Principles of the Heat Treatment of Plain Carbon and Low Alloy Steels

Charlie R. Brooks

Materials Science and Engineering Department
The University of Tennessee, Knoxville, TN

Manager Book Acquisitions
Veronica Flint

Manager Book Production
Grace M. Davidson

Production Project Coordinators
Randall L. Boring
Cheryl L. Powers
Alexandru Popaz Pauna

**The Materials
Information Society**

Library of Congress Cataloging Card Number: 96-78934

ISBN: 0-87170-538-9

SAN: 204-7586

ASM International®
Materials Park, OH 44073-0002

Printed in the United States of America

Dedication

This book is dedicated to my wife Sue for her editing assistance with this project and my other books, and for her patience and support (usually) in my other endeavors.

Acknowledgments

I thank many researchers and organizations for allowing me to use information from their works and publications; the sources are acknowledged where the information appears in the book. I particularly acknowledge ASM International for permission to use material from many of their publications. Special appreciation is expressed to Professor George Krauss for permission to use information from his own research and that of his co-workers. Also, special appreciation is expressed to Mrs. Iris Thelning for permission to use information from *Steel and its Heat Treatment*, Butterworths, London (1975) by her late husband Karl-Erik Thelning. I also am indebted for the assistance of Veronica Flint of ASM International in editing and publishing this book. Mrs. Carla Lawerence is thanked for her patient typing of the manuscript, and Mrs. Deb Basak kindly fitted some of the data to polynomials.

Preface

In the current highly competitive field of materials, steels continue to be widely used, and of these the plain carbon and low alloy steels usually are the material of choice for structural and machine components. The purpose of this book is to provide background information on the practical physical metallurgy of the heat treatment and choice of these steels. The material presented here should be of value to engineers involved in the application of steels in manufacturing who must be aware of all aspects which provide a competitive benefit. This will be of particular interest to metallurgists and metallurgical engineers, but also to other engineers involved in the design and use of components made from steel.

Considerable information from the literature has been used to illustrate the points made, but no serious attempt has been made to convert the data to SI units. Conversion tables are given in appendices.

Table of Contents

Chapter 1

Introduction

The materials used in components are now highly diversified, with many applications historically reserved for steels now taken by plastics, composites and ceramics. This change has been brought about by economic factors, environmental factors (e.g., lighter weight automobiles for better gas mileage and less air pollution), and (at least certainly in the United States) by international competition. These three factors are not independent of each other.

There are, of course, many applications for which steels are still clearly the most suitable material. And there are former applications of steels which may in the future be reclaimed if the factors listed in the preceding paragraph become more favorable for the use of steels. Thus, at the present time it is especially important that the type of steel chosen for a given application, and the heat treatment given it, be critically examined in order to justify its use.

The choice of steel in general for an application, and specific steels in particular, rests not just on the cost of the starting stock material (e.g., bars, plates), which is closely related to the alloy content, but also on the cost of the heat treatment, and on the subsequent success of the manufactured component. For example, the best choice may require a more expensive steel which can be hardened with less concern about control of the cooling process in order to reduce rejections because of inadequate hardening during quenching.

The current (and future) manufacturing climate requires extremely careful consideration of the choice of steel and the design of its heat treatment. To do this requires understanding the factors that affect the response of steels to heat treatment and knowing how to use these factors in choosing the steel and in designing the heat treatment. Methods to do this have been under close scrutiny and continue to be under development.

The purpose of this book is to review current methods of examining the suitability of a given steel for an application in which the main property of concern is hardness (or strength). Some of the methods are quantitative (at least approximately) and others are correlative. Taken together, they serve as a powerful guide and method of choosing steels and designing their heat treatment. In the following chapters, a brief review of the concepts of the common method of graphically depicting the decomposition of austenite, the time-temperature-transformation (TTT) diagrams, is given first. Then the concept of hardenability is presented, and the methods of calculating hardenability from the chemical composition and the austenite grain size are reviewed. Then the heat transfer process during quenching is examined. Methods of estimating the temperature-time curve during quenching at various locations in simple shapes (e.g., bars, plates) are presented. This information, coupled with the hardenability information, allows estimating the hardness distribution which is developed by the hardening heat treatment. Tempering is reviewed since most steels require subsequent tempering (mainly for improved toughness). Austenitizing, the precursor to hardening, is covered, followed by a treatment of annealing, normalizing, martempering, austempering and intercritical heat treatment. The heat treatment of steels is being increasingly modeled with computer programs, and this is reviewed. In the last chapter, examples of the use of the material in the preceding chapters to the design of heat treatments are given.

It is assumed that the reader is familiar with the general concepts and terminology (e.g., austenite, martensite, etc.) of the heat treatment of steels. These are covered in introductory physical metallurgy and materials science books, and in specific books on heat treatment.

The first three listed here are recommended for background information on heat treatment of steels.

The last book has an excellent selection of microstructures.

C.R. Brooks, *Heat Treatment of Ferrous Alloys*, McGraw-Hill Book Company/Hemisphere Publishing Company, New York (1979)

A.K. Sinha, *Ferrous Physical Metallurgy*, Butterworths, Boston (1989)

G. Krauss, *Steels: Heat Treatment and Processing Principles*, American Society for Materials, Materials Park, Ohio (1990)

L.E. Samuels, *Optical Microscopy of Carbon Steels*, American Society for Metals, Metals Park, Ohio (1980)

The Iron-Carbon Phase Diagram and Time-Temperature-Transformation (TTT) Diagrams

"I vividly recall our surprise at the great delay and slowness in transformation at temperatures above about 1200 degrees F (680 degrees C)…"

E.C. Bain, *Metals Structure and the Hardenability of Steel, 1920 to 1940: Personal Recollections, in The Sorby Centennial Symposium on the History of Metallurgy, C.S. Smith, editor, Gordon and Breach, New York (1965).*

In the heat treatment of steels, the time and temperature dependence of the formation of the microconstituents of steels (pearlite, bainite, martensite, primary ferrite, primary iron carbide) is of critical importance. As a guide in understanding and choosing heat treatments, it is convenient to have a graphical method of displaying these events for a given thermal history. Basically, a diagram which does this is called a *Time-Temperature-Transformation diagram*, frequently abbreviated *TTT diagram*. In this chapter, the two types of TTT diagrams used are described and the methods of determining them are outlined. These diagrams are affected by the carbon and alloy content and by the prior austenite grain size, and the way in which these factors affect them is examined.

It is important to keep in mind that the TTT diagrams depict what happens to austenite, *and only austenite*, upon certain heat treatments. These diagrams do not give guidance as to what happens to the austenite transformation products (e.g., pearlite, martensite) if they are heat treated.

As a precursor to examination of the decomposition of austenite, the phases and microconstituents found in steels are the first reviewed. This includes a presentation of the iron-carbon phase diagram and of the equilibrium phases. The common microconstituents which form in steels are also described, including the nomenclature used

to describe them. A definition of the phases and microconstituents is listed in Table 2-1.

Phases in the Iron-Carbon System

If pure iron is heated from 25°C to the liquid state, the change in length (or volume) with temperature is that shown in Fig. 2-1. From 25 to 910°C, there is an increase in length, almost linear, with a slight perturbation near the Curie temperature (768°C) where iron changes from the ferromagnetic (very strongly magnetic) to the paramagnetic (very weakly magnetic) form. At 910°C, there is a marked *decrease* in length. The length increases until 1400°C, at which temperature the length *increases*, attaining a length essentially that obtained by an extrapolation of the curve in the low temperature range. Then the iron expands until the melting temperature (1560°C) is reached, whereupon it expands as it melts.

From 25 to 910°C, iron exists as the body-centered cubic (BCC) structure (Fig. 2-2). From 910 to 1400°C, it exists as the face-centered cubic (FCC) structure (Fig. 2-2). The abrupt changes in length noted at 910 and 1400°C are explained by the difference in the specific volume (or density) of these two types of atomic packing. If the iron atoms are considered to be spheres of the same diameter for either structure, then the volume difference between the two types of atom arrangements can be calculated. The basis must be the same mass. The body-centered cubic unit cell (Fig. 2-2) has two atoms in it, and the face-centered cubic unit cell (Fig. 2-2) has four. Thus we must compare the volume of two body-centered cubic cells to that of one face-centered cubic cell. The calculation in Fig. 2-2 shows that the change from the body-centered cubic arrangement to the face-centered cubic arrangement causes a 9% *decrease* in volume (and length). This difference in atomic packing is the origin of the decrease in the length at 910°C shown in Fig. 2-1. Likewise, the abrupt increase in length at 1400°C (Fig. 2-1) is caused by the compact face-centered cubic structure changing *back* to the body-centered cubic structure.

The lower temperature body-centered cubic form of iron is designated α, and is called α-*ferrite*, or normally just *ferrite*. The high temperature body-centered cubic form is designated δ, and is called δ-*ferrite*. The face-centered cubic form of iron is designated γ, and is called *austenite*, after the famous English metallurgist Robert Austins.

The atomic structure of iron and carbon are considerably different, so it is expected that these two elements may combine to form compounds. The common compound is *iron carbide*, which is Fe_3C. That is, it is a compound of three iron atoms and one carbon atom. Thus it contains 25 at.% C, which corresponds to 6.67 wt.% C. Its structure is shown in Fig. 2-3.

If pure carbon is present in any steels, it occurs as *graphite*, since the diamond form will only be present for pressures much higher than associated with the use of steels.

The Iron-Carbon Phase Diagram

The Fe-C phase diagram is a graphical representation of the phases present for a given alloy composition and temperature. A common way of representing composition is to use weight percent, and in this book it will be abbreviated %. (Other methods are used, such as atomic percent.) The Fe-C phase diagram is shown in Fig. 2-4.

In pure iron there are four critical temperatures associated with phase changes, and thus the addition of carbon will affect these temperatures. In Fig. 2-4 it is seen that the addition of carbon to liquid iron lowers the melting point to a minimum of about 1133°C at about 4.3 wt.% C, and then this temperature increases. Line a-b-c-d is the liquidus temperature, the temperature at which on cooling crystallization begins. The line a-b-c-d can also be considered to be the solubility limit of iron in the iron-carbon liquid. For example, at 1400°C and 3% C, the liquid phase is present. If iron is added to this liquid, decreasing the % carbon, when the composition reaches about 2.3% C, continuing addition of iron to the liquid only results in the presence of the γ phase along with the liquid, but the composition of the liquid phase remains at 2.3% C. That is, at 1400°C, 97.7% Fe (2.3% C) is the solubility limit of iron in the liquid.

Likewise, the boundary f-g-h represents the solubility limit of carbon in the γ phase. For example, an alloy containing 1.0% C at 1150°C is in the γ phase region. Carbon can be added to the γ phase at this temperature and maintain only the face-centered cubic structure until the line g-h is reached, at about 1.9% C. This is the solubility limit of carbon in austenite. Continued addition of carbon to the alloy results in the formation of iron carbide (Fe_3C) in the austenite. The chemical composition of the austenite remains at 1.9%.

In a similar fashion, the line i-j-k represents the solubility limit of carbon in the α phase (ferrite). Note that the ability to absorb carbon is considerably less than austenite. The maximum solubility of carbon in ferrite is about 0.02% C at 723°C (point j), whereas in austenite it is about 2.0% C at 1133°C (point g). Austenite has the close-packed face-centered cubic structure, and hence the percent of open space between the iron atoms is less than

Table 2-1   Definition of phases, microconstituents and critical temperatures in steels

Term	Definition
Austenite	Designated by γ. Face-centered cubic iron with elements such as carbon and manganese dissolved to form a solid solution. In most steels, not stable at low temperatures (e.g., 25°C). Can dissolve up to about 2.0 wt.% C. Relatively soft.
Ferrite	Designated by α. Body-centered cubic iron with elements such as manganese dissolved to form a solid solution. The solubility of carbon in α is very low, 0.025 wt.% maximum. Relatively soft.
Iron carbide	Iron-carbon compound, Fe_3C. Unstable phase, will decompose to iron and graphite, but takes a relatively long time and thus is a common phase in steels. Very hard.
Cementite	Iron carbide.
Pearlite	Two phase mixture of ferrite and iron carbide having a lamellar morphology. Forms from austenite.
Bainite	Two phase mixture of ferrite and iron carbide, which consists of fine rods of iron carbide in acicular ferrite. Exact morphology depends upon temperature range of formation. Forms from austenite.
Martensite	Single phase body-centered tetragonal iron with carbon dissolved in it. Morphology is lath or acicular plates. Forms from austenite. Very hard.
Graphite	Equilibrium phase in steels and cast irons. However, it forms very slowly and doesn't appear in most steels.
Tempered martensite	Ferrite and iron carbide aggregate formed from martensite. Note that it is a two phase mixture. The structure consists of small rounded carbide particles in the ferrite grains.
Eutectoid temperature and composition	The temperature at which α, γ and Fe_3C are in equilibrium. In plain carbon steels, it is about 723°C. The eutectoid composition is about 0.8 wt.% C in plain carbon steels.
A_1	Eutectoid temperature
A_3	Temperature-composition line which gives the chemical composition (wt.% C) of γ in equilibrium with α. Also temperature at which primary ferrite begins to form from γ upon "equilibrium" cooling in steels with less than 0.8% C.
A_{cm}	Temperature-composition line which gives the chemical composition (wt.% C) of γ in equilibrium with Fe_3C. Also temperature at which primary Fe_3C begins to form from γ upon "equilibrium" cooling in steels with greater than 0.8% C.
$A_{r1}, A_{r3}, A_{rcm}, A_{c1}, A_{c3}, A_{ccm}$	Designation of the temperatures at which the decomposition of austenite associated with the A_1, A_3, and A_{cm} temperature begins upon cooling ("r" subscript) and heating ("c" subscript). The temperatures depend on the cooling rate and heating rate.

for the body-centered cubic structure (see Fig. 2-2). Carbon is a relatively small atom, and will dissolve in these two crystal structures by locating in the interstices between the iron atoms, forming an *interstitial solid solution*. Thus it may appear that more carbon would dissolve in the ferrite since it has more open space. However, the important consideration is the size of the interstitial sites, not the total open space. In the face-centered cubic structure, the interstitial sites are considerably larger than those

in the body-centered cubic structure. Thus the face-centered cubic austenite dissolves considerably more carbon than the body-centered cubic α-ferrite or δ-ferrite.

The eutectoid temperature (723°C, Fig. 2-4) is sometimes referred to as the A_1 temperature. The solubility line of iron in austenite, i-f in Fig. 2-4, is called the A_3 temperature, and that for carbon in austenite, f-g, is called the A_{cm} temperature. These designations are for the equilibrium transformation temperatures.

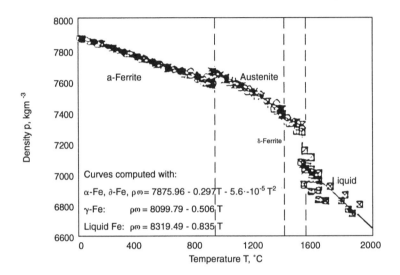

(a)

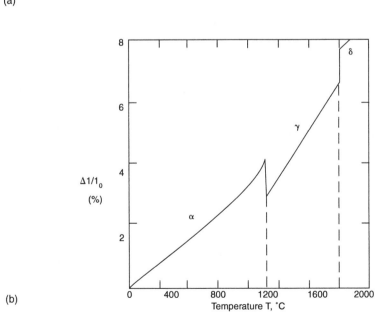

(b)

Fig. 2-1 (a) Density versus temperature (measured values and chosen function given by lines and equations) for pure iron. The sources of the experimental data are cited in the reference. (b) Length changes (relation to 20°C) versus temperature for pure iron derived from the information in (a). ((a) Adapted from A. Jablonka, K. Harste and K. Schwerdtfeger, *Steel Research*, Vol 62, p 24 (1991))

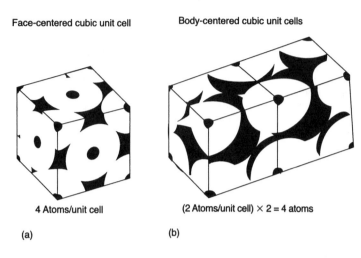

Face-centered cubic unit cell   Body-centered cubic unit cells

4 Atoms/unit cell   (2 Atoms/unit cell) × 2 = 4 atoms

(a)   (b)

$$[V_{FCC} - V_{BCC}]/[V_{FCC}] \times 100 = -8.9\%$$

Thus FCC structure about 9% more dense
(less volume) than BCC structure

Fig. 2-2   Model of (a) the body-centered cubic and (b) the face-centered cubic crystal structures. The calculation of the difference in volume for the two structures is shown, where it is assumed that the atoms are spheres and have the same radius in both structures. The close-packed face-centered cubic structure is about 9% more dense than the body-centered cubic structure.

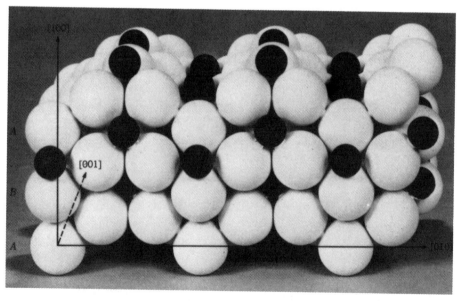

*(Courtesy E. J. Fasiska, Fundamental Research Laboratory, U.S. Steel Corpora-
tion, and G. A. Jeffrey, Crystallography Laboratory, University of Pittsburgh.)*

Fig. 2-3   A model of the crystal structure of Fe$_3$C, which is a complex compound of iron and interstitial carbon. (A.G. Guy, *Introduction to Materials Science*, McGraw-Hill Book Company, New York (1972))

The phase diagram shown in Fig. 2-4 is that commonly used in analyzing the heat treatment of plain carbon and low alloy steels. Iron carbide is actually not an equilibrium phase, but is metastable. For example, below the eutectoid temperature (723°C), Fe₃C will decompose into ferrite and graphite given enough time. However, the rate of decomposition is sufficiently low that the formation of graphite need not be considered for the steels of interest in this book. Its formation becomes important in the high temperature (e.g., 500°C) application of steels and in the higher carbon content cast irons.

Microconstituents and Non-Equilibrium Phases

The area of the Fe-C phase diagram of interest here is that of austenite and the two-phase ferrite + iron carbide region below it. In this section the common microconstituents and phases found in steels are described. The details of their formation are not given here, but some will be found in subsequent sections and others in references listed at the end of Chapter 1.

The phase diagram in Fig. 2-4 shows that an equilibrated Fe-C alloy containing 0.8% C will be austenite above 723°C and a mixture of ferrite and iron carbide below this temperature down to 25°C. Right at 723°C, the three phases co-exist. Thus upon cooling this alloy slowly (e.g., 50°C/h) from the austenite region, upon passing 723°C the austenite will change to the two-phase mixture of α and Fe₃C. A reaction of a single solid phase transforming upon cooling to two other solid phases is called a *eutectoid* reaction. The phase diagram does not indicate the morphology (e.g., size, shape and arrangement) of the two phases. In Fe-C alloys, the two-phase mixture will form as alternating plates of α and Fe₃C, which is called *pearlite*. This structure is so fine an optical microscope must be used to resolve it. It is a common *microconstituent* in steels. Examples of its appearance are shown in Fig. 2-5.

If the steel is not of eutectoid carbon content, then upon slow cooling from the austenite region a *proeutectoid* or *primary* phase will form prior to the formation of pearlite. This is depicted in Fig. 2-6a. If the steel contains less than the eutectoid carbon content it is called a *hypoeutectoid* steel, and the primary phase is ferrite. Upon cooling, when the line f-i (Fig. 2-4) is reached, ferrite begins to form in the austenite. These α crystals nucleate at the austenite grain boundaries, so that after the decomposition of austenite is complete, their arrangement reveals the prior austenite grain size. This is illustrated by the microstructures in Fig. 2-6b.

If the carbon content of the steel is greater than the eutectoid value, the steel is referred to as *hypereutectoid*, and the primary phase is iron carbide. These primary Fe₃C crystals form at the austenite grain boundaries (Fig. 2-7a), but, unlike primary α, they form as a thin layer along the entire austenite boundary, giving a microstructure such as shown in Fig. 2-7b. Originally, the primary Fe₃C was referred to as *cementite*, but this word is now used to also mean Fe₃C in general.

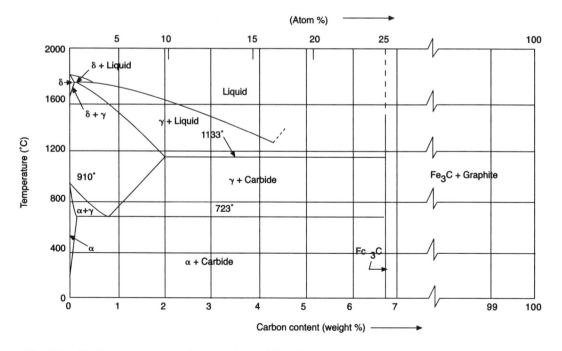

Fig. 2-4   The iron-carbon phase diagram. (Adapted from *Metals Handbook*, 8th edition, Vol 8, American Society for Metals, Metals Park, Ohio (1973))

The morphology of the α-Fe$_3$C mixture is determined by the heat treatment. For some treatments, the mixture will consist of roughly spherical particles of Fe$_3$C dispersed in α. This microconstituent is called *spheroidite*. Its origin is discussed in Chapters 5 and 7. An example of the microstructure of spheroidite is shown in Fig. 2-8.

Another morphology of the α-Fe$_3$C mixture which forms for certain heat treatments consists of short rods of Fe$_3$C in α and is called *bainite*. (This structure is named after E.C. Bain, the American metallurgist who contributed greatly to the physical metallurgy of steels.) The exact structure depends on the steel and the heat treatment. Examples of the bainite microstructure are shown in Fig. 2-9.

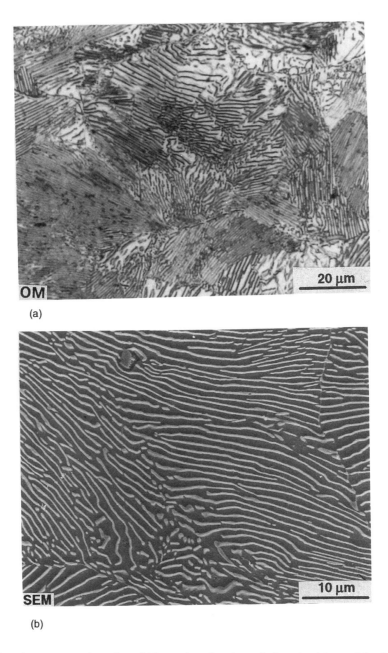

(a)

(b)

Fig. 2-5   The microstructure of pearlite, which consists of regions of alternate plate crystals of ferrite and iron carbide. The structure is revealed by careful polishing of the surface and then etching with a chemical which dissolves the ferrite, leaving the Fe$_3$C plates standing in relief. In optical microscopy, at low magnification (a), the carbide plates appear as black lines. In scanning electron microscopy (b), the carbide plates appear white at high magnification.

If Fe-C alloys are equilibrated in the austenite region, then cooled very rapidly (e.g., water quenched) to 25°C, a non-equilibrium phase is formed during cooling. It has a body-centered tetragonal crystal structure (Fig. 2-10), and since it is a single phase, it has the same chemical composition (% C) as the parent austenite. This phase is called *martensite*. (This structure is named after the German scientist Adolf Martens.) Upon cooling, when the austenite reaches a certain temperature (the martensite-start temperature, M_s), lath or needle-like crystals of martensite form very rapidly inside the austenite grains. The center plane of these crystals is approximately parallel to a close-packed plane (a {111} plane) of the austenite. Below a sufficiently low temperature (the martensite-finish temperature, M_f), the austenite will have been converted to martensite. Thus each former austenite grain will consist of many thin crystals of martensite. Upon metallographic preparation and etching of a sample, the structure will have a "brush-stroke" appearance due to this crystallographically oriented

structure. Examples of the microstructure are shown in Fig. 2-11. For the lower carbon martensite, the crystals have a lath-like nature; for higher carbon, they are acicular or plate-like.

It is seen in Fig. 2-4 that martensite is not shown as an equilibrium phase. It is unstable, and if heated in the temperature range below the eutectoid temperature (723°C), it will decompose into ferrite and carbide. The heat treatment to produce this effect is called *tempering* and is treated in detail in Chapter 5. The ferrite-carbide structure formed from the decomposition of martensite is called *tempered martensite*. Examples of the microstructure are shown in Fig. 2-12. The size and density of the carbide particles depends upon the tempering temperature and time. Note that the tempered martensite may retain a "brush-stroke" appearance reminiscent of that of the parent martensite.

Details of the terminology of the phases and microconstituents of steels have been summarized by Samuels, including the history of the names used (L.E. Samuels,

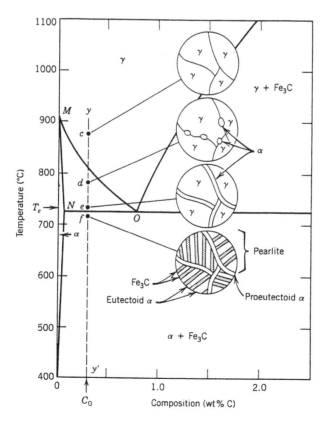

Fig. 2-6(a) Depiction of the formation of proeutectoid or primary ferrite from austenite upon cooling slowly a hypoeutectoid steel. (Adapted from W.D. Callister, *Materials Science and Engineering*, Wiley, New York (1985). Reprinted by permission of John Wiley & Sons, Inc.) *(continued)*

Optical Microscopy of Carbon Steels, American Society for Metals, Metals Park, Ohio (1980)). Definitions of the phases and microconstituents are summarized in Table 2-1.

Isothermal TTT Diagram

To systematically study the formation of the microconstituents of steels, such as pearlite and bainite, it is best

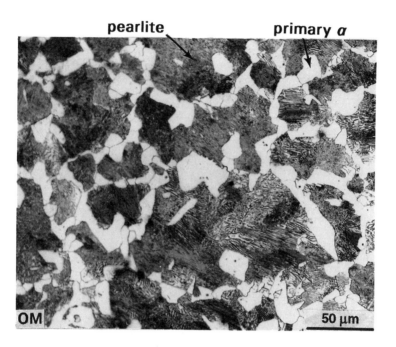

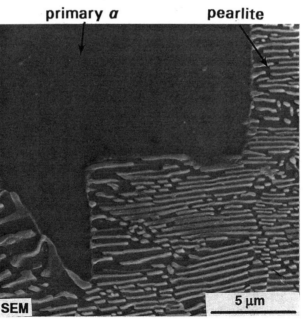

Fig. 2-6(b) (continued) Microstructures showing primary ferrite and pearlite in hypoeutectoid steels cooled slowly from austenite. In optical microscopy, the primary ferrite appears white, but in scanning electron microscopy, it appears dark.

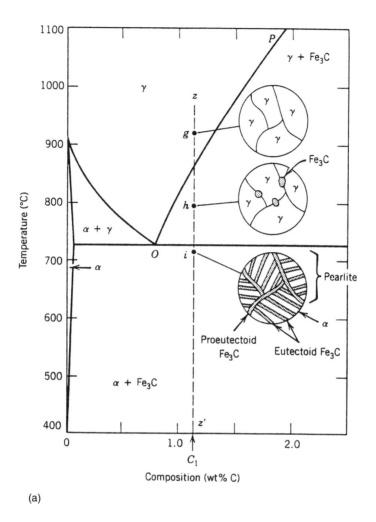

(a)

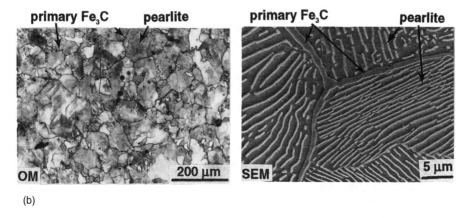

(b)

Fig. 2-7 (a) Depiction of the formation of proeutectoid or primary iron carbide from austenite upon cooling slowly a hypereutectoid steel from W.D. Callister, *Materials Science and Engineering*, Wiley, New York (1985). Reprinted by permission of John Wiley & Sons, Inc. (b) Microstructures showing primary iron carbide and pearlite in a hypereutectoid steel cooled slowly from the austenite region. In the low magnification optical micrograph on the left, the primary carbide appears as dark lines outlining the prior austenite grain boundaries. The primary carbide is resolved at higher magnification in the scanning electron micrograph on the right.

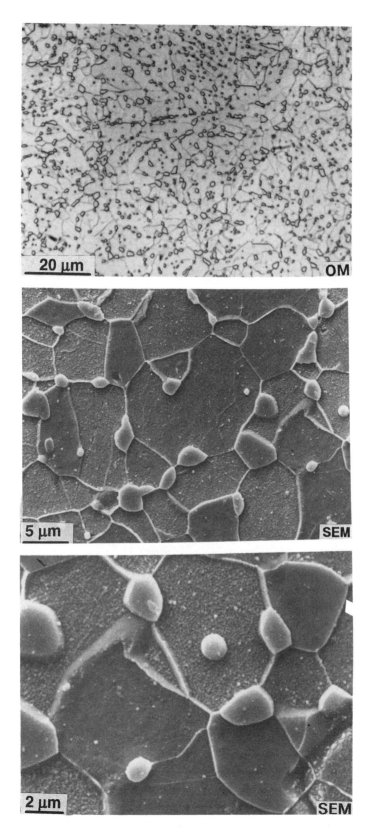

Fig. 2-8   The microstructure of spheroidite, consisting of spherical "globs" of carbide crystals in ferrite

to examine the transformation of austenite upon isothermal transformation at a series of sub-critical temperatures. (This procedure is to be contrasted to that where the heat treatment involves the temperature changing with time.) The isothermal transformation procedure maintains the temperature constant while time is varying, which makes the kinetics of the transformation easier to analyze at a given temperature. Then the temperature

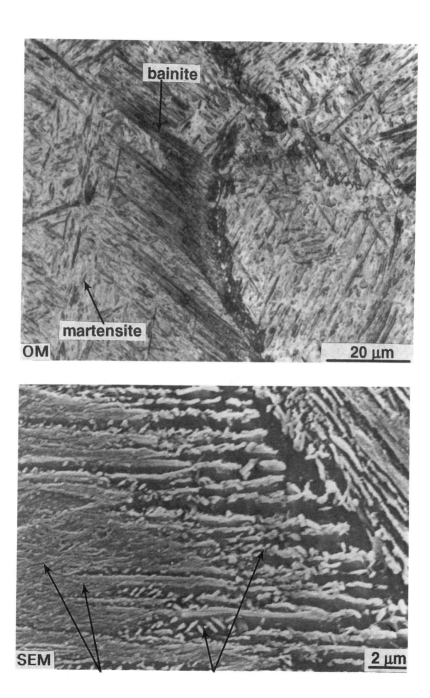

Fig. 2-9   Example of the microstructure of bainite in an oil quenched 0.47% C steel. The details of the structure are best revealed by the higher resolution scanning electron micrograph (b), where the carbide particles appear white in a grayer ferrite background.

dependence of the process is examined from the observations made at different temperatures.

The first detailed study of the decomposition of austenite upon isothermal transformation was by Davenport and Bain (E.S. Davenport and E.C. Bain, *Trans. AIME*, Vol 90, p. 117 (1930)). They presented the sequence of the decomposition of austenite on a temperature-time diagram, indicating at each isothermal transformation temperature the time at which a given microconstituent first appeared, and the time at which it ceased to form. This diagram is the *isothermal TTT diagram*, sometimes abbreviated *IT diagram*. Since that time, many isothermal TTT diagrams have been determined, and sources of diagrams have been reviewed by Eldis (G.T. Eldis, p. 126 in *Hardenability Concepts with Applications to Steel*, D.V. Doane and J.S. Kirkaldy, editors, The Metallurgical Society, Warrendale, PA (1978)).

In the isothermal TTT diagram a key premise is that the steel sample is cooled from the austenitizing temperature to the transformation temperature sufficiently rapidly that its temperature equilibrates before any transformation occurs. Thus in steels which have a relatively high

rate of formation of bainite and pearlite, considerable care must be exercised in the experiments. In steels of low alloy content, and especially low carbon content, the rate of formation of bainite and pearlite is so high that it is often difficult to determine the TTT diagram accurately. To minimize such problems, the samples used are usually thin (e.g., 2 mm) discs, and they are placed in salt or lead baths at the transformation temperature to provide rapid heat transfer and hence cause rapid cooling from the austenitizing temperature. In the low alloys steels, even transfer by hand from the austenitizing furnace to the transformation bath is too slow, and special devices must be used.

There are two common methods of following the transformation of austenite to martensite. One is to examine the microstructures of a set of samples which been cooled to the transformation temperature, then each sample cooled rapidly to 25°C after progressively longer transformation times. The rapid cooling from the transformation temperature will convert any austenite present to martensite, which can easily be distinguished from any austenite transformation products (e.g., pearlite and bainite). This procedure is shown schematically in Fig.

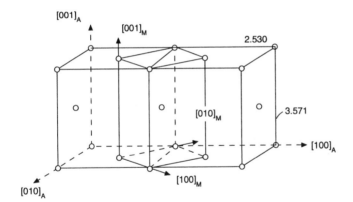
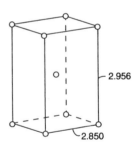

Face-centered cubic austenite, showing body-centered tetragonal cell. A stands for austenite, M for martensite.

Body-centered tetragonal martensite

Lattice parameters of austenite:	$a_a = 3.571 \times 10^{-8}$ cm
Lattice parameters of bct cell in fcc austenite:	$a = 2.530 \times 10^{-8}$ cm $c = 3.571 \times 10^{-8}$ cm
Lattice parameters of bct martensite:	$a = 2.850 \times 10^{-8}$ cm $c = 2.950 \times 10^{-8}$ cm

Fig. 2-10 Illustration of the relationship between the face-centered cubic austenite cell and the martensite body-centered cubic cell derived from it. The lattice parameters are based on a 0.8% C steel and 25°C. (From C.R. Brooks, *Heat Treatment of Ferrous Alloys*, Hemisphere/McGraw-Hill, New York (1979))

2-13. A series of microstructures obtained by such a procedure is shown in Fig. 2-14. In this case, the microconstituent which formed was pearlite.

The other common method of determining the transformation process is to measure the length of a sample using a dilatometer designed to be used at elevated temperatures. The sample with the dilatometric instrumentation on it is austenitized, then removed from the austenitizing furnace and the sample with the assembly placed in the transformation furnace (usually a salt or metal bath for rapid heat transfer). The length of the sample is recorded as a function of time at the transformation temperature. This method of determining the TTT diagram relies on detecting the volume expansion when the close-packed face-centered cubic austenite decomposes to the less dense products. After attaining what appears to be com-

pletion of the reaction, the sample is cooled to 25°C and the microstructure examined to determine the microconstituent which was forming during the transformation. An example of data obtained by the dilatometric method is shown in Fig. 2-15. The initial contraction is due to the sample cooling from the austenitizing temperature to the transformation temperature. This is followed by a time period during which the length is constant. Then an expansion occurs due to the transformation.

It is customary and useful to place on the isothermal TTT diagram the martensite start temperature M_S and the finish temperature M_f. However, strictly speaking, these should not be on this diagram, as martensite forms (usually) only upon cooling, and not upon isothermal holding (except in very high alloy steels). These two temperatures can be determined by use of a quenching dilatometer,

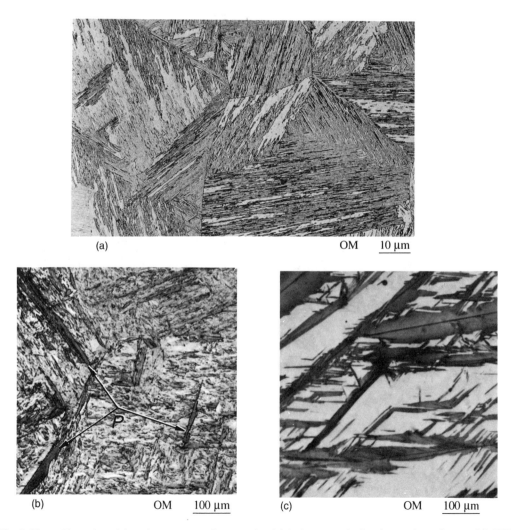

(a)   OM   10 μm

(b)   OM   100 μm   (c)   OM   100 μm

Fig. 2-11   Examples of the microstructure of martensite. (a) Lath martensite in a low-carbon alloy steel (0.03% C, 2% Mn); (b) Plate martensite (marked *P*) and lath martensite in medium-carbon (0.57% C) steel; (c) Plate martensite in a high-carbon (1.2% C) steel. Matrix is retained austenite. (From *Metals Handbook*, 9th edition, Vol 9, *Metallography and Microstructures*, American Society for Metals, Metals Park, Ohio (1985))

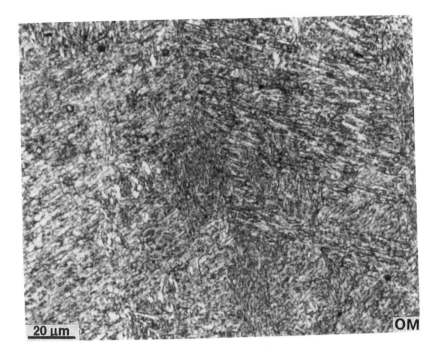

(a)

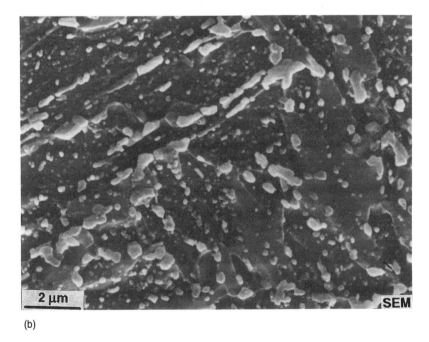

(b)

Fig. 2-12   Microstructures typical of those of tempered martensite. In (a) the dark regions in the optical micrograph (OM) are caused by scattering of light from clusters of carbides standing in relief above the etched ferrite. In the scanning electron micrograph (SEM) (b), the carbides are resolved and are the light particles in the darker ferrite background.

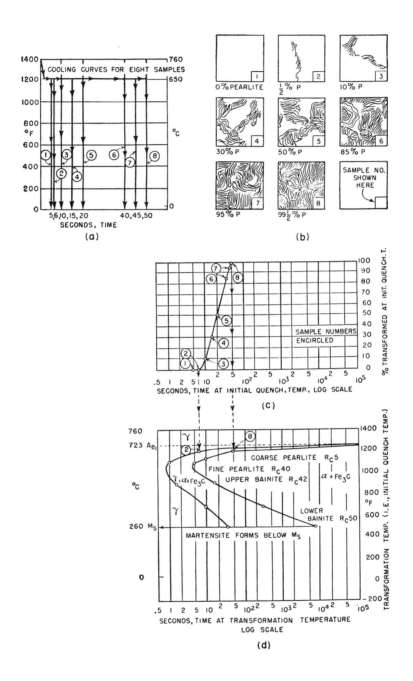

Fig. 2-13   Schematic illustration of the metallographic method used to determine at a fixed temperature the start and finish times of the formation of a microconstituent from austenite. In Fig. 2-14 are shown actual microstructures which would correspond to the letters shown on the schematic microstructures shown in this figure. (From C.A. Keyser, *Basic Engineering Metallurgy*, p. 178-179 (1959). Reprinted by permission of Prentice-Hall, Inc., Englewood Cliffs, NJ)

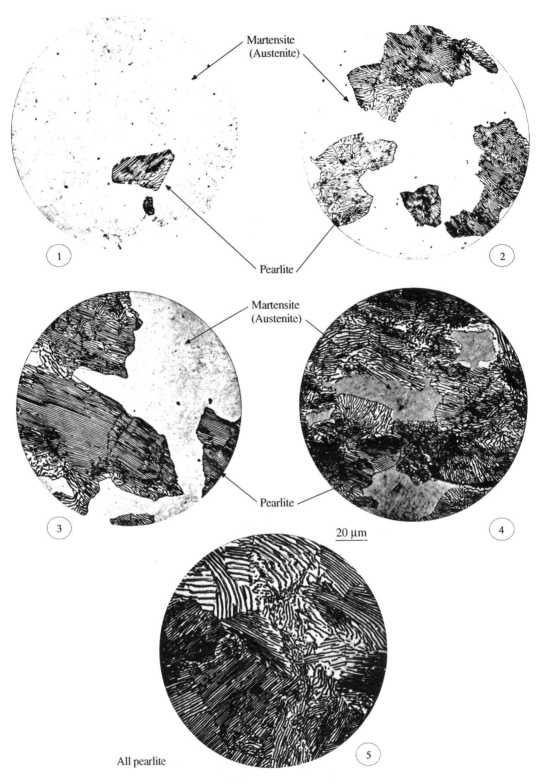

Fig. 2-14 Microstructures illustrating the isothermal formation of pearlite in a eutectoid steel. At the transformation temperature, the structures were mixtures of pearlite and austenite, but the austenite transformed to martensite upon cooling rapidly to 25°C. (Taken from E.C. Bain and H.W. Paxton, *Alloying Elements in Steel*, 2nd edition, American Society for Metals, Metals Park, Ohio, p. 22-26 (1961))

noting the temperature at which, upon cooling rapidly, a volume expansion begins and the temperature at which it ceases. An example is shown in Fig. 2-16.

Another method of determining the M_s and M_f temperatures is a microstructural technique which relies on the fact that fresh martensite will etch lightly, but even slightly tempered (reheated) martensite will etch dark. The heat treatments are illustrated schematically in Fig. 2-17. The sample processed along the path marked A will be all austenite at the quench temperature of 375°C. The sample is only held about two sec., so bainite will not

form. Thus upon quenching to 25°C after holding for two sec., the austenite will convert to all martensite. Hence, the M_s temperature is below 375°C.

The sample which is quenched to 250°C forms about 90% martensite. Upon holding for two sec. at this temperature, the austenite will not form bainite. However, the martensite will temper, forming a fine dispersion of carbides in ferrite. Upon cooling rapidly to 25°C after the 2 sec., the remaining 10% austenite will transform to *fresh* martensite, but the tempered martensite will not change. At 25°C the structure consists of 90% dark etching,

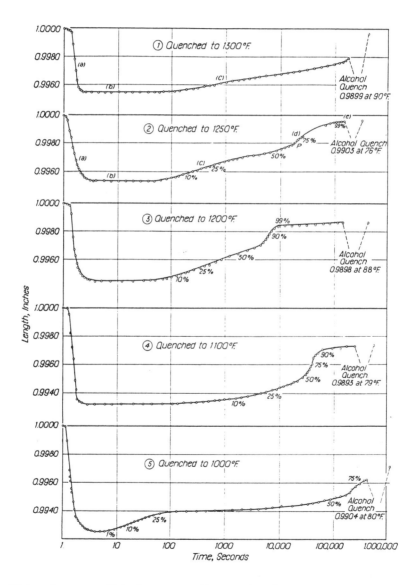

Fig. 2-15 Dilatometer curves obtained upon quenching samples of a steel to the temperatures noted, and holding to allow the austenite to transform to pearlite. These data are used to determine the start and finish time at each temperature for pearlite formation. The steel contained 0.30% C, 1.63% Mn, 0.49% Si, 0.44% Cr, and 0.33% Mo. The samples were austenitized at 1650°F (900°C) from which they were cooled to the transformation temperature. (From R.A. Flinn, E. Cook and J.A. Fellows, *Trans. ASM*, Vol 31, p. 41 (1943))

martensite-appearing structure and 10% of a light etching martensite (fresh martensite). Thus the M_s temperature is above 250°C. Microstructures formed by this method are shown in Fig. 2-18.

A TTT diagram determined by the two methods outlined above is shown in Fig. 2-19. The two methods give similar results. Note that the microstructural method is sensitive to detecting the beginning of transformation.

Fig. 2-20 shows one of the isothermal TTT diagrams constructed by Bain and Davenport. This was for a eutectoid steel. Note that no data are shown for times less than one sec., because samples could not be cooled sufficiently

rapidly from the austenitizing temperature to the transformation temperature to prevent any transformation before reaching the transformation temperature. Also note the distortion in the region of martensite formation, which is also due to experimental problems. This early diagram can be compared to a later one for a similar eutectoid steel shown in Fig. 2-21. Note that the M_f temperature is not given because of difficulties in estimating at which temperature the steel becomes exactly 100% martensite. Instead, the temperature M_{90} at which 90% martensite is present is shown.

The curvature of the isothermal TTT diagrams for low alloy steels displays a "C" shape. However, in the

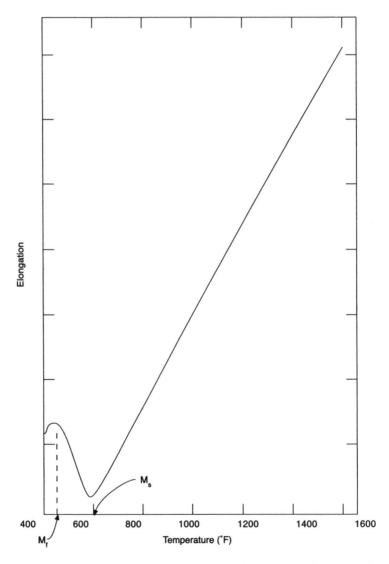

Fig. 2-16   Dilatometer curve showing the length change upon the formation of martensite from austenite upon cooling rapidly. From this curve the M_s and M_f temperatures can be determined. These data are for a modified 4130 steel. (Adapted from A.L. Christenson, E.C. Nelson and C.E. Jackson, *Trans. AIME*, Vol 162, p. 606 (1945))

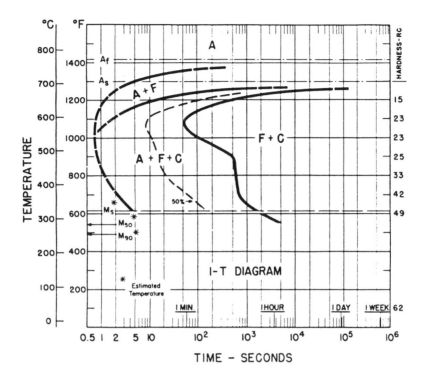

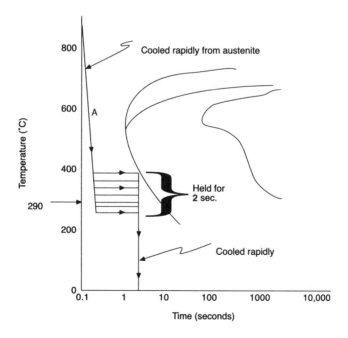

Fig. 2-17 Schematic illustration of the heat treatment used to develop metallographic samples used to determine the M_s and M_f temperatures. Any martensite formed upon the initial quench is tempered when held for the 2 sec. at the indicated temperatures. Upon quenching from these temperatures, the remaining austenite forms fresh (untempered) martensite, which can be distinguished from the tempered martensite because the latter etches dark. Such microstructures are shown in Fig. 2-18

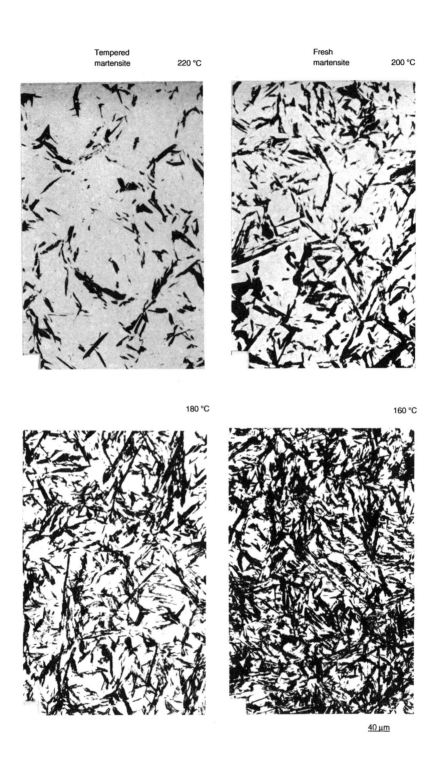

Fig. 2-18 Microstructures illustrating the determination of the M_s and M_f temperatures by a metallographic method. Each sample was quenched to the temperature noted, held for one second to temper any martensite which had formed, then quenched to 25°C. The short heat treatment tempered any martensite formed upon the initial quench, and it etched dark. Any martensite formed upon quenching from the initial quenching temperature to 25°C etched relatively light. The M_s temperature was determined to be 240°C. (Adapted from A.B. Greninger and A.R. Troiano, *Trans. ASM*, Vol 28, p. 537-563 (1940))

temperature range of 550°C both bainite and pearlite may form, and careful examination can detect a start curve for each microconstituent. Usually this distinction is not made, and the temperature range of overlap of the formation of pearlite and bainite is not distinguished on the diagram. This was the case in Fig. 2-21. However, as will be shown in a later section, the addition of alloying elements can cause marked separation of the bainite formation and pearlite formation regions.

For a steel of eutectoid carbon content (close to 0.8% in plain carbon steels), the start and finish curves of pearlite formation approach the eutectoid temperature asymptomatically, as shown in Fig. 2-22. If the steel contains less than (hypoeutectoid) or greater than (hypereutectoid) the eutectoid carbon content, then the TTT diagram should include the decomposition of austenite in the two phase region above the eutectoid temperature. This is illustrated in Fig. 2-22. In the two phase region (γ + α for hypoeutectoid steel, γ + Fe$_3$C for hypereutectoid steels), some austenite will be present at equilibrium. Thus no finish curve is shown. Isothermal TTT diagrams for a hypoeutectoid and a hypereutectoid steel are shown in Fig. 2-23.

Continuous Cooling TTT Diagram

Studying the decomposition of austenite upon isothermal transformation at different temperatures is necessary for fundamental examination of the process. However, few commercial heat treatments involve isothermal transformation. Instead, most heat treatments involve cooling a steel from the austenite region in a continuous manner. That is, the steel piece is removed from the austenitizing furnace and placed in a quenchant (e.g., air, oil, water) and allowed to cool to 25°C. Note that this is not a constant cooling rate, but the temperature usually does decrease monotonically and "smoothly." Therefore, for heat treating purposes it would be more useful to have a TTT diagram which indicates the structures forming for different cooling rates. This is a *continuous cooling TTT diagram*, sometimes called a *CCT diagram*.

The continuous cooling TTT diagram is determined in a manner similar to that used for the isothermal TTT diagram. One method involves microstructural examination of samples of a given steel which have been cooled from austenite at a given rate, with each sample cooled rapidly to 25°C after reaching a certain different temperature. This is illustrated schematically in Fig. 2-24. The

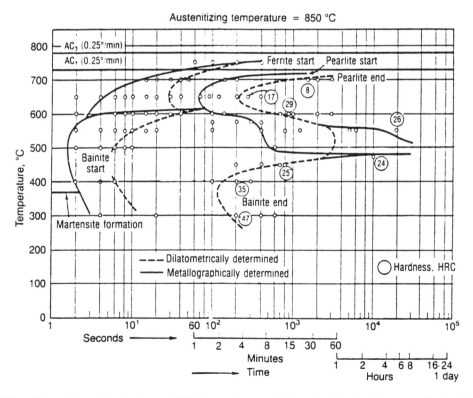

Fig. 2-19   Comparison of the isothermal TTT diagram for a steel determined by the dilatometry (dashed lines) and metallography (continuous lines). (From *Atlas zur Warmebehandlung der Stahle*, Vol 1-4, Verlag Stahleisen mbH, Dusseldorf, Germany (1954), as given in G. Krauss, *Steels: Heat Treatment and Processing Principles*, ASM International, Materials Park, Ohio, p 93 (1990))

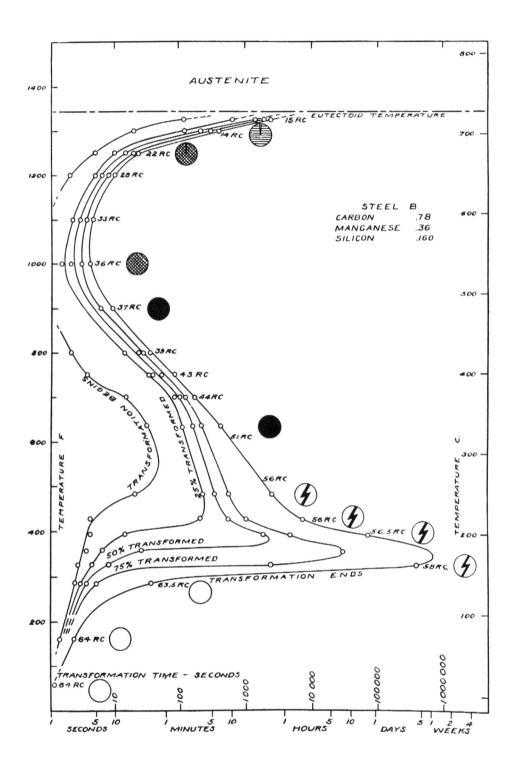

Fig. 2-20　Isothermal TTT diagram for a steel determined by Davenport and Bain. (From E.S. Davenport and E.C. Bain, *Trans. AIME*, Vol 90, p. 117 (1930))

microstructural examination indicates which microconstituent has formed along the cooling curve, an example of which is shown in Fig. 2-25. This procedure is then repeated for different cooling rates. The beginning of the formation of each microconstituent is noted on the temperature-time diagram, as well as the location for the completion of the decomposition of austenite. The other method uses a dilatometer; typical data are shown in Fig. 2-26.

A continuous cooling TTT diagram is shown in Fig. 2-27 for a eutectoid steel, and in Fig. 2-28 for a hypoeutectoid and for a hypereutectoid steel. For the hypereutectoid steel, note that no region for the formation of primary iron carbide is shown, as was indicated by the curves in Fig. 2-22. The reason is that in this case the samples were austenitized in the two phase austenite-iron carbide region, and thus the structure upon beginning transformation was austenite and iron carbide. Upon cooling, no significant amount of additional iron carbide formed.

It is common in continuous cooling TTT diagrams to place some cooling curves on the diagram, and to give the hardness at 25°C at the lower end of each curve. Such cooling curves are shown on the diagrams in Figs. 2-28 and 2-29. Note that the cooling curves for which primary ferrite and pearlite form show a perturbation, with the temperature rising for a small time period, before continuing to decrease, and that this effect occurs when the primary ferrite (in hypoeutectoid steels) or pearlite (in eutectoid and hypereutectoid steels) begins to form. This effect is caused by the heat release upon the transformation, which is sufficiently rapid that it compensates for heat loss by the sample to the surroundings, resulting in a temperature rise. The heat effect is also present when forming martensite or bainite, but usually the cooling rate

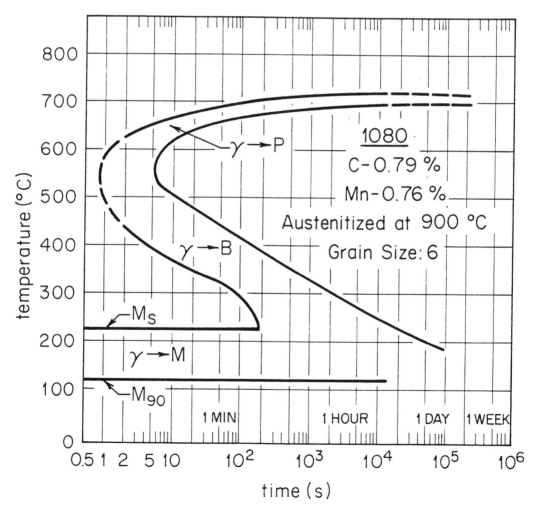

Fig. 2-21   Isothermal TTT diagram for a eutectoid, plain carbon steel. Legend: A = Austenite; F = Ferrite; C = Carbide; M = Martensite; B = Bainite; P = Pearlite. (Adapted from *Atlas of Isothermal Transformation and Cooling Transformation Diagrams,* American Society for Metals, Metals Park, Ohio (1977))

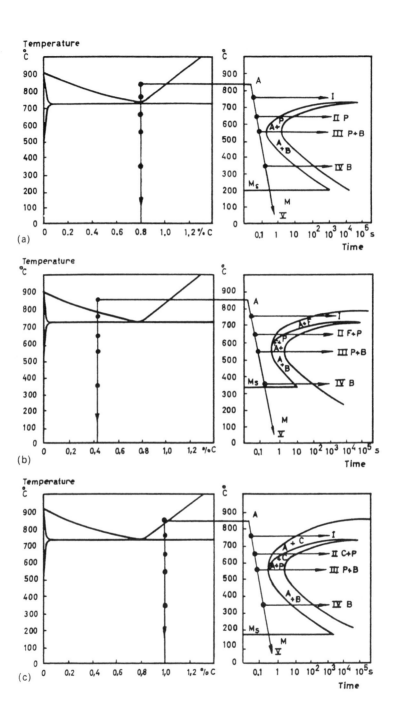

Fig. 2-22 Part 1   Schematic illustration of the effect of carbon content on the isothermal TTT diagrams of plain carbon steels. (Part 1) Structural transformations resulting from various cooling programs for steels containing: (a) 0.80% C; (b) 0.45% C; (c) 1.0% C. Legend: A = austenite; B = bainite; C = cementite; F = ferrite; P = pearlite; M = martensite; M_3 = start of martensite formation. ((Part 1) Adapted from K.E. Thelning, *Steel and Its Heat Treatment*, Butterworths, London (1975)) *(continued)*

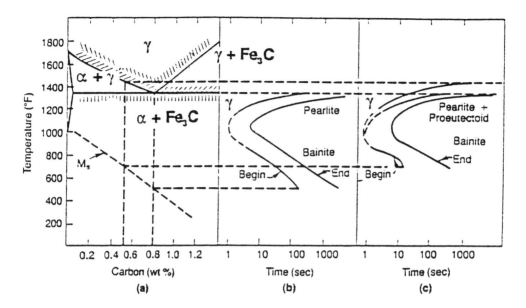

Fig. 2-22 Part 2 (continued) Relationship to Fe-C diagram (a) of IT diagrams of eutectoid steel (b) and steel containing 0.5% carbon(c). ((Part 2) adapted from G. Krauss and J.F. Libsch, *Phase Diagrams in Ceramic, Glass and Metal Technology*, A.M. Alper, editor, Academic Press, New York (1970))

Type: 1021
Composition: Fe - 0.20% C - 0.81% Mn Grain size: 8-9
Austenitized at 927°C (1700°F)

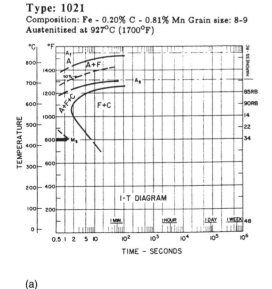

(a)

Type: W1 Tool Steel
Composition: Fe - 1.13% C - 0.30% Mn Grain size: 7-8
Austenitized at 910°C (1670°F)

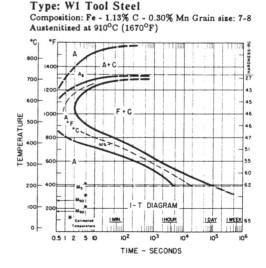

(b)

Fig. 2-23 Actual isothermal TTT diagram for a plain carbon steel showing the effect of carbon content. (From same source as Fig. 2-21)

is greater in this range of the TTT diagram, and hence the heat release cannot compensate for the heat extraction. One can usually detect a slight change in slope of the cooling curve when martensite begins to form (see curve marked "901" in Fig. 2-27).

As the cooling rate increases, the hardness increases. Once a cooling rate is attained which will not allow formation of any pearlite, bainite, primary ferrite or primary iron carbide, then the structure will be all martensite for this rate or higher (if the M_f is above 25°C), and these rates will give the maximum hardness for the given steel. The cooling rate which will just miss the "nose" of the diagram is called the *critical cooling rate* or *critical cooling velocity*.

A continuous cooling TTT diagram for a 0.37% C alloy steel is shown in Fig. 2-29. (In this diagram, the start of primary ferrite formation is shown, and the completion of pearlite, but the region indicating the start of pearlite formation is not shown.) The samples cooled along the curve marked at the bottom by "585" (which is the Diamond Pyramid hardness) passed through the bainite region, but formed only a few percent bainite. The rest of the structure is martensite, as seen in the microstructures shown below the TTT diagram. The sample cooled along the line marked "215" passed only through the region of formation of primary ferrite and pearlite, which are labeled on the micrograph. Upon cooling considerably slower, along the line marked "185," the sample also passed through the primary ferrite and pearlite region. However, the microstructure shown below the diagram shows that the amount of primary ferrite has increased, but this feature is not noted on the TTT diagram. The greater amount of primary ferrite makes this steel cooled along this curve considerably softer than samples cooled through the same region on the TTT diagram but at faster rates.

On continuous cooling, the austenite does not begin to decompose at the equilibrium transformation temperatures A_1, A_3 and A_{cm} to the transformation products pearlite, primary ferrite or primary Fe_3C. Instead, undercooling is required to initiate these transformations. A common nomenclature to indicate the temperatures at

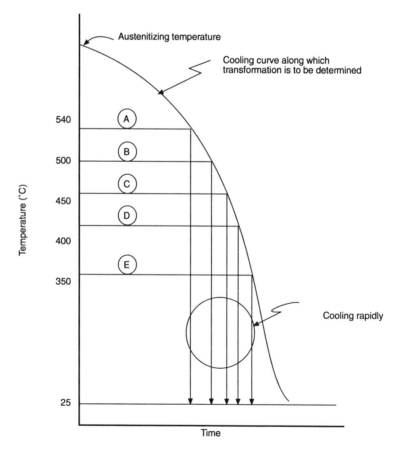

Fig. 2-24   Schematic illustration of the heat treatment of samples in order to determine the sequence of the decomposition of austenite along the cooling curve. Actual microstructures corresponding to the letters are shown in Fig. 2-25

which these transformations begin upon cooling is with an additional subscript, A_{r1}, A_{r3} and A_{rcm} (See Table 2-1). The subscript "r" is for the French word *refroidissement* (cooling). It is important to note that fixed temperatures cannot be set since the transformation is dependent on the cooling rate, the temperature being lower the more rapid the cooling.

Another method of presenting the transformation upon continuous cooling is shown by Fig. 2-30. Here the cooling curve is represented by the cooling rates at 700°C. (The reasons for the choice of this temperature will be given in Chapter 3.) For example, if the sample is cooled continuously along a temperature-time curve (which is not linear) which has a slope of 1000°C/min.

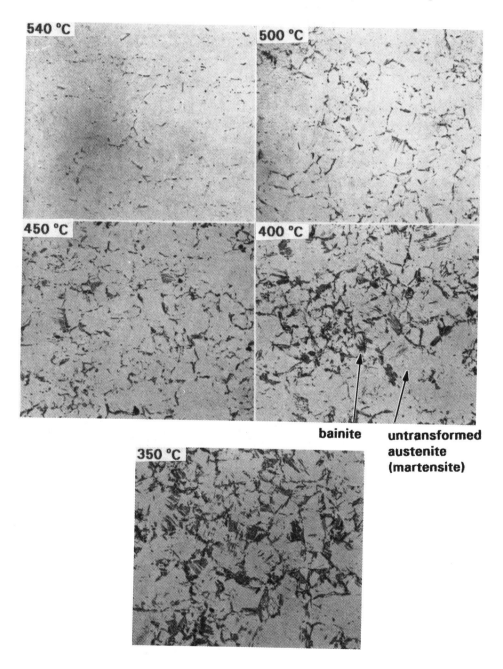

bainite   untransformed austenite (martensite)

Fig. 2-25   Microstructures of 0.054 in. dia. specimens of the B.S. En 12 steel, air cooled to the temperatures indicated, and then water quenched. The dark features are bainite and the whiter background is untransformed austenite, converted to martensite upon finally cooling to 25° C. (From W. Steven and G. Mayer, *J. Iron and Steel Institute*, Vol 174, p. 36 (1953))

(17°C/sec.) at 700°C, martensite begins to form at 340°C; at 280°C the steel has 50% martensite-50% austenite, and the M_f is reached at 120°C. Thus the structure at 25°C is all martensite. This sequence is shown by the heavy line marked A in Fig. 2-30. If the steel is cooled corresponding to a rate of 50°C/min. (0.8°C/sec.) (curve marked B), then upon cooling, bainite begins to form at 420°C. At 340°C there is 50% bainite and 50% austenite. At 320°C, there is about 60% bainite and 40% austenite, and at this temperature the austenite begins to transform to martensite. At 145°C, all of the austenite has transformed to martensite, giving at 25°C a structure of 60% bainite and 40% martensite.

Comparison of Isothermal and Continuous Cooling TTT Diagrams

Isothermal TTT diagrams and continuous cooling TTT diagrams for two steels are shown in Fig. 2-31. Note that the continuous cooling TTT diagram is displaced to lower temperatures and longer times than the isothermal TTT diagram. The M_s and M_f temperatures are, of course, the same for the two diagrams.

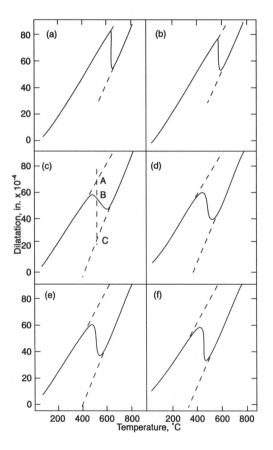

Fig. 2-26   Dilation curves illustrating the volume changes which occur during continuous cooling upon the formation of decomposition products from austenite. (From same source as Fig. 2-25)

Factors Affecting the TTT Diagram

The TTT diagrams are affected by any factor that affects the rate of nucleation and rate of growth of pearlite, bainite, primary ferrite and primary iron carbide. The factors can be described under two categories: chemical composition and austenite grain size.

Chemical composition

The common alloying elements decrease the rate of nucleation and rate of growth of primary ferrite, pearlite and bainite. It is also found that increasing carbon has a similar effect. These effects occur if the carbon and alloying elements are in solid solution in the austenite, and randomly distributed on an atomic scale. The effect of increasing carbon content is shown by comparing Fig. 2-21 to Fig. 2-23a. Note two effects here. One is that increasing carbon content displaces the TTT diagram to slightly longer times, and another is that increasing carbon content lowers the M_s and M_f temperatures.

The effect of alloying additions on the isothermal and continuous cooling TTT diagram is illustrated in Fig. 2-32. Note that the primary ferrite, pearlite and bainite curves are displaced to longer times. Also note that the alloying elements do not affect the kinetics of the formation of the different microconstituents in the same manner. In some steels, the primary ferrite and pearlite curves are much more affected than the bainite curves (Fig. 2-32b).

In examining the effect of chemical composition on the TTT diagram, it is very important to understand that if the austenite is not chemically homogeneous, the rate of formation of the transformation products will be increased. Thus if undissolved carbides are present, then nucleation of pearlite and bainite will be enhanced. This is why in Fig. 2-23 the TTT diagram for the hypereutectoid steel is displaced to shorter times than in the diagram in Fig. 2-21 for a eutectoid steel. For the high carbon steel, austenitization was carried out in the two phase austenite-iron carbide region, and the iron carbides already present in the austenite acted as nuclei for pearlite and bainite formation.

If the austenitization time is too short to allow the dispersion of alloying additions upon forming austenite from the starting structure (e.g., pearlite), then these chemical gradients in the austenite (even if the structure is all austenite) will allow the transformation products to nucleate more easily than if the austenite is chemically homogeneous. The homogenization of the austenite is affected by the austenitizing temperature and time and the starting microstructure.

Empirical relations have been determined which relate the M_s temperature to the chemical composition, and two are given in Fig. 2-33a. Note the limitations given for the validity of these equations. Of more interest is a relation which allows a determination of the amount of retained austenite for a given quench temperature, such as shown in Fig. 2-33b. The M_s temperature is known (or estimated from equations) and the quench temperature (T_q) is then used in the abscissa in the figure to determine the amount of retained austenite upon quenching to temperature T_q.

Austenite grain size

The prior austenite grain size has a significant effect on the location of the TTT diagram on the time axis. The microconstituents (e.g., pearlite, bainite) nucleate primarily at the austenite grain boundaries. Thus, the austenite grain size affects the start of the transformation, and indirectly the completion of the transformation. Consider the nucleation of pearlite occurring at the austenite grain boundaries. The nucleation rate is the number of pearlite nuclei formed per austenite grain boundary area per time. This is independent of the grain size. However, the important factor here is the number of nuclei per time, which is the surface nucleation rate times the austenite grain boundary area. Thus, a steel which has a smaller (finer) grain size (larger ASTM grain size number) will have more surface area available for nucleation, and pearlite will nucleate faster. This is illustrated in Fig. 2-34. Therefore, a smaller grain size will displace the TTT diagram

to shorter times. The higher nucleation rate will also decrease the time for completion of the formation of pearlite, and thus on the TTT diagram a smaller grain size will also shift the completion of the reaction to shorter times. Similar arguments about the effect of austenite grain size on the formation of bainite and primary ferrite are valid.

Fig. 2-35 shows isothermal TTT diagrams for the same steel but with two different austenite grain sizes. The diagram is displaced to longer times for the larger grain size (smaller ASTM grain size number).

There are sparse data which indicate that the M_s and M_f temperatures may be dependent on the austenite grain size. For example, for a 52100 steel, Kern reports a M_s of 500°F for an ASTM grain size of 9 (austenitized at 1550°F) and of 300°F for a grain size of 3 (austenitized at 1950°F) (R. Kern, *Heat Treating*, November 1990). The cause does not appear to have been established. It could be associated with the heterogeneity of the austenite (note that this is a high carbon steel and 1550°F is in the two phase austenite + carbide region) and not directly with the austenite grain size.

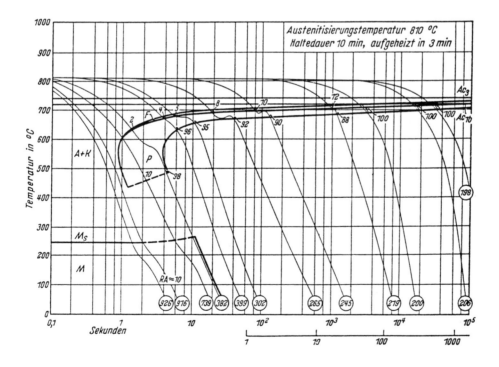

Fig. 2-27   Continuous cooling TTT diagram for a eutectoid, plain carbon steel. A is austenite, K is Fe$_3$C, M is martensite. (From L. Habraken and J.-L. de Brouwer, *De Ferri Metallographica, Vol. 1, Fundamentals of Metallography*, W.B. Saunders, Philadelphia (1966))

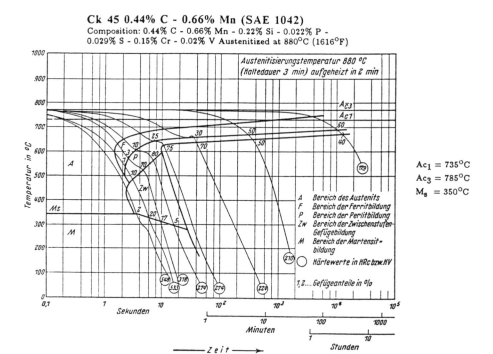

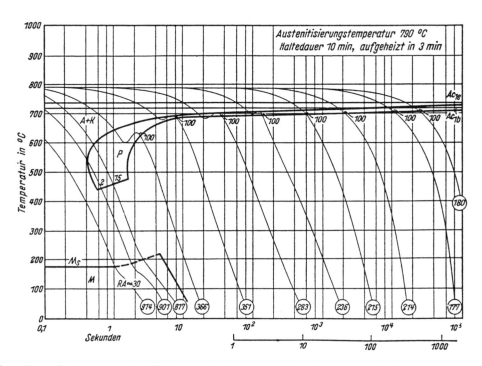

Fig. 2-28 Continuous cooling TTT diagram for hypoeutectoid and hypereutectoid, plain carbon steels. (A is austenite, F is primary ferrite, K is Fe₃C, P is pearlite, M is martensite and Zw is bainite) (From same source as Fig. 2-27)

Continuous cooling transformation diagram for the steel containing 0.37% C, 0.36% Si, 0.85% Mn, 1.44% Ni, and 0.02% Mo, austenitized at 800 C (1470 F) for 20 minutes.

Typical micro-structures of the steel described above continuously cooled at various rates (X1000, etched with 2% nital).

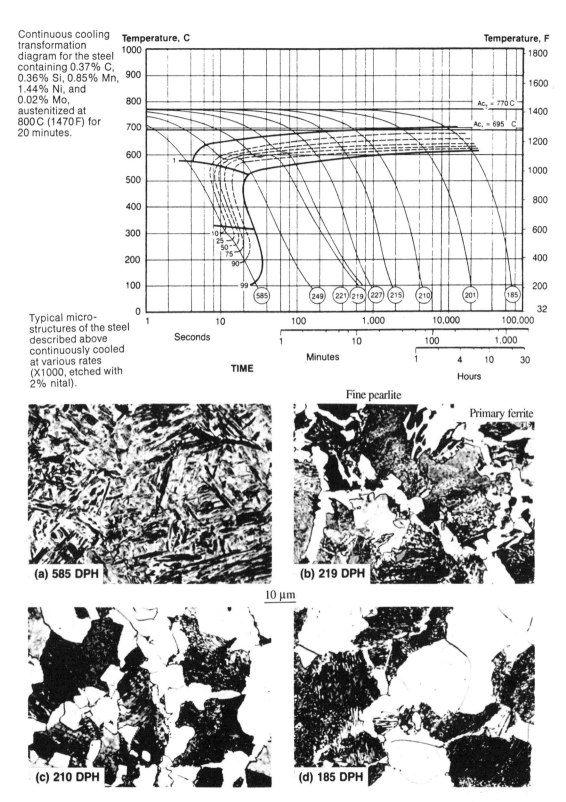

Fig. 2-29   Continuous cooling TTT diagram for an alloy steel, with microstructure shown for four cooling rates. (Adapted from W.W. Cias, *Phase Transformation, Kinetics and Hardenability of Medium-Carbon Steels*, Climax Molybdenum Co., Greenwich, Conn. (1972))

2 Ni Cr Mo

Composition: 0.30% C - 0.48% Mn - 0.25% Si - 0.020% P -
0.020% S - 2.00% Cr - 0.40% Mo - 2.00% Ni Grain size: 8-9
Austenitized at 850°C (1562°F)

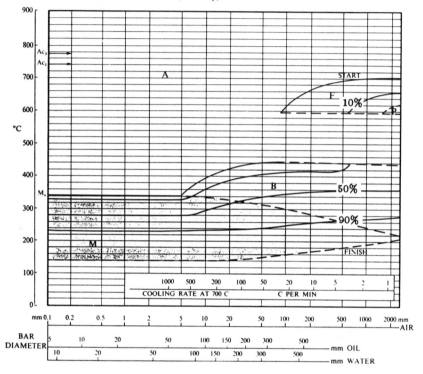

Fig. 2-30 Continuous cooling TTT diagram for an alloy steel, showing a different method of presenting the transformation process compared to that in the preceding figures. (From M. Atkins, *Atlas of Continuous Cooling Transformation Diagrams for Engineering Steels*, American Society for Metals, Metals Park, Ohio, p. 16 (1980))

0.73% C - 1.62% Si (71 Si 7)

Composition: 0.73% C - 0.73% Mn - 1.62% Si - 0.019% P -
0.012 S - 0.10% Cr - 0.19% Cu - 0.12% Ni - 0.01% V
Austenitized at 845°C (1555°F)

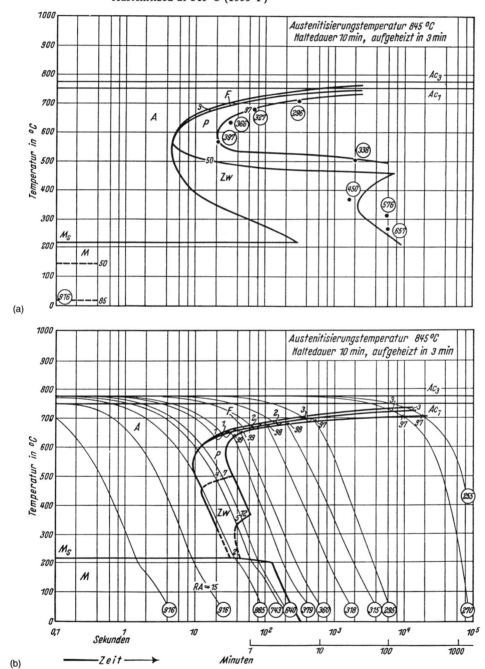

(a)

(b)

Fig. 2-31   Comparison of the isothermal TTT diagram (a) and the continuous cooling TTT diagram (b) for two steels (From same source as Fig. 2-27) *(continued)*

50 CrV 4 (SAE 6145)
Composition: 0.47% C - 0.82% Mn - 0.35% Si - 0.035% P -
0.015% S - 1.20% Cr - 0.14% Cu - 0.04% Ni - 0.11% V
Austenitized at 880°C (1616°F)

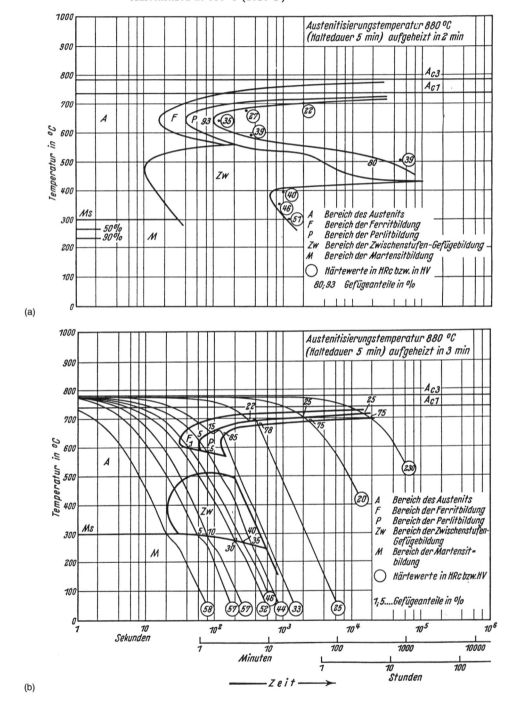

(a)

(b)

Fig. 2-31 (continued) Comparison of the isothermal TTT diagram (a) and the continuous cooling TTT diagram (b) for two steels (From same source as Fig. 2-27)

1335

C-0.35

Mn-1.85

Austenitized at 1550°F

Grain Size:
70% 7, 30% 2

LEGEND

A = Austenite   M = Martensite
F = Ferrite   B = Bainite
C = Carbide   P = Pearlite

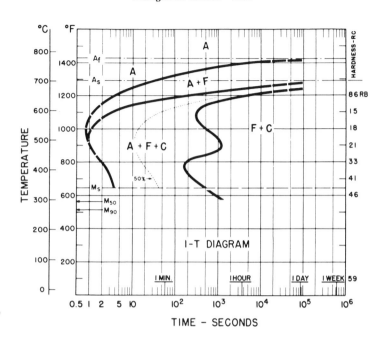

4140

C-0.37   Mn-0.77

Cr-0.98   Mo-0.21

Austenitized at 1550°F

Grain Size: 7-8

LEGEND

A = Austenite   M = Martensite
F = Ferrite   B = Bainite
C = Carbide   P = Pearlite

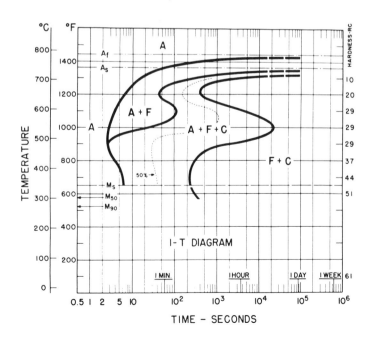

Fig. 2-32   Isothermal TTT diagrams showing the effect of alloying elements on the shape and location of the diagram (From same source as Fig. 2-27) *(continued)*

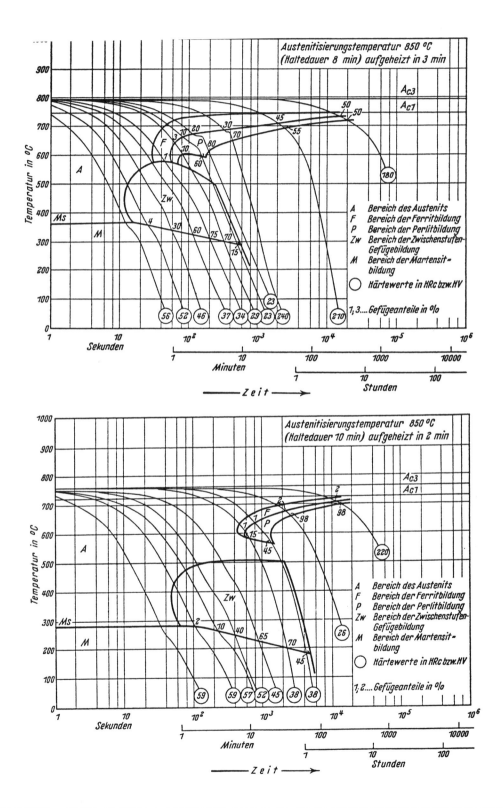

Fig. 2-32(b) (continued) Continuous cooling TTT diagrams showing the effect of alloying elements on the shape and location of the diagram. (From same source as Fig. 2-27)

The alloying elements must be completely dissolved in the austenite.

Stevens and Haynes

M_S (°C) = 561 - 474 % C - 33 % Mn - 17- % Ni - 17 % Cr -21 % Mo

Stuhlmann

For high alloy and medium alloy steels.

M_S (°C) = 550 - 350 % C - 40 % Mn - 20 % Cr -10 % Mo
- 17 % Ni - 8 % W - 35 % V - 10 % Cu + 15 % Co + 30 % Al

(a)

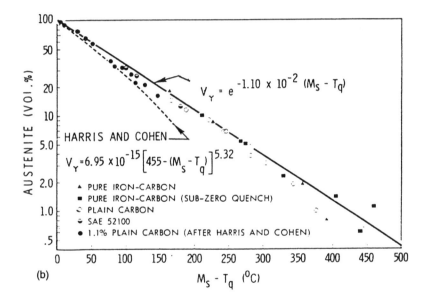

(b)

Fig. 2-33   Relations which allow estimation of the (a) M_S temperature and (b) amount of retained austenite from the chemical composition. ((a) from W. Stevens and A.G. Haynes, *J. Iron and Steel Inst.*, Vol 183, p 349 (1956), and W. Stuhlmann, *Harterei Techn. Mitt.*, Vol 6, p. 31 (1954); (b) adapted from D.P. Koistinen and R.E. Marburger, *Acta Metallurgica*, Vol 7, p. 59 (1959))

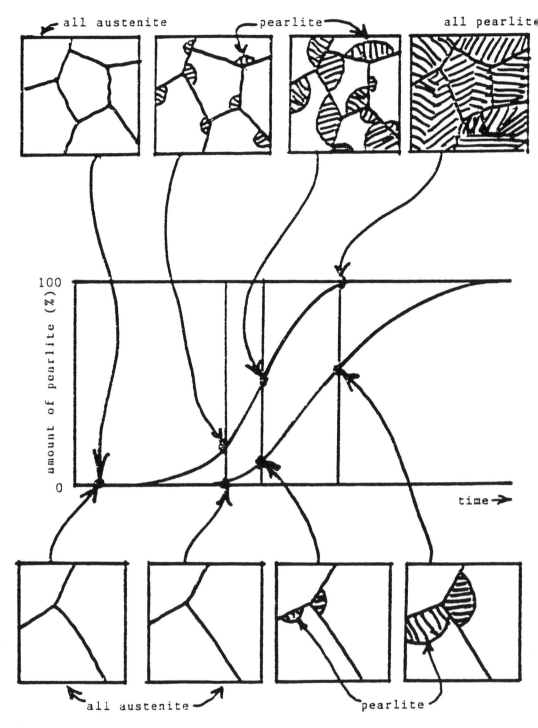

Fig. 2-34   Schematic diagram showing the effect of austenite grain size on the rate of isothermal transformation of austenite to pearlite

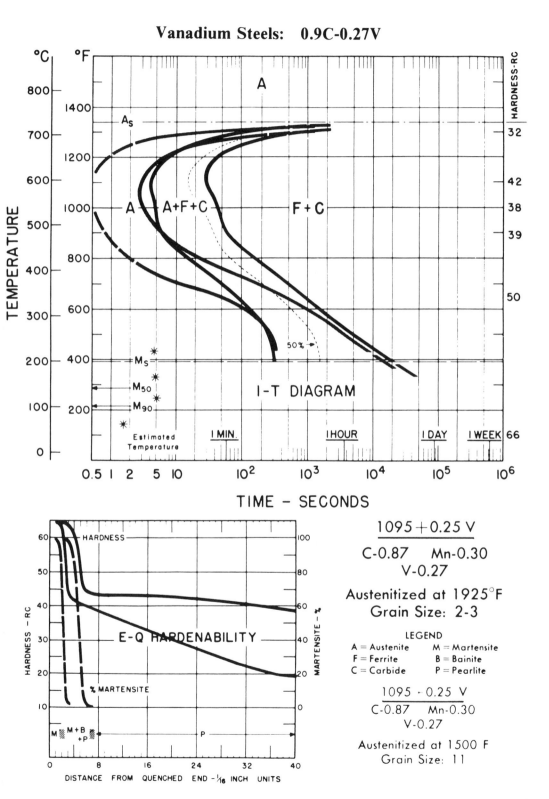

Fig. 2-35 Isothermal TTT diagram showing that the diagram is displaced to longer times for the larger austenite grain size. (From *Atlas of Isothermal Transformation Diagrams*, U.S. Steel Corporation, Pittsburgh (1950))

Chapter 3

Hardenability

Introduction

In heat treating steels for hardening, the part is usually continuously cooled from austenite to develop the desired mechanical properties (usually specified in terms of hardness). For relatively high strength requirements, it is necessary to form a martensitic structure (with its accompanying low toughness) having a hardness higher than the required value, then temper the part appropriately (to form tempered martensite with improved toughness) to lower the hardness to the required value. This approach requires forming a martensitic structure (or a structure containing martensite with other microconstituents). To obtain this structure requires that the cooling curve at each location in the steel part, which must be all martensite, miss the nose of the continuous cooling TTT diagram.

Clearly, to form all martensite is easier if the TTT diagram is displaced to longer times. In this sense, easier means that slower cooling can be employed. This is a very important practical aspect to quenching for hardening, because several advantages accrue from being allowed to use slower cooling to form martensite. One of the most important advantages is that less rigid control of the heat transfer is required. In quenching steels which have the TTT diagram displaced to short times (e.g., the nose at 1 sec.), rapid cooling is required to form all martensite, and very little variation in this rapid cooling is allowed. For example, water quenching may be required along with a high circulation velocity, and the temperature of the water may have to be closely regulated because a slight rise in the water temperature may reduce the cooling rate, although only slightly, sufficiently to allow formation of less than all martensite. On the other hand, if the TTT diagram is displaced to long times (e.g., the nose at 60 sec.), control of the water temperature is less critical, and circulation of the water may not be required.

Thus, it is seen that it is advantageous in hardening to use a steel which has a TTT diagram displaced to long times. (The choice may have to be consistent with other

requirements and, of course, cost.) This is brought about basically by use of steels containing appropriate amounts of alloying elements (e.g., Cr, Ni, Mo).

On a relative basis, using a steel which has the TTT diagram located at longer times allows slower cooling to form martensite. Thus this steel is more *hardenable* than one with its TTT diagram located at shorter times, since

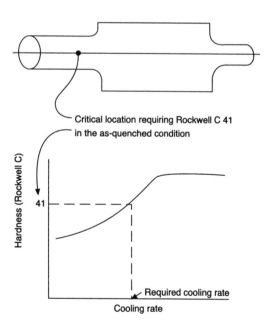

Fig. 3-1 Schematic illustration of how the hardness can be determined at a location in a steel part if (a) the cooling rate at that location is known, and (b) the hardness-cooling rate curve is known for the steel from which the part is made. (This curve depends upon the chemical composition and the austenite grain size.)

the more hardenable steel can form martensite over a wider range of cooling rates than can a less hardenable steel. Thus it is said that the former steel has a higher *hardenability*. That is, the term hardenability is used (at this stage) to denote the ability of a steel to form martensite over a range of cooling rates.

[In the Metals Handbook (*Metals Handbook, Desk Edition*, H.E. Boyer and T.L. Gall, editors, American Society for Metals, Metals Park, Ohio (1985)), the following definition is given of hardenability: "The relative ability of a ferrous alloy to form martensite when quenched from a temperature above the upper critical temperature. Hardenability is commonly measured as the distance below a quenched surface at which the metal exhibits a specific hardness (50 HRC, for example) or a specific percentage of martensite in the microstructure."]

It was clearly demonstrated in Chapter 2, with regard to the continuous cooling TTT diagrams, that there is a cooling rate above which all martensite will form upon cooling to 25°C. (This assumes that the M_f is above 25°C.) This is the *critical cooling rate* or the *critical cooling velocity*. The cooling curve for this critical cooling rate is not linear, so to properly characterize or assign some numerical value, the method employed to determine the cooling rate must be specified. For example, the time to cool half-way from the austenitizing temperature

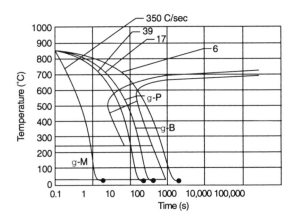

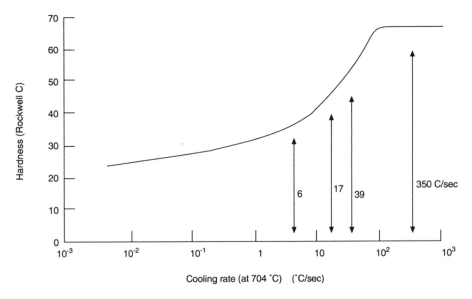

Fig. 3-2 The continuous cooling TTT diagram for a 1080 steel, with cooling curves superimposed, and showing the relation of the TTT diagram to the hardness-cooling rate curve for this steel. (TTT diagram from C.R. Brooks, *Heat Treatment of Ferrous Alloys*, Hemisphere Publishing Corporation/McGraw-Hill Book Company, New York (1979))

to the quench temperature (e.g., 25°C) could be employed. Or the "average" cooling rate could be used, being defined as the difference in the austenitizing temperature and the quench temperature divided by the time to cool to within some value of the quench temperature (e.g., to within 100°C of the quench temperature). Or the cooling rate could be taken as the slope of the tangent at a given temperature, such as 700°C. This latter definition appears to be more quantitative, but it is not obvious at what temperature the derivative dT/dt should be taken.

The crux of this chapter is to develop a method to quantitatively define hardenability. Empirical methods to estimate the hardenability knowing the chemical composition and prior austenite grain size will be described, and their utility examined. However, the Jominy end-quench test is first described and its relation to hardenability explained.

The Jominy End-quench Test

In this chapter the hardness obtained at 25°C after continuous cooling from austenite is being treated, and thus a useful curve to have for each steel of interest is a graph of hardness versus cooling rate. (As mentioned in the previous section, we must decide how to specify this rate.) If a steel component of a given shape and size is to be made of the steel which has this hardness-cooling rate curve, and the hardness at any given point is specified, this curve can be used to determine the required cooling rate at this location. Then one must examine the heat transfer conditions which will give this cooling rate. This is the subject of Chapter 4. This concept is illustrated schematically in Fig. 3-1.

Let us look more closely at the hardness-cooling rate curve. We will do this by using a continuous cooling TTT diagram for a plain carbon steel (1080, 0.8% C) and for an alloy steel (4340, 0.38% C, 0.75% Mn, 1.85% Ni,

0.80% Cr, 0.25% Mo). Since the TTT diagram depends on the prior austenite grain size, each of these diagrams is for a specific austenite grain size. As shown in Fig. 3-2, the hardness-cooling rate curve is determined by the continuous cooling TTT diagram. Although in Fig. 3-2 this curve is schematic, approximate hardness values are shown at four specific cooling rates. (These cooling rates are the slope of the temperature-time curve at 704°C.) The critical cooling rate is approximately 350°C/sec. Thus, on the hardness-cooling rate curve, the hardness is constant at the maximum value corresponding to an all-martensite structure above a cooling rate of about 350°C/sec.

It can be seen that the hardness-cooling rate curve will shift upwards towards the maximum value if the TTT diagram shifts to longer times. However, the hardness in the region of the curves representing the formation of all martensite will be determined essentially only by the carbon content of the martensite. (Analytical expressions to represent the hardness of martensite are given in Chapter 9.) Thus this region of the hardness-cooling rate curve increases as the carbon content increases, but only up to about 0.6% C (see Fig. 3-3). These effects are shown in Fig. 3-4, which compares the continuous cooling TTT diagrams of the 1080 steel and the 4340 steel, and shows their relation to the hardness-cooling rate curves. Note that in these two diagrams, the cooling curves (temperature-time curves) for the four chosen cooling rates of 350, 39, 17 and 6°C/sec. are shown on both TTT diagrams. For the 1080 steel, all martensite is formed only at a cooling rate of 350°C/sec. formed. However, for the 4340 steel, all martensite is formed only at a cooling rate of 350°C/sec. For the 4340 steel, the critical cooling rate is about 22°C/sec., so at a cooling rate of 350 and 39°C/sec., all martensite is formed in this steel. However, in the cooling rate range where all martensite is formed, the

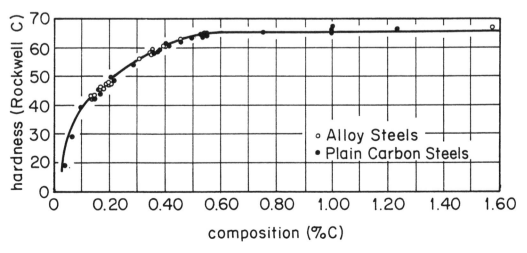

Fig. 3-3   Hardness of martensite as a function of the carbon content of the martensite. The data for both the plain carbon steels and the alloy steels are fitted by a single curve, showing that the hardness of martensite does not depend on the alloy content. (From same source as Fig. 3-2)

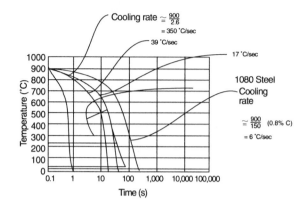

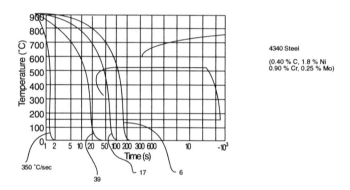

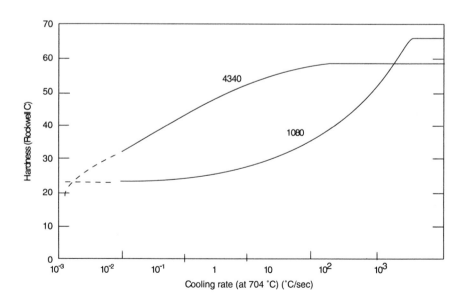

Fig. 3-4 Hardness versus cooling rate for a 1080 steel and a 4340 steel. For each steel, the curve is for a specific austenite grain size

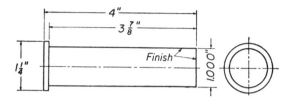

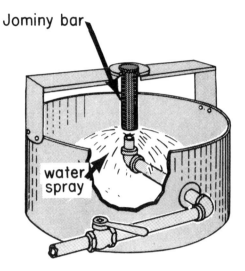

Jominy test specifications

The test specimen is normalized at about 150 °F above the Ac3 point, then machined to remove any decarburization and to obtain the correct dimensions. Following this, the specimen is heated to about 75 °F above the Ac3 point in a closed container that has a layer of cast-iron chips in the bottom. The specimen is held at this temperature 30 min and is cooled immediately thereafter on the hardenability fixture. The time spent in transferring to the fixture should not be more than 5 sec. This fixture is constructed so that the test specimen is held 1/2 in. above the water opening, in order that a column of water may be directed against the bottom of the piece. The water opening is 1/2 in. in diam and adjustment is made so that before the specimen is placed over it, a column of water 2½ in. high comes from the opening. The water temperature is kept at 75 °F plus or minus 5 °F and a condition of still air is maintained around the specimen during cooling. The piece is permitted to remain on the fixture until cold, or at least for 10 min., and is then quenched in cold water.

Schematic Illustration of Jominy Test

After cooling, two parallel flats, 180 deg apart and 0.015 in. deep, are ground along the entire length of the bar, and hardness measurements are taken at intervals of 1/16 in. for the first inch, then usually at intervals of 1/8 in. for the second inch, and 1/4 in. for the remainder of the bar. These hardnesses may be plotted to give a stanadard hardenability curve.

Fig. 3-5   Description of the Jominy test. (From same source as Fig. 3-2)

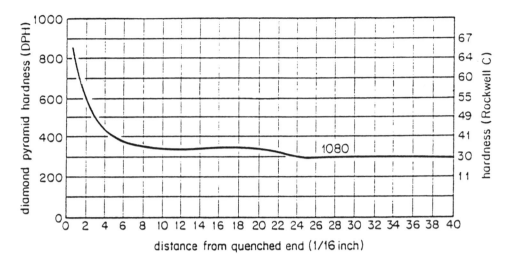

Fig. 3-6 A typical Jominy curve, for a 1080 steel. This curve is for a specific chemical composition and a specific austenite grain size. (From same source as Fig. 3-2)

1080 steel is harder, because it has the higher carbon martensite (see Fig. 3-3).

When the 1080 steel is cooled at 39°C/sec., a mixed structure of pearlite, bainite and martensite is formed, and the hardness is considerably less than that of the 4340 steel cooled at this same rate. When the 1080 steel is cooled at 17 and 6°C/sec., only pearlite is formed. At 17°C/sec., the pearlite is finer than that formed upon cooling at 6°C/sec., and hence harder. However, the hardness of the all-pearlite structure is considerably less than that of the mixed structure formed upon cooling at 39°C/sec., because of the presence of the hard martensite.

In the 4340 steel, cooling at 17 and 6°C/sec. produces a structure of martensite and bainite. As the cooling rate decreases, more bainite and less martensite are present.

The relative amount of these two microconstituents is not shown on the TTT diagram in Fig. 3-4, but for these two cooling rates only a small amount (e.g., <5%) of bainite is present. Thus the hardness is high (Fig. 3-4) and close to that of the martensite structure.

In the 1080 steel, reducing the cooling rate from the critical values of about 350°C/sec. to about 30°C/sec. produces a great decrease in hardness. Thus, in this range the hardness is quite sensitive to the cooling rate, which is shown in Fig. 3-4. This reflects the point made above that in low hardenability steels, slight differences in the cooling rate when high cooling rates are used (e.g., water quenching) allow wide differences in hardness. Note that this effect will not occur in the high hardenability 4340 steel.

From the curves in Fig. 3-4, it is seen that they can be taken as a measure of hardenability, since they show the cooling rate range over which all martensite can be formed. Thus, the 4340 steel clearly has the higher hardenability. *However*, note that it is incorrect to say that this steel is harder. Which of these two steels is harder depends upon the cooling rate range being considered.

The hardness-cooling rate curves can be obtained experimentally by austenitizing a set of samples of the steel of interest (which sets the austenite grain size), then cooling each sample at a different rate by the use of different quenchants (e.g., air, water, oil). The temperature-time curve for each sample must be known so that the cooling rate can be determined. This procedure was simplified by Jominy, who developed a method to obtain a range of cooling rates from a single sample. The method is illustrated schematically in Fig. 3-5. A bar of specified dimensions made from the steel of interest is austenitized at the desired temperature for the desired time, then is placed in a fixture which allows water to be sprayed at high velocity on the end. Any given location in the bar

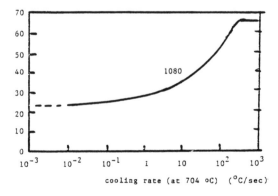

Fig. 3-7 A hardness-cooling rate curve derived from the Jominy curve in Fig. 3-6

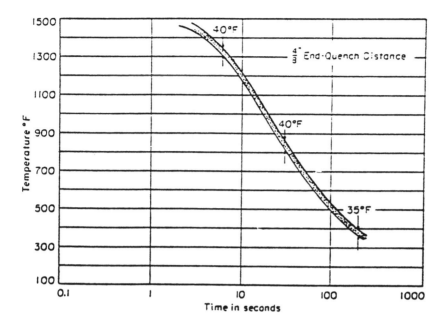

Fig. 3-8 Temperature-time data obtained at 0.5 inch from the end of a Jominy bar. The points represent data from 14 different tests using the same steel. (From J. Birtalan, R.G. Henley and A.L. Christenson, *Trans. ASM*, Vol 46, p 936 (1954))

loses heat to the water-quenched end, to the surrounding air, and by radiation. However, measurements show that the heat lost by these last two methods is negligible compared to that extracted out the water-quenched end. Also, it has been established that, at any distance from the water-quenched end, the temperature on the circular plane is essentially identical at any time. After the bar cools to 25°C, the hardness is measured on the surface along the axis. (A narrow flat surface is frequently ground to remove any oxidized material and to get below any decarburized layer. Extreme care must be taken to not affect the structure (burning) in the grinding operation.) Then the hardness is plotted as a function of distance from the quenched end, as shown in Fig. 3-6. This test is called the *Jominy end-quench test* and the plot is called a *Jominy curve*.

Clearly, the temperature-time curve at any location can be measured, so that the cooling rate can be established at each location. Thus from this the data could be plotted as a hardness-cooling rate plot as in Fig. 3-7.

It would appear that this method requires determining the temperature-time curves at various locations on the Jominy bar each time a steel sample is end-quenched. Certainly the thermal conductivity of steels is dependent upon the chemical composition, and the heat effects associated with the phase transformations which occur affect the cooling curve differently for different steels. The reproducibility for a given steel of the cooling curve at a given location is quite adequate, as shown by the data in Fig. 3-8. However, measurable differences in cooling

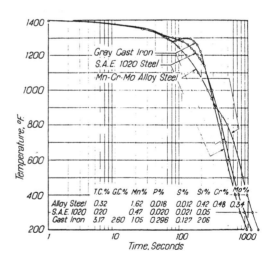

Fig. 3-9 Temperature-time cooling curves for two steels and a cast iron. These curves were for cooling at the center of 7.9 in. diameter cylinders quenched form 1650°F. (From C.R. Wilks, E. Cook and H.S. Avery, *Trans. ASM*, Vol 35, p 1 (1945))

curves are obtained for different steels, as illustrated by the cooling curves in cylinders shown in Fig. 3-9.

In Chapter 4 we will correlate the cooling conditions on the Jominy bar to those of steels quenched into various media. It will be seen that for these correlations to work best requires using a cooling rate at 704°C (1300°F). In Fig. 3-9 it is seen that at this temperature the curves for the different steels give about the same cooling rate. Thus the cooling rate at 704°C for any location on the Jominy bar is essentially independent of the steel composition. This is very important in being able to develop the heat transfer correlations described in Chapter 4. The cooling rate as a function of location on the Jominy bar is shown in Fig. 3-10.

The curve in Fig. 3-10 can be used to convert the hardness-cooling rate curves in Fig. 3-4 into a Jominy curve. In actuality, the curves in Fig. 3-4 were obtained by the curve in Fig. 3-10 and the Jominy curves in Fig. 3-11. In Fig. 3-4 the four cooling rates used (350, 39, 17

and 6°C/sec.) were chosen because they correspond to the cooling rates at 1/16, 1/4, 1/2 and 1 inch from the quenched end of the Jominy bar. The relation of the cooling curves at these locations and the Jominy curve is shown in Fig. 3-12. Note that on the Jominy curve plots the cooling rate is sometimes given at the top.

The Jominy test, when done properly, is quite reproducible. The reproducibility of the cooling rate at given locations was referred to earlier (Fig. 3-8). Fig. 3-13 shows Jominy curve data obtained on Jominy specimens from the same steel but for which the Jominy tests were performed at different laboratories.

It is thus seen that the hardness-cooling rate curve can be obtained from a single Jominy test. However, the lowest cooling rate is about 1°C/sec., which is consider-

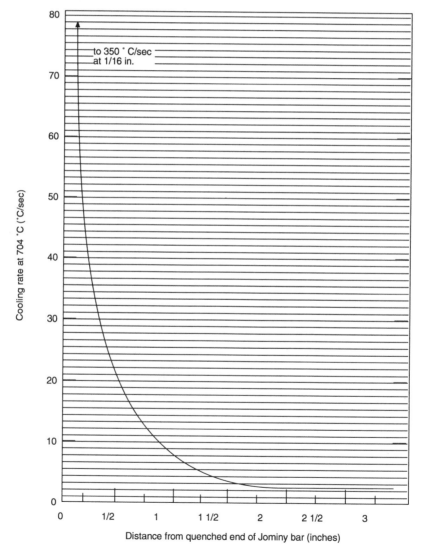

Fig. 3-10   The relationship between the cooling rate (at 704°C) and the position on the Jominy bar. (From W.E. Jominy in *Hardenability of Alloy Steels*, American Society for Metals, Metals Park, Ohio (1939))

ably above that associated with annealing (furnace cooling) and even normalizing (air cooling). Thus to obtain hardness data for cooling rates <1°C/sec. requires additional heat treatments. Also, steels of very high hardenability, such as "air hardenable" tool steels, require special heat treatments to obtain hardness-cooling rate curves.

The Jominy end-quench test is a relatively easy test to perform and is quite reproducible. Thus it is widely used to examine the hardenability of a steel and to provide information for the design of heat treatments of steels.

The Critical Diameter and the Ideal Critical Diameter

The concepts outlined in this section, leading to establishing a quantitative measure of hardenability, are given in more detail in Grossmann's book on hardenability (M.A. Grossmann, *Elements of Hardenability*, American Society for Metals, Metals Park, Ohio (1952)).

Critical diameter

As an introduction to establishing a quantitative measure of hardenability, we examine the concept of critical diameter. The *critical diameter* D_c is defined as that diameter which will form 50% martensite at the center when quenched into a given medium (or quenchant). (In Chapter 4 we will examine a quantitative method of characterizing the medium.) Note that stating a value of D_c for a given steel requires also stating how the steel was quenched.

The utility of using 50% martensite at the center instead of, say, 100% martensite, lies in the sensitivity of hardness and the microstructural etching effect (the darkness) to the amount of martensite present. In Fig. 3-14 is shown (at low magnification) the appearance of the polished and etched surface of a sample which has all martensite at the left, and all fine pearlite at the right. Note that the location of the region containing 50% martensite can be well correlated with the position in the microstructure where the dark etching begins.

The relationship between the diameter of cylinders of various sizes and the location across the diameter which contains 50% martensite when the cylinders are quenched into the same medium is illustrated by Fig. 3-15. Here are photographs of the cross-section of a set of cylinders of a given steel which have been quenched into a given medium. The cross-sections have been ground and heavily etched. The demarcation between the light and the dark regions shows the location of 50% martensite; the diametrical distance across this region is called the unhardened diameter D_u. Measurements of D_u were made from the photographs, and the ratio D_u/D versus D is plotted in Fig. 3-16. The diameter at which $D_u/D = 0$ is that diameter which has 50% martensite at the center; this is the critical diameter D_c for that quench. Thus D_c is obtained by extrapolation of the curve of a plot of D_u/D versus D to $D_u/D = 0$. This is shown in Fig. 3-16, giving a value of $D_c = 1.05$ inches for the steel of the bars in Fig. 3-15.

If the microstructure of a Jominy bar is determined along the axis of the bar, it is found that the position on

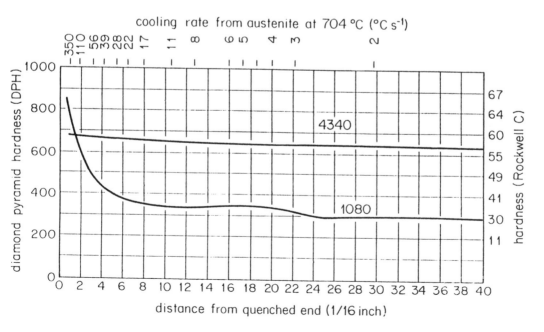

Fig. 3-11   Jominy curves of a 1080 and a 4340 steel. For each steel, the chemical composition and the austenite grain size was fixed. (From same source as Fig. 3-2)

the Jominy curve (hardness versus distance from quenched end) at which the rate of change in hardness is greatest (the inflection point) almost always contains 50% martensite. Thus, the critical diameter of the steel of

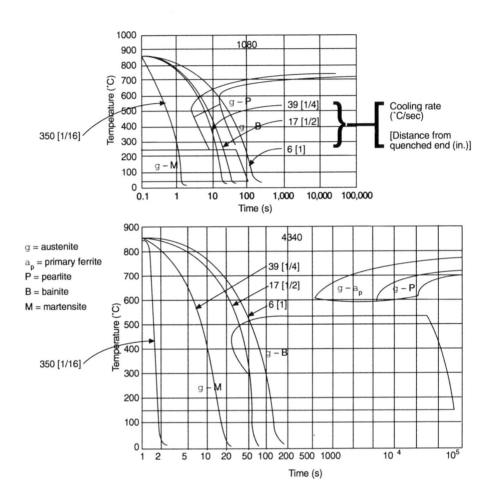

g = austenite
a_p = primary ferrite
P = pearlite
B = bainite
M = martensite

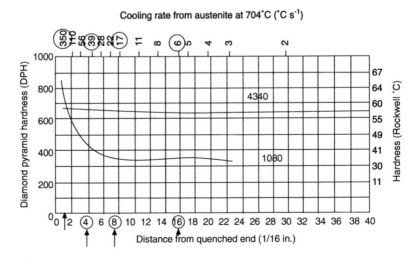

Fig. 3-12   Relationship of the continuous cooling TTT diagram to the Jominy curve

the bars shown in Fig. 3-15 can be obtained by measuring the hardness at the center of each, plotting these values versus the diameter, and determining the diameter of the inflection point. As shown in Fig. 3-16, this gives a critical diameter of 1.05 inches, in excellent agreement with that obtained by measuring the hardness at the center and plotting the data as shown in Fig. 3-17. Thus, the critical diameter can be obtained by appropriate hardness measurements at the center of cylinders.

The relationship between the TTT diagram, the Jominy curve and the critical diameter is shown in Fig. 3-18.

Severity of quench

The heat transfer process during quenching of a steel part will be discussed in detail in Chapter 4. However, it is necessary here to introduce a term which is a quantita-

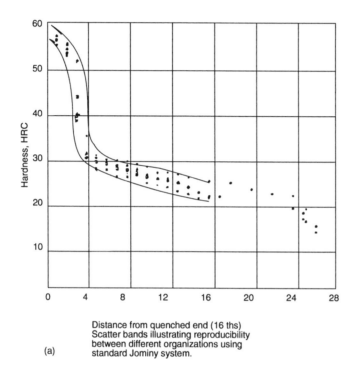

Distance from quenched end (16 ths)
Scatter bands illustrating reproducibility between different organizations using standard Jominy system.

(a)

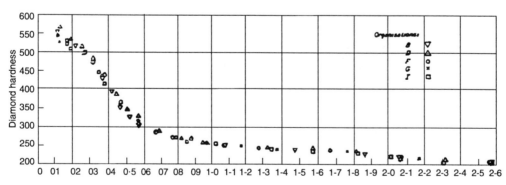

Distance from quenched end of Jominy bar, in.

(b)

Fig. 3-13   Jominy curves showing the reproducibility of the Jominy test. (a) From G.E. Totten, C.E. Bates and N.A. Clinton, *Handbook of Quenchants and Quenching Technology*, ASM International, Materials Park, Ohio (1993). (b) From *Symposium on the Hardenability of Steel*, Iron and Steel Institute, London (1946)

tive measure of the "cooling power" or "cooling ability" of a quenchant. This is the *severity of quench*, H, defined by the equation

$$H = h/2k$$

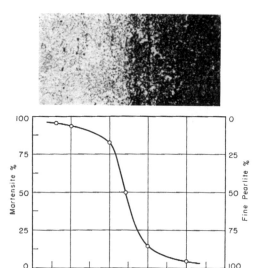

Fig. 3-14   Low magnification micrograph showing the transition from a predominantly martensite structure (at left) to a predominantly pearlite structure (at right), and the corresponding amount of martensite. (From M.A. Grossmann, *Elements of Hardenability*, American Society for Metals, Metals Park, Ohio (1952))

where h is the film coefficient associated with the heat transfer in the quenchant and k is the thermal conductivity of the steel. For a given steel, both are assumed to be temperature independent. Typical values of H range from 5.00 for a violently agitated brine quench to 0.2 for still oil; still water has a value of about 1.00. If the quench immediately brings the temperature of the surface of the steel to that of the quenchant, the H = ∞, and this quench is called an *ideal quench*.

In terms of cylinders, the heat transfer equations can be solved (making suitable assumptions) so that relationships can be obtained between the diameter of bars which will give the same cooling rate at the center when cooled into different (but given) quenchants. The results are shown in Fig. 3-19.

Ideal critical diameter

Note that the curves in Fig. 3-19 are based on heat transfer correlations, and in the strict sense they have nothing to do with hardenability. However, since these curves refer to the center of cylinders, they can be used with experimental data of D_c to determine the ideal critical diameter D_i.

In Fig. 3-15 are photographs of the etched cross-section through cylinders of the same steel after each was quenched into the same medium; thus the severity of quench H was fixed. It was found that the critical diameter D_i of this steel for this H value was 1.05 inches. For this steel, a cylinder having a diameter of 1.05 inches produced 50% martensite at the center when quenched into this quenchant of known severity of quench of about H = 1.0 (still water). We want to know what diameter cylinder

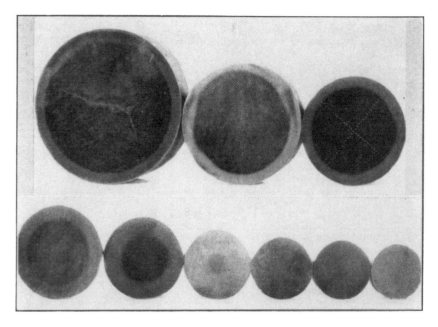

Fig. 3-15   Etched cross-sections of cylinders of a 1090 steel which were quenched in water. (From M.A. Grossmann, M. Asimov and S.F. Urban, in *Hardenability of Alloy Steels*, American Society for Metals, Metals Park, Ohio (1939))

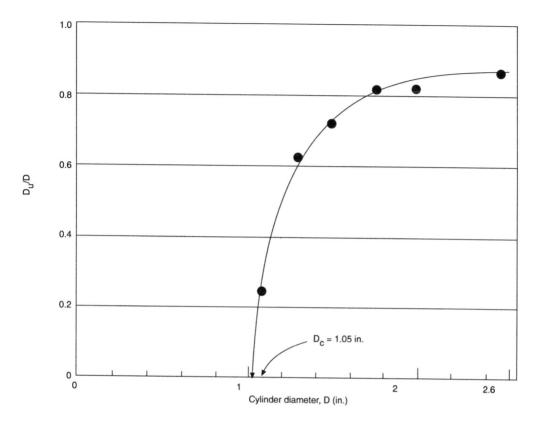

Fig. 3-16   The ratio of the unhardened diameter D_u to that of the diameter D versus the diameter D, from the photographs in Fig. 3-15. Note that at $D_u/D = 0$, the diameter is the critical diameter $D_c = 1.05$ inch for the quench used

made of this steel will be required to produce just 50% martensite at the center when using an ideal quench of H = ∞. (This diameter will be smaller than D_c, since an ideal quench is being used (H = ∞) which will cool the steel faster.) This is then a heat transfer problem, already solved and graphed in Fig. 3-19, from which D_i can be obtained, as illustrated in Fig. 3-20.

The procedure described above is one that can be used to determine the ideal critical diameter of a steel. It does require determining the critical diameter for a quenchant of known H value.

Another method recently described is as follows. (It is from J.M. Tartaglia and G.T. Eldis, *Met. Trans.*, Vol 15A, p 1172 (1984).) This method relies on using the curve in Fig. 3-21, which shows the relationship between the cooling rate at the center of cylinders when quenched into an ideal quench (H = ∞) and the location along the Jominy bar which has the same cooling rate. Since these cooling rates refer to the center of the cylinders and the quench is an ideal quench, then the diameter is the ideal critical diameter D_i. Thus, for a given steel (given chemical composition and austenite grain size), the Jominy curve can be determined experimentally, then the location along it at which 50% martensite is present (at the inflec-

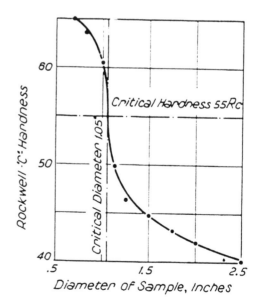

Fig. 3-17   A plot of center hardness versus bar diameter for the bars shown in Fig. 3-15. (From same source as Fig. 3-14)

tion point in the Jominy curve) can be determined. From this and the curve in Fig. 3-21, the ideal critical diameter can be determined.

In low carbon steels, microstructural determination of the location of 50% martensite is difficult. Also, in high hardenability steels, use of the inflection point in the Jominy curve to locate the position of 50% martensite is not as accurate as in low hardenability steels. Thus, Tartaglia and Eldis uses different hardness criteria. They utilized the hardness data in Fig. 3-22 (which were determined by microstructural examination of Jominy bars). They assumed that the location at 1/16 inch from the quenched end of the Jominy bar was all martensite, and they subtracted the difference in hardness of the curves in Fig. 3-22 from this value to locate the position of 50% martensite. They then used the curve in Fig. 3-21 to obtain D_i. Their method is illustrated in Fig. 3-23.

Calculation of the Ideal Critical Diameter

In this section we examine methods that have been developed which allow estimation of the ideal critical diameter from the chemical composition and the austenite grain size. This subject tends to be confusing, so that sometimes it is difficult to assess the applicability of the various methods. Details of the various methods and their limitations and suitability for use are treated in two books: (1) C.A. Siebert, D.V. Doane and D.H. Breen, *The Hardenability of Steels*, American Society for Metals, Metals Park, Ohio (1970); and (2) *Hardenability Concepts with Applications to Steel*, D.V. Doane and J.S. Kirkaldy, editors, AIME, Warrendale, PA (1978).

The methods involve determination of the ideal critical diameter, by the methods described in the preceding section, for steels of various compositions and austenite

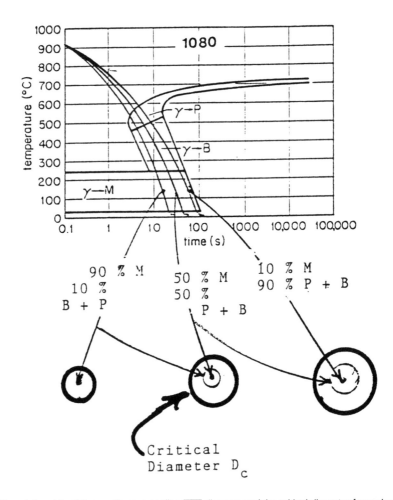

Fig. 3-18   The relationship of the continuous cooling TTT diagram and the critical diameter for a given quench

grain sizes. For example, D_i can be determined for a series of plain carbon steels with various carbon contents for various austenite grain sizes. This allows the development of a plot of D_i versus carbon content with curves for each austenite grain size. Then to examine the effect of Mn on D_i, cylinders of a series of steels of a given carbon content and austenite grain size, but with various Mn contents, are processed and analyzed to obtain D_i for each

Mn content. For this carbon content and austenite grain size, D_i can be plotted versus Mn content. Strictly speaking, this curve is valid only for this carbon content and austenite grain size.

The main problem in developing methods to calculate D_i from the chemical composition is the synergistic effects of the elements. For example, the effect of Mn on D_i for a given carbon content can be determined, but the

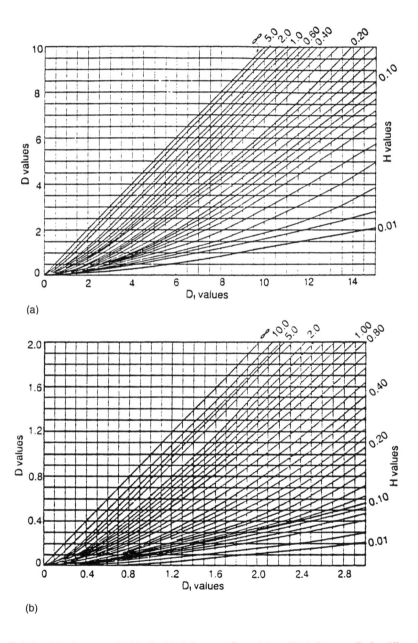

(a)

(b)

Fig. 3-19 Relationships between the ideal critical diameter D_I and the critical diameter D_C for different severity of quench values H. (a) Relationship between actual critical diameter (D), ideal critical diameter (D_I) and severity of quench (H). (b) Relationships similar to those shown but at a larger scale. (From M.A. Grossmann and E.C. Bain, *Principles of Heat Treatment*, 5th edition, American Society for Metals, Metals Park, Ohio (1964))

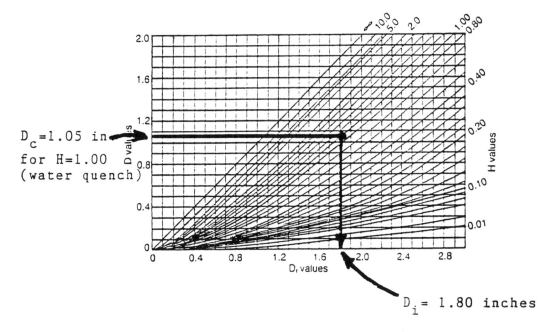

$D_c = 1.05$ in
for H=1.00
(water quench)

$D_i = 1.80$ inches

Fig. 3-20 Illustration of how the ideal critical diameter can be obtained from the curves in Fig. 3-19 if the severity of quench is known (H = 1.0 in this case) for a given critical diameter (1.05 inches in this case)

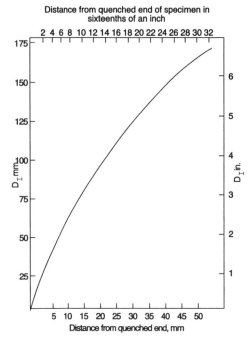

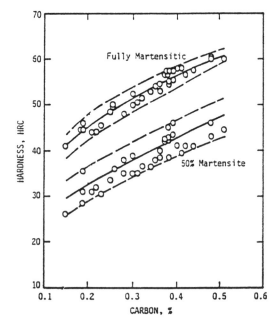

Fig. 3-21 Position along the Jominy bar having the same cooling rate as the center of cylinders of various diameters when quenched in an ideal quench (H = ∞). (Adapted from D.J. Carney, *Trans. ASM,* Vol 46, p 882 (1954))

Fig. 3-22 Hardness as a function of carbon content for structures which are all martensite and for structures containing 50% martensite. (Adapted from J.M. Hodge and M.A. Orehoski, *Trans. AIME,* Vol 167, p 627 (1946))

use of these results to estimate the effect of Mn in steels of other carbon contents and containing Cr and Ni may not be valid.

Grossmann was the first to develop in detail factors which could be used to calculate D_i knowing the austenite grain size and carbon and alloy content. We will briefly indicate the method he, and many others, used. Then we will show more recent and reliable data to use in the calculation of D_i.

Ideal critical diameters were determined (by the methods described in the preceding section) for both plain carbon steels and high purity iron-carbon alloys for various austenite grain sizes. Results such as those shown in Fig. 3-24 were found. Curves such as these serve as the

basis for corrections for alloying additions. Grossmann determined the effect of individual elements (e.g., Mn, Cr) on D_i. He found that he could predict the D_i of the alloy steel by multiplying that of the plain carbon steel (for a given austenite grain size, as in Fig. 3-24) by factors (called *multiplying factors*) for each element, depending upon the amount of each element. He, and others, presented the factors for determining D_i for alloy steels in plots of multiplying factors versus the amount of alloying additions. Examples are shown in Fig. 3-25 for Cr and Mo. Note that the multiplying factors differ greatly, depending upon the source of the determination.

In recent years, the methods of determining the multiplying factors have been refined and extended to higher

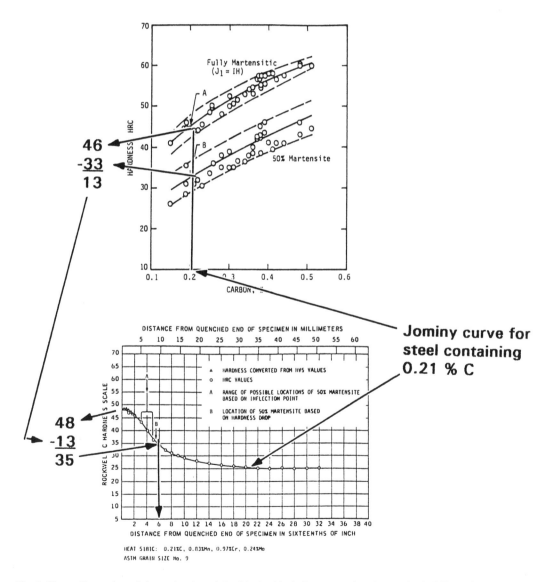

Fig. 3-23   Illustration of determination of the ideal critical diameter using the method of Tartaglia and Eldis. (Adapted from J.M. Tartaglia and G.T. Eldis, *Met. Trans.*, Vol 15A, p 1173 (1984)) *(continued)*

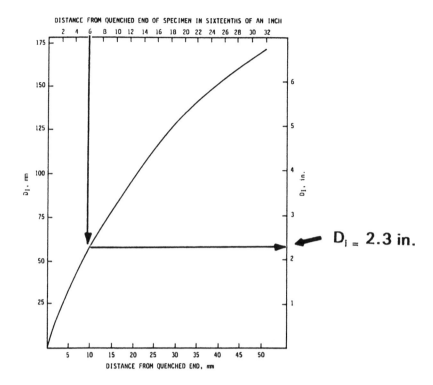

Fig. 3-23 *(continued)* Illustration of determination of the ideal critical diameter using the method of Tartaglia and Eldis. (Adapted from J.M. Tartaglia and G.T. Eldis, *Met. Trans.*, Vol 15A, p 1173 (1984))

carbon contents. Fig. 3-26 shows some D_i data for various carbon contents and austenite grain sizes, and Fig. 3-27 shows multiplying factors considered to be especially valid for lower carbon steels (0.15-0.25% C). These were developed by first determining the effect of individual elements in ternary alloys. The multiplying factors derived from these steels were tested against the experimentally determined D_i for multicomponent steels. The multiplying factors were then modified to obtain a set of average factors, given in Fig. 3-27.

In Fig. 3-28 is shown the ideal critical diameter as a function of carbon content and austenite grain size, and in Fig. 3-29 the alloy multiplying factors, from the work of Moser and Legat. Note that these data extend to higher carbon content than those in Fig. 3-26. The reduction in D_i beyond about 0.8% C is because austenitization was in the two phase $\gamma + Fe_3C$ region, and the presence of the carbides enhances the transformation of austenite to pearlite and bainite and hence lowers the hardability (lower D_i).

Jatczak developed factors for carburizing steels. These required special consideration because the effects of the higher carburizing temperatures were included. Even in the low carbon core, in some cases the higher austenitizing temperature affects the homogeneity of the

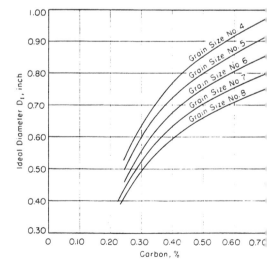

Fig. 3-24 The ideal critical diameter for iron-carbon alloys as a function of carbon content and austenite grain size. (Adapted from I.R. Kramer, S. Siegel and J.G. Brooks, *Trans. AIME*, Vol 167, p 670 (1946))

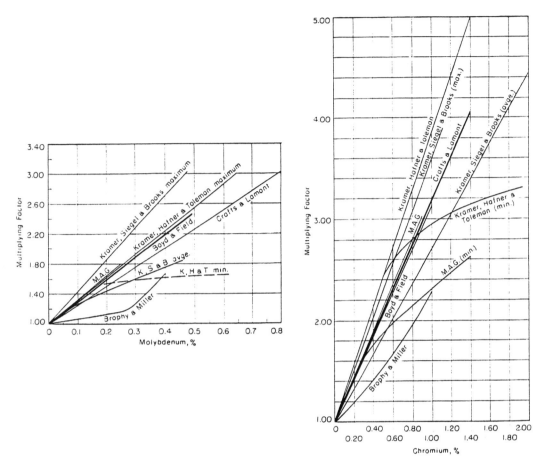

Fig. 3-25   Multiplying factors for Cr and Mo from several sources, as given by Grossmann. (From same source as Fig. 3-14)

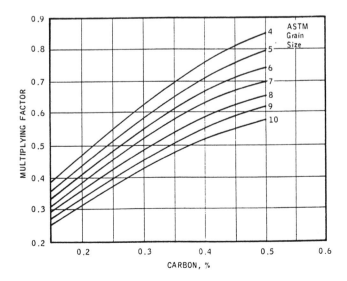

Fig. 3-26   The ideal critical diameter for iron-carbon alloys as a function of carbon content and austenite grain size. (From C.A. Siebert, D.V. Doane and D.H. Breen, *The Hardenability of Steels*, American Society for Metals, Metals Park, Ohio (1977))

austenite, and hence the hardenability. Fig. 3-30 shows the base ideal critical diameter as a function of carbon content and austenitizing temperature. Note that the hardenability decreases with higher carbon contents (see previous paragraph). The multiplying factors developed by Jatczak are shown in Fig. 3-31. Some of the restrictions in the use of these factors are listed in the figure captions.

The procedure described above has been summarized in the American Society for Testing and Materials (ASTM) Standards A255-89 and A255-67. These are reproduced in Appendices 1a and 1b. The data in Table

1a.1 is for only one austenite grain size, ASTM grain size number 7, but this is a common value for deoxidized steels. Tables in Appendix 1b give data for grain sizes 5, 6, 7 and 8.

Calculation of the Jominy Curve

The Jominy curve can be determined experimentally relatively easily. However, in the design of steel components in which the choice of steel and the heat treatment must be made, it is not convenient experimentally to examine the effects on the Jominy curve of changes in chemical composition or austenite grain size. Fortunately,

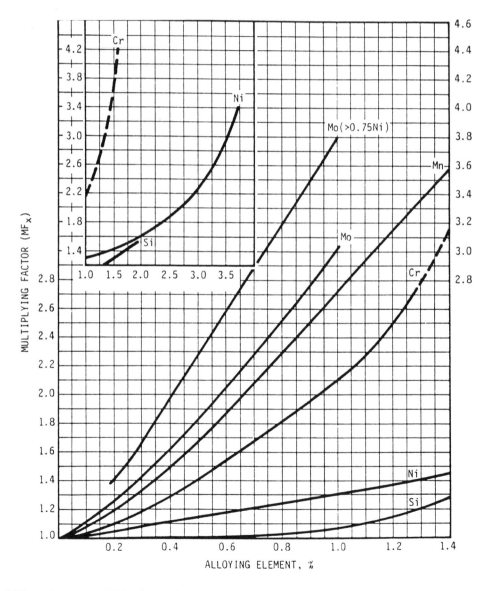

Fig. 3-27   Average multiplying factors for several elements in alloy steels containing 0.15 to 0.25% C. (From *Metal Progress*, Vol 100, p 69 (Sept 1971))

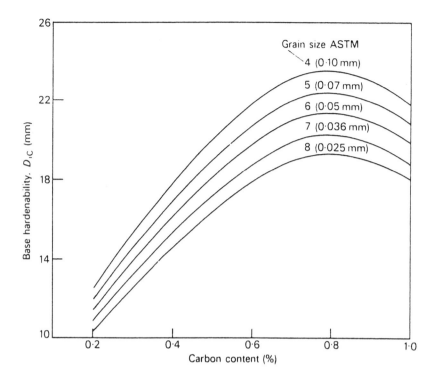

Fig. 3-28 The ideal critical diameter as a function of carbon content and austenite grain size as given by Moser and Legat. (After Moser and Legat, *Harterei Techn. Mitt.*, Vol 24, p 100 (1969), as referenced in R.W.K. Honeycombe, *Steels—Microstructure and Properties*, American Society for Metals, Metals Park, Ohio (1981))

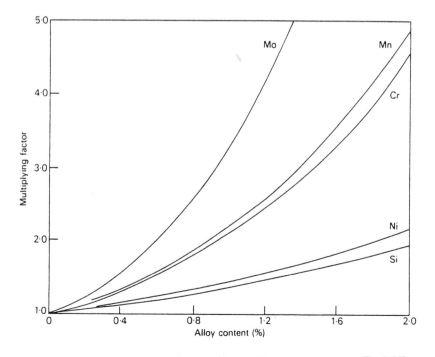

Fig. 3-29 Multiplying factors as given by Moser and Legat. (From same source as Fig. 3-28)

methods have been developed which allow calculation of the Jominy curve from a value of the ideal critical diameter. D_i can be calculated as described in the previous section.

Field and Boyd determined experimentally the Jominy curve for 14 steels. From these data, they developed a correlation between the ratio of the initial hardness IH to the hardness at various distances from the quenched end (distance hardness DH) and the D_i for each Jominy bar. They used for IH the value at 1/16 inch and assumed it to be all martensite (see Fig. 3-3). It was found that the data could be represented by the plot in Fig. 3-32. An example of a calculation of a Jominy curve from these data is shown in Fig. 3-33.

The approach taken by Field and Boyd was used by Sponzilli, Keith and Walter to develop similar data. The results are tabulated in Table 3-1. The values of IH (hardness at 1/16 inch) are tabulated in Table 3-2. Eldis developed a similar table for carburizing grade steels, shown in Table 3-3.

Tartaglia and Eldis used data from 32 carburizing steels, containing from 0.20 to 0.23% C. They fitted their data to a polynomial for IH/DH as a function of D, by a best fit computer method. Their results are shown in Fig. 3-34. The agreement of their method and that of Boyd and Field is shown in Fig. 3-35. Their results are tabulated in Table 3-4. Note that at the 1/16 inch position (J_1) the values at low D_i are greater than unity. This is because they are using for IH the data in Table 3-2, which they

showed underestimated the hardness of martensite for low carbon steels (such as 0.2% C for Table 3-4).

[Note that the symbol J is being introduced. This is the Jominy distance. In English units, the subscript stands for sixteenths of an inch along the Jominy bar. Thus J_1 means 1/16 inch and J_4 means 4/16 inch.]

In some cases Jominy data have been treated to develop an equation for the Jominy curve. One developed by Just is given in Table 3-5.

The ASTM standard in Appendix 1a gives tables for dividing factors to calculate DH knowing D_i, and it also lists polynomial equations to allow calculating the dividing factor.

All of the above treatments are based on correlations, either to calculate D_i and then the Jominy curve, or experimental Jominy curve data treated statistically to obtain an expression of hardness-Jominy distance as a function of chemical composition and austenite grain size.

By using a theoretical model, Kirkaldy has treated the problem more analytically, and his treatment is outlined in Chapter 9. In summary, the rate of the formation of pearlite or primary ferrite as a function of temperature could be calculated from the chemical composition and austenite grain size. The start of the transformation of austenite was taken as inversely proportional to this curve, as shown in Fig. 3-36, so that the transformation start line of the continuous cooling TTT diagram could be calculated. The inflection point on the Jominy curve is taken as that which corresponds to the cooling curve for

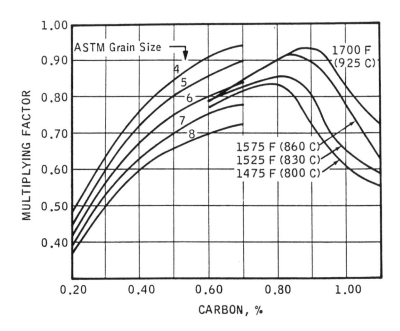

Fig. 3-30 The ideal critical diameter for (inches) iron-carbon alloys as a function of carbon content and austenite, grain size showing data in the higher carbon range applicable to carburized cases. (From C.F. Jatczak, *Met. Trans.*, Vol 4, p 2267 (1973))

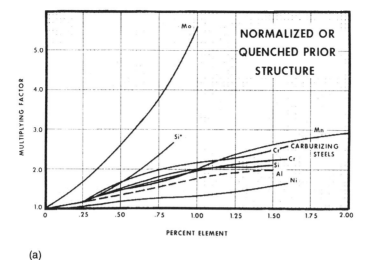

(a)

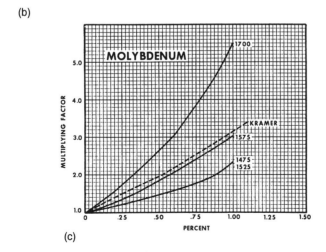

(b)

(c)

Fig. 3-31 Multiplying factors recommended by Jatczak for carburizing steels. (a) Revised factors for calculation of hardenability at high carbon levels when quenched from 1525 °F (830 °C). (b) Revised factors for calculation of hardenability at high carbon levels when quenched from 1700 °F (927 °C). (c) Effect of austenitizing temperature on multiplying factors for Mo at high carbon levels. (From same source as Fig. 3-30) *(continued)*

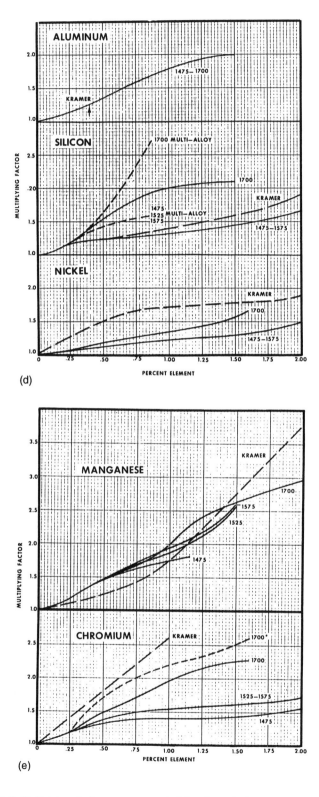

Fig. 3-31   (continued) Multiplying factors recommended by Jatczak for carburizing steels. (d) Effect of austenitizing temperature on multiplying factors for Mn and Cr at high carbon levels. (e) Effect of austenitizing temperature on mulitplying factors for Si, Ni, and Al at high carbon levels. (From same source as Fig. 3-30) *(continued)*

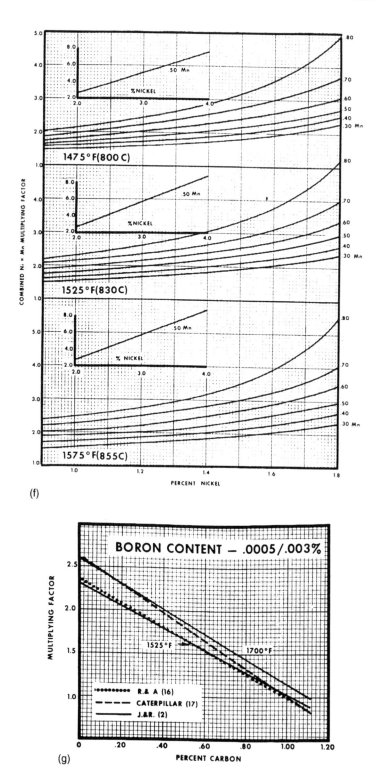

(f)

(g)

Fig. 3-31 (continued) Multiplying factors recommended by Jatczak for carburizing steels. (f) Combined multiplying factor for Ni and Mn in bainitic high carbon steels quenched from 1475 to 1575 °F (800 to 855 °C). Use in place of standard factors when composition contains more than 1.0% Ni and 0.15%t Mo. (g) Multiplying factors for boron at 1525 and 1700 °F when hardenability criterion is 10% transformation. (From same source as Fig. 3-30)

which the steel begins austenite decomposition at the temperature corresponding to the temperature of maximum austenite decomposition velocity (see Fig. 3-36).

This "inflection point predictor" was calibrated by use of Jominy curves for over 800 steels. The quality of the prediction of the inflection point is illustrated by the curves in Fig. 3-37. Some of the scatter is because of uncertainty in the original data; for example, the austenite grain size may not have been known.

From the equation for the inflection point hardness, the entire Jominy curve could be calculated. The agreement with the procedure and experimental Jominy data is illustrated in Fig. 3-38. Thus it appears that this approach is quite good.

Table 3-1   IH/DH as a function of distance on the Jominy bar, as given by Sponzilli, Keith and Walter. (From J.T. Sponzilli, C.J. Keith and G.H. Walter, *Metal Progress*, Vol 108, p 86 (Sept 1975))

Ideal critical diameter (D_i), in.	J1	J2	J3	J4	J5	J6	J7	J8	J9	J10	J11	J12	J13	J14	J15	J16	J20	J24	J28	J32
1.0	1.0	1.29	1.91	2.48	2.72	2.93	3.14	3.33	3.60	3.87	4.13	4.40	...	...	...	...	...	...	...	...
1.1	1.0	1.22	1.65	2.17	2.43	2.63	2.84	3.08	3.29	3.50	3.72	3.93	4.14	4.34	4.55	4.75	5.70	...	...	...
1.2	1.0	1.18	1.56	1.96	2.22	2.42	2.63	2.86	3.06	3.25	3.44	3.60	3.79	3.95	4.11	4.15	4.58	5.00	6.00	...
1.3	1.0	1.15	1.47	1.80	2.01	2.21	2.42	2.66	2.83	2.99	3.16	3.32	3.44	3.55	3.67	3.78	4.13	4.40	4.72	5.25
1.4	1.0	1.11	1.39	1.67	1.88	2.09	2.29	2.49	2.66	2.82	2.97	3.10	3.23	3.34	3.44	3.53	3.77	4.02	4.26	4.53
1.5	1.0	1.08	1.31	1.57	1.76	1.97	2.16	2.34	2.49	2.64	2.78	2.93	3.02	3.12	3.21	3.30	3.53	3.73	3.91	4.10
1.6	1.0	1.06	1.24	1.49	1.69	1.87	2.06	2.21	2.36	2.50	2.63	2.75	2.85	2.94	3.03	3.10	3.33	3.51	3.67	3.83
1.7	1.0	1.04	1.18	1.43	1.63	1.82	1.96	2.11	2.23	2.35	2.47	2.59	2.68	2.76	2.85	2.93	3.16	3.33	3.47	3.59
1.8	1.0	1.04	1.17	1.38	1.56	1.74	1.86	2.01	2.12	2.23	2.35	2.45	2.55	2.63	2.72	2.80	3.00	3.17	3.29	3.40
1.9	1.0	1.04	1.16	1.34	1.50	1.66	1.80	1.91	2.02	2.12	2.23	2.33	2.42	2.51	2.59	2.68	2.88	3.04	3.14	3.25
2.0	1.0	1.03	1.14	1.30	1.44	1.59	1.71	1.83	1.94	2.03	2.13	2.23	2.32	2.41	2.50	2.58	2.78	2.92	3.02	3.11
2.1	1.0	1.02	1.12	1.26	1.38	1.52	1.63	1.75	1.85	1.94	2.04	2.13	2.22	2.32	2.41	2.50	2.69	2.82	2.91	3.00
2.2	1.0	1.01	1.11	1.24	1.36	1.48	1.58	1.69	1.79	1.88	1.97	2.06	2.15	2.25	2.33	2.42	2.61	2.73	2.83	2.91
2.3	1.0	1.0	1.11	1.22	1.34	1.45	1.54	1.64	1.73	1.82	1.91	1.99	2.09	2.18	2.26	2.35	2.53	2.65	2.75	2.83
2.4	1.0	1.0	1.10	1.20	1.30	1.40	1.50	1.60	1.69	1.76	1.85	1.93	2.02	2.10	2.19	2.27	2.47	2.58	2.67	2.75
2.5	1.0	1.0	1.09	1.18	1.28	1.37	1.46	1.55	1.63	1.72	1.80	1.88	1.97	2.05	2.14	2.22	2.40	2.51	2.60	2.68
2.6	1.0	1.0	1.08	1.17	1.26	1.34	1.43	1.52	1.60	1.68	1.76	1.84	1.94	2.00	2.08	2.16	2.34	2.44	2.53	2.61
2.7	1.0	1.0	1.06	1.15	1.24	1.32	1.41	1.48	1.57	1.65	1.73	1.80	1.88	1.96	2.03	2.10	2.28	2.38	2.47	2.54
2.8	1.0	1.0	1.06	1.14	1.22	1.30	1.38	1.45	1.54	1.61	1.69	1.76	1.84	1.91	1.98	2.05	2.23	2.33	2.41	2.48
2.9	1.0	1.0	1.05	1.13	1.21	1.28	1.36	1.42	1.50	1.58	1.65	1.72	1.80	1.87	1.94	2.00	2.18	2.28	2.35	2.42
3.0	1.0	1.0	1.05	1.11	1.18	1.25	1.32	1.39	1.46	1.54	1.60	1.68	1.75	1.81	1.88	1.94	2.12	2.22	2.28	2.36
3.1	1.0	1.0	1.04	1.10	1.17	1.24	1.30	1.37	1.44	1.50	1.57	1.65	1.70	1.77	1.84	1.90	2.08	2.18	2.24	2.32
3.2	1.0	1.0	1.03	1.09	1.16	1.23	1.29	1.35	1.41	1.48	1.54	1.61	1.67	1.73	1.80	1.86	2.04	2.13	2.20	2.27
3.3	1.0	1.0	1.03	1.08	1.15	1.21	1.27	1.33	1.40	1.46	1.52	1.58	1.65	1.71	1.77	1.83	2.00	2.08	2.15	2.22
3.4	1.0	1.0	1.02	1.07	1.13	1.19	1.25	1.31	1.37	1.44	1.50	1.55	1.60	1.66	1.73	1.80	1.95	2.04	2.11	2.17
3.5	1.0	1.0	1.02	1.07	1.13	1.19	1.24	1.29	1.35	1.40	1.45	1.51	1.56	1.62	1.69	1.76	1.91	2.00	2.07	2.13
3.6	1.0	1.0	1.02	1.06	1.11	1.17	1.22	1.27	1.32	1.39	1.43	1.48	1.55	1.60	1.66	1.72	1.87	1.96	2.03	2.08
3.7	1.0	1.0	1.01	1.06	1.11	1.15	1.20	1.25	1.30	1.35	1.40	1.46	1.51	1.56	1.62	1.68	1.83	1.92	1.98	2.04
3.8	1.0	1.0	1.01	1.05	1.10	1.14	1.19	1.23	1.28	1.33	1.38	1.43	1.48	1.53	1.59	1.65	1.80	1.88	1.94	2.00
3.9	1.0	1.0	1.01	1.05	1.09	1.14	1.18	1.22	1.27	1.31	1.36	1.41	1.46	1.51	1.56	1.62	1.76	1.84	1.90	1.96
4.0	1.0	1.0	1.0	1.04	1.08	1.12	1.16	1.20	1.25	1.29	1.33	1.38	1.43	1.48	1.53	1.59	1.72	1.80	1.86	1.92
4.1	1.0	1.0	1.0	1.04	1.08	1.11	1.15	1.18	1.23	1.28	1.32	1.36	1.41	1.46	1.51	1.56	1.68	1.77	1.82	1.88
4.2	1.0	1.0	1.0	1.03	1.06	1.10	1.14	1.17	1.22	1.25	1.29	1.34	1.38	1.42	1.48	1.53	1.65	1.73	1.78	1.84
4.3	1.0	1.0	1.0	1.03	1.06	1.10	1.13	1.16	1.20	1.24	1.28	1.32	1.37	1.41	1.46	1.50	1.62	1.70	1.75	1.80
4.4	1.0	1.0	1.0	1.02	1.05	1.09	1.12	1.15	1.19	1.23	1.27	1.30	1.35	1.39	1.43	1.47	1.58	1.66	1.72	1.76
4.5	1.0	1.0	1.0	1.02	1.05	1.08	1.11	1.14	1.18	1.22	1.25	1.28	1.32	1.36	1.40	1.44	1.55	1.63	1.68	1.73
4.6	1.0	1.0	1.0	1.02	1.05	1.07	1.10	1.12	1.15	1.19	1.22	1.26	1.29	1.33	1.37	1.41	1.52	1.59	1.64	1.69
4.7	1.0	1.0	1.0	1.01	1.04	1.06	1.09	1.11	1.14	1.17	1.20	1.24	1.28	1.31	1.35	1.38	1.49	1.56	1.61	1.65
4.8	1.0	1.0	1.0	1.01	1.02	1.05	1.07	1.10	1.13	1.16	1.19	1.22	1.25	1.28	1.32	1.36	1.46	1.53	1.57	1.62
4.9	1.0	1.0	1.0	1.0	1.0	1.03	1.06	1.08	1.11	1.14	1.17	1.20	1.23	1.26	1.29	1.33	1.43	1.49	1.53	1.58
5.0	1.0	1.0	1.0	1.0	1.0	1.02	1.05	1.07	1.10	1.13	1.15	1.18	1.20	1.25	1.28	1.31	1.40	1.46	1.50	1.54
5.1	1.0	1.0	1.0	1.0	1.0	1.01	1.04	1.06	1.09	1.11	1.14	1.17	1.19	1.22	1.25	1.28	1.37	1.43	1.47	1.51
5.2	1.0	1.0	1.0	1.0	1.0	1.0	1.03	1.05	1.08	1.10	1.13	1.15	1.18	1.20	1.23	1.25	1.34	1.39	1.43	1.47
5.3	1.0	1.0	1.0	1.0	1.0	1.0	1.02	1.04	1.06	1.09	1.11	1.13	1.16	1.18	1.21	1.23	1.31	1.36	1.39	1.43
5.4	1.0	1.0	1.0	1.0	1.0	1.0	1.02	1.03	1.05	1.08	1.11	1.12	1.15	1.18	1.20	1.21	1.28	1.33	1.36	1.40
5.5	1.0	1.0	1.0	1.0	1.0	1.0	1.01	1.03	1.05	1.07	1.08	1.10	1.12	1.13	1.15	1.18	1.25	1.29	1.33	1.37
5.6	1.0	1.0	1.0	1.0	1.0	1.0	1.01	1.02	1.04	1.05	1.07	1.09	1.10	1.12	1.14	1.16	1.22	1.26	1.28	1.33
5.7	1.0	1.0	1.0	1.0	1.0	1.0	1.01	1.02	1.03	1.04	1.06	1.07	1.09	1.10	1.11	1.13	1.19	1.23	1.25	1.29
5.8	1.0	1.0	1.0	1.0	1.0	1.0	1.0	1.01	1.02	1.04	1.05	1.06	1.07	1.09	1.10	1.11	1.17	1.19	1.22	1.25
5.9	1.0	1.0	1.0	1.0	1.0	1.0	1.0	1.01	1.01	1.02	1.03	1.04	1.05	1.06	1.08	1.09	1.13	1.16	1.18	1.21
6.0	1.0	1.0	1.0	1.0	1.0	1.0	1.0	1.0	1.01	1.01	1.02	1.03	1.04	1.05	1.06	1.07	1.10	1.13	1.15	1.18

Table 3-2 The hardness of steels containing 99.9% martensite as a function of carbon content. (After L.C. Boyd and J. Field, as given in C.A. Siebert, D.V. Doane and D.H. Breen, *The Hardenability of steels*, American Society for Metals, Metals Park, Ohio (1977))

			Carbon-Hardness Factors				
Carbon, %	Maximum hardness, HRC	Carbon, %	Maximum hardness, HRC	Carbon, %	Maximum hardness, HRC	Carbon, %	Maximum hardness, HRC
0.10	38	0.23	46	0.36	54	0.49	60
0.11	39	0.24	46	0.37	55	0.50	60
0.12	40	0.25	47	0.38	55	0.51	60
0.13	40	0.26	48	0.39	56	0.52	61
0.14	41	0.27	49	0.40	56	0.53	61
0.15	41	0.28	49	0.41	57	0.54	61
0.16	42	0.29	50	0.42	57	0.55	61
0.17	42	0.30	50	0.43	58	0.56	61
0.18	43	0.31	51	0.44	58	0.57	62
0.19	44	0.32	51	0.45	58	0.58	62
0.20	44	0.33	52	0.46	59	0.59	62
0.21	45	0.34	53	0.47	59	0.60	62
0.22	45	0.35	53	0.48	59		

Table 3-3 IH/DH as a function of distance on the Jominy bar, as developed by Eldis. (From D.V. Doane in *Hardenability Concepts with Applications to Steel*, D.V. Doane and J.S. Kirkaldy, editors, AIME, Warrendale, PA (1978))

	IH/DH ratios for various J_D in carburizing steels of different DI								
					IH/DH[a]				
DI, in. (mm)	J_1	J_2	J_3	J_4	J_6	J_8	J_{10}	J_{12}	J_{16}
0.8 (20.3)	1.14	1.48	2.28	2.79	3.57	4.32	5.14	5.88	7.75
0.9 (22.9)	1.10	1.36	2.00	2.47	3.16	3.79	4.46	5.09	6.61
1.0 (25.4)	1.08	1.27	1.78	2.20	2.81	3.34	3.88	4.41	5.64
1.1 (27.9)	1.06	1.20	1.60	1.97	2.52	2.96	3.40	3.84	4.82
1.2 (30.5)	1.04	1.15	1.45	1.78	2.27	2.64	3.00	3.37	4.14
1.3 (33.0)	1.03	1.12	1.34	1.63	2.06	2.38	2.67	2.97	3.58
1.4 (35.6)	1.03	1.09	1.26	1.50	1.89	2.16	2.40	2.65	3.13
1.5 (38.1)	1.02	1.08	1.20	1.40	1.75	1.98	2.18	2.39	2.77
1.6 (40.6)	1.02	1.07	1.16	1.33	1.64	1.84	2.01	2.19	2.48
1.7 (43.2)	1.02	1.06	1.13	1.27	1.55	1.73	1.88	2.03	2.27
1.8 (45.7)	1.02	1.05	1.11	1.23	1.48	1.65	1.79	1.91	2.10
1.9 (48.3)	1.02	1.05	1.09	1.19	1.42	1.59	1.71	1.82	1.98
2.0 (50.8)	1.02	1.05	1.09	1.17	1.38	1.54	1.66	1.77	1.90
2.1 (53.3)	1.02	1.04	1.08	1.15	1.35	1.50	1.63	1.74	1.84
2.2 (55.9)	1.01	1.04	1.08	1.14	1.32	1.47	1.60	1.71	1.81
2.3 (58.4)	1.01	1.04	1.08	1.13	1.30	1.45	1.58	1.68	1.78
2.4 (61.0)	1.01	1.03	1.08	1.12	1.29	1.44	1.56	1.66	1.75
2.5 (63.5)	1.01	1.03	1.07	1.10	1.28	1.42	1.54	1.63	1.72
2.6 (66.0)	1.01	1.02	1.07	1.09	1.26	1.40	1.51	1.60	1.69
2.7 (68.6)	1.01	1.02	1.06	1.08	1.25	1.38	1.48	1.57	1.66
2.8 (71.1)	1.00	1.02	1.06	1.07	1.23	1.36	1.46	1.54	1.63
2.9 (73.7)	1.00	1.01	1.05	1.06	1.22	1.34	1.43	1.51	1.60
3.0 (76.2)	1.00	1.01	1.04	1.06	1.20	1.32	1.41	1.48	1.57
3.1 (78.7)	1.00	1.01	1.03	1.05	1.19	1.29	1.38	1.46	1.54
3.2 (81.3)	1.00	1.01	1.02	1.05	1.18	1.27	1.36	1.43	1.51
3.3 (83.8)	1.00	1.01	1.02	1.04	1.16	1.25	1.33	1.40	1.48
3.4 (86.4)	1.00	1.01	1.02	1.04	1.15	1.23	1.31	1.37	1.45
3.5 (88.9)	1.00	1.01	1.02	1.04	1.13	1.21	1.28	1.34	1.41
3.6 (91.4)	1.00	1.01	1.02	1.03	1.12	1.19	1.26	1.31	1.38
3.7 (94.0)	1.00	1.00	1.01	1.02	1.10	1.17	1.23	1.28	1.35

(a) For J_D in sixteenths of an inch. Metric J_D values are J_1 = 1.6 mm, J_2 = 3.2 mm, J_3 = 4.8 mm, J_4 = 6.4 mm, J_6 = 9.5 mm, J_8 = 13 mm, J_{10} = 16 mm, J_{12} = 19 mm, J_{16} = 25 mm

Based on regression analysis of 338 heats of steel, Kern obtained expressions for the hardness as a function of alloy content for locations on the Jominy bar. These are given in Table 3-6, along with the range of chemical composition for which these expressions are valid.

H-Band Steels

When a common steel is purchased, the supplier guarantees the chemical composition of key elements to be within certain limits. However, in applications involv-

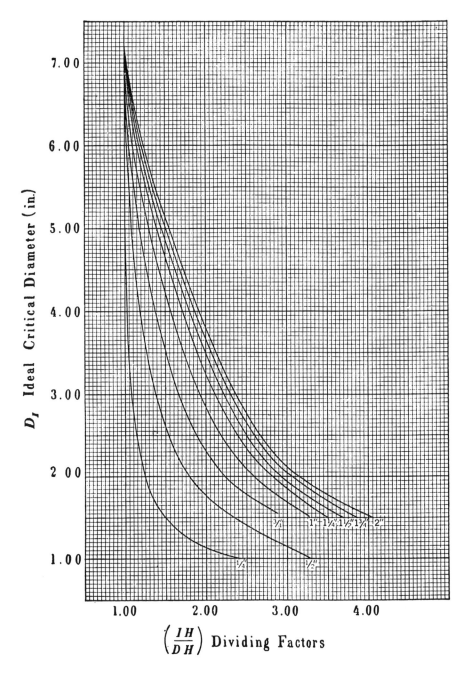

$$\left(\frac{IH}{DH}\right) \text{ Dividing Factors}$$

Fig. 3-32 Relation between D_i and IH/DH given by Boyd and Field. (From D.S. Clark and W.R. Varney, *Physical Metallurgy for Engineers*, 2nd edition, PWS Publishing Company, Boston (1993))

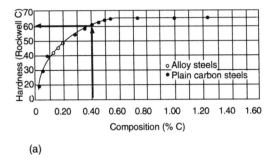

(a)

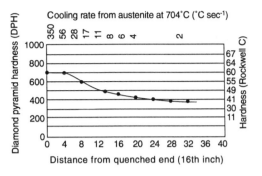

(b)

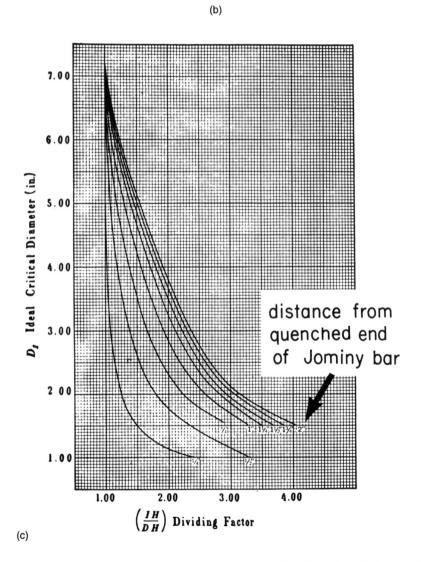

(c)

Fig. 3-33   Illustration of the calculation of the Jominy curve for a steel having a D_i = 4.9 inches. The steel contained 0.40% C, from which IH = 60 Rockwell C. The calculated values of the Jominy curve are the closed circles (a) The hardness of martensite as a function of the carbon content of the martensite. (b) The calculated Jominy curve of a 4140 steel. (c) For the chemical composition and austenite grain size of this 4140 steel, the calculated D_i = 4.9 in. The carbon content was 0.40%, so IH = 60 Rockwell C

ing hardening, the user may be more interested in the hardenability instead of the specific chemistry. The user may choose a steel based on the minimum alloy content consistent with the required hardenability. However, once the steel is purchased, if the carbon and alloying elements are all on the low side of the allowed chemical composi-

tion, still meeting chemical composition specifications, the steel may be of lower hardenability than the user anticipated.

Thus if the user is interested in hardenability, a more lax chemistry tolerance may be accommodated if there is some guarantee of the hardenability. This is the essence

Table 3-4   IH/DH as a function of distance on the Jominy bar and D_i in carburizing steels. (From same sources as Table 3-2)

	IH/DH ratios calculated for various Jominy distances (J_b) in carburizing steels of different D_1								
					IH/DH(a)				
D_i, in. (mm)	J_1	J_2	J_3	J_4	J_6	J_8	J_{10}	J_{12}	J_{16}
0.8 (20.3)	1.12	1.43	2.27	2.72	3.53	4.26	5.01	5.66	7.16
0.9 (22.9)	1.09	1.32	1.94	2.39	3.09	3.69	4.31	4.88	6.15
1.0 (25.4)	1.07	1.24	1.69	2.12	2.72	3.22	3.72	4.21	5.30
1.1 (27.9)	1.05	1.18	1.51	1.90	2.42	2.83	3.24	3.66	4.57
1.2 (30.5)	1.04	1.14	1.38	1.71	2.17	2.51	2.85	3.21	3.97
1.3 (33.0)	1.03	1.11	1.29	1.57	1.97	2.26	2.53	2.84	3.47
1.4 (35.6)	1.03	1.09	1.23	1.45	1.81	2.06	2.29	2.55	3.06
1.5 (38.1)	1.02	1.07	1.19	1.37	1.69	1.91	2.10	2.31	2.73
1.6 (40.6)	1.02	1.07	1.16	1.30	1.59	1.79	1.96	2.14	2.47
1.7 (43.2)	1.02	1.06	1.14	1.25	1.52	1.70	1.85	2.00	2.27
1.8 (45.7)	1.02	1.05	1.13	1.22	1.46	1.64	1.78	1.90	2.12
1.9 (48.3)	1.02	1.05	1.12	1.20	1.42	1.59	1.72	1.83	2.00
2.0 (50.8)	1.02	1.05	1.11	1.18	1.40	1.56	1.69	1.78	1.92
2.1 (53.3)	1.01	1.04	1.10	1.17	1.37	1.54	1.66	1.74	1.85
2.2 (55.9)	1.01	1.04	1.08	1.16	1.36	1.52	1.64	1.72	1.81
2.3 (58.4)	1.01	1.03	1.07	1.16	1.34	1.50	1.63	1.69	1.78
2.4 (61.0)	1.01	1.03	1.06	1.15	1.32	1.48	1.61	1.67	1.75
2.5 (63.5)	1.01	1.03	1.05	1.14	1.31	1.45	1.57	1.64	1.72
2.6 (66.0)	1.01	1.02	1.05	1.13	1.29	1.43	1.55	1.61	1.69
2.7 (68.6)	1.01	1.02	1.05	1.12	1.27	1.41	1.52	1.58	1.66
2.8 (71.1)	1.01	1.02	1.05	1.11	1.25	1.38	1.49	1.55	1.63
2.9 (73.7)	1.01	1.02	1.05	1.10	1.24	1.36	1.46	1.52	1.60
3.0 (76.2)	1.00	1.02	1.04	1.09	1.22	1.33	1.43	1.49	1.58
3.1 (78.7)	1.00	1.02	1.04	1.09	1.20	1.31	1.40	1.46	1.55
3.2 (81.3)	1.00	1.02	1.04	1.08	1.19	1.29	1.37	1.43	1.52
3.3 (83.8)	1.00	1.01	1.04	1.07	1.17	1.26	1.34	1.40	1.49
3.4 (86.4)	1.00	1.01	1.03	1.06	1.15	1.24	1.31	1.37	1.46
3.5 (88.9)	1.00	1.01	1.03	1.05	1.14	1.22	1.29	1.34	1.43
3.6 (91.4)	1.00	1.01	1.03	1.04	1.12	1.19	1.26	1.32	1.40
3.7 (94.0)	1.00	1.01	1.03	1.03	1.10	1.17	1.23	1.29	1.37
3.8 (96.5)	1.00	1.01	1.02	1.02	1.08	1.14	1.20	1.26	1.34

Table 3-5   Equations by Just relating DH to chemical composition, austenite grain size and Jominy distance. (From E. Just, *Metal Progress*, Vol 96, p 288 (Nov 1969))

Just Equation

$$DH = 88\sqrt{(\%C)} - 0.0135J^2\sqrt{(\%C)} + 19(\%Cr) + 6.3(\%Ni) + 16(\%Mn) + 35(\%Mo) + 5(\%Si) - 0.82(GS) - 20\sqrt{J} + 2.1$$

The distance J is in sixteenths of an inch and the hardness is in Rockwell C. The equation is valid from 4/16 to 40/16 inches, and for the following composition and grain sizes:

0.08-0.56% C; 0.20-1.88% Mn; 0-8.94% Ni; 0-1.97% Cr; 0-0.53% Mo; 0-3.8% Si; 1.5-11 ASTM grain size

For the initial hardness, at 1/6 in., the equation

$$IH = 60\sqrt{\% C} + 20$$

is used. This equation is valid only up to 0.6% C.

of the *H-band steels* or *H-steels*. To illustrate the concept, consider a 4140 steel which has the chemical composition specifications shown in Table 3-7. Now if the Jominy curve is calculated (by the method shown in Fig. 3-33 and using a specific set of factors for carbon content, alloy content and austenite grain size to calculate D_i) using the lower and the upper limit of the chemical composition specification, the two curves shown in Fig. 3-39 are obtained. These calculated curves will depend upon the

grain size chosen; here an "average" austenite grain size of ASTM 6 was used.

However, a 4140 steel can be purchased with a hardenability *and* a chemical guarantee; this is a 4140 H steel. The chemical specification is also shown in Table 3-7 where it is seen that the chemical tolerances are more lax than they are for the 4140 steel. But for such an H-steel, the supplier guarantees that the Jominy curve determined experimentally from a Jominy bar made from

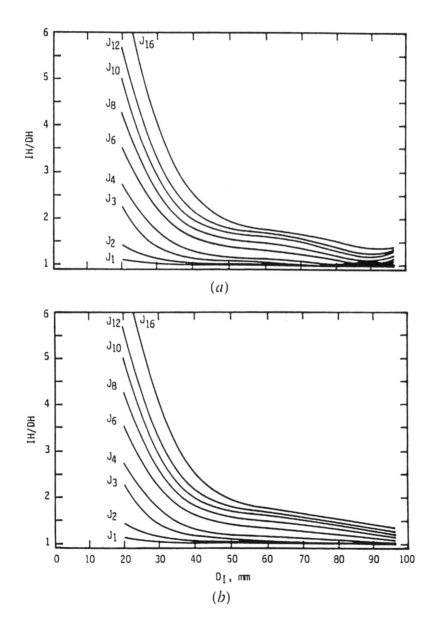

(a)

(b)

Fig. 3-34   Calculated curves of IH/DH versus D_i as given by Tartaglia and Eldis. (From J.M. Tartaglia and G.T. Eldis, *Met. Trans.*, Vol 15A, p 1173 (1984))

the purchased steel will fall between two extremes, called the *H-band*. For 4140 H steel, the limits are shown in Fig. 3-39. Note that over much of the Jominy curve, the 4140 H steel has a more restrictive hardenability than the 4140 steel.

This more restrictive hardenability is attainable in spite of the wider tolerances on the chemical composition by modifying the heat of steel so that if one element (e.g., Mo) is below the desired average, then another element (e.g., Ni) is adjusted to be above the desired average, to bring the hardenability up to within the band.

Note that if the heat treatment and choice of steel for a steel component are being examined, then in considering hardenability the worst case should be used, which is the lower limit of the hardenability band. Thus, in some compilations of the H-band steels only the lower curve is given. In Fig. 3-40 are shown examples of Jominy bands and in Fig. 3-41 the minimum hardenability curves. Some bands are given in Appendix 19.

The Boron Hardenability Effect

The effect of boron on the hardenability of steels is treated separately because of its rather unusual effect. It is very potent in retarding the formation of primary ferrite and pearlite, especially in low carbon steels, when in very small concentrations (e.g., 0.001%). However, boron usually has little effect on the bainite transformation rate. The continuous cooling TTT diagrams in Fig. 3-42 illustrate these effects. Such behavior is important in the development of structures which are primarily bainite.

The effect of boron was discovered when heats were made with boron additions added as grain refiners. The influence of boron is modified greatly by the carbon content and elements such as Ti and N in low concentrations.

Grossmann gave the multiplying factors for B shown in Fig. 3-43. This general effect has been confirmed by many investigators since, and an example is shown in Fig.

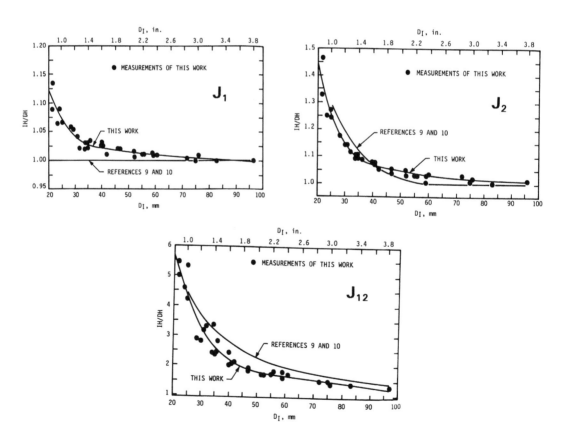

Fig. 3-35 Comparison of IH/DH versus D_i as determined by Tartaglia and Eldis and by Boyd and Field (references 9 and 10). The Jominy distances to which the curves apply are shown as J_i, where the subscript is in mm. (From J.M. Tartaglia and G.T. Eldis, *Met. Trans.*, Vol 15A, p 1173 (1984))

Table 3-6 Equations for hardness at various Jominy distances as a function of chemical composition. The element symbol represents the amount of that element in weight percent. (From R.F. Kern and M.E. Suess, *Steel Selection*, Wiley, New York (1979))

Jominy distance (1/16ths)	Hardness (Rc)
1	$204.C + 4.3Si + 8.32Cu - 241.3C^2 + 11.03$
2	$207.9C + 7.06Cu - 246.3C^2 + 400MnB + 9.94$
3	$226.3C + 2.28Mn + 6.15Cu - 281.7C^2 + 7.43 \times 10^3 C^2 B + 4.176$
4	$7.02Ni - 13.07Cr + 23.9 \times 10^3 \, CB - 9.01 \times 10^6 CB^2 + 47.76$
5	$17.88Ni - 11.76Cr + 33.8 \times 10^3 CB - 19.0 \times 10^6 CB^2 + 5.29 \times 10^3 \, MnB + 39.8$
6	$41.73Ni - 80.32MnS + 23.5 \times 10^3 CB - 23.1 \times 10^6 CB^2 + 10.27 \times 10^3 MnB + 32.9$
7	$8.46Mn - 115.6S + 64.4Ni + 24.7Cr - 17.4 \times 10^6 CB^2 + 12.47 \times 10^3 Mn^2 B + 18.1$
8	$14.34Mn - 80.34S + 68.77Ni + 36.84Cr - 16.13 \times 10^6 CB^2 + 9.89 \times 10^3 Mn^2 B + 7.7$
9	$27.15Mn + 136.3P + 69.07Ni + 33.6Cr + 1.715Mn^2 B - 9.329$
12	$14.01Mn + 87.59P + 31.33Ni + 21.17Cr + 70.76Mo + 5.49$
16	$22.93C + 9.173Mn + 50.54P + 16.36Ni + 13.29Cr + 57.44Mo + 1.696$
20	$29.11C + 10.41Mn + 10.2Ni + 12.71Cr + 50.43No - 2.93$

Carbon	0.28	−0.46%
Manganese	0.80	−1.40%
Silicon	0.13	−0.39%
Nickel	0.00	−0.28%
Chromium	0.05	−0.25%
Molybdenum	0.01	−0.06%
Copper	0.08	−0.22%
Boron	0.0001	−0.0019%

Grain size was not included, but was within the range of ASTM 8-12

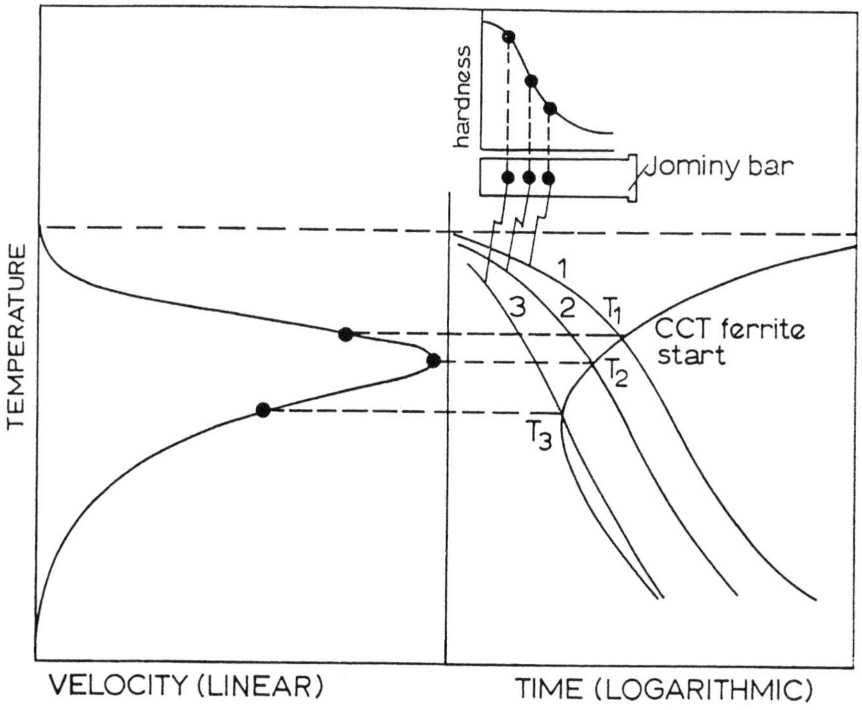

Fig. 3-36 Illustration of the method of locating the inflection point on the Jominy curve from the curve of the velocity of formation of primary ferrite or pearlite versus temperature curve. (From J.S. Kirkaldy, G.O. Pazionis and S.E. Feldman in *Heat Treatment '76*, The Metals Society, London (1976))

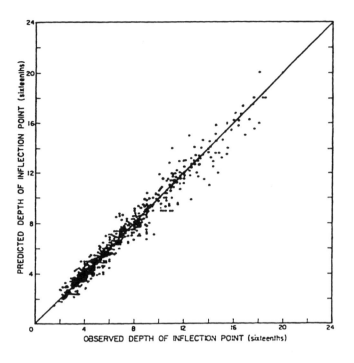

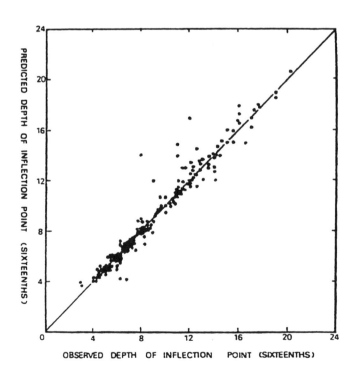

Fig. 3-37   Comparison of the predicted inflection point on the Jominy curve to that observed. (From S.E. Feldman in *Hardenability Concepts with Applications to Steel*, D.V. Doane and J.S. Kirkaldy, editors, The Metallurgical Society, Warrendale, PA (1978))

3-44. The reduction in the effect of B at higher concentrations is probably due to the precipitation of the borocarbide $Fe_{23}(C,B)_6$. Kapadia, Brown and Murphy studied the synergistic effect of B, Ti and Zr, and correlated the hardenability to an "effective" boron content (designated β), defined as

$$\beta = (\% \text{ B}) - \{(\% \text{ N}) - 0.002) - [((\% \text{ Ti})/5) - ((\%Zr)/15)]\}$$

The hardenability multiplying factor as a function of this effective boron content is shown in Fig. 3-45.

The carbon content has a potent influence on the boron effect, as shown in Fig. 3-46. Note that for the higher carbon steels the boron effect is negligible. This is the basis for utilizing boron mainly in low carbon steels.

It also has been reported that too high an austenitizing temperature may reduce or eliminate the B effect. However, there are conflicting data on this point.

For further information on the effect of B on hardenability, the reader should consult the following articles in *Hardenability Concepts with Applications to Steel*, D.V. Doane and J.S. Kirklady, editors, The Metallurgical Society, Warrendale, PA (1978):

- Ph. Maitrepierre, D. Thivellier, J. Rofes-Vernis, D. Rousseau and R. Tricot, "Microstructure and Hardenability of Low-Alloy Boron-Containing Steels," p 421.
- B.M. Kapadia, "Prediction of the Boron Hardenability Effect in Steel—A Comprehensive Review," p 448.

Table 3-7 Chemical specification for 4140 steel and 4140 H steel

Element	Chemical composition, wt.%	
	4140H	4140
Carbon	0.37-0.45	0.38-0.43
Manganese	0.70-1.05	0.75-1.00
Silicon	0.20-0.35	0.20-0.35
Chromium	0.80-1.15	0.80-1.10
Molybdenum	0.15-0.25	0.15-0.25

Closure

A descriptive summary of the effects of alloying elements on hardenability is presented in Table 3-8. The effect of copper is noteworthy. This element is added only in special steels, not the kind being considered here. However, its concentration in steels has been increasing due to continued recycling of steel with entrained copper scrap, and thus its effect of hardenability may become increasingly important.

Table 3-8 A summary of the effects of alloying elements on hardenability. (From *Metals Handbook*, 10th edition, Vol 1, Properties and Selection: Irons, *Steels and High-Performance Alloys*, ASM International, Materials Park, Ohio (1990))

Manganese contributes markedly to hardenability, especially in amounts greater than 0.8%. The effect of manganese up to 1.0% is stronger in low- and high-carbon steels than in medium-carbon steels.

Nickel is similar to manganese at low alloy additions, but is less potent at the high alloy levels. Nickel is also affected by carbon content, the medium-carbon steels having the greatest effect. There is an alloy interaction between manganese and nickel that must be taken into account at lower austenitizing temperatures.

Copper is usually added to alloy steels for its contribution to atmospheric-corrosion resistance and at higher levels for precipitation hardening. The effect of copper on hardenability is similar to that of nickel, and in hardenability calculations it has been suggested that the sum of copper plus nickel be used with the appropriate multiplying factor of nickel.

Silicon is more effective than manganese at low alloy levels and has a strengthening effect on low-alloy steels. However, at levels greater than 1% this element is much less effective than manganese. The effect of silicon also varies considerably with carbon content and other alloys present. Silicon is relatively ineffective in low-carbon steels but is very effective in high-carbon steels.

Molybdenum is most effective in improving hardenability. Molybdenum has a much greater effect in high-carbon steels than in medium-carbon steels. The presence of chromium decreases the multiplying factor, whereas the presence of nickel enhances the hardenability effect of molybdenum.

Chromium behaves much like molybdenum and has its greatest effect in medium-carbon steels. In low-carbon steels and carburized steels, the effect is less than in medium-carbon steels, but is still significant. As a result of the stability of chromium carbide at lower austenitizing temperatures, chromium becomes less effective.

Vanadium is usually not added for hardenability in quenched and tempered structural steels (such as ASTM A 678, grade D) but is added to provide secondary hardening during tempering. Vanadium is a strong carbide former, and the steel must be austenitized at a sufficiently high temperature and for a sufficient length of time to ensure that the vanadium is in solution and thus able to contribute to hardenability. Moreover, solution is possible only if small amounts of vanadium are added.

Tungsten has been found to be more effective in high-carbon steels than in steels of low carbon content (less than 0.5%). Alloy interaction is important in tungsten-containing steels, with manganese-molybdenum-chromium having a greater effect on the multiplying factors than silicon or nickel additions.

Titanium, niobium, and zirconium are all strong carbide formers and are usually not added to enhance hardenability, for the same reasons given for vanadium. In addition, titanium and zirconium are strong nitride formers, a characteristic that affects their solubility in austenite and hence their contribution to hardenability.

Boron can considerably improve hardenability, the effect varying notably with the carbon content of the steel. The full effect of boron on hardenability is obtained only in fully deoxidized (aluminum-killed) steels.

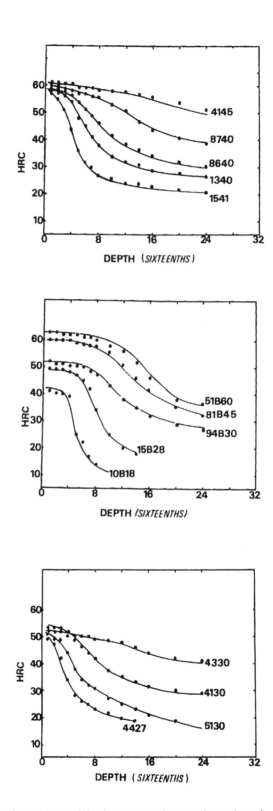

Fig. 3-38 Comparison of the calculated Jominy curve to the experimental one for several steels. (From same source as Fig. 3-37)

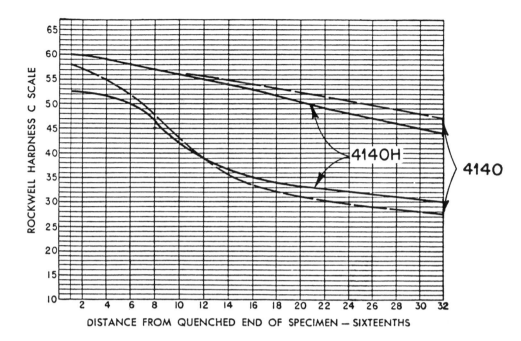

Fig. 3-39 Calculated Jominy curves (dashed lines) for 4140 steel, using an austenite grain size of ASTM 6 and the maximum (top curve) and minimum (bottom curve) allowable amount of each element (see Table 3-7), compared to the H-band for 4140 H steel (solid lines) (From same source as Fig. 3-2)

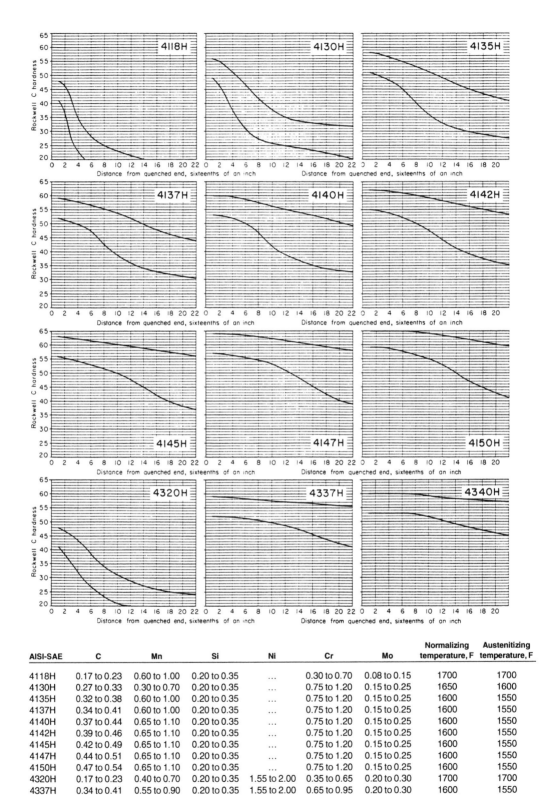

AISI-SAE	C	Mn	Si	Ni	Cr	Mo	Normalizing temperature, F	Austenitizing temperature, F
4118H	0.17 to 0.23	0.60 to 1.00	0.20 to 0.35	...	0.30 to 0.70	0.08 to 0.15	1700	1700
4130H	0.27 to 0.33	0.30 to 0.70	0.20 to 0.35	...	0.75 to 1.20	0.15 to 0.25	1650	1600
4135H	0.32 to 0.38	0.60 to 1.00	0.20 to 0.35	...	0.75 to 1.20	0.15 to 0.25	1600	1550
4137H	0.34 to 0.41	0.60 to 1.00	0.20 to 0.35	...	0.75 to 1.20	0.15 to 0.25	1600	1550
4140H	0.37 to 0.44	0.65 to 1.10	0.20 to 0.35	...	0.75 to 1.20	0.15 to 0.25	1600	1550
4142H	0.39 to 0.46	0.65 to 1.10	0.20 to 0.35	...	0.75 to 1.20	0.15 to 0.25	1600	1550
4145H	0.42 to 0.49	0.65 to 1.10	0.20 to 0.35	...	0.75 to 1.20	0.15 to 0.25	1600	1550
4147H	0.44 to 0.51	0.65 to 1.10	0.20 to 0.35	...	0.75 to 1.20	0.15 to 0.25	1600	1550
4150H	0.47 to 0.54	0.65 to 1.10	0.20 to 0.35	...	0.75 to 1.20	0.15 to 0.25	1600	1550
4320H	0.17 to 0.23	0.40 to 0.70	0.20 to 0.35	1.55 to 2.00	0.35 to 0.65	0.20 to 0.30	1700	1700
4337H	0.34 to 0.41	0.55 to 0.90	0.20 to 0.35	1.55 to 2.00	0.65 to 0.95	0.20 to 0.30	1600	1550

Fig. 3-40 Examples of Jominy curve hardenability bands for H band steels. (From *Metals Handbook*, 8th edition, Vol 1, *Properties and Selection of Metals*, American Society for Metals, Metals Park, Ohio (1961))

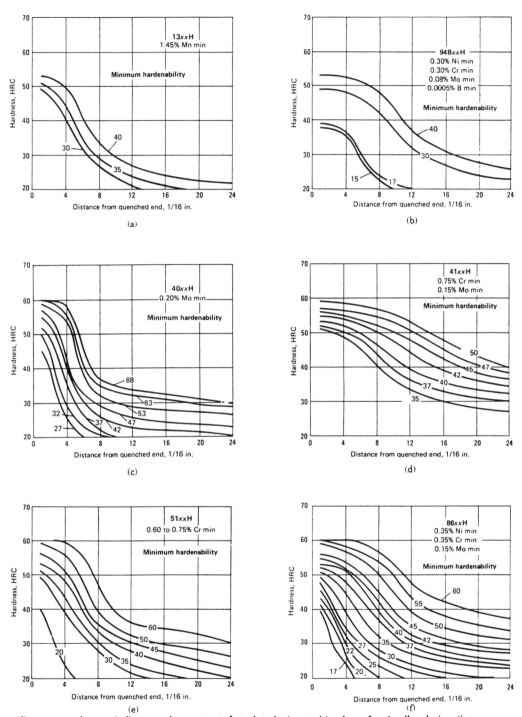

Number adjacent to each curve indicates carbon content of steel, to be inserted in place of *xx* in alloy designation.

Fig. 3-41   Examples of minimum curves of H bands. (From *Metals Handbook*, 9th edition, Vol 1, *Properties and Selection: Iron and Steels*, American Society for Metals, Metals Park, Ohio (1978))

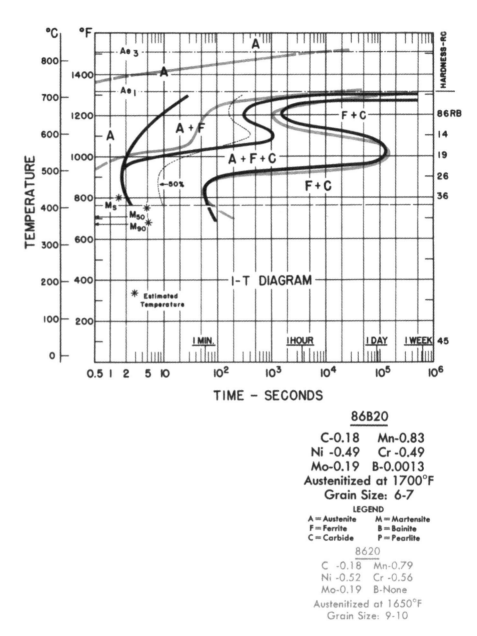

(a)

86B20

C-0.18   Mn-0.83
Ni -0.49   Cr -0.49
Mo-0.19   B-0.0013
Austenitized at 1700°F
Grain Size: 6-7

LEGEND
A = Austenite   M = Martensite
F = Ferrite   B = Bainite
C = Carbide   P = Pearlite

8620

C -0.18   Mn-0.79
Ni -0.52   Cr -0.56
Mo-0.19   B-None
Austenitized at 1650°F
Grain Size: 9-10

Fig. 3-42   TTT diagrams illustrating the effect of boron. ((a) and (b) from *Atlas of Isothermal Transformation and Cooling Transformation Diagrams*, American Society for Metals, Metals Park, Ohio (1977); (c) from W.W. Cias, *Austenite Transformation Kinetics of Ferrous Alloys*, Climax Molybdenum Company, Greenwich, Conn., undated) *(continued)*

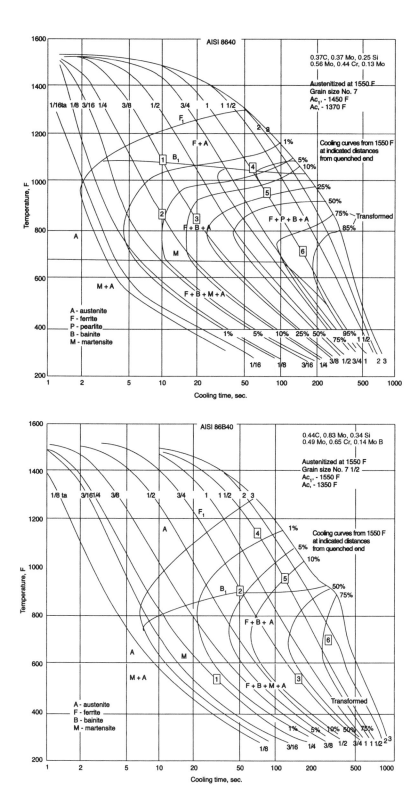

Fig. 3-42 (continued) TTT diagrams illustrating the effect of boron. ((a) and (b) from *Atlas of Isothermal Transformation and Cooling Transformation Diagrams*, American Society for Metals, Metals Park, Ohio (1977); (c) from W.W. Cias, *Austenite Transformation Kinetics of Ferrous Alloys*, Climax Molybdenum Company, Greenwich, Conn., undated) (continued)

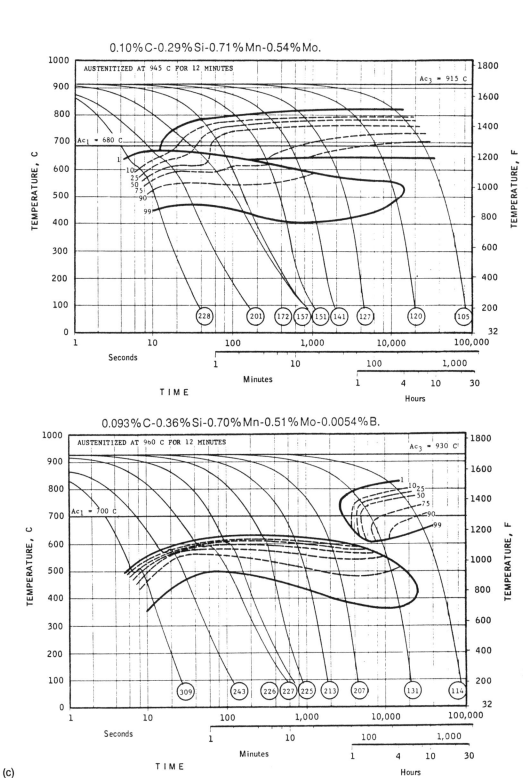

Fig. 3-42   (continued) TTT diagrams illustrating the effect of boron. ((a) and (b) from *Atlas of Isothermal Transformation and Cooling Transformation Diagrams*, American Society for Metals, Metals Park, Ohio (1977); (c) from W.W. Cias, *Austenite Transformation Kinetics of Ferrous Alloys*, Climax Molybdenum Company, Greenwich, Conn., undated)

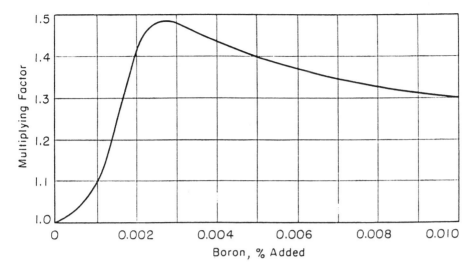

Fig. 3-43   The boron multiplying factors as given by Grossmann. (From same source as Fig. 3-14)

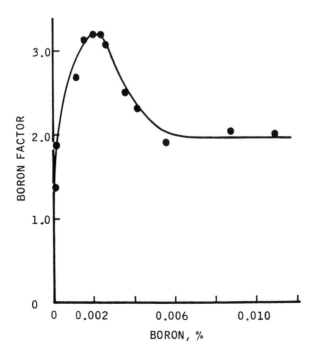

Fig. 3-44   The boron multiplying factors as given by Melloy, Slimmon and Podgursky. (From G.F. Melloy, P.R. Slimmon and P.P. Podgursky, *Met. Trans.*, Vol 4, p 2279 (1973))

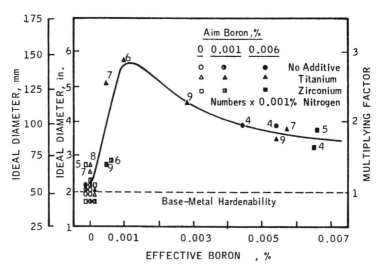

Fig. 3-45   The boron multiplying factors as a function of the "effective" boron content. (From B.M. Kapadia, R.M. Brown and W.J. Murphy, *Trans. AIME*, Vol 242, p 1689 (1968))

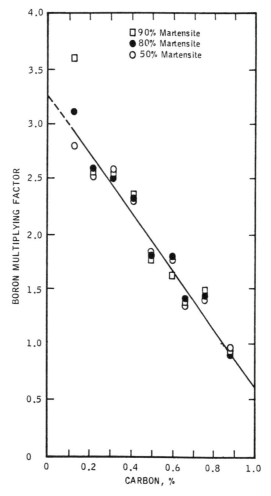

Fig. 3-46   The effect of carbon on the boron multiplying factors. The steels contained 0.8% Mn. (From D.T. Lewellyn and W.T. Cook, *Metals Tech.*, p 517 (Dec 1974))

Chapter 4

Quenching of Steels

The Heat Transfer Process During Quenching

In this chapter, the cooling of steels from the austenite region is examined. This is a crucial step in hardening, and improper cooling causes difficulties which cannot be relieved by treatments in subsequent steps in the heat treating process. Thus, it is important to understand the factors which affect the cooling process. Since most heat treatments for hardening involve cooling in a liquid (e.g., oil, water), normalizing (cooling in air) or annealing (e.g., furnace cooling) will not be considered. Also, only quenching from the austenite region will be examined.

Cooling during quenching is a rather complicated process, but it can be conveniently separated into three stages. When the hot steel is placed in contact with the quenchant at low temperatures (e.g., 25°C), the liquid in contact with the steel immediately boils, forming a vapor blanket around the steel part. The relatively low thermal conductivity of the vapor prevents the steel from cooling rapidly. This is stage one of cooling. For rapid cooling, it is considered best to minimize this stage.

Eventually a temperature is reached where the vapor begins to break into bubbles and separate from the surface. This allows fresh cold fluid to contact the still hot steel, and the fluid boils, forming another bubble, which breaks free. This process continues to sweep fresh fluid onto the hot surface. Thus in this second stage, cooling is most rapid. This stage is sometimes called the *boiling stage* or *nucleate boiling stage*.

When the surface of the steel part attains a temperature such that the fresh liquid contacting it does not boil, stage three is entered. Here heat transfer is achieved by conduction and convection in the quenchant, and is relatively slow compared to stage two. [Note that radiation is neglected in all stages.]

These three stages are depicted schematically in Fig. 4-1a. Cooling curves for several quenchants are shown in

Fig. 4-2. It is seen that the type of quench can affect the time over which the three stages exist. A better feeling of the heat transfer rate can be obtained by plotting, from the data in Fig. 4-2, the cooling rate, as shown in Fig. 4-3. Hardness profiles across a specific steel after quenching into four of these media are shown in Fig. 4-4. It is seen that the highest hardness curve corresponds to quenching in tap water, which has the highest cooling rate. The distinction between the hardness profiles for the other three media is more difficult to predict from the data in Fig. 4-3. This may be due to the fact that the data in Fig. 4-2 were obtained on silver spheres, a material having a higher thermal diffusivity than steel.

The data in the preceding figures illustrate that it may be difficult to characterize a quench quantitatively. It was pointed out in Chapter 3 that the cooling rate at 704 °C is used for some heat transfer correlations (to be discussed), but the data in the previous figures indicate that this may not be a good indicator of the relative effectiveness of a quench. It has been found that the most useful quantity is the *severity of quench H*, which was defined in Chapter 3. Here we will examine this quantity in more detail.

There are two considerations. One is the heat flux from the surface to the quenchant, which controls the temperature of the surface of the steel part. The other consideration is the temperature distribution inside the steel part, which is controlled by the thermal diffusivity of the steel part. The flux from heat conduction at the surface is equal to that by heat transfer into the quenchant.

The rate of heat transfer dQ/dt into the quenchant is taken to be given by Newton's law of cooling, so that

$$(dQ/dt)_s = h(T_s - T_f)$$

where h is the film coefficient, T_s is the temperature of the surface of the steel, and T_f is the temperature of the quenchant, or the final temperature. Note that T_s is time

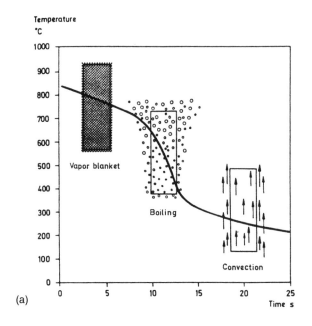

(a)

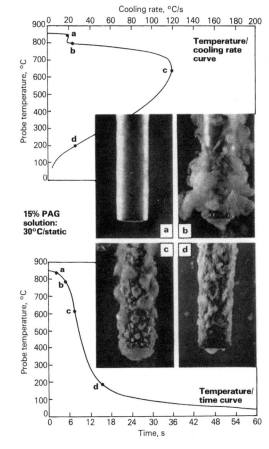

(b)

Fig. 4-1 (a) Schematic illustration of the three stages of cooling upon quenching a steel into a liquid. (b) Photographs of a cylinder quenched into a polymer quenchant, showing the three stages of cooling. ((a) from J. Bodin and S. Segerberg in *Quenching and Distortion Control,* G.E. Totten, editor, p 1, ASM International, Materials Park, Ohio, (1992), (b) from *Heat Treatment of Metals,* Vol 13, p 3 (1986))

dependent. Now a reduced temperature U can be defined as

$$U = (T - T_f)/(T_i - T_f)$$

where T is the temperature at a point inside the solid and is a function of time, and T_i is the initial temperature at that point, which is the austenitizing temperature in the case of quenching of steels being considered. Differentiating this equation with respect to distance X gives

$$dU/dx = [1/(T_i - T_f)] [dT/dx]$$

Now at any point in the steel part, the flux of heat dQ/dt is given by

$$dQ/dt = k (dT/dx)$$

and at the surface of the steel part, this is

$$dQ/dt = k (dT/dx)_s$$

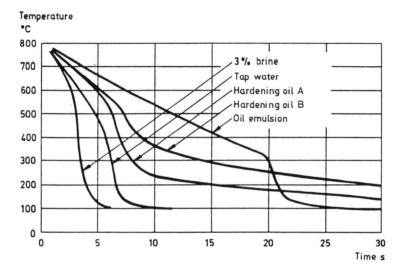

Fig. 4-2   Cooling curves at the center of silver spheres upon quenching into the media indicated. (From same source as Fig. 4-1a)

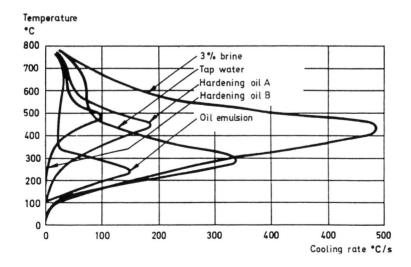

Fig. 4-3   Cooling rate as a function of cooling temperature derived from the curves in Fig. 4-2. (From same source as Fig. 4-1a)

which is equal to the flux cited above, so that

$$(dT/dx)_s = [h/k] (T_s - T_f)$$

so

$$(dU/dx)_s = [(1/T_i - T_f)] [h/k] [(T_s - T_f)]$$

$$= [h/k] [(T_s - T_f)/(T_i - T_f)]$$

$$= [h/k] U$$

or

$$(dU/dx)_s = H' U$$

To obtain the temperature distribution inside a steel part requires using Fourier's second law in appropriate form. For example, in one dimension, this is

$$dT/dt = \alpha (d^2T/dx^2)$$

where α is the thermal diffusivity of the steel. This equation must be solved for the appropriate boundary conditions, one of which is that the temperature of the surface

is given by the equations above. Thus the temperature as a function of time for any location in a steel part can be determined. The solutions can also be put in terms of the reduced temperature U. This is examined in detail in Chapter 9.

The Severity of Quench H

Solutions to the heat transfer equations exist for simple geometries, such as cylinders and plates, and can be obtained for more complicated shapes. Thus temperature, as a function of time, for any location in the steel part can be obtained if the pertinent heat transfer coefficients are specified. The thermal conductivity and thermal diffusivity of the steel are reasonably well known as a function of temperature, so their temperature dependence can be taken into account (although many solutions assume them to be constant). However, the film coefficient depends on a number of factors, which makes it difficult to characterize h in terms of the physical parameters of the quenchant. It depends upon, for example, the viscosity of the quenchant, but also on the surface roughness of the steel and the flow rate of the quenchant. Therefore, the

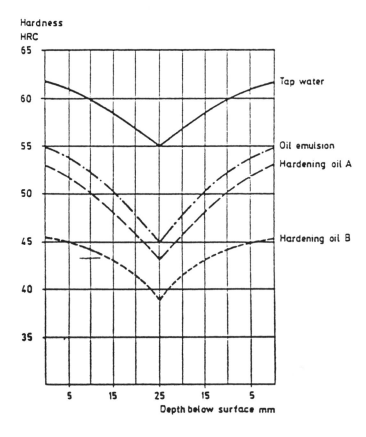

Fig. 4-4   Hardness profiles across a 50 mm diameter cylinder after quenching into the media indicated. (From same source as Fig. 4-1a)

heat transfer ability of the quenchant must be evaluated for each case.

The film coefficient h is usually combined with the thermal conductivity of the steel part to define a *severity of quench* or *Grossmann number* H, given by

$$H = h/2k$$

This quantity is then used as a parameter in the solution to the heat transfer equations. Thus, the temperature as a function of time at any location in a steel part is given as a function of the severity of quench. The calculation of cooling curves is described in detail in Chapter 9.

A very important result of the solutions to the heat transfer equations is that the *relative* cooling curves are identical for the same value of the product HD (for cylinders of diameter D) and HL (for plates of thickness L). The meaning of this is shown in Fig. 4-5.

Determination of the Severity of Quench

Consider a cylinder 1.00 inch in diameter quenched into a medium with H = 1.00 (e.g., water). The product HD = 1.00. The center of the cylinder cools to give the cooling curve shown in Fig. 4-6. Now we quench a cylinder 2.00 inches in diameter into the same quenchant. The position that cools at the same rate as that of the center of the 1 inch diameter bar will not be in the center, but near the surface, as shown in Fig. 4-6. Heat transfer calculations show that this location is about 0.88 of the

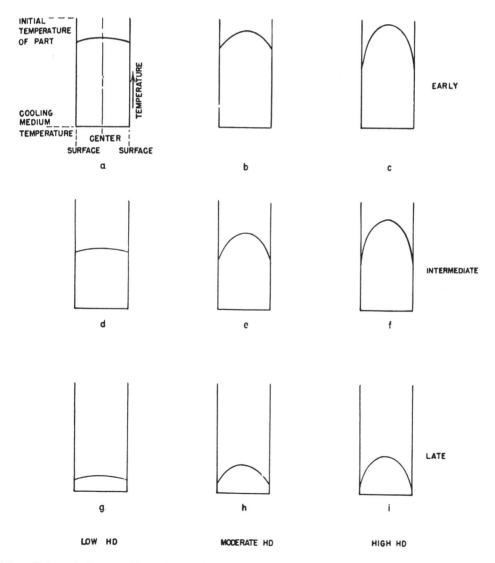

Fig. 4-5   Schematic diagrams illustrating significance of the product HD (or HL) on the temperature distribution across a cylinder. Time during quenching increases from top to bottom. (From J.H. Hollomon and L.D. Jaffee, *Ferrous Metallurgical Design*, Wiley, New York (1947). Reprinted by permission of John Wiley & Sons, Inc.)

distance from the center to the surface. We will represent this position by the ratio $D_u/D = 0.88$. We can repeat this procedure for cylinders with other diameters, and from these calculations a plot of D_u/D versus D can be made, as shown in Fig. 4-6.

If we use a cylinder of a diameter of 0.50 inches, and a quenchant with H = 2.00, then we get the curve shown in Fig. 4-7. Note that for a 1 inch diameter cylinder quenched into H = 2.00, the position $D_u/D = 0.88$ cools at the same rate as the center of the 0.5 inch cylinder. This is the same ratio as for the case of the 2 inch diameter cylinder quenched in H = 1.00. The connecting factor in the two cases is that the product HD = 1.00. It was pointed out in the preceding section that different cylinders will cool identically if the product HD is the same. Thus the curves in Fig. 4-7 will be identical if D_u/D is plotted against HD. Therefore, for each value of HD at $D_u/D = 0$ a curve is obtained similar to that in Fig. 4-7. These curves are shown in Fig. 4-8.

Using the curves in Fig. 4-8, the following method can be used to determine the severity of quench. A series of cylinders of different diameters of a given steel are austenitized and then quenched into the quenchant. There are then sectioned across the diameter and D_u is measured

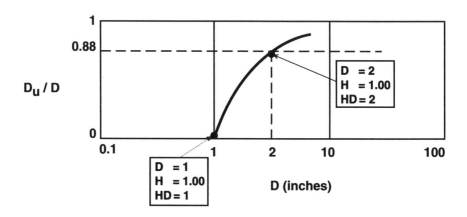

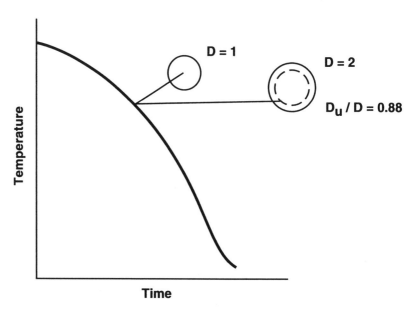

Fig. 4-6   Schematic diagram illustrating the relation between D_u/D and HD

by the methods outlined in Chapter 3. From this the ratio D_u/D is obtained, and this is plotted versus the diameter D, as shown in Fig. 4-9.

The unhardened interface position corresponds closely to that of 50% martensite. Thus, the diameter D at which $D_u/D = 0$ gives the critical diameter for the quench used. The curve in Fig. 4-9 has the same shape as the corresponding curve for D_u/D versus HD for the quench used. Thus, to determine the severity of quench H, the curve in Fig. 4-9 is plotted on the same scale as Fig. 4-8, overlaid on Fig. 4-8, and moved along the ordinate until the experimental curve (Fig. 4-9) matches one of the calculated curves. Then the matching value of HD is read off for $D_u/D = 0$, and knowing the critical diameter D_c (from Fig. 4-9), the value of H is determined. This is shown in Fig. 4-10, giving a value of H = 1.5.

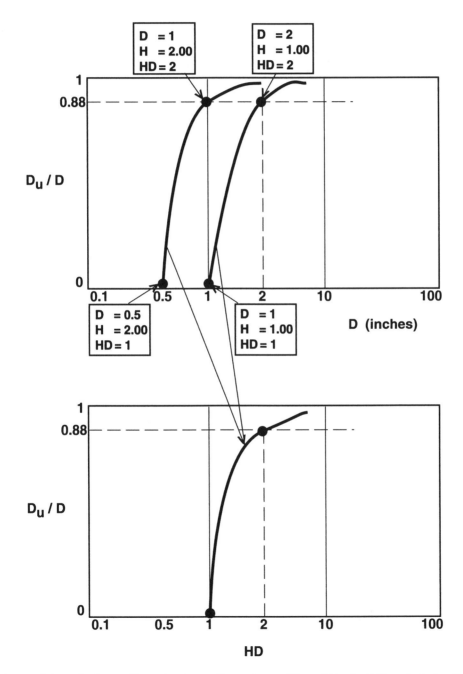

Fig. 4-7 Schematic diagram illustrating that cooling under conditions of identical HD product gives the same D_u/D versus HD curve

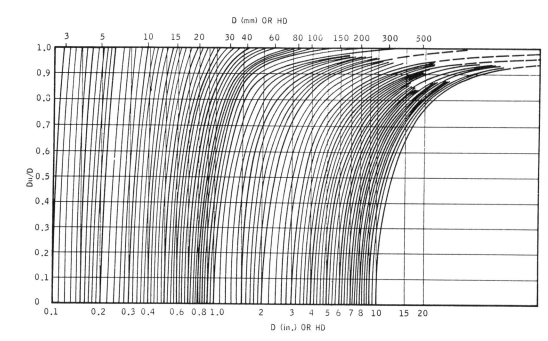

Fig. 4-8   Calculated curves of D_u/D versus HD. (From M.A. Grossmann, M. Asimow and S.F. Urban, in *Hardenability of Alloy Steels*, American Society for Metals, Metals Park, Ohio (1939))

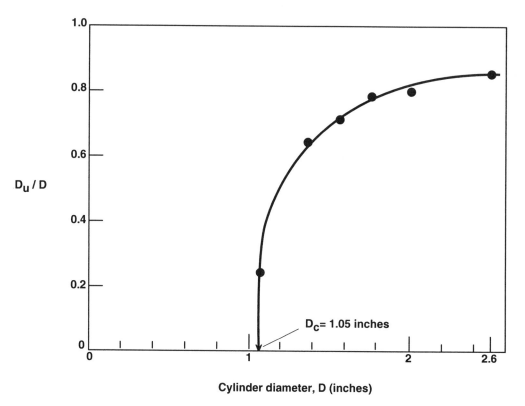

Fig. 4-9   Experimental data of the ratio of the unhardened diameter D_u to that of the diameter D versus the diameter D, from the photographs in Fig. 3-15

Table 4-1   Sample calculations of the severity of quench. (From same source as Fig. 4-11)

For 1½-inch round		Date 6-27-50
$a^2 = 0.0099$	Heat No. 220,952	Grade 9460M
$b^2 = 0.5625$ inch	Spec. No. 2	Pos. of T/u.c.—Ctr.
$r = a^2t/b^2$	Instrument No. 3	
$r/b = 0.0$	Temp. of quenchant	
b = Radius of test piece; $H_a = hb$	Water 70°F	
r = Radius of position considered; $H_G = ½h$	Oil.............	
a^2 = Diffusivity, in²/sec	Other........	
t = Time	FCC condition—Spent carb. compound	

τ	t (sec.)	T (°F)	U	$H_a = hb$	$H_G = ½h$
0.02	1.14	1550	1.0	0	0
0.04	2.27	1550	1.0	0	0
0.06	3.41	1547	0.997	...	...
0.08	4.55	1543	0.996	0.3	0.2
0.10	5.68	1523	0.982	0.52	0.35
0.20	11.36	1273	0.814	1.53	1.02
0.30	17.05	999	0.628	1.89	1.26
0.40	22.73	798	0.492	1.89	1.26
0.50	28.41	650	0.392	1.79	1.19
0.60	34.09	557	0.329	1.65	1.10
0.70	39.77	507	0.295	1.52	1.01
0.80	45.45	461	0.264	1.34	0.89
0.90	51.14	406	0.227	1.30	0.87
1.0	56.82	350	0.189	1.30	0.87
1.2	68.18	271	0.136	1.27	0.85
1.4	79.55	221	0.102	1.19	0.79
1.6	90.91	196	0.085	1.08	0.72

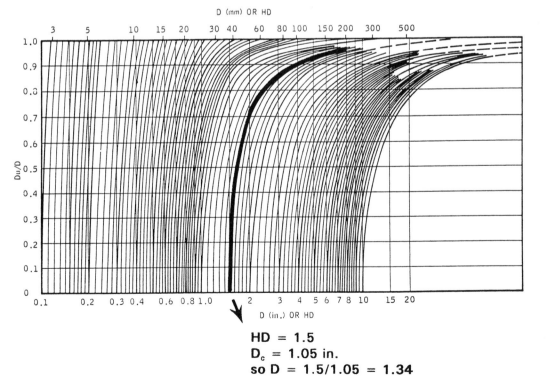

HD = 1.5
D_c = 1.05 in.
so D = 1.5/1.05 = 1.34

Fig. 4-10   The curve in Fig. 4-9 drawn on the plot in Fig. 4-8, showing how the severity of quench is obtained from the ordinate intercept

Carney determined the severity of quench more directly by measuring the cooling curves in metal cylinders and using these values in conjunction with Russell's tables. This is illustrated by the sample calculation in Table 4-1. The 1.5 inch diameter cylinder was quenched into water. The cooling curves were measured with a thermocouple at the center and at the mid-radius. From these data, the reduced temperature U was calculated, and

from Russell's tables a value of H was obtained as a function of temperature.

Figure 4-11 shows some of the results. It is seen that H is temperature dependent, and also varies with the location from which the cooling curve came which was used for the calculation. Carney points out that the variable H values found just reflect the lack of applicability of the assumptions used to construct Russell's

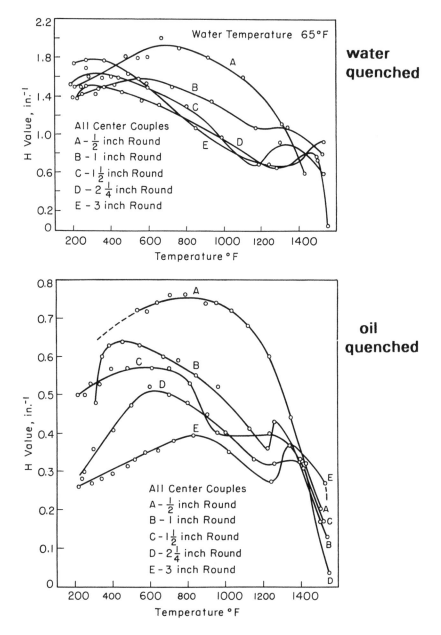

Fig. 4-11 Variation of the severity of quench H with temperature and size of the cylinders. The steel was a plain carbon 1080 steel. (From D.J. Carney, *Trans. ASM*, Vol 46, p 883 (1954))

tables. He presents other data which show that the main source of error is probably the assumption of a constant film coefficient. These results point out the importance of recognizing the uncertainty in values of the severity of quench.

Monroe and Bates [R.A. Monroe and C.E. Bates, *J. Heat Treating*, Vol 3, p 83 (1984)] solved the necessary heat transfer equations by a finite element heat transfer program to obtain a polynomial describing the relationship between the cooling rate at 704°C and the severity of quench. They then quenched cylinders and obtained the cooling curves, from which they calculated the cooling rate at 704°C. Using this experimental cooling rate, they calculated the severity of quench from the mathematical expression relating H and cooling rate. This method is similar to that of Carney using Russell's tables. The H values were reported only for the cooling rate at 704°C, but their method would give variations at other temperatures similar to those found by Carney, as described in the preceding paragraph.

The data examined in this section show that, in using the severity of quench values in designing heat treatments, it must be kept in mind that the values are only approximate. Calculations using H values are useful in outlining ranges of cooling rates required to obtain a given hardness, and in indicating the types of quenchants that might be usable and hence should be tried in establishing the final commercial quenching process.

Table 4-2 gives the range of H values typical of the different quenchants listed. The exact value depends critically upon the degree of agitation or the flow rate of the quenchant past the surface of the steel parts.

Correlation of the Cooling Rate of Cylinders and Plates with that in the Jominy Bar

It was pointed out in Chapter 3 that if a hardness is required at a certain location in a steel component, the required cooling rate could be determined if a plot of hardness versus cooling rate from austenite were available for the steel from which the part was to be made. This plot is obtained by the Jominy curve, and in Chapter 3 methods were examined by which the Jominy curve could be estimated from the chemical composition and the austenite grain size. In this section, we examine methods to estimate the quench (H value) required if the size and shape of the part are known and the required cooling rate is known.

The heat transfer equations can be solved so that the cooling rate at 704°C can be calculated as a function of the location in various shapes, such as cylinders and plates. These locations can then be correlated with positions on the Jominy bar having the same cooling rate (via Fig. 3-10). These results are subject to the same concerns as those found for determining the severity of quench, so that the correlations are not exact, but should be used as guidelines in establishing heat treatments.

Figure 4-12 shows the correlation between cylinders and the Jominy bar, and Fig. 4-13 shows that for plates and bars. Alternate methods of presenting these data for cylinders are shown in Fig. 4-14 and 4-15. In Fig. 4-16 the curves are not labeled with H values, but with the type of quenchant, including, for some of the curves, the flow rate of the quenchant past the quenched steel cylinders.

Table 4-2   Typical range of H values for different quenchants. ((a) from *Metals Handbook*, 9th edition, Vol 4, *Heat Treating*, American Society for Metals, Metals Park, Ohio (1981). (b) from M.A. Grossmann and M. Asimow, *The Iron Age*, p 39 (May 2, 1940))

(a)

Circulation or agitation	H-value or quenching power		
	Oil	Water	Caustic soda or brine
None	0.25 to 0.30	0.9 to 1.0	2
Mild	0.30 to 0.35	1.0 to 1.1	2 to 2.2
Moderate	0.35 to 0.40	1.2 to 1.3	...
Good	0.4 to 0.5	1.4 to 1.5	...
Strong	0.5 to 0.8	1.6 to 2.0	...
Violent	0.8 to 1.1	4	5

(b)

Mode of cooling	H-values			
	Air	Oil	Water	Brine
Specimen and coolant still	0.02	0.30	1.0	2.2
Specimen moved moderately in still coolant	...	0.4 to 0.6	1.5 to 3.0	...
Specimen moved strongly in still coolant	...	0.6 to 0.8	3.0 to 6.0	7.5
Strong to violent current or spray of coolant	...	1.0 to 1.7	6.0 to 12.0	...

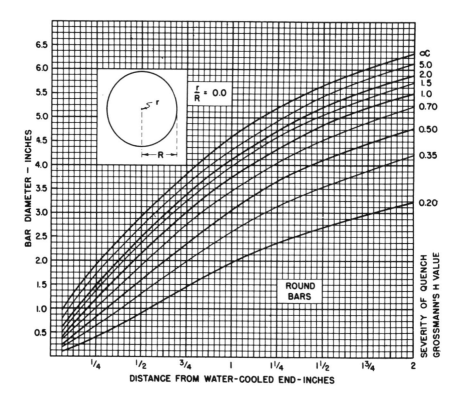

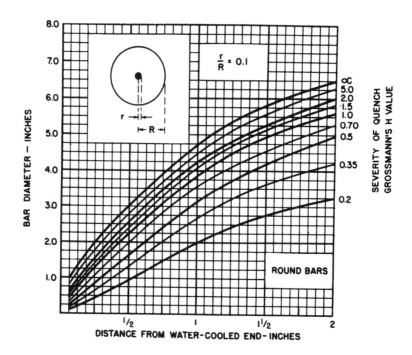

Fig. 4-12   Relation between locations in cylinders and the positions on the Jominy bar which have the same cooling rate at 704°C for different severity of quench values. (Adapted from J.L. Lamont, *Iron Age*, Vol 152, No. 16, p 64 (1943)) *(continued)*

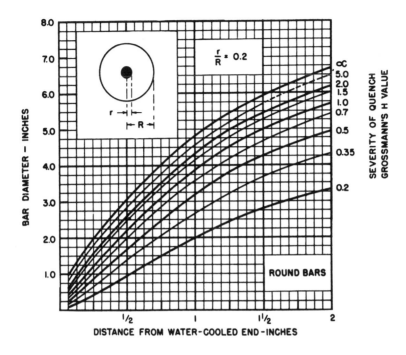

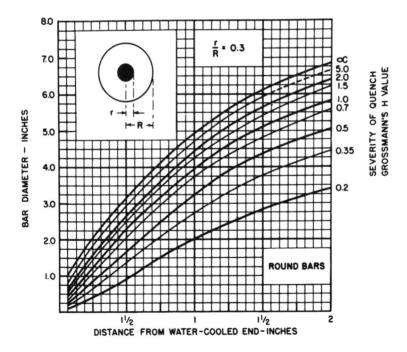

Fig. 4-12 (continued) Relation between locations in cylinders and the positions on the Jominy bar which have the same cooling rate at 704°C for different severity of quench values. (Adapted from J.L. Lamont, *Iron Age*, Vol 152, No. 16, p 64 (1943)) *(continued)*

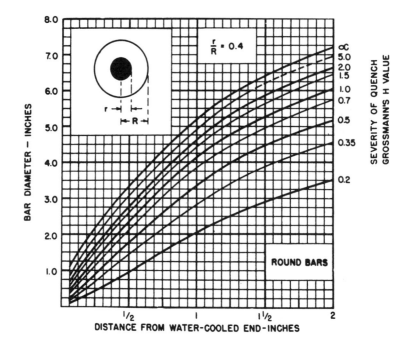

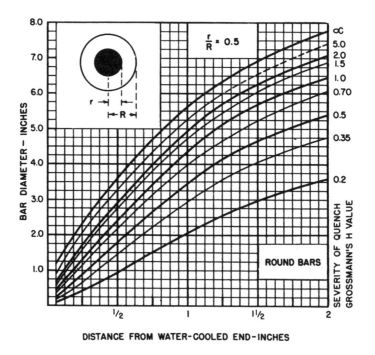

Fig. 4-12   (continued) Relation between locations in cylinders and the positions on the Jominy bar which have the same cooling rate at 704°C for different severity of quench values. (Adapted from J.L. Lamont, *Iron Age*, Vol 152, No. 16, p 64 (1943)) (*continued*)

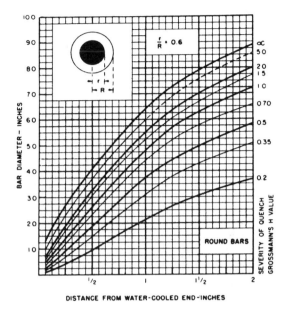

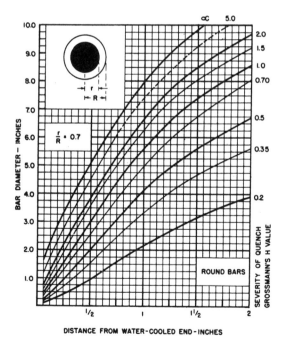

Fig. 4-12   (continued) Relation between locations in cylinders and the positions on the Jominy bar which have the same cooling rate at 704°C for different severity of quench values. (Adapted from J.L. Lamont, *Iron Age*, Vol 152, No. 16, p 64 (1943)) *(continued)*

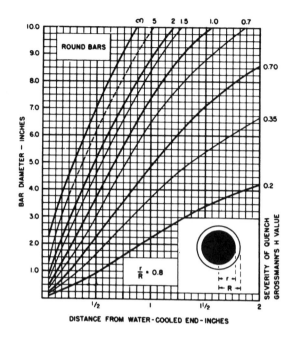

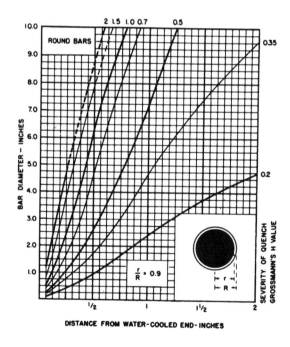

Fig. 4-12 (continued) Relation between locations in cylinders and the positions on the Jominy bar which have the same cooling rate at 704°C for different severity of quench values. (Adapted from J.L. Lamont, *Iron Age*, Vol 152, No. 16, p 64 (1943)) *(continued)*

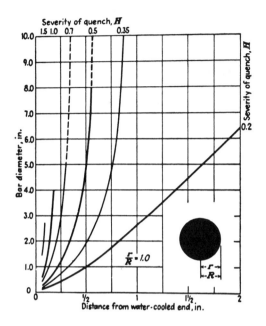

Fig. 4-12 (continued) Relation between locations in cylinders and the positions on the Jominy bar which have the same cooling rate at 704°C for different severity of quench values. (Adapted from J.L. Lamont, *Iron Age,* Vol 152, No. 16, p 64 (1943))

"H" or severity of quench values for various quenching conditions

H value	Quenching condition
0.10	Poor oil quench-no agitation
0.35	Good oil quench-moderate agitation
0.50	Very good oil quench-good agitation
0.70	Strong oil quench-violent agitation
1.00	Poor water quench-no agitation
1.50	Very good water quench-strong agitation
2.00	Brine quench-no agitation
5.00	Brine quench-violent agitation
∞	Ideal quench

Calculation of Hardness Distribution in Cylinders

In this section the cooling rate correlation will be used to calculate the hardness distribution across the diameter of cylinders. The calculations will be used to illustrate the sensitivity of the hardness distribution to the severity of quench and the hardenability.

Since the cooling rate at 704°C in various locations in cylinders can be correlated to that of locations on the Jominy bar, the hardness distribution across the diameter can be calculated if the Jominy curve is known. To illustrate this, we will use the heat transfer correlation in

Fig. 4-12, and the minimum in the Jominy band for a low alloy, Mn steel, 1340H. The Jominy band is shown in Fig. 4-17a. The hardness distribution will be determined for a 1 and a 3 inch diameter cylinder when quenched into oil of H = 0.20 and water of H = 1.00. The procedure is outlined in Fig. 4-18. The results for the 1 inch diameter cylinder are plotted in Fig. 4-19. The hardness is almost constant across the diameter for both quenchants, and it is obvious that the curves will rise, maintaining this constancy, as the severity of quench increases from 0.20 to 1.00. Also, shown in Fig. 4-19 is the hardness distribution for the steel if quenched into an ideal quench (H = ∞). It is clear that there is negligible difference between

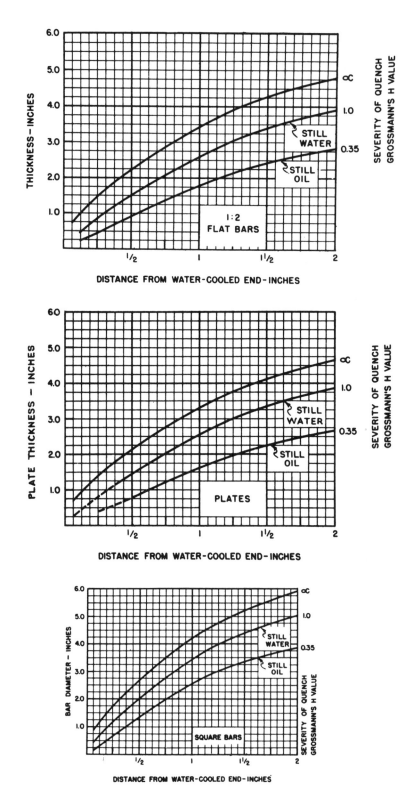

Fig. 4-13   Relation between locations in plates and the positions on the Jominy bar which have the same cooling rate at 704°C for different severity of quench values. (From same source as Fig. 4-12)

a water quench of H = 1.00 and an ideal quench, within the hardness measurement uncertainty of about ±2 Rockwell C.

In Fig. 4-19 are also shown results of the same calculation for a 3 inch diameter bar. Here the difference between the center and the surface hardness is more affected by the quenchant. Also note that there is a measurable difference in hardness using H = 1.00 and using an ideal quench, except at the surface, where the difference is slight.

To observe the effect of hardenability on the hardness distribution, the calculations were made using the lower limit of the hardenability band of the high hardenability 4340H steel (see Fig. 4-17b). The results are shown in Fig. 4-20. The hardness distribution, of course, is less sensitive to the quenchant, and even for the 3 inch diameter cylinder there is negligible difference between the result using H = 1.00 and using an ideal quench. For all three quenchants, the surface hardness is essentially that of an all-martensite structure.

The approach illustrated above can be used to examine the effect of a number of variables on the hardness distribution. For example, the hardenability factors examined in Chapter 3 can be used to calculate the effect of variation in chemical composition and austenite grain size on the ideal critical diameter. From the values of D_i, the Jominy curves can be calculated, and these can be used as described above to calculate the hardness

distribution to see how sensitive it is to the variation in chemical composition and austenite grain size.

Also, the approach above can be used to determine how sensitive the hardness distribution may be to variations in the severity of quench. This may be an important factor, especially when batch quenching components where locally H may vary due to variations in fluid flow, quenchant heating, etc.

Methods of Determining Cooling Rates in Quenched Steel Components

Most machine components do not have a simple shape (e.g., cylindrical) and thus the methods outlined above can be used only as a guide for other shapes. However, there is a method which can be used to determine the cooling rate in quenched steel components. This method is applicable if the component is of sufficient size to machine a Jominy bar from it. This bar is then austenitized as the component will be, and then end quenched, from which the Jominy curve is obtained. Then if the hardness at any location is measured, the cooling rate at that location can be obtained form this hardness value and the Jominy curve. For internal locations, the component must be sectioned to make the measurement. The procedure is described in detail in Fig. 4-21.

If the component is too small to machine a Jominy bar, the method in Fig. 4-21 cannot be applied. However, if the Jominy curve for the steel used to make the compo-

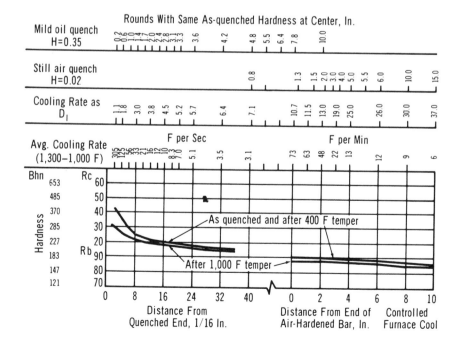

Fig. 4-14   Heat transfer correlations between the position in cylinders and the position on the Jominy bar. (From C.F. Jatczak, *Metal Progress*, Vol 100, No. 3, p 60 (1971))

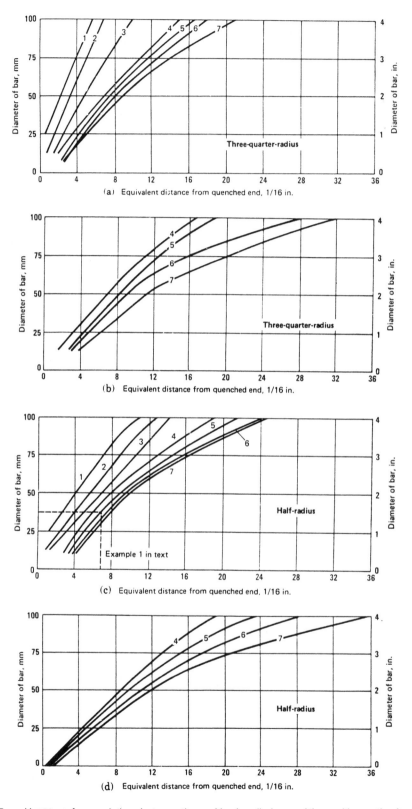

Fig. 4-15   Heat transfer correlations between the position in cylinders and the position on the Jominy bar. (From *Metals Handbook*, 9th edition, Vol 1, *Properties and Selection: Irons and Steels*, American Society for Metals, Metals Park, Ohio (1978))

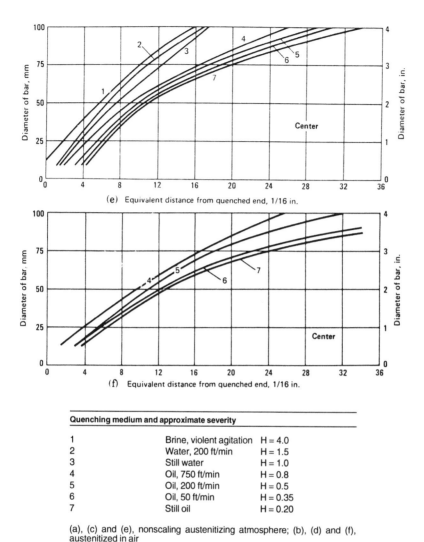

(e) Equivalent distance from quenched end, 1/16 in.

(f) Equivalent distance from quenched end, 1/16 in.

Quenching medium and approximate severity		
1	Brine, violent agitation	H = 4.0
2	Water, 200 ft/min	H = 1.5
3	Still water	H = 1.0
4	Oil, 750 ft/min	H = 0.8
5	Oil, 200 ft/min	H = 0.5
6	Oil, 50 ft/min	H = 0.35
7	Still oil	H = 0.20

(a), (c) and (e), nonscaling austenitizing atmosphere; (b), (d) and (f), austenitized in air

Fig. 4-15   (continued)

nent is known, or if the chemical composition of the stock material is known and hence the Jominy curve can be calculated, then the cooling rate can still be estimated from the hardness measured at any location in the component.

The Formation of Residual Stresses During Quenching

When quenching steels, the uneven cooling causes the formation of residual stresses. These stresses play an important role in application of steel parts, and they also play a prominent role in quench cracking. In quenched steels of the type being discussed here, these stresses originate from two sources. One is the thermal stresses

due to uneven contraction (thermal residual stresses). These stresses can be induced upon cooling (and on heating) materials which undergo no phase change. The other source is the volume change which occurs upon the decomposition of austenite. As will be seen, the sign (tension or compression) of the thermal residual stresses usually can be reasoned. Indeed, the final stress distribution can be calculated with appropriate data (e.g., coefficient of expansion, yield strength as a function of temperature, temperature-time curves as a function of position in the part). However, it is much more difficult to determine the stresses due to the phase changes; even the sign of the stresses is sometimes difficult to rationalize. This is because the temperature-time curves must be coupled with the continuous cooling TTT diagram, which requires a complicated procedure. Approaches to analytical treatments of the development of residual stresses during quenching are presented in Chapter 9.

In this section, the formation of residual stresses in materials in which no phase change occurs on cooling is described first. Then the effect on the residual stresses of the phase changes in austenite is examined.

Quenching stresses developed without phase changes

To demonstrate the formation of thermal residual stresses, we describe the development of stresses during cooling of a cylinder. We only consider longitudinal stresses, but the tangential and radial stresses can be taken into account quantitatively.

First, we will describe what must happen to *not* have thermal residual stresses develop. This process is shown schematically in Fig. 4-22. For convenience of description, the cylinder will be divided into a center (or core) region and a surface region. We begin with the cylinder at a uniform high temperature T_h; the quenchant temperature is T_l. Upon placing the material in the quenchant, the surface region cools to T_l. Thus the surface wants to contract to a length l_2 which can be calculated if the

coefficient of expansion of the material is known. However, the center is still hot and at temperature T_h, so it tends to remain at the length it has. Since the center and the surface are intimately connected, upon cooling the contracting surface pulls down on the center, placing it in compression. The center, tending to remain at the length it has, resists this force, and only partly contracts, so that the surface cannot contract to a length characteristic of temperature T_l. This places the surface in tension. The length is l_1 and the residual stress distribution is shown in Fig. 4-22b. Note that at this stage the surface is at temperature T_l, but the center is still at temperature T_h. Now as the center cools, it contracts, and the residual stresses are gradually reduced (Fig. 4-22c to 4-22d). When the center attains temperature T_l, both the center and the surface are at the correct length for this temperature, and the residual stresses are zero (Fig. 4-22e).

It is important to note that in the description above no plastic deformation occurs. Thus the material has a sufficiently high yield strength (which is a function of temperature) so that at no time do the *elastic* stresses cause the yield strength to be exceeded. This situation is best attained if the yield strength is high at all temperatures, and if the strain at any time during cooling is small. (This

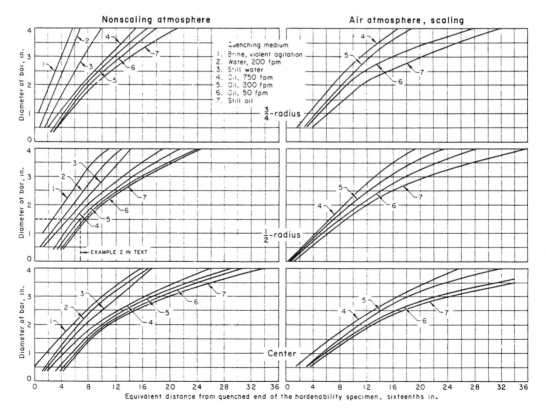

Fig. 4-16   Heat transfer correlations between the position in cylinders and the position on the Jominy bar. (From *Metals Handbook*, 8th edition, Vol 1, *Properties and Selection of Metals*, American Society for Metals, Metals Park, Ohio (1961))

SAE/AISI 1340H   UNS H13400

Heat-treating temperatures recommended by SAE
Normalize (for forged or rolled specimens only): 870 °C (1600 °F)
Austenitize: 845 °C (1550 °F)

Approximate diameters of rounds with same as-quenched hardness (HRC), mm											Location in round	Quench
50 75											Surface	Mild water quench
20 30		60		90							3/4 radius from center	
	20	30	40	50	60		80		100		Center	
	20	40	60	80		100					Surface	Mild oil quench
	15		30	45		60		75		90	3/4 radius from center	
		10	20	30	40		50		60	75	Center	

Hardness, HRC vs. Distance from quenched end, mm

Hardness limits for specification purposes

J distance, mm	Hardness, HRC	
	Maximum	Minimum
1.5	60	53
3	60	52
5	59	50
7	58	48
9	57	42
11	56	36
13	54	32
15	52	30
20	47	26
25	41	24
30	39	23
35	37	22
40	36	21
45	35	20
50	34	20

Fig. 4-17   Jominy band for 1340H steel and 4340H steel. (From ASTM specification A 304-70, American Society for Testing and Materials, Philadelphia (1984). Copyright ASTM. Reprinted with permission) *(continued)*

SAE/AISI 4340H UNS H43400

Heat-treating temperatures recommended by SAE
 Normalize (for forged or rolled specimens only): 870 °C (1600 °F)
 Austenitize: 845 °C (1550 °F)

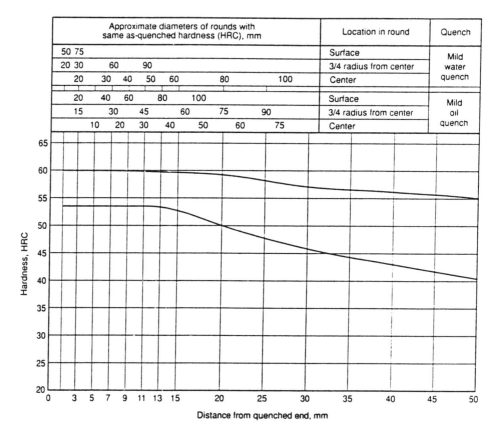

Hardness limits for specification purposes

J distance, mm	Hardness, HRC	
	Maximum	Minimum
1.5	60	53
3	60	53
5	60	53
7	60	53
9	60	53
11	60	53
13	60	52
15	60	52
20	59	50
25	58	48
30	58	46
35	57	44
40	57	43
45	56	42
50	56	40

Fig. 4-17 (continued) Jominy band for 1340H steel and 4340H steel. (From ASTM specification A 304-70, American Society for Testing and Materials, Philadelphia (1984). Copyright ASTM. Reprinted with permission)

latter characteristic is met for materials with low coefficients of expansion, such as ceramics.)

The process above is altered to allow *plastic* deformation to occur. The process is shown schematically in Fig. 4-23. When the cylinder is first quenched, and the surface is at temperature T_l but the center is still at temperature T_h, it is assumed that the residual stresses shown in Fig. 4-23b are sufficient to cause plastic deformation. [This causes distortion, of course, which is not depicted here.] This plastic deformation may occur in both the surface and the center, depending upon the relative cross-section area of the two regions. As this

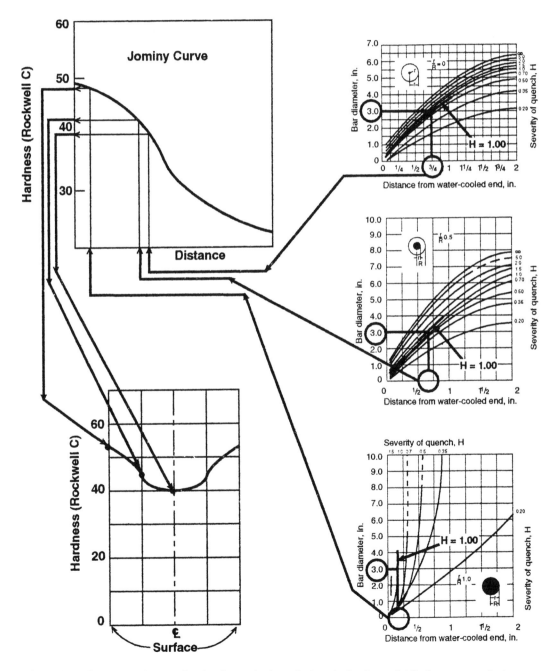

Fig. 4-18   Schematic diagram showing the method to calculate the hardness distribution across cylinders

deformation occurs, the center contracts and the surface expands, relieving the stresses and changing the stress distribution from that in Fig. 4-23c to that in Fig. 4-23d.

Note in Fig. 4-23d that the stress distribution is low. The center is still at temperature T_h, but it now has a length about the same as the surface. Thus, upon lowering the temperature of the center to T_l, the center tries to contract to a length which can be calculated from the coefficient of expansion, and this length will be less than that of the surface which is at temperature T_l. Therefore, as the center cools and contracts, it places the surface in compression. The surface resists this compressive stress

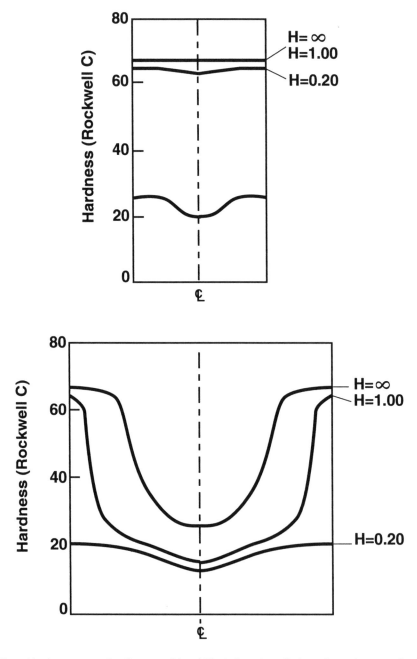

Fig. 4-19 Hardness across the diameter of 1 and 3 inch diameter cylinders when using quenchants of H = 0.20, 1.00 and ∞. These curves are based on the minimum in the hardenability band of a 1340H steel

so that the center cannot contract to the desired length; it is too long, and thus is in tension. The final stress distribution is that shown in Fig. 4-23e. The final length is greater than l_2.

The development of thermal residual stresses is depicted schematically also in Fig. 4-24. Here the distortion that will occur is indicated. If no plastic deformation occurs, the longitudinal residual stresses at the surface will follow the upper curve as cooling progresses. Note that when the surface and the center attain the quenchant temperature (25°C), the residual stress is zero. However, if plastic deformation occurs about the time marked by B, then the surface residual stress will decrease from a to b. Then upon further cooling, the surface will attain a compressive residual stress. This must be balanced by a tensile residual stress in the center (shown by the dashed line).

Another way to look at the longitudinal residual stresses in a cylinder is illustrated by Fig. 4-25. Here two springs at the equilibrium length are shown, the one in the center being the longer. If these are intimately joined at the top by a plate, the outer spring becomes longer than it was, and the inner spring becomes shorter. Hence the center spring is in compression, and the outer is in tension. This points out the principle of the common method of measuring residual stresses (from any origin). The technique involves machining off layers and measuring the dimensional changes accompanying the removal of each layer. Thus in Fig. 4-25, if the outer spring is removed (machined off), the center spring is free to expand. From this dimensional change and the elastic modulus, the longitudinal stress that was present before removal of the layer can be estimated. The shape changes are illustrated schematically in Fig. 4-26, where the center expands when the outside is removed. This is also illustrated in Fig. 4-27 for a plate. In actually making the measurements, of course, the layers are removed in small increments.

The magnitude of the thermal residual stresses is illustrated by the data in Fig. 4-28. Here are shown the longitudinal, tangential and radial stresses across the diameter of a cylinder. Note that the material is 1045 steel, *but* the samples were *not* heated into the austenite region. Thus, the stresses do not contain any contribution from phase changes. The stresses are compressive at the surface and tension at the center, and the stresses are less the lower the temperature from which quenching occurred, and less if quenched into oil compared to quenching into water. At the surface and the center, the magnitude of these stresses is comparable to the yield strength.

Quenching stresses developed with phase changes

When a steel is quenched from austenite, an additional important contribution to the residual stresses is from the volume change associated with the decomposition of austenite. The magnitude of the stresses is related to the volume (or length) data shown in Fig. 4-29. In Fig. 4-29a is shown schematically the length of an eutectoid steel sample with temperature for two thermal treatments. If the steel is austenitized then cooled slowly, the curve a-b-c-d is obtained. The volume expansion occurs in the temperature range $T_b - T_c$, when austenite goes to pearlite. Some actual length versus temperature data are shown in Fig. 4-29b.

If the steel is quenched from high temperature, then the contraction curve of austenite (a-b) is followed down to temperature T_e, the martensite-start temperature. Below this temperature, the steel sample expands as cooling progresses because the volume increase with the formation of martensite exceeds the contraction of the remaining austenite. Thus, the curve a-b-e-f is followed. Once all martensite is formed, the steel sample contracts upon further cooling with a slope (the coefficient of expansion) characteristic of that of martensite.

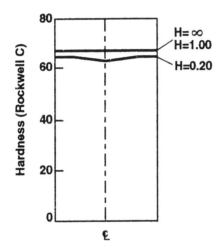

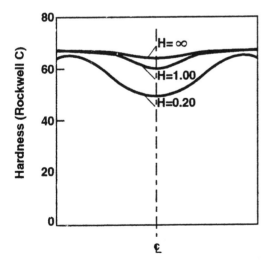

Fig. 4-20 Hardness across the diameter of 1 and 3 inch diameter cylinders when using quenchants of H = 0.20, 1.00 and ∞. These curves are based on the minimum in the hardenability band of a 4340H steel

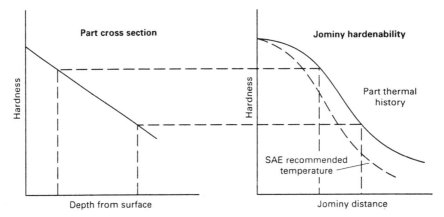

Procedure to determine quench cooling rates at important locations in a workpiece:

- *Step 1:* Obtain at least two test parts (a) made from the same heat of steel and manufactured as close as possible to the proposed production method. Castings will do if forging dies are not available
- *Step 2:* Machine parts to condition in which they will be hardened. Copper plate or otherwise protect parts from any carburizing or decarburizing action. Process parts through heat-treating operations for times estimated to be approximately that for the production part. Quench part No. 1 in a manner as close to production as possible (no temper)
- *Step 3:* Cut, grind, and polish hardened sections from part No. 1 so hardness readings may be taken as shown on example below:

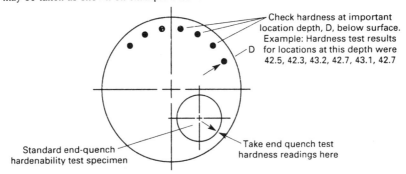

Check hardness at important location depth, D, below surface. Example: Hardness test results for locations at this depth were 42.5, 42.3, 43.2, 42.7, 43.1, 42.7

Standard end-quench hardenability test specimen

Take end quench test hardness readings here

- *Step 4:* Machine end-quench hardenability test specimens from part No. 2 test location on hardenability specimens to correspond to depth D, below surface. Harden end-quench specimens from same temperature as part No. 1. Example test results as follows:

Distance from quenched end, $\frac{1}{16}$ in.	1	2	3	4	5	6	8
Hardness, HRC	56	55	55	54	52	48	43

- *Step 5:* By comparing hardness results obtained at reference location of step 3 (HRC 42.7) to end-quench results (step 4), it can be seen that this hardness occurs at $\frac{8}{16}$ in. on end-quench curve. Quench cooling rate at reference point is approximately equal to $\frac{8}{16}$ in. in end-quench test
- *Step 6:* Confirm cooling rate subsequently on a number of different heats of production parts and adjust material or heat treatment or both to obtain the engineering requirements more precisely

(a) Can be used on gear teeth, roots of splines, and other part shapes. If section in which cooling rate must be determined (such as a gear tooth) is too small for an end-quench hardenability specimen, test results from a separate test may be used. An attempt should be made to make end-quench hardness tests on metal of same location in cross section as gear tooth.

Fig. 4-21   Procedure to determine the cooling rate at any location in a quenched steel component. (J.L. Lamont, *Iron Age*, Vol 152, p 64 (Oct 14, 1943))

The magnitude of the expansion when martensite forms depends upon the carbon content, but only slightly, as shown in Fig. 4-30. Note that the volume difference is less the higher the carbon content. However, the residual stresses will be greater the higher the carbon content (and alloy content) because of the effect of composition on M_s and M_f temperatures. This will be treated in the next section.

The temperature dependence of the volume change when a steel cools depends upon both the cooling rate and the hardenability of the steel. When austenite decomposes to primary ferrite, pearlite, bainite or martensite, there is a volume expansion. Thus residual stresses may develop even if martensite does not form.

We consider first the case of transformation stresses when both the center and the surface of a cylinder form martensite. This is shown schematically in Fig. 4-31. Note in this case that the surface is completely martensite while the center is still completely austenite. This is shown by the temperature profiles in Fig. 4-31b. Upon cooling, when the surface transforms to martensite, this

region expands. However, this is resisted by the center, which is still austenite. Thus the surface is in compression and the center is in tension (Fig. 4-31c). Then when the center transforms to martensite (time t_b to t_c), the center expands, placing the surface in tension and the center in compression (Fig. 4-31c). (Also see Fig. 4-33c.) Since martensite is very brittle in tensile loading, cracking may occur at this stage, and this is discussed in the next section.

If the cylinder had cooled as shown schematically in Fig. 4-32a, a different situation exists. The residual stresses which develop can be visualized by considering what occurs if the cylinder were cooled to 25°C and still was entirely austenite, then the surface transformed to martensite and the center to pearlite. The surface would expand as it changed to martensite, and would have an unimpeded length as shown in Fig. 4-32b. Likewise, the center would also expand, but to a shorter unimpeded length. If the center and the surface are then connected, the surface must be compressed and the surface expanded to attain a length match. Thus the surface is in compres-

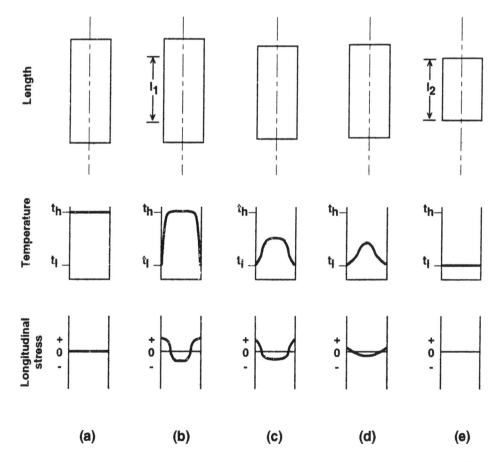

(a) **(b)** **(c)** **(d)** **(e)**

Fig. 4-22 Schematic illustration of the development of longitudinal thermal residual stresses in a cylinder during cooling. At (a), the cylinder is at a high temperature T_h, and from (b) to (e) it is cooling to the lower temperature T_l. In this sequence, it is assumed that no plastic deformation occurs, so that after cooling to T_l no residual stresses are present (e)

sion and the center in tension. The actual stresses will be lowered if plastic deformation occurs in either the center or the surface during the cooling and transformation process.

Figure 4-33 shows residual stresses developed in a steel for three cases with different cooling rates at the surface and the center. Cooling to form all martensite (Fig. 4-33c) produces tension at the surface, for the reason described in association with Fig. 4-31. Note that the tensile residual stresses at the surface from the transformation have been large enough to compensate for the expected compressive residual thermal stresses. Figure 4-33a shows the case of the surface transforming to martensite but the center to a softer product. This is the case described in Fig. 4-32, which leads to compressive residual stresses at the surface.

Quench Cracking in Steels

There are two types of quench cracks in quenched steels. One is microcracks which occur in the martensite.

These occur at the points of impingement of martensite plates with each other or with austenite grain boundaries, and they form only in the higher carbon steels because they only occur in plate martensite, not lath martensite. These cracks are usually only revealed upon microscopic examination. The other type of cracks are gross cracks, which frequently cause the steel component to break into pieces upon quenching. These cracks are usually quite visible at low magnification. The formation of the cracks is related to the residual stresses developed in quenching. It is possible that microcracks may act as nuclei for the formation of the gross cracks, so that the formation of microcracks may be quite important in considering gross quench cracking.

Microcracking

It has been shown that microcracking is associated with the impingement of martensite plates on one another or on austenite grain boundaries. Since the plate martensite morphology only forms in the higher carbon steels, microcracking does not occur in the lower carbon steels.

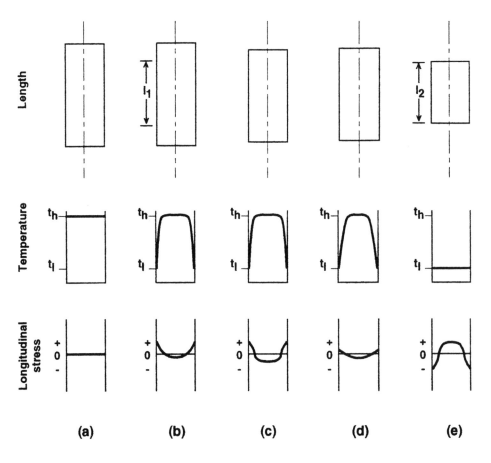

| (a) | (b) | (c) | (d) | (e) |

Fig. 4-23   Schematic illustration of the development of longitudinal thermal residual stresses in a cylinder during cooling. Here it is assumed that plastic deformation occurs (between (c) and (d)), and the final residual stresses are compression at the surface and tension at the center (e). (From C.R. Brooks, *Heat Treatment of Ferrous Alloys*, Hemisphere Publishing Corporation/McGraw-Hill Book Company, New York (1979))

steels. In fact, a study of a 1.39% C hypereutectoid steel which was austenitized in the two phase austenite + iron carbide region, at a temperature so that the austenite carbon content was about 0.8%, showed that microcracks did not develop. The microcrack density increased with austenitizing temperature. It also has been shown that prior austenite grain size will affect the microcrack density; the smaller the grain size, the lower the microcrack density. Of direct interest in hardening steels, it was found that the density of microcracks was not affected by the severity of quench, and therefore the formation of microcracks is not related to the development of gross residual stresses during quenching. [For details of these effects, see A.R. Marder, A.O. Benscoter and G. Krauss, *Met. Trans.*, Vol 1, p 1545 (1970); R.P. Brobst and G. Krauss, *Met. Trans.*, Vol 5, p 457 (1974); M.G. Mendiratta, J. Sasser and G. Krauss, *Met. Trans.*, Vol 3, p 351 (1972).]

Gross cracking during quenching

Quench cracking of steels is associated with the stresses created during quenching and the strength and toughness of the structures. In quenching, cracking oc-

curs in the martensitic structure because of its high brittleness. Other structures which might be present are susceptible to cracking in principle, but in practice their ductility usually precludes cracking.

The higher the carbon content, the more susceptible steels are to quench cracking. However, this is not due to the effect of carbon on the volume difference between austenite and martensite, because, as was shown in Fig. 4-30, the volume change decreases slightly with increasing carbon content. The important factor is the influence that carbon content (and alloy content) have on the M_s and M_f temperatures. The higher the carbon content (and alloy content), the lower the M_s and M_f temperatures. Since the coefficient of expansion (or contraction) of austenite and martensite differ, as shown in Fig. 4-29, the amount of expansion which occurs when martensite forms is greater if this occurs at lower temperatures. This is illustrated in Fig. 4-34. Note that when the martensite begins to form just below the M_s temperature, the volume change (denoted ΔV in Fig. 4-34) is greater if this occurs at a lower temperature. Also, when martensite forms at relatively high temperatures, there is more stress relaxation and hence the transformation residual stresses are not so large.

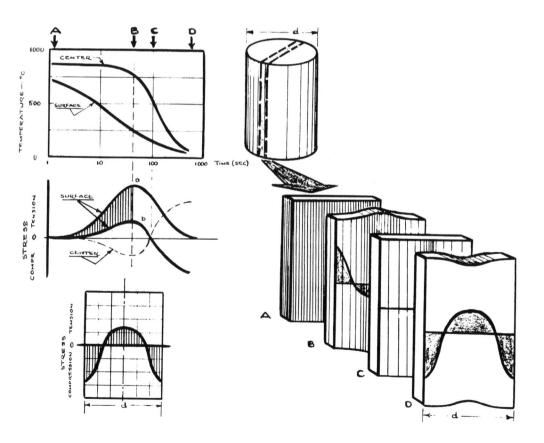

Fig. 4-24 Schematic illustration showing the development of thermal residual stresses on cooling. (From L.J. Ebert, *Met. Trans.*, Vol 9A, p 1537 (1978))

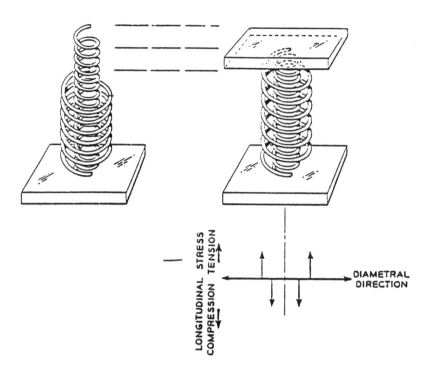

Fig. 4-25 Illustration of the concept of residual stresses using springs. (From R.G. Treuting in *Residual Stress Measurements*, American Society for Metals, Metals Park, Ohio (1952))

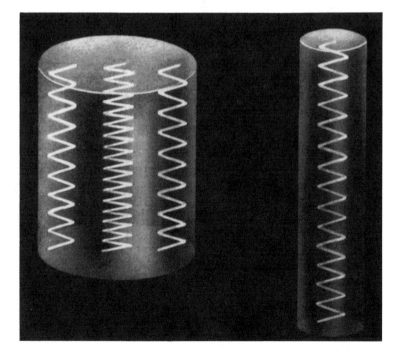

Fig. 4-26 Schematic illustration of the change in length of the center of a cylinder which has residual compressive stresses in the center and tensile stresses in the surface, when the surface layer is removed. (From J.J. Lynch, p 42 in *Residual Stress Measurements*, American Society for Metals, Metals Park, Ohio (1952))

Fig. 4-27   Schematic illustration of the change in length of a plate which has residual compressive stresses in the center and tensile stresses in the outside, when the righthand side is removed. (From J.J. Lynch, p 42 in *Residual Stress Measurements*, American Society for Metals, Metals Park, Ohio (1952))

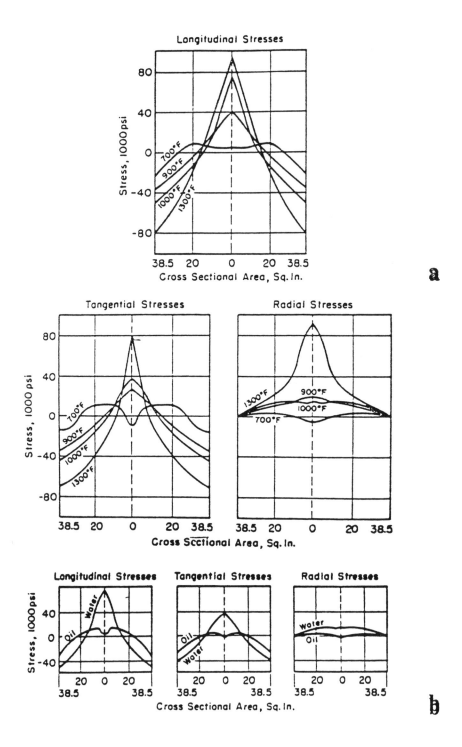

Fig. 4-28 Thermal residual stress distribution in cylinders of a 1045 steel for various cooling treatments. Note that the samples were not austenitized before quenching, so that these stresses are thermal residual stresses. (From H.B. Wichart in *Residual Stress Measurements*, American Society for Metals, Metals Park, Ohio, p. 97 (1952))

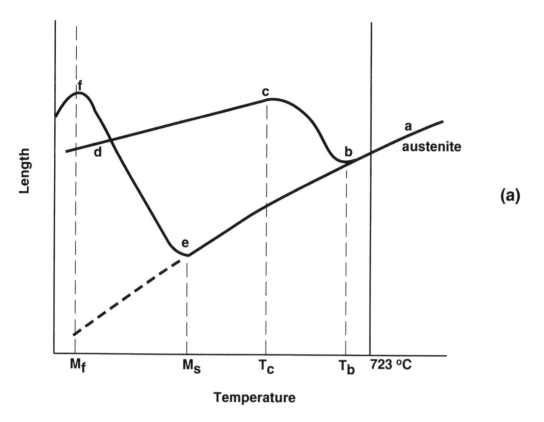

Fig. 4-29 The variation of the length of a 0.8% C steel sample upon slow cooling and upon rapid cooling. (a) is schematic. ((b) from same source as Fig. 4-1a)

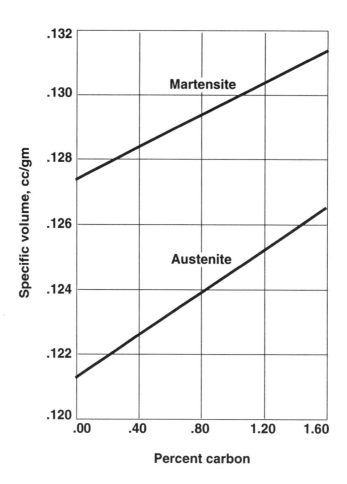

Fig. 4-30 The specific volume of austenite and martensite as a function of carbon content, showing that the volume change upon forming martensite is not very dependent on the carbon content. (Adapted from L.D. Jaffe and J.H. Hollomon, *Trans. AIME*, Vol 167, p 617 (1946))

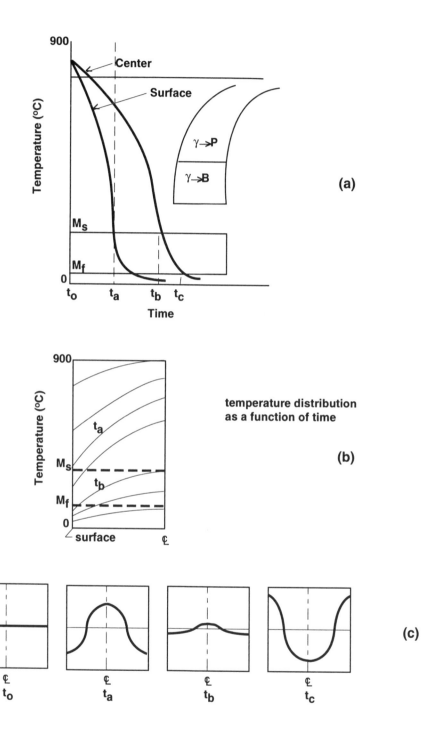

temperature distribution
as a function of time

(b)

(c)

Fig. 4-31   Schematic illustration of the development of transformation residual stresses in a eutectoid steel cooled rapidly so that both the surface and the center form martensite

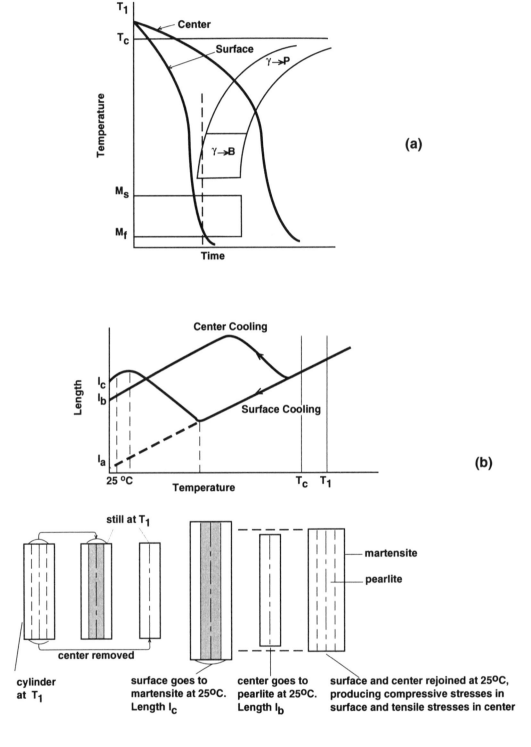

Fig. 4-32   (a) Schematic CCT diagram showing cooling curves at the surface and the center of a cylinder of a eutectoid steel cooled so that the surface forms martensite and the center forms pearlite. (b) Length versus temperature curves for a sample cooled as depicted in (a). (c) A schematic diagram illustrating the formation of residual transformation stresses

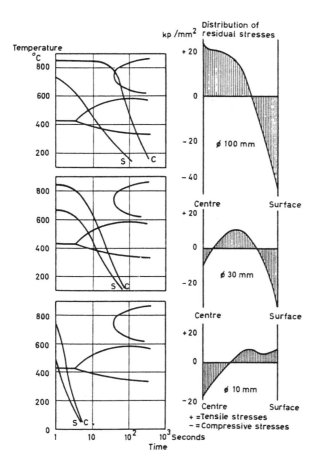

Fig. 4-33   Longitudinal residual stresses in three cylinders of a steel, each of which had the cooling curves shown for the surface and the center. (From A. Rose, *Harterei Techn. Mitt.*, Vol 21, p 1 (1966), as given in K.-E. Thelning, *Steel and Its Heat Treatment*, Butterworths, London (1975))

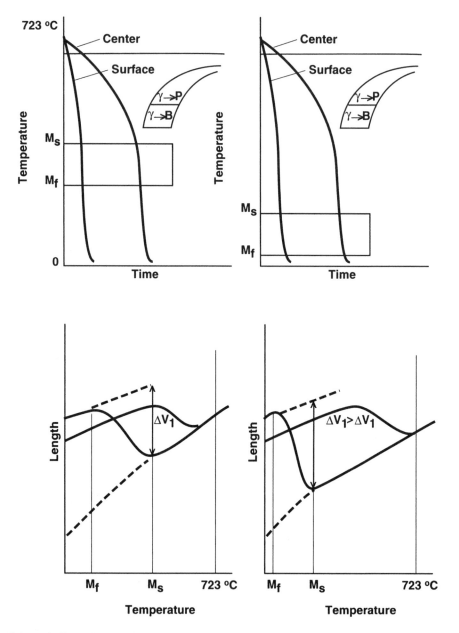

Fig. 4-34 Schematic illustration showing the influence of the M_s and M_f temperatures on the volume change which occurs when martensite forms

Chapter 5

Tempering

The main difficulty with using steels in the hardened condition in which the structure is martensitic is that the toughness is low. Thus, in most applications where relatively high hardness is required, the steel part is quenched to form a martensitic structure harder than that required, then it is heated in the ferrite + iron carbide region of the phase diagram (i.e., below 723°C) to convert the martensite to a structure of fine carbide particles in ferrite. This structure has a lower hardness than that of martensite, but by proper choice of the temperature and time used, the structure developed will be sufficiently fine to give the desired hardness. In this condition, martensite is not present, but has been replaced by the tougher ferrite-iron carbide structure.

This heat treatment is called *tempering*, and the main purpose is to develop a usable combination of hardness (strength) and toughness. The structure which forms is called *tempered martensite*. However, it is important to understand and to remember that tempered martensite usually contains *no* martensite. It is a structure of fine carbide particles in ferrite which has formed from the martensite during the tempering heat treatment.

In this chapter, the tempering behavior of plain carbon steels will be examined first, then that of alloy steels. Then some correlations will be examined which allow estimations of the tempered hardness from the chemical compositions, tempering temperature and tempering time. Finally the important problem of temper embrittlement will be discussed.

There are many detailed reviews of tempering in steels. For example, see G. Krauss in *Phase Transformations in Ferrous Alloys* (A.R. Marder and J.I. Goldstein, editors, The Metallurgical Society, Warrendale, PA (1984)) and the June 1983 issue of *Metallurgical Transactions*. Also see M. Wisti and M. Hingwe, "Tempering of Steel" in *ASM Handbook*, Vol 4, *Heat Treating*, ASM International, Materials Park, Ohio (1991).

Effect of Tempering on Mechanical Properties of Plain Carbon Steels

In obtaining data on the effect of tempering on properties, the as-quenched condition must be kept in mind. Generally, it is assumed that the as-quenched structure is martensite, or mostly martensite. However, if quenching is only made to 25°C, then retained austenite may be present, and during tempering this isothermally decomposes, which gives a different effect on the hardness than does the decomposition of martensite. In the data to be presented in this section on hardness and tensile mechanical property data, the presence of a small amount of retained austenite or of structures other than martensite, such as a small amount of pearlite or bainite, will not significantly affect the tempering results. However, this may not be true of the effect on toughness, and this will be examined in some detail in the section on temper embrittlement.

It also must be kept in mind that from a practical standpoint, some tempering usually has occurred before property measurements can be made. This is due to the very rapid diffusion of carbon in martensite. Thus in the strict sense we are not examining tempering of martensite, but of "conditioned" martensite. However, this is not a practical problem in terms of heat treatment.

Effect of tempering on hardness

Hardness data typical of those of plain carbon steel are shown in Fig. 5-1. In Fig. 5-1a the shortest tempering time used was 10 min. The as-quenched hardness for the two carbon contents is shown in the figures. The rapidity with which martensite decomposes into the ferrite-carbide structure is reflected by the large decrease in hardness upon tempering for only 10 min. at 204°C. The reduction in hardness shown by the curves is associated with the coarsening of the carbides, as will be illustrated in a subsequent section. The higher carbon steel is the harder because of the greater amount of iron carbide

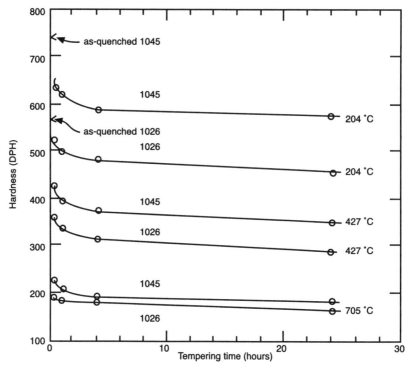

(a)

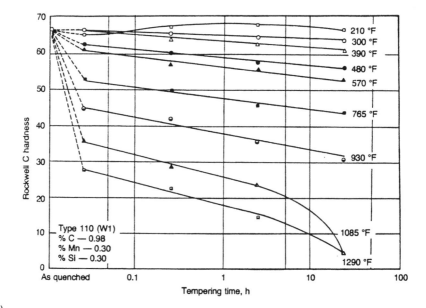

(b)

Fig. 5-1 Effect of time and tempering temperature on hardness of type 110 (W1). Specimens hardened by brine quenching after 1 h at 1600°F and cooling to −95°F in dry ice and alcohol. ((a) From R.A. Grange and R.W. Baughman, *Trans. ASM,* Vol. 48, p. 165 (1956)). ((b) Adapted from J.H. Hollomon and L.D. Jaffe, *Trans. AIME,* Vol. 162, p. 223 (1945))

present. Figure 5-1b shows hardness data for a high carbon steel.

Tempering hardness data are more commonly plotted as a function of tempering temperature, for a fixed tempering time, usually in the range to be used commercially. Such data are shown in Fig. 5-2. The general effect of the carbon content is exemplified by Fig. 5-3.

If the effect of tempering for short times is to be studied, then the samples must be small so that they can be heated to the tempering temperature rapidly. This requires that the tempering temperature environment must be molten metal or molten salt, so that the heat transfer is rapid. Some data showing the effect of very short tempering times are shown in Fig. 5-4. Note that a measurable reduction in hardness is obtained in 0.3 sec. at 200°C. This again reflects the rapidity of the diffusion of carbon in martensite.

Effect of tempering on tensile mechanical properties

The effect of tempering on tensile mechanical properties is typified by the data in Fig. 5-5 and 5-6. Note that the tensile strength and yield strength decrease with in-

creasing tempering temperature, similar to that of hardness. The ductility increases with increasing tempering temperature.

It is important to recognize that it is difficult to measure the tensile mechanical properties of martensite. The material is so brittle that unreliable results are sometimes obtained. The yield strength may be less than that after low-temperature tempering, probably due to the presence of microcracks in the martensite.

Effect of tempering on toughness

A common method of measuring the toughness of steels is the impact test, which measures the energy absorbed in fracturing a sample in a specified impact loading for a specified specimen size and geometry (Fig. 5-7a). The results can be reported in several ways (Fig. 5-7b). One is to report the impact energy (for fracture) at a specific temperature. Another is to give the impact energy as a function of the test temperature. Still another way is to give the temperature where the impact energy-temperature curve changes from a relatively high value to a relatively low value. This temperature is usually called the impact transition temperature, and is often taken as the

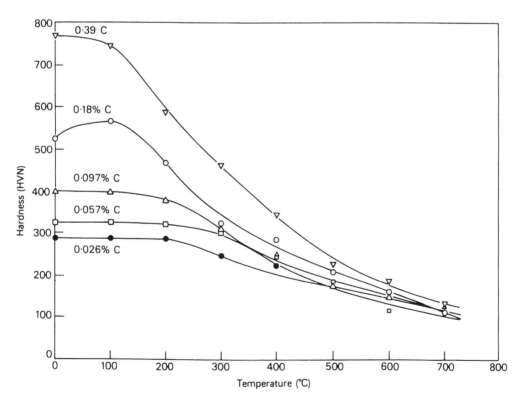

Fig. 5-2   The effect of tempering temperature on the hardness of plain carbon steels. The tempering time was 1 hour. (Adapted from G.R. Speich, *Trans. Met. Soc. AIME*, Vol 245, p 2553 (1969))

temperature at the inflection point in the impact energy-temperature curve. In most impact fractures of steels, the fracture surface has a region associated with the crack propagating from the crack notch, then on the periphery a shear lip. A measure of toughness is sometimes taken as the relative amount of the fracture surface covered by the shear lip. This is shown in Fig. 5-7c.

One difficulty encountered in obtaining the impact energy-temperature curve is that at sufficiently high temperatures, the structure of the steel will change before the

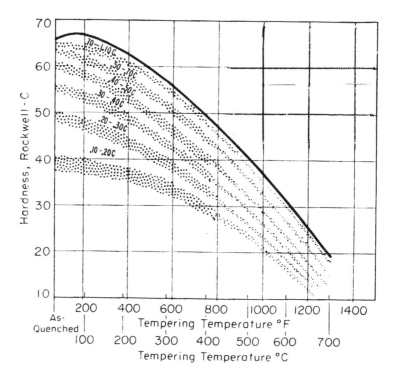

Fig. 5-3   Hardness of plain carbon steels as a function of tempering temperature. (Adapted from M.A. Grossmann and E.C. Bain, *Principles of Heat Treatment,* American Society for Metals, Metals Park, Ohio (1964))

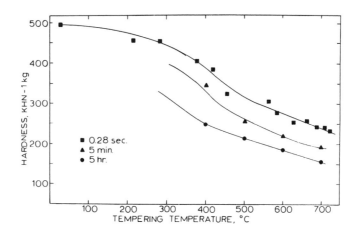

Fig. 5-4   Knoop 1-kg microhardness number as a function of tempering temperature for three tempering times. The effect of tempering temperature and time on the hardness for a 0.2% C steel. (Adapted from R.N. Caron and G. Krauss, *Met. Trans.,* Vol 3, p 2382 (1972))

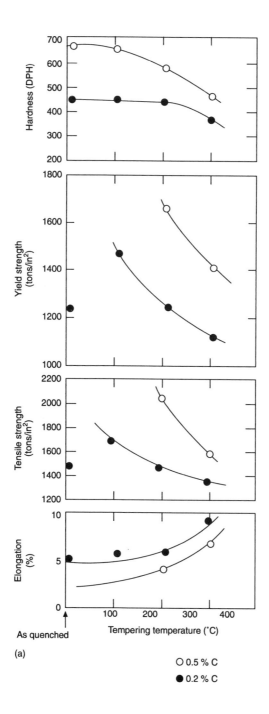

Fig. 5-5　The effect of tempering temperature on the tensile mechanical properties of plain carbon steels. In (a), the tempering time was 7 hr.; in (b), the tempering time was not known. ((a) Adapted from K.J. Irvine, F.B. Pickering and J. Garstone, *J. Iron and Steel Inst.,* Vol 196, p 66 (1960). (b) Adapted from H. Muir, B.L. Averback and M. Cohen, *Trans. ASM,* Vol 47, p 380 (1955)) *(continued)*

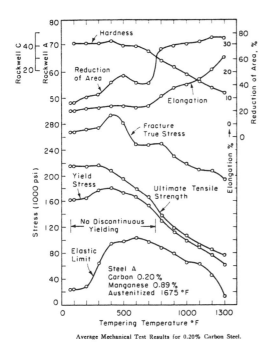

Average Mechanical Test Results for 0.20% Carbon Steel.

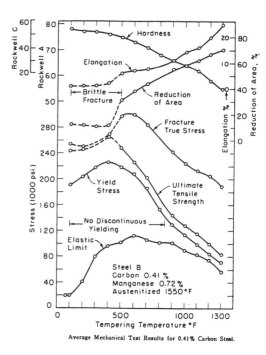

Average Mechanical Test Results for 0.41% Carbon Steel.

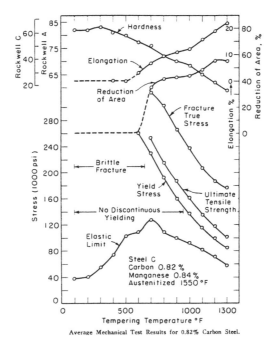

Average Mechanical Test Results for 0.82% Carbon Steel.

(b)

Fig. 5-5 (continued) The effect of tempering temperature on the tensile mechanical properties of plain carbon steels. In (a), the tempering time was 7 hr.; in (b), the tempering time was not known. ((a) Adapted from K.J. Irvine, F.B. Pickering and J. Garstone, *J. Iron and Steel Inst.*, Vol 196, p 66 (1960). (b) Adapted from H. Muir, B.L. Averback and M. Cohen, *Trans. ASM,* Vol 47, p 380 (1955))

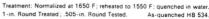

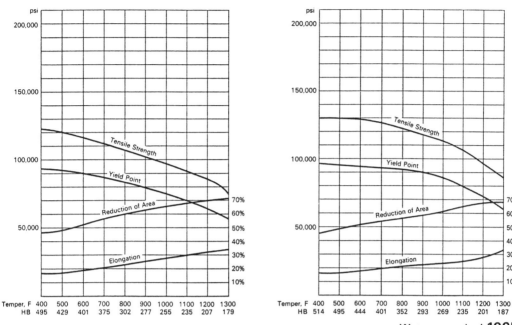

Water-quenched **1030**

Treatment: Normalized at 1700 F; reheated to 1600 F; quenched in water,
1-in. Round Treated; .505-in. Round Tested.   As-quenched HB 514.

Temper, F	400	500	600	700	800	900	1000	1100	1200	1300
HB	495	429	401	375	302	277	255	235	207	179

Water-quenched **1040**

Treatment: Normalized at 1650 F; reheated to 1550 F; quenched in water.
1-in. Round Treated; .505-in. Round Tested.   As-quenched HB 534.

Temper, F	400	500	600	700	800	900	1000	1100	1200	1300
HB	514	495	444	401	352	293	269	235	201	187

Water-quenched **1050**

Treatment: Normalized at 1650 F; reheated to 1525 F; quenched in water.
1-in. Round Treated; .505-in. Round Tested.   As-quenched HB 601.

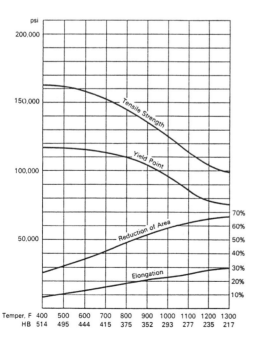

Temper, F	400	500	600	700	800	900	1000	1100	1200	1300
HB	514	495	444	415	375	352	293	277	235	217

Water-quenched **1095**

Treatment: Normalized at 1650 F; reheated to 1450 F; quenched in water.
1-in. Round Treated; .505-in. Round Tested.   As-quenched HB 601.

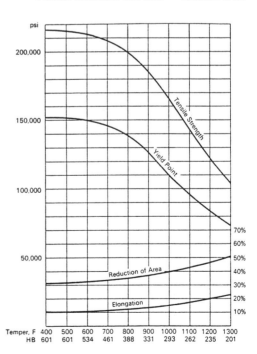

Temper, F	400	500	600	700	800	900	1000	1100	1200	1300
HB	601	601	534	461	388	331	293	262	235	201

Fig. 5-6   The effect of tempering temperature (no tempering time given) on the tensile mechanical properties of plain carbon steels. (Adapted from *Modern Steels and Their Properties*, Handbook 3310, Bethlehem Steel Corp., Bethlehem, PA)

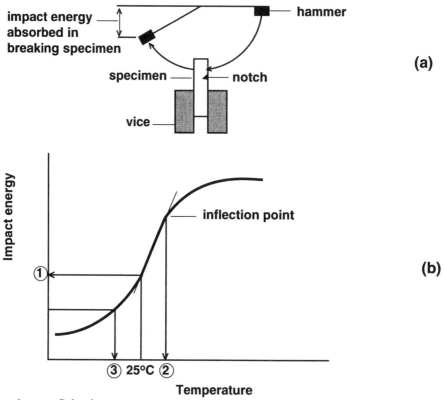

(a)

(b)

Toughness Criterion:

①- Impact energy at 25°C

②- Temperature of the inflection point in the impact energy-temperature curve

③- Temperature for specified impact energy (e.g., 15 ft-lb)

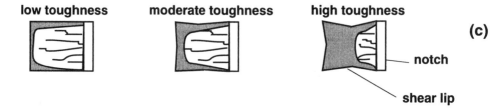

Schematic diagram of impact sample fracture surface appearance

Fig. 5-7   Schematic illustration of measures of the toughness of a steel based on the impact test

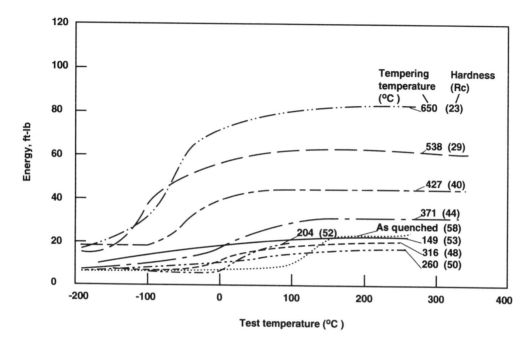

Fig. 5-8　Impact curves for a steel which has been tempered at different temperatures. (Adapted from F.R. Larson and J. Nunes, *Proc. ASTM,* Vol 62, p. 1192-1209 (1962))

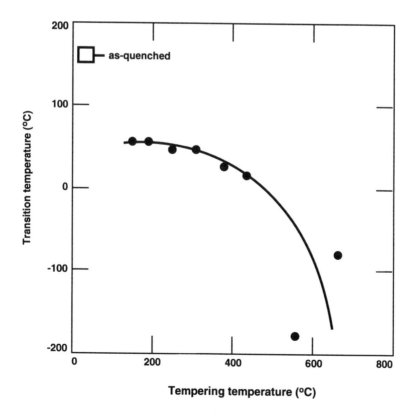

Fig. 5-9　The transition temperature as a function of tempering temperature, derived from the curves in Fig. 5-8

measurement can be made. Thus, there is an upper temperature limit to the measurement, depending on the tempering temperature used. For the martensitic structure, this is very low. In the strict sense (as pointed out earlier), tempering occurs even at 25°C (or even below), since the rapid carbon migration allows the formation of some fine carbides.

Figure 5-8 shows an impact energy-temperature curve for a plain carbon steel tempered at different temperatures. From these data, the transition temperature can be obtained as the inflection point temperature, and the results are shown in Fig. 5-9.

The general effect of tempering in plain carbon steels on the impact energy is illustrated by the data in Fig. 5-10. (Note that there may be a slight reduction in impact energy (measured at 25°C) around 250°C. This effect will be discussed in more detail in the section on temper embrittlement.)

Effect of Tempering on the Microstructure of Plain Carbon Steels

Microstructural examination of the structure which develops during tempering is crucial in explaining the effects of tempering on properties. In this section, examples of the structure of plain carbon steels are shown. First, the optical microstructure is examined, in which it

will be seen that the carbide-ferrite structure is too fine to be resolved, except for very high tempering temperatures. Then the microstructure will be examined using electron microscopy in which the fine details are resolved.

Microstructure as revealed by optical microscopy

When martensite is etched with the common steel etchants, such as nital, the structure is attacked relatively slowly, so that the microstructure is relatively light. However, when the tempered structure (even for tempering at very low temperatures and for short times) is etched, the microstructure is markedly darker. [In fact, this effect can usually be seen with the unaided eye on a cut surface, a method of detecting "burning" having occurred during cutting of a steel.] The dark structure results because the etchant removes the ferrite, leaving carbides in relief. These carbides cause light scattering, so that the surface appears dark.

Although the microstructure will darken upon tempering, the fine details are not resolved. Microstructures of three steels are shown in Fig. 5-11, 5-12 and 5-13; these are typical of plain carbon steels of these carbon contents. Note that the structure is markedly different compared to the as-quenched, martensitic structures shown in Fig. 5-14.

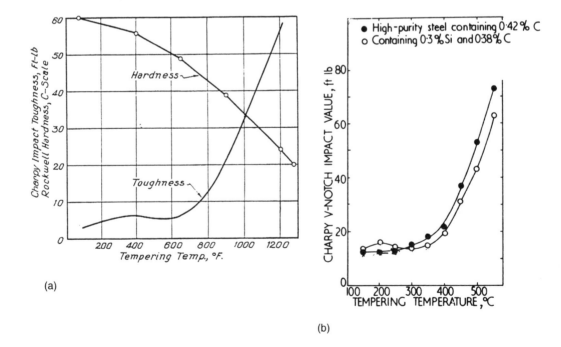

(a)

(b)

Fig. 5-10 Impact energy and hardness (both measured at 25 °C) as a function of tempering temperature of a 0.45% C steel. ((a) From H.H. Allison, Jr. in *Modern Steels*, E.E. Thum, Ed., American Society for Metals, Metals Park, Ohio (1939). (b) Adapted from J.M. Capus and G. Mayer, *J. Iron and Steel Inst.*, Vol 196, p 149 (1960))

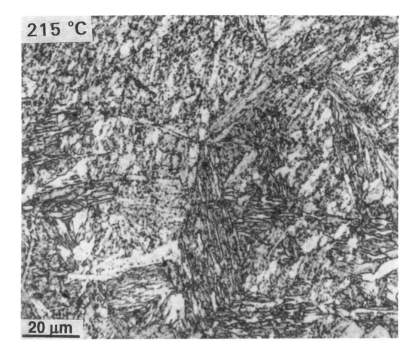

(a)

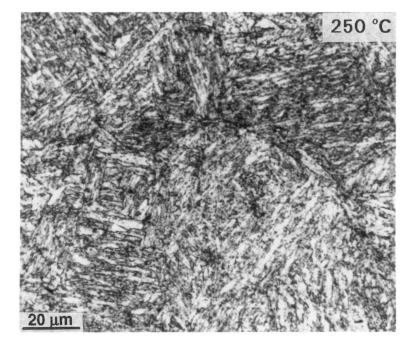

(b)

Fig. 5-11   Optical micrographs showing the effect of tempering temperature 1 hr on the microstructure and hardness of a 0.4% C steel. *(continued)*

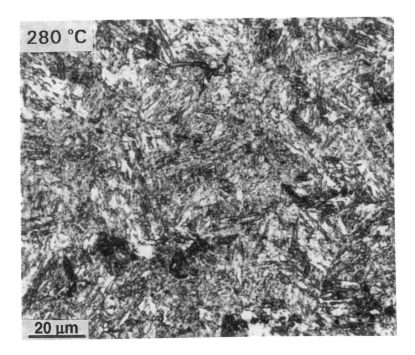

(c)

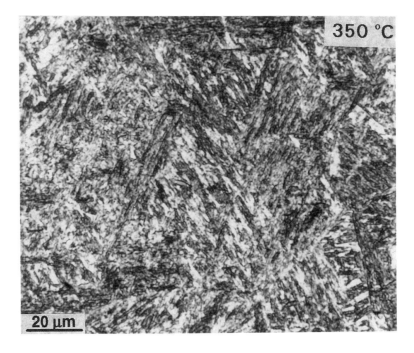

(d)

Fig. 5-11   (continued) Optical micrographs showing the effect of tempering temperature 1 hr on the microstructure and hardness of a 0.4% C steel. *(continued)*

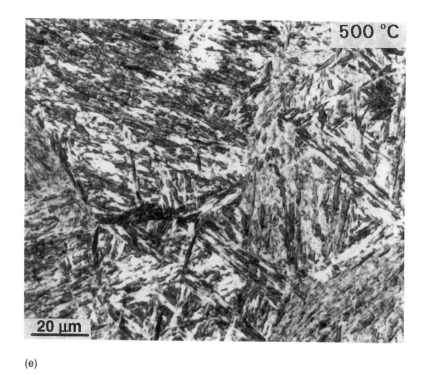

(e)

(f)

Fig. 5-11 (continued) Optical micrographs showing the effect of tempering temperature 1 hr on the microstructure and hardness of a 0.4% C steel.

The structure which darkens upon tempering still retains the "brush-stroke" appearance of martensite. Although small, local, dark regions can be seen in the micrographs for the higher tempering temperatures (e.g., Fig. 5-12b), these may not be individual carbides, but rather due to scattering of light from carbide clusters. This will be illustrated in the next section. It is clear from these micrographs that the structure becomes coarser the longer the tempering time and the higher the temperature. Indeed, at the highest tempering temperature, the individual

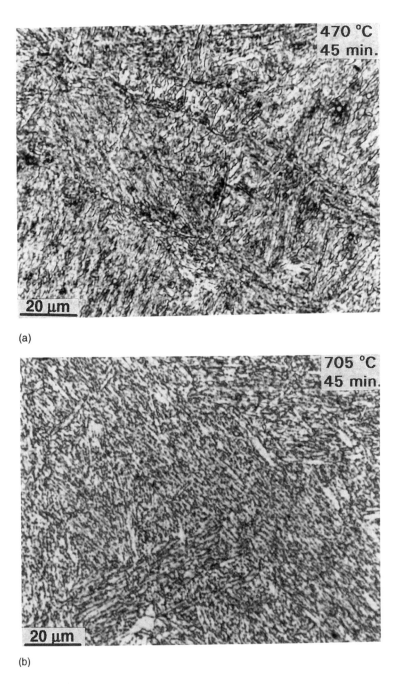

(a)

(b)

Fig. 5-12   Optical micrographs showing the effect of tempering temperature and time on the microstructure of a 0.4% C steel. *(continued)*

black spots are individual carbides. For the higher carbon steel tempered at 705°C for 100 h, the individual carbide spheroids can be resolved (Fig. 5-12c).

As will be demonstrated in the next section, the structures in the micrographs in Fig. 5-11, 5-12 and 5-13 consist of carbide particles in a ferrite matrix. Thus this "tempered martensite" structure contains no martensite. This is seen in the optical micrographs in Fig. 5-15 for a 0.2% C steel. Tempering at low temperature (Fig. 5-15a) reveals an appearance similar to that of the lath martensite characteristic of the low carbon steel, but in this tempered structure the pattern is more distinct. Indeed, this is due to etching along the ferrite grain boundaries. This is shown more clearly in Fig. 5-15b and 5-15c, which are micrographs for this steel tempered at higher temperatures so that the structure is coarser. Here the grain boundaries in the ferrite are clear. An original austenite grain boundary (now a ferrite grain boundary) can be seen in Fig. 5-15b. The carbides are still small, but they are resolved in Fig. 5-15c.

Microstructure as revealed by electron microscopy

We will first examine electron micrographs for plain carbon steel tempered for the times and temperatures similar to those for the optical micrographs in the previous section (that is, for one hour or greater and for temperatures >200°C).

In Fig. 5-16a is an optical micrograph of the microstructure of an 0.5% C steel after tempering at 470°C for 1 h. The appearance is similar to that shown in the previous optical micrographs (e.g., Fig. 5-12a). In Fig. 5-16b and 5-16c are shown scanning electron micrographs of the same sample. The resolution of the electron microscope has allowed the individual carbides and also the ferrite grain boundaries to be revealed. (In this imaging, smooth areas tend to be dark, and carbides standing in relief above the etched ferrite are brighter; this is generally opposite to the contrast seen using optical microscopy.) Note that the dark spots in Fig. 5-16a are not individual carbides, but are due to scattering of light from clusters of carbides, such as those outlined in Fig. 5-16c.

When this 0.5% C steel is tempered for one hour at 700°C, the carbide structure is coarser, as shown in Fig. 5-17. Note that these individual carbides are larger, but that there are fewer of them. Thus the hard carbides are further apart, and hence this structure will be softer (Rockwell C 26) than for the sample tempered at 470°C (see Fig. 5-16c), which had a hardness of Rockwell C 35.

Additional examples of the tempered structure are shown in Fig. 5-18. The optical micrographs associated with some of these structures are shown in Fig. 5-11 and 5-13. The coarsening of the carbides with increasing tempering temperature is clearly seen. Figure 5-19 shows a plot of carbide size versus tempering temperature for the 0.8% C steel; the sizes were estimated from the micrographs.

In the lower temperature tempering range (e.g., 25-300°C) for typical tempering times (e.g., 30 min. to 2 h), and perhaps for short tempering times at higher

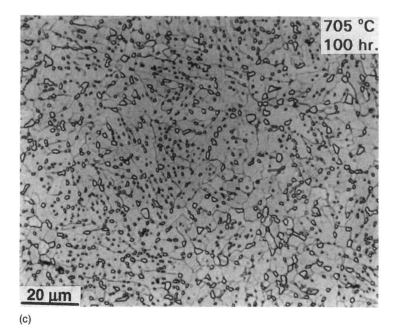

(c)

Fig. 5-12 (continued) Optical micrographs showing the effect of tempering temperature and time on the microstructure of a 0.4% C steel.

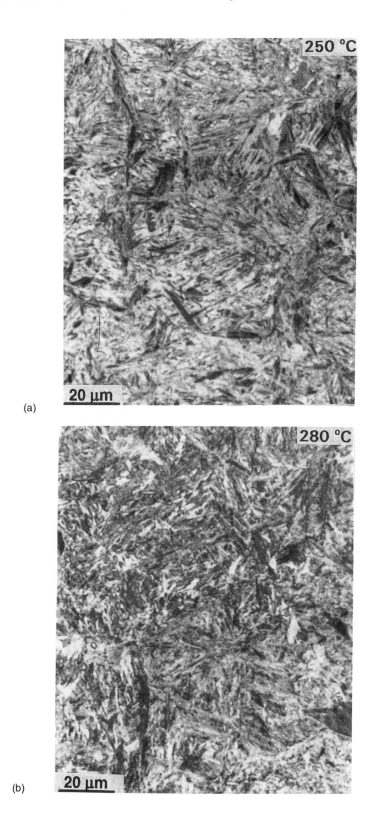

(a)

(b)

Fig. 5-13 Optical micrographs showing the effect of tempering temperature 1 hr on the microstructure of a 0.8% C steel. *(continued)*

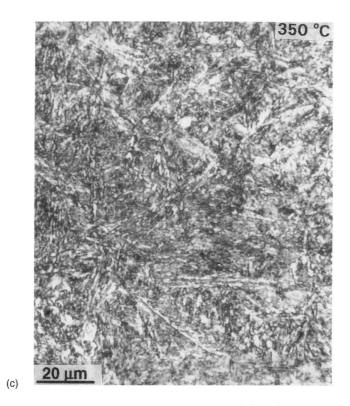

(c)

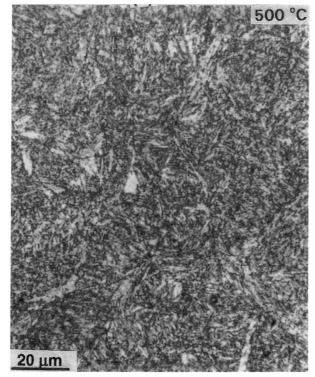

(d)

Fig. 5-13   (continued) Optical micrographs showing the effect of tempering temperature 1 hr on the microstructure of a 0.8% C steel.

temperatures, metastable carbides form. The type of carbide may depend upon the carbon content and the tempering temperature (and time), but these all contain more carbon than Fe_3C and have a different crystal structure or different lattice parameter. In Table 5-1 are listed some of the carbides which have been reported to be present.

Stages of Tempering in Plain Carbon Steels

To examine the stages in tempering of plain carbon steels, the expected behavior of a eutectoid steel will be explored. The changes in the steel during tempering can be followed by a number of experimental methods: hardness measurements, x-ray diffraction, magnetic measurements, dimensional changes, etc. One of the most useful experimental methods is the change in length. The advantage of this method is illustrated in Fig. 5-20. In Fig. 5-20a is shown schematically the change in length of an eutectoid steel for different heat treatments. If the steel is cooled relatively slowly from austenite, the curve a'-a-b-c is followed. The expansion from a to b is due to the formation of pearlite from the close-packed austenite. If the steel is cooled rapidly from the austenite region to 25°C, the steel expands beginning at the M_s temperature (point d), and continues to expand as cooling progresses. In this eutectoid steel, at 25°C, some retained austenite will be present (point e), but cooling to a sufficiently low temperature (point f) will convert nearly all the austenite to martensite. If this steel is then heated to 25°C, the length will be that at point g.

If the steel at 25°C, consisting of martensite, is heated, it expands along the curve g-h. However, a temperature is soon attained, depending on the heating rate,

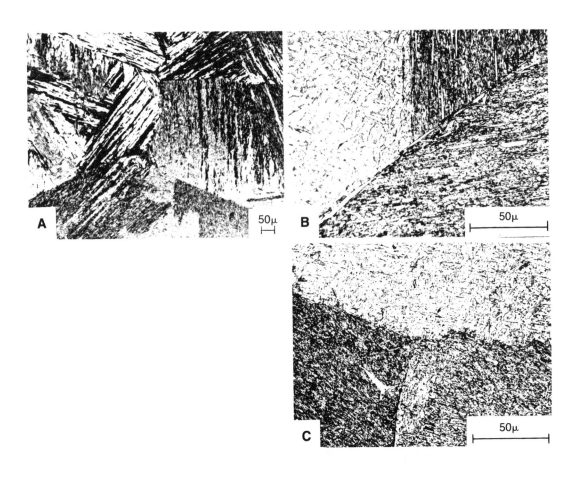

Fig. 5-14 Part 1 Optical micrographs showing the microstructure of martensite of plain carbon steels. (Adapted from A.R. Marder and G. Krauss, *Trans. ASM,* Vol 60, p 651-660 (1967)). Lath martensite microstructures in (A) Fe-0.2C, (b) Fe-0.4C, and (c) Fe-0.6C alloys. Light micrographs *(continued)*

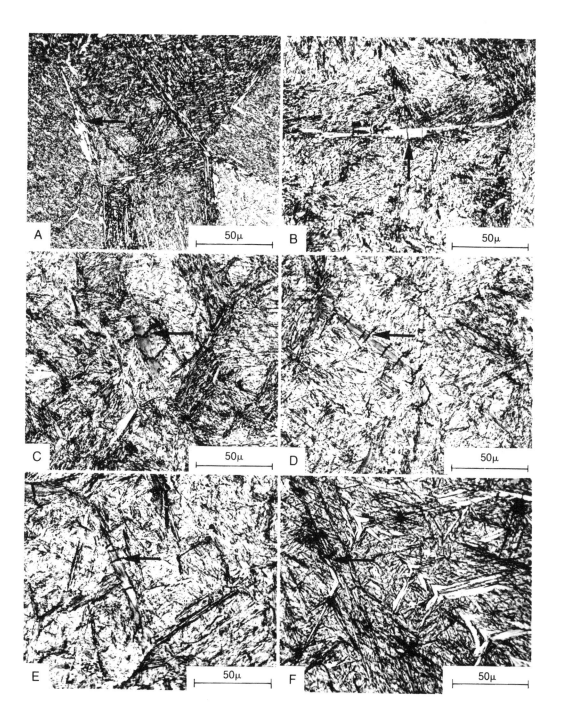

Fig. 5-14 Part 2 (continued) Optical micrographs showing the microstructure of martensite of plain carbon steels. (Adapted from A.R. Marder and G. Krauss, *Trans. ASM,* Vol 60, p 651-660 (1967)). Transition from lath to plate martensite microstructures in Fe-C alloys between 0.67 and 1.00% carbon. (A) 0.67% (B) 0.75% (C) 0.82% (D) 0.85% (E) 0.93% (F) 1.00%. Light micrographs. Sodium bisulfite etch

such that the martensite begins to decompose. This is accompanied by a contraction, so the length begins to decrease. When the martensite is converted completely to ferrite and carbide, the length will be that at point i, reaching the length-temperature curve for pearlite (b-i-c).

If it is desired to study the decomposition of martensite isothermally, the steel, initially all martensite and at 25°C, is heated rapidly to the tempering temperature of interest, then the length is measured as a function of time at the tempering temperature. Thus the length should follow the curve g-j-k, as depicted in Fig. 5-20b and 5-20c.

During tempering, as the carbides nucleate in the martensite, the carbon content of the remaining marten-

site decreases, manifesting itself in a reduced c/a ratio, which becomes unity when the matrix becomes ferrite. The c/a ratio can be determined from x-ray diffraction methods. Also, by this method the amount of martensite can be measured. Microstructural examination allows determination of the amount of Fe_3C present, as well as the average size of the carbides and the average separation distance between them. These quantities are plotted schematically as a function of tempering time in Fig. 5-21. Also shown is the hardness as a function of tempering time.

If retained austenite is present at 25°C, then the length is that at point e (Fig. 5-22). Then upon heating, or upon holding at the tempering temperature, T_1, the martensite

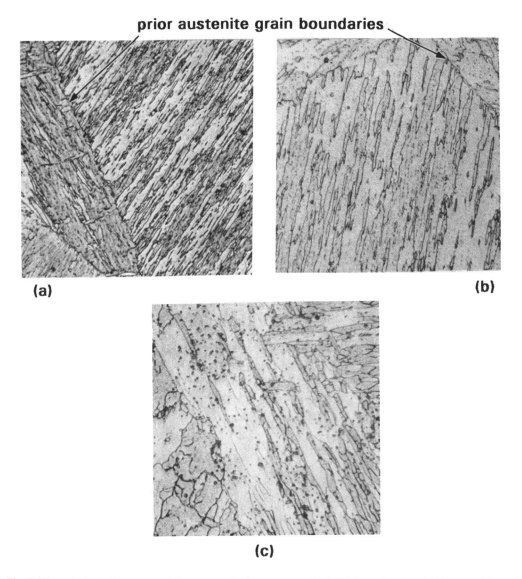

Fig. 5-15 Optical micrographs of the tempered microstructure of a 0.2% C steel. 500 ×. (a) Tempered for 200 hr at 400 °C. (b) Tempered for 12 hr at 600 °C. (c) Tempered for 12 hr at 700 °C. (From R.N. Caron and G. Krauss, *Met. Trans.,* Vol 3, p 2381 (1972))

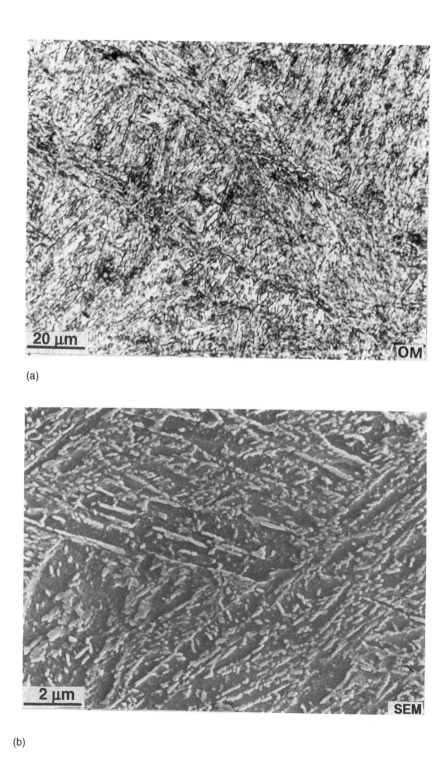

(a)

(b)

Fig. 5-16   Micrographs of the microstructure of a 0.5% C steel tempered for 45 min. at 470 °C. (a) is an optical micrograph, and (b) and (c) are scanning electron micrographs *(continued)*

tempers, causing a reduction in length, and the austenite decomposes to pearlite or bainite, depending upon the temperature T_1, causing an expansion. Whether the steel is expanding or contracting at a given time depends upon the kinetics of the decomposition of the martensite and the austenite. The tempering rate is relatively rapid, so that it is expected that tempering will be completed before any austenite begins to decompose. Thus the steel sample will undergo a contraction, then an expansion as the austenite decomposes. Although the decomposition of retained austenite to pearlite or bainite will increase the hardness, this may not be apparent because of the softening associated with the tempering of the martensite.

The decomposition of martensite can occur at quite low temperatures, due to the high diffusion rate of carbon. This is illustrated in Fig. 5-23a. The data are for a 1% C, low alloy steel which was austenitized, quenched to 25°C, then cooled to –196°C, so that the structure was essentially all martensite. Then the length was monitored at 25°C, whereupon a contraction was observed. This reflects the decomposition of the martensite. At this low temperature, however, Fe_3C is not forming, but the metastable ε carbide.

If this steel is austenitized and quenched to 25°C, with no low temperature treatment, then about 4% retained austenite is present. Then upon measuring the length at 25°C, the curve shown in Fig. 5-23b is obtained. The length first increases, then decreases. This is associated with the isothermal decomposition of austenite to martensite. (This is an effect that we haven't examined before. This wasn't shown on the TTT diagrams that we have been using, because usually these steels contained no retained austenite at 25°C.) The subsequent contraction is caused by the tempering of the martensite. The net effect of the decomposition of the martensite and the austenite is to give a curve which passes through a maximum.

The effect on hardness of the low temperature decomposition of austenite is illustrated in Fig. 5-24. In this steel, the hardness increase due to the decomposition of austenite was greater than any reduction due to tempering of the martensite.

The high dislocation and interface density of martensite provides a high density of nucleation sites for the formation of carbides, whether Fe_3C or metastable carbides. Thus the nucleation rate is high. When the metastable carbides form, the martensite matrix is reduced in

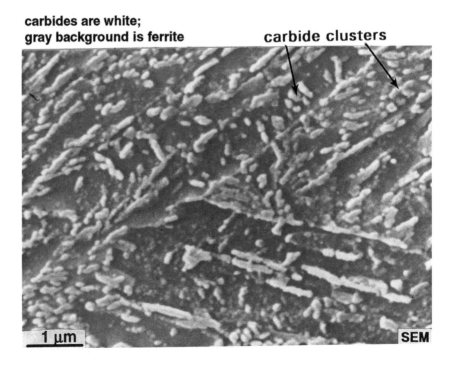

carbides are white;
gray background is ferrite

carbide clusters

1 μm

SEM

(c)

Fig. 5-16 (continued) Micrographs of the microstructure of a 0.5% C steel tempered for 45 min. at 470 °C. (a) is an optical micrograph, and (b) and (c) are scanning electron micrographs

carbon content, becoming essentially low carbon martensite. Thus, the steel will consist of low carbon martensite with metastable carbides precipitating in it. When Fe₃C forms, the martensite has its carbon content reduced continuously, until it becomes ferrite. Since the carbides are nucleating very close together, they do not grow very large before the matrix between them is ferrite. This is illustrated schematically in Fig. 5-25. At this stage, the density of fine carbides is high, and hence the hardness is relatively high. From this point on, the structural changes only involve coarsening, and the hardness decreases.

The ferrite which forms during tempering undergoes recovery and recrystallization because it inherits some of the dislocation structure of the parent martensite. This causes the development initially of a rather fine ferrite grain size. The rate of growth of these grains is inhibited by the numerous carbides which are present.

In Fig. 5-26 are shown hardness data for tempering plain carbon steels, with the stages of the structural changes noted. A tabulation of the stages by Krauss is shown in Table 5-2. (The stages which correspond to alloy steels will be discussed in a subsequent section.)

Kinetics of Tempering in Plain Carbon Steels

It is expected that the rate of tempering will depend upon the tempering sequence which is occurring, as tabulated in Table 5-2. However, in terms of affecting the hardness, the temperature and time tempering response can be put into surprisingly simple terms. Consider the schematic depiction in Fig. 5-27. Shown are hardness-tempering time curves for three temperatures. We take the

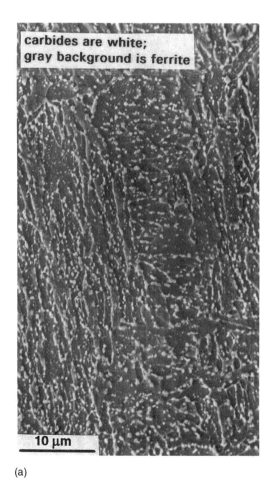

(a)

Fig. 5-17 Scanning electron micrographs of the microstructure of a 0.5% steel tempered for 1 hr at 700 °C.
(continued)

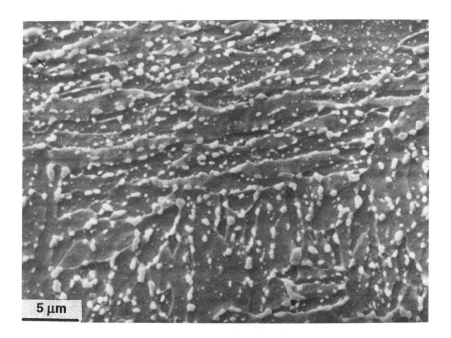

(b)

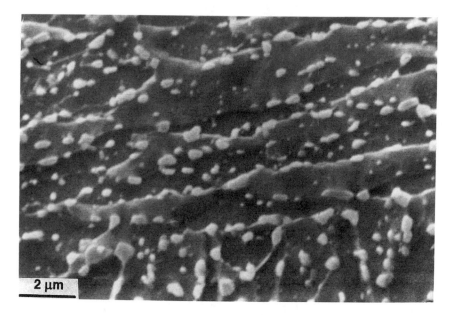

(c)

Fig. 5-17 (continued) Scanning electron micrographs of the microstructure of a 0.5% steel tempered for 1 hr at 700 °C.

1 μm, 0.2% C

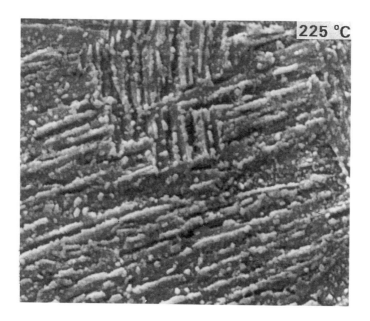

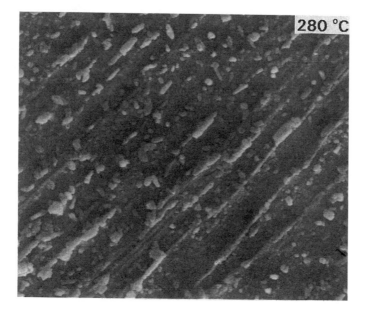

(a)

Fig. 5-18   Scanning electron micrographs showing the effect of tempering temperature (1 hr) on the microstructure of 0.2, 0.4 and 0.8% C steels. In these micrographs, the carbides are white and the gray background is ferrite. *(continued)*

1 μm, 0.2% C

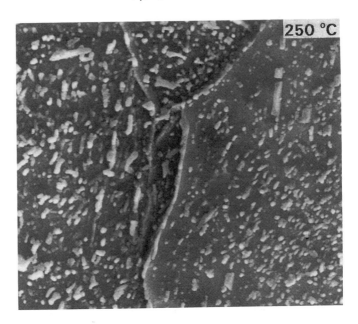

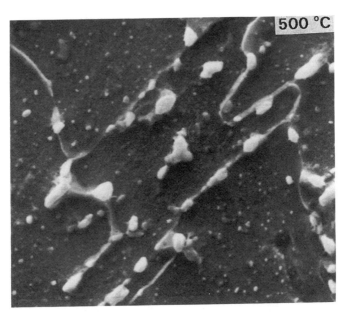

(b)

Fig. 5-18   (continued) Scanning electron micrographs showing the effect of tempering temperature (1 hr) on the microstructure of 0.2, 0.4 and 0.8% C steels. In these micrographs, the carbides are white and the gray background is ferrite. *(continued)*

1 μm, 0.4% C

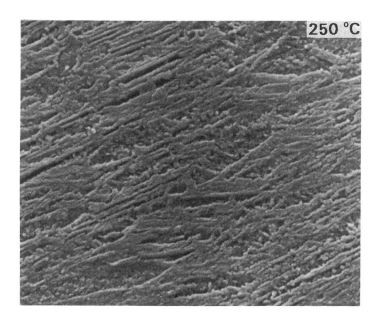

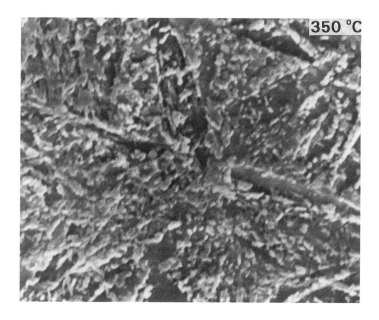

(c)

Fig. 5-18   (continued) Scanning electron micrographs showing the effect of tempering temperature (1 hr) on the microstructure of 0.2, 0.4 and 0.8% C steels. In these micrographs, the carbides are white and the gray background is ferrite. *(continued)*

1 μm, 0.4% C

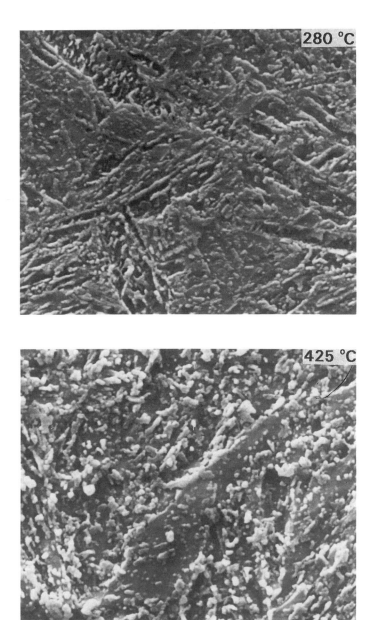

(d)

Fig. 5-18   (continued) Scanning electron micrographs showing the effect of tempering temperature (1 hr) on the microstructure of 0.2, 0.4 and 0.8% C steels. In these micrographs, the carbides are white and the gray background is ferrite. *(continued)*

rate of hardness decrease to be proportional to [ex (–Q/RT)]. Thus we write

Rate of hardness change = $dH/dt = A \exp(-Q/RT)$

where A is a constant, Q is the activation energy for the process, R is the ideal gas constant, and T is the absolute temperature. This can be written as

$$dH = A [\exp(-Q/RT)] dt$$

and

$$H = H_0 + A [\exp(-Q/RT)] t_0 + A [\exp(-Q/RT)] t$$

where H_0 is the hardness at time $t = t_0$. From this we get

$$H = f \{t \exp(-Q/RT)]$$

Thus the temperature and time to attain the same hardness (see Fig. 5-27) is given by

$$T_1 \exp(-Q/RT_1) = t_2 \exp(-Q/RT_2) = t_3 \exp(-Q/RT_3)$$
$$= C'$$

where C' is a constant. Thus we can write

$$t \exp(-Q/RT) = C'$$

and

$$\ln t - Q/RT = \ln C'$$

and

$$T \ln t - T \ln C' = Q/R$$

or

$$T (\ln t + c) = \text{constant}$$

or

$$T (\log T + c') = \text{constant, where c and c' are constants.}$$

However, it is found that the activation energy depends upon the hardness level H being considered. Thus

$$Q = RT (\ln t - \ln C') = RT \ln (t/C') = f(H)$$

or

$$H = f (T \ln t)$$

or

$$H = f (T \ln t + \text{constant})$$

1 µm, 0.4% C

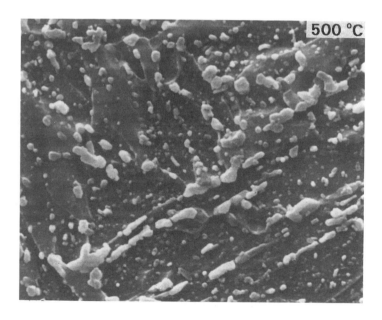

(e)

Fig. 5-18   (continued) Scanning electron micrographs showing the effect of tempering temperature (1 hr) on the microstructure of 0.2, 0.4 and 0.8% C steels. In these micrographs, the carbides are white and the gray background is ferrite. *(continued)*

1 μm, 0.8% C

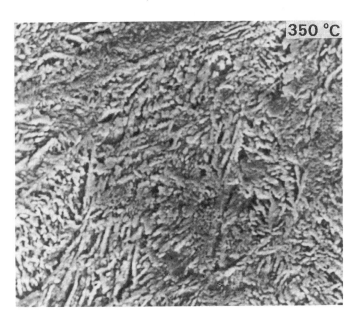

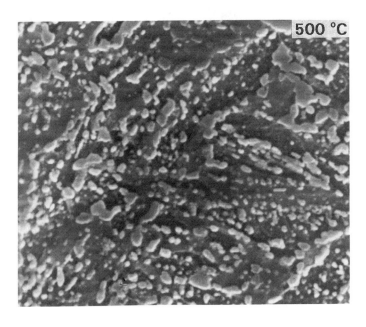

(f)

Fig. 5-18 (continued) Scanning electron micrographs showing the effect of tempering temperature (1 hr) on the microstructure of 0.2, 0.4 and 0.8% C steels. In these micrographs, the carbides are white and the gray background is ferrite. *(continued)*

0.8% C

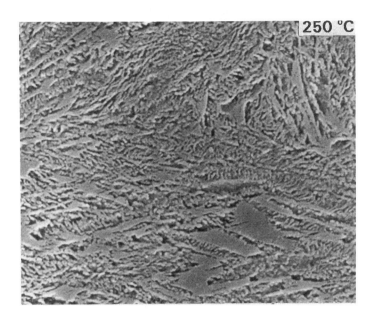

250 °C

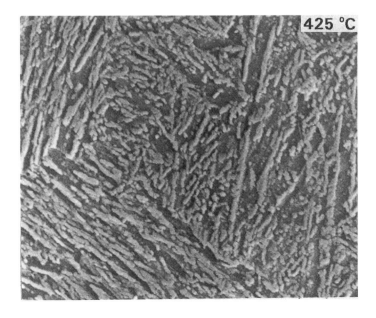

425 °C

(g)

Fig. 5-18 (continued) Scanning electron micrographs showing the effect of tempering temperature (1 hr) on the microstructure of 0.2, 0.4 and 0.8% C steels. In these micrographs, the carbides are white and the gray background is ferrite.

or

$$H = f(T \log t + C)$$

where C is a constant. (This is sometimes called the Hollomon-Jaffe parameter.)

The relations above allow hardness data of a given steel obtained for a variety of tempering temperatures and times to be plotted on a common plot of hardness versus the parameter (T (C + log t). T must be absolute temperature (K or R). The data must be manipulated to find the value of C which gives the best fit. Thus for each steel, C will have a specific value.

The correctness of the above derivation is shown by the tempering data for plain carbon steels shown in Fig. 5-28. Note that the tempering times range from 10 sec. to 24 h. These data are for steels which were quenched to form martensite, and for the higher carbon steels they were cooled to lower temperatures to ensure the subsequent tempering of an all-martensite structure.

However, the parametric plotting is valid for steels containing retained austenite, as shown by the data in Fig. 5-29. In this high carbon steel, retained austenite was present, so that the data include a contribution to the hardness from the decomposition of the retained austenite to pearlite or bainite.

It is also found that the parametric plot is valid for tempering structures other than martensite. This is shown by the data in Fig. 5-30 for a 0.94% C steel which was isothermally transformed to fine pearlite (Fig. 5-30a) or to bainite (Fig. 5-30b) prior to tempering.

If a comparison is made of the tempering of martensite and of other starting structures, it is found that in the region of high values of the parameter, corresponding to high tempering temperatures and long times, the data fall close to a common curve (for a given steel). This is shown in Fig. 5-31. This agreement reflects the fact that the structural change is coarsening of the Fe_3C carbides.

The agreement of the hardness data with the tempering parameter in the range where coarsening alone is occurring should be predictable from the theory which deals with the growth of large precipitates at the expense of the solution of the smaller ones. (This is often called *Ostwald ripening*.) The basis for the phenomenon is the dependence of the solubility of carbon in ferrite at the

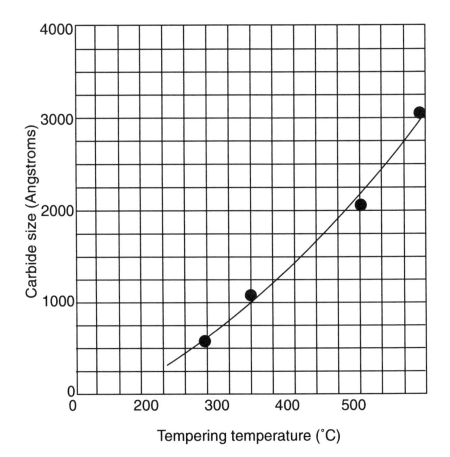

Fig. 5-19 Approximate carbide size as a function of tempering temperature for 0.8% C steel, from micrographs
in Fig. 5-18

of the solution of the smaller ones. (This is often called *Ostwald ripening*.) The basis for the phenomenon is the dependence of the solubility of carbon in ferrite at the ferrite-carbide interface on the curvature of this interface. The *Gibbs-Thompson equation* and a diffusion model is used to obtain an equation similar to the following.

$$r^3 - r_0^3 = [(D_c \, \gamma \, X_c \, V^2)/RT] \, t$$

where r is the average radius of the carbides at time t, r_0 is the initial radius (at time t = 0), D_c is the diffusion coefficient of carbon in ferrite, X_c is the solubility of carbon in ferrite in equilibrium with carbides of infinite radius of curvature, γ is the ferrite-carbide interface surface energy, V is the molar volume, T is the absolute temperature and R is the ideal gas constant. If the hardness follows the Hall-Petch relation, with the hardness

Table 5-1 Carbides claimed to have formed during tempering of plain carbon steels. (From G.R. Krauss, *Principles of Heat Treatment of Steel*, American Society for Metals, Metals Park, Ohio (1980))

Designation	Name and structure		Composition
η, eta		orthorhombic	$Fe_2C(a)(b)(c)$
χ, chi	Hägg carbide	monoclinic	$Fe_{2.2}C(d)$
ε, epsilon		hexagonal	$Fe_{2.4}C(e)$
θ, theta	Cementite	orthorhombic	Fe_3C

(a) Y. Hirotsu, S. Nagakura, and S. Oketani, *Proc. Int. Conf. Tech. Iron Steel*, Tokyo, p 1140 (1971). (b) Y. Hirotsu and S. Nagakura, *Acta Metall.*, Vol 20, p 645 (1972). (c) D.L. Williamson, K. Nakazawa, and G. Krauss, *Met. Trans. A*, Vol 10A, p 1351 (1979). (d) J. Chipman, *Met. Trans.*, Vol 3, p 55 (1972). (e) E.W. Langer, *Met. Sci. J.*, Vol 2, p 59 (1968)

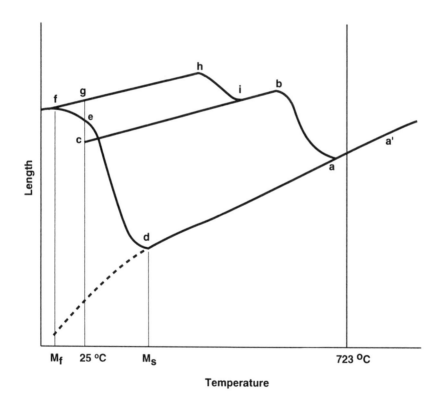

(a)

Fig. 5-20 Schematic illustration of the length changes in a 0.8% C steel for different heating and cooling processes *(continued)*

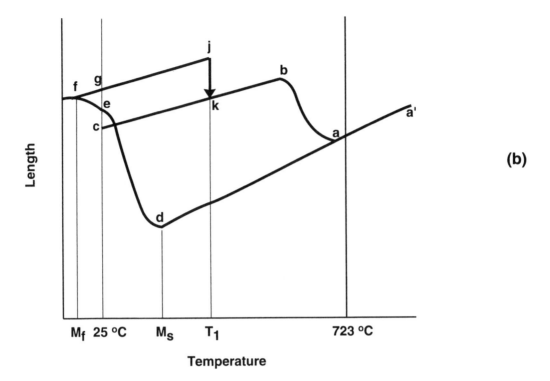

(b)

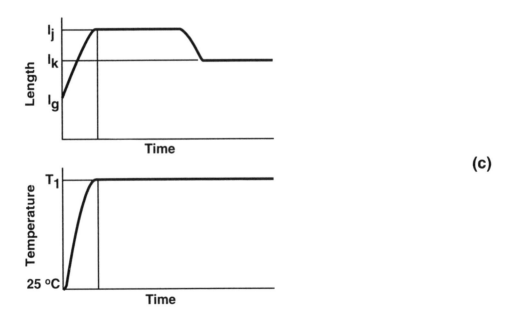

(c)

Fig. 5-20   (continued) Schematic illustration of the length changes in a 0.8% C steel for different heating and cooling processes

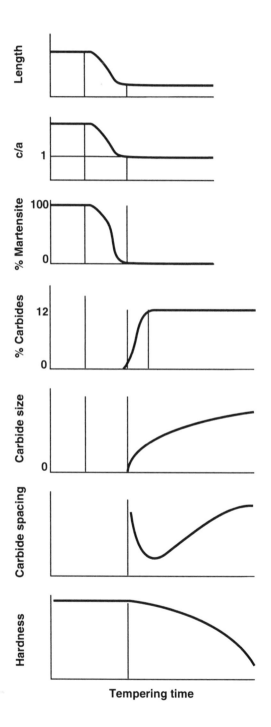

Fig. 5-21   Schematic illustration of the changes in several quantities for a 0.8% C steel during tempering

inversely proportional to the average separation distance between the carbides, then the hardness as a function of tempering time can be obtained if the radius of the carbides can be linked to the carbide separation. The relation is

$$P = [4/3] [(1 - f)/f] r$$

and

$$\lambda = [(\pi\, r\, P)/2\, (1 - f)]^{1/2} - [\pi\, r/2]$$

where P is the mean free carbide path, λ is the intercarbide spacing, and f is the fraction of carbides present. This latter term is assumed to be the equilibrium amount of carbides present. The hardness is taken to be inversely proportional to the square root of the mean carbide path (Hall-Petch relation).

Using these equations to obtain the hardness H as a function of tempering time yields an expression making H proportional to $t^{-1/6}$. Thus a plot of log H versus log t should give a straight line with a slope of $-1/6$. Using the hardness data in Fig. 5-32 yields the plot in Fig. 5-33. However, the slope is about -0.07, whereas $-1/6 = -0.17$.

Tempering in Alloy Steels

In alloy steels, it is observed that, in general, the rate of hardness decrease is reduced. This is associated with the influence of the substitutional solutes (e.g., Mn, Si, Cr) on the diffusion of carbon. Also, when the alloy content is sufficiently high, carbides other than Fe$_3$C may form which have a high solute content. These alloying elements must diffuse during formation and growth of the carbides, and these elements diffuse much slower in ferrite than does carbon. Thus the rate of softening will be less than in plain carbon steels.

In this section the mechanical properties of alloy steels will be examined and compared to those of plain carbon steels. The steels examined will contain no more than about 5% alloy content.

Effect of tempering on hardness

The effect of alloying elements on tempered hardness can be compared by examining conventional tempering curves (hardness versus tempering temperature), such as those shown in Fig. 5-34. Here the tempering curves appear similar to those for plain carbon steels, except the alloy steel does not soften as much.

For many alloy steels, there is a reduction in hardness as the tempering time or temperature increase, then an increase in hardness followed by a decrease. This increase is referred to as *secondary hardening*, and in the high carbon, high alloy steels and in tool steels this effect is quite prominent and important. It is illustrated by the data in Fig. 5-35 and Fig. 5-36.

The hardness of alloy steels can be plotted parametrically, showing higher values compared to plain carbon steels of the same carbon content. Examples are shown in Fig. 5-37.

Effect of tempering on tensile mechanical properties

In general, the tensile mechanical properties of alloy steels compared to those of plain carbon steels are reflected in their comparative hardness data. The alloy steels have a higher yield and tensile strength than do the plain carbon steels, and the elongation (ductility) is lower. An example is shown in Fig. 5-38.

Effect of tempering on toughness

In alloy steels, the toughness increases with tempering temperature, as illustrated in Fig. 5-39, the same as for plain carbon steels. (The minimum occurring around 260°C (350°F) is due to temper embrittlement, which will be discussed in a following section.) Also, in some cases the toughness is higher than in plain carbon steels of the same carbon content. Figure 5-40a shows the impact energy-temperature curves for a 1013 steel and a 4315 steel, both having a martensite structure and the same

prior austenite grain size. Note that this alloy steel has a slightly greater toughness. Upon tempering at 400°F for one hour, the curves in Fig. 5-40b show that the alloy steel has a better toughness. More importantly, it is seen that if the two steels are tempered to the same hardness (290 DPH), the alloy steel has better toughness.

Stages of Tempering in Alloy Steels

In alloy steels, the stages of tempering involve those described for plain carbon steels. In addition, however, alloy carbides may form, as well as the ε carbide and Fe_3C. Generally, for 1 or 2 h tempering times, the alloy carbides appear in the higher temperature range, 500-700°C, as shown in Table 5-2.

Kinetics of Tempering in Alloy Steels

The tempering response of alloy steels also depends upon the beginning structure, which is influenced by the

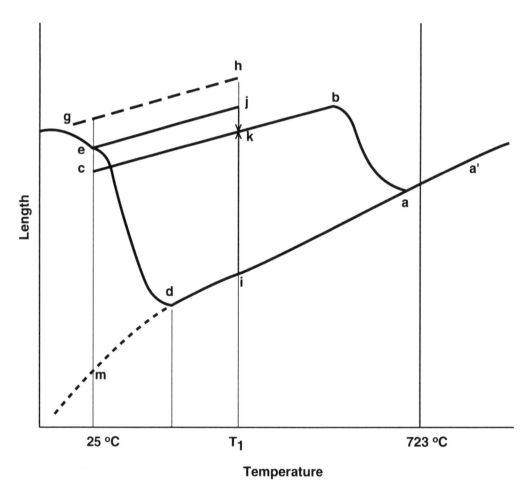

Fig. 5-22 Schematic illustration of the change in length of a 0.8% C steel during tempering at a temperature T_1

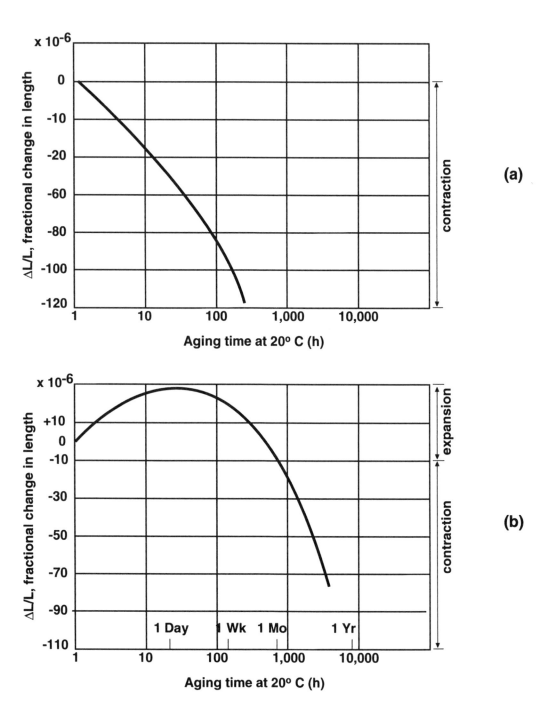

Fig. 5-23 (a) Change in length for a 1.0% C-1.5% Cr-0.2% V steel after austenitizing at 845 °C followed by oil quenching, cooling to −195 °C, then length measured at 20 °C. (b) Change in length at 20 °C after austenitizing at 845 °C followed by quenching into oil at 20 °C. (Adapted from B.L Averback, M. Cohen, and S.G.Fletcher, *Trans. ASM*, Vol 40, p 728 (1948))

Ms and Mf temperatures. Thus for alloy steels, the Ms will be lower than for plain carbon steels of the same carbon content, and therefore the martensite formed will not have undergone as much *auto-tempering* (tempering during cooling before reaching 25°C). In principle, this will influence the response to tempering.

In many alloy steels, the Fe₃C carbide forms in the lower temperature regime, even though this is not the equilibrium carbide. However, kinetically, Fe₃C is easier to form since only the diffusion of carbon is required, and not the slower diffusing alloying elements. Eventually a sufficiently high tempering temperature is used which (for the tempering time used) allows time for the alloying elements to diffuse in the ferrite and form the alloy carbides. As noted in Table 5-2, this is in the general range of 300-700°C. In many alloy steels, when a temperature is reached so that these alloy carbides begin to appear, they have a finer dispersion than the Fe₃C, so that the hardness increases. This is one of the causes of secondary hardening. At higher temperatures, for the tempering time used, these alloy carbides become sufficiently coarse that the hardness decreases.

Even in alloy steels where the equilibrium carbide is Fe₃C, the rate of formation and of coarsening is reduced. This could be reflecting the influence of these alloying elements in the ferrite on the diffusion of carbon. This is most likely accomplished by the influence of the elements on lowering the metastable equilibrium carbon content in the ferrite at the ferrite-carbide interface, and thus lowering the carbon gradient (see Fig. 5-25). The influence of alloying elements on the diffusivity of carbon in ferrite may be secondary.

The hardness as a function of tempering time and tempering temperature can be plotted parametrically (Fig. 5-37), so the mechanism of Ostwald ripening is controlling the coarsening as it was in plain carbon steels.

It is interesting to note that such parametric plot is obtained even for steels which show secondary hardening.

Methods of Estimating Tempered Hardness by Correlations in Plain Carbon and Alloy Steels

The parametric plots of tempered hardness, such as Fig. 5-28 and 5-37, are quite useful for determining tempering temperatures and times to attain a required hardness. They do require some experimental data, obtained over a sufficient tempering temperature and time range to establish the constant c. However, it is useful to have methods available which allow estimation of the tempered hardness of steels based on chemical composition and other variables (e.g., prior austenite grain size) so that at least some indication of the expected tempered hardness can be obtained without conducting heat treatments. Such an approach would be quite useful in assisting in the choice of steels to meet required hardnesses.

In this section some methods of estimating the hardness are described. The techniques are usually based on correlations, and their accuracy is limited by the method used and their applicability is limited by the range of chemistry of the steels used in establishing the correlation. In using these correlations, these limitations should be kept in mind.

Several methods have been developed for estimating hardness of tempered steels. We will first examine the relatively recent treatment by Grange, Hribal and Porter. This method is valid *only* for tempering martensite. They used both plain carbon and alloy steels ranging in carbon content from about 0.2 to about 1.0%, and the alloy content was up to as high as about 2% for certain elements. The hardness data for the plain carbon steels are shown in Fig. 5-41, for tempering one hour. They then

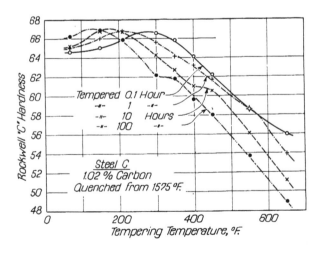

Fig. 5-24   The effect of tempering time on the hardness of a 1.02% C steel. (From S.G. Fletcher and M.Cohen, *Trans. ASM*, Vol 32, p 333 (1944))

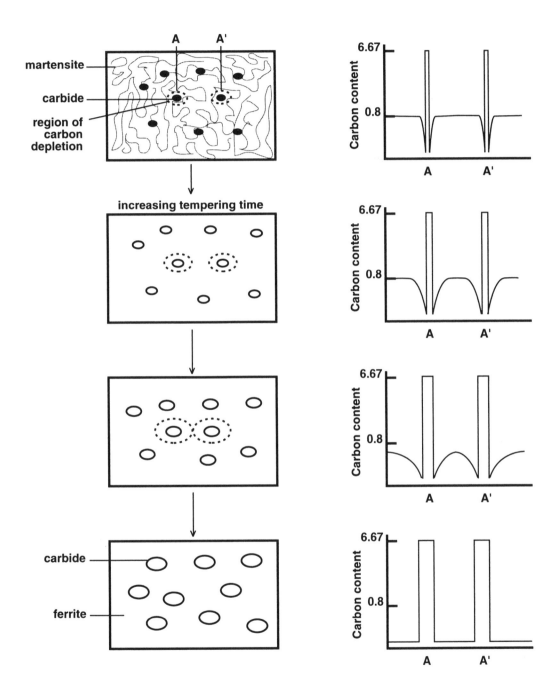

Fig. 5-25 Schematic illustration of the nucleation and growth of carbides in martensite, and the formation of ferrite

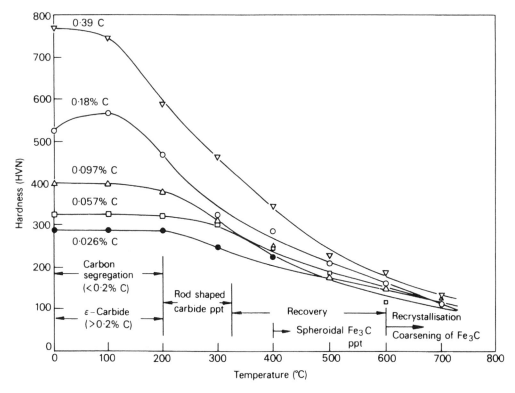

Fig. 5-26   The effect of tempering temperature on the hardness of plain carbon steels, showing the tempering stages. The tempering time was one hour. (Adapted from G.R. Speich, *Trans. Met. Soc. AIME,* Vol 245, p 2553 (1969))

Table 5-2   Sequence of events in tempering of steels. (From G. Krauss in *Phase Transformations in Ferrous Alloys*, A.R. Marder and J.I. Goldstein, editors, The Metallurgical Society, Warrendale, PA (1984))

Temperature range (°C)	Reaction and symbol (if designated)	Comments
−40 to 100	Clustering of 2 to 4 carbon atoms on octahedral sites of martensite segregation of carbon atoms to dislocations boundaries	Clustering is associated with diffuse spikes around fundamental electron diffraction spots of martensite
20 to 100	Modulated clusters of carbon atoms on (102) martensite planes (A2)	Identified by satellite spots around electron martensite
60 to 80	Long period ordered phase with ordered carbon atoms arranged (A3)	Identified by superstructure spots in electron diffraction patterns
100 to 200	Precipitation of transition carbide as aligned 2 nm diameter particles (T1)	Recent work identifies carbides as eta (orthorhombic, Fe_2C); earlier studies identified the carbides as epsilon (hexagonal, $Fe_{2.4}C$)
200 to 350	Transformation of retained austenite to ferrite and cementite (T2)	Associated with tempered martensite embrittlement in low and medium carbon steels
250 to 700	Formation of ferrite and cementite; eventual development of well spheroidized carbides in a matrix of equiaxed ferrite grains (T3)	This stage now appears to be initiated by chi-carbide formation in high carbon Fe-C alloys
500 to 700	Formation of alloy carbides in Cr, Mo, V, and W containing steels. The mix and composition of the carbides may change significantly with time (T4)	The alloy carbides produce secondary hardening and pronounced retardation of softening during tempering or long time service exposure around 500°C
350 to 550	Segregation and cosegregation of impurity and substitutional alloying elements	Responsible for temper embrittlement

examined the effect of different elements on the hardness, to obtain an incremental increase in hardness as a function of alloy content and tempering temperature. Based on the data in Fig. 5-41, they developed the base curves shown in Fig. 5-42. The incremental additions for alloying elements are obtained from the curves in Fig. 5-43. The validity of this method is illustrated by the data in Fig. 5-44. They only used prior austenite grain sizes (ASTM) from 2 to 4, for which they found no effect on the tempered hardness.

As an example of the use of this method, consider a 4140 steel containing 0.40% C, 0.83% Mn, 0.31% Si, 0.10% Ni, 1.00% Cr and 0.19% Mo, which has been tempered at 700°F for one hour. From Fig. 5-42, the base hardness will be 373 DPH. Then from Fig. 5-43, the addition factors are 45, 14, 1, 28, and 27, respectively. Thus the tempered hardness is 497, a considerable increase over the 373 for the plain carbon steel (e.g., 1040 steel).

This method is limited to tempering for one hour. However, estimates of the tempering temperature required to bring about the same hardness at different times can be made based on the assumption that the hardness is related to the tempering parameter T (c + log t). Note in Fig. 5-37 that the constant c used for the five steels was 18. Thus, assuming c = 18, the curves in Fig. 5-45 can be calculated. These allow estimates of other tempering times. For example, if tempering for one hour at 700°F gives a hardness of 497 DPH, the same hardness will be obtained by tempering at 700°F for a time which corresponds to the value of (700 + 460) (18 + log 1) = 20.88 × 10^3. Note that this value falls on the 700°F curve for one hour tempering. Thus for 2 h tempering time, Fig. 5-45 yields a temperature of 680°F (interpolated between the 600 and the 700°F curves).

The disadvantage of using the method of Grange, Hribal and Porter outlined above is that it is valid only for a starting microstructure of martensite. Crafts and Lamont developed a correlation which they found valid for other starting microstructures (e.g., bainite, martensite + bainite). Their procedure is outlined below.

The relation between the quenched hardness and the tempered hardness and the parameters in their method is illustrated in Fig. 5-46. The tempered hardness R_T is related to the quenched hardness R_Q by the equation below, where f is called the disproportionate softening, D the temper decrement, B the critical hardness, and the quantity A is a term which takes into account the alloying additions. The quantities in this equation are obtained from the curves in Fig. 5-47 and 5-48.

$$R_T = (R_Q - B - D) f + B + A$$

A limitation of this method is that it is valid only for a tempering time of 2 h.

Since this method is applicable to starting structures other than just martensite, it can be used to determine the change in the Jominy curve if the Jominy bar had been tempered, or the hardness profile across a quenched bar after tempering.

Embrittlement in Tempered Steels

It was shown earlier that the hardness, yield strength and tensile strength decrease with increased tempering temperature (if secondary hardening does not occur), and the elongation at fracture increases, as shown in Fig. 5-6 and 5-38. This shows that the ductility is increasing with the tempering temperature. However, this does not mean that the toughness is increasing. For many steels the impact energy (measured at 25°C) as a function of tempering temperature shows a minimum in the lower temperature tempering region, as shown in Fig. 5-10a and 5-39. This reduction in toughness is referred to generally as *temper embrittlement*.

The details of temper embrittlement are complicated, and in some cases still not well understood. In this section, no attempt is made to give a thorough review of the many studies of temper embrittlement or to discuss in detail the causes. Instead, the reader is referred to a list at the end of this section, of review papers in the last few years on this subject.

The embrittlement of martensite during tempering heat treatments may involve the decomposition of retained austenite, segregation of elements present in minor amount to prior austenite grain boundaries (now ferrite grain boundaries) or to other ferrite grain boundaries, the morphology of carbides which form during tempering, etc., and combinations of these structural features. Fracture may be along the prior austenite grain boundaries or occur along other ferrite boundaries, it may involve cleavage in the ferrite, or it may occur in carbide plates.

There are two types of temper embrittlement which will be examined. One is called *tempered martensite embrittlement* (TME), and is associated with tempering at about 260°C. The other type is called *temper embrittle-*

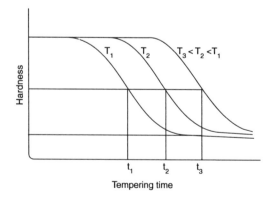

Fig. 5-27 Schematic illustration of the relation between the tempering time, tempering temperature and hardness, showing how the rate of tempering is related to the tempering time and temperature

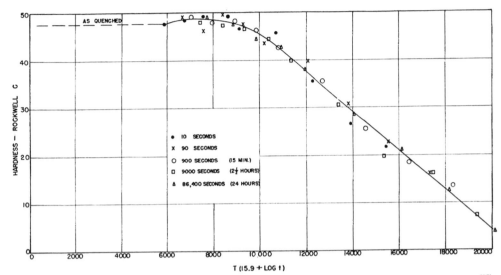

HARDNESS VS. TIME-TEMPERATURE PARAMETER FOR TEMPERING FULLY QUENCHED 0.31 PER CENT CARBON STEEL (U).
Constant = 15.9.
Time t in seconds.
Temperature T in deg. K.

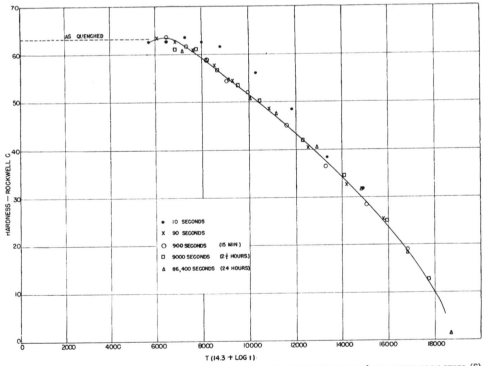

HARDNESS VS. TIME-TEMPERATURE PARAMETER FOR TEMPERING FULLY QUENCHED 0.56 PER CENT CARBON STEEL (S).
Constant = 14.3.
Time t in seconds.
Temperature T in deg. K.

Fig. 5-28 Tempering data for several plain carbon steels plotted parametrically. The structure was all martensite prior to tempering. (From J.H. Holloman and L.D. Jaffe, *Trans. AIME,* Vol 162, p 223 (1945)) *(continued)*

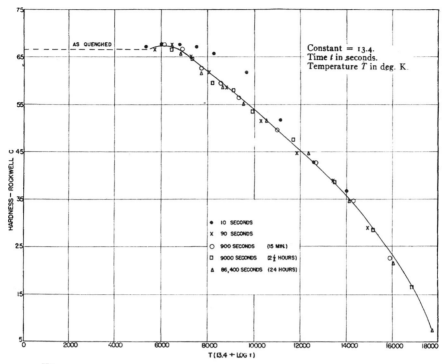

HARDNESS VS. TIME-TEMPERATURE PARAMETER FOR TEMPERING FULLY QUENCHED 0.74 PER CENT CARBON STEEL (T).

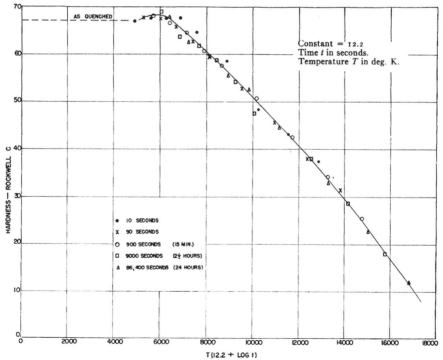

-HARDNESS VS. TIME-TEMPERATURE PARAMETER FOR TEMPERING FULLY QUENCHED 0.89 PER CENT CARBON STEEL (W).

Fig. 5-28 (continued) Tempering data for several plain carbon steels plotted parametrically. The structure was all martensite prior to tempering. (From J.H. Holloman and L.D. Jaffe, Trans. AIME, Vol 162, p 223 (1945)) (continued)

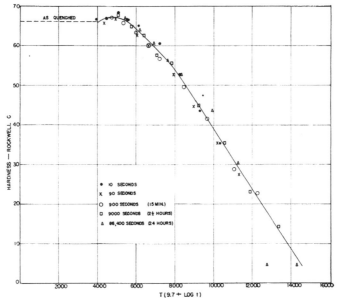

HARDNESS VS. TIME-TEMPERATURE PARAMETER FOR TEMPERING FULLY QUENCHED 0.96 PER
CENT CARBON STEEL (R).
Constant = 9.7.
Time t in seconds.
Temperature T in deg. K.

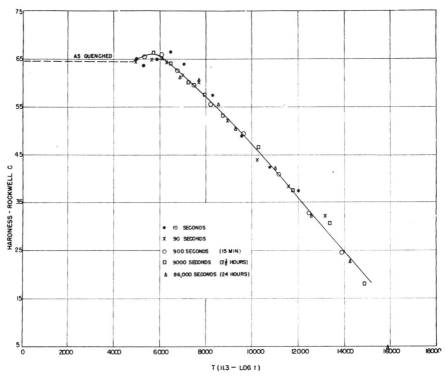

HARDNESS VS. TIME-TEMPERATURE PARAMETER FOR TEMPERING FULLY QUENCHED 1.15 PER CENT CARBON
STEEL (V).
Constant = 11.3.
Time t in seconds.
Temperature T in deg. K.

Fig. 5-28   (continued) Tempering data for several plain carbon steels plotted parametrically. The structure was all martensite prior to tempering. (From J.H. Holloman and L.D. Jaffe, Trans. AIME, Vol 162, p 223 (1945))

ment (TE) and is associated with slowly cooling through, or holding, in the range 370-565°C.

The usual and easiest method of detecting embrittlement is by impact testing. However, it may be misleading to use just the impact energy measured at 25°C for comparison of the effect of tempering. This is illustrated in Fig. 5-49, which shows impact curves for two steels, A and B; for each steel, two curves are shown, one for the steel heat treated to be tough and the other heat treated to be embrittled. Although in steel B, testing at 25°C clearly distinguishes the embrittling effect, for steel A, testing at 25°C does not show much difference in the impact energy. However, examination of the complete impact energy-temperature curves does allow detection of the embrittlement. Thus, it is important to determine the impact energy-temperature curves, and from these a transition temperature (see Fig. 5-7) can be obtained as a comparative measure of embrittlement.

Tempered martensite embrittlement

Tempered martensite embrittlement (abbreviated TME) is sometimes referred to as one step temper embrittlement (OSTE). The origin of this term is illustrated in Fig. 5-50. To develop this type of embrittlement, the steel is quenched from the austenite region to form martensite, then it is tempered. In the range of 200-500°C, it is found that the toughness is reduced. This type of embrittlement is also referred to as 260°C (500°F) embrittlement and 350°C embrittlement because for some steels the embrittlement is most pronounced after tempering near these temperatures.

There are two structural features which are important in TME. One is the segregation of minor elements, especially P, to austenite grain boundaries. The other is the formation during tempering of deleterious carbide morphologies from thin layers of retained austenite. These two factors are not necessarily independent. We will look first at the problem of segregation of elements to the austenite grain boundaries, then the decomposition of retained austenite to carbides.

TME is intimately associated with segregation to austenite grain boundaries of certain elements present in minor amounts (e.g., 0.01%); Sn, Sb, As and especially P are important in effecting this embrittlement. Figure 5-51 shows the effect of P. Figures 5-52 and 5-53 show fractographs illustrating the effect of P content on the fracture

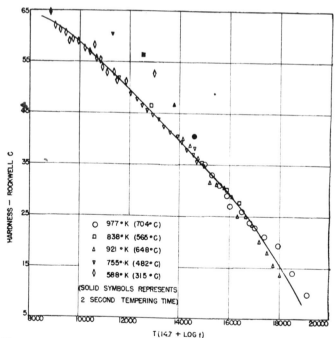

HARDNESS VS. TIME-TEMPERATURE PARAMETER FOR TEMPERING 0.94 PER CENT CARBON STEEL. (Data from Engel.)
Structure before tempering: martensite (plus retained austenite)
Treatment before tempering: 1500°F., 10 min., brine quench.
Constant = 14.7.
Time t in seconds.
Temperature T in deg. K.

Fig. 5-29   Tempering data plotted parametrically for a steel which contained retained austenite prior to tempering. (From J.H. Hollomon and L.D. Jaffe, Trans. AIME, Vol 162, p 223 (1945))

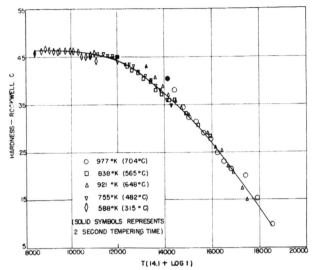

HARDNESS VS. TIME-TEMPERATURE PARAMETER FOR TEMPERING 0.94 PER CENT CARBON STEEL. (*Data from Engel.*)

Structure before tempering: fine pearlite.
Treatment before tempering: 1500°F., 10 min. Quench in lead at 900°F., hold 30 sec. Quench in water.

Constant = 14.1.
Time t in seconds.
Temperature T in deg. K.

(a)

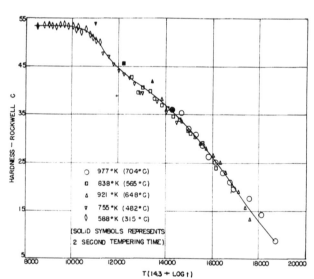

HARDNESS VS. TIME-TEMPERATURE PARAMETER FOR TEMPERING 0.94 PER CENT CARBON STEEL. (*Data from Engel.*)

Structure before tempering: bainite (plus retained austenite).
Treatment before tempering: 1500°F., 10 min.; quench in lead-bismuth at 600°F., hold 30 min. Quench in water.

Constant = 14.3.
Time t in seconds.
Temperature T in deg. K.

(b)

Fig. 5-30   Tempering data plotted parametrically for a steel which had different microstructures prior to tempering. (From J.H. Hollomon and L.D. Jaffe, *Trans. AIME,* Vol 162, p 223 (1945))

surface morphology of impact samples. In this study, in the range of temper embrittlement the fracture was markedly intergranular (Fig. 5-53). There was less intergranular fracture in the lower P steel (Fig. 5-52). Such fractographic observations have confirmed the intergranular fracture nature of tempered martensite embrittlement in some steels. It is important to understand that the fracture is occurring along prior austenite grain boundaries, which are now high angle ferrite grain boundaries.

Chemical analysis of the fracture surface can be obtained by use of Auger electron spectroscopy. This method gives the chemical composition of a layer of

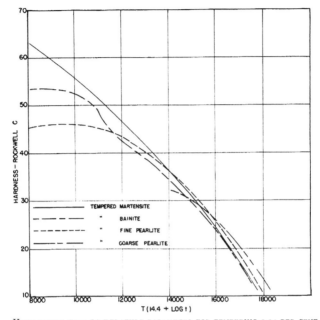

HARDNESS VS. TIME-TEMPERATURE PARAMETER FOR TEMPERING 0.94 PER CENT CARBON STEEL FROM VARIOUS INITIAL STRUCTURES. (*Data from Engel.*[2])
Temperature of formation of isothermal structures: bainite, 600°F.; fine pearlite, 900°F.; coarse pearlite, 1200°F.

Constant = 14.4
Time t in seconds.
Temperature T in deg. K.

Fig. 5-31   Tempering data plotted parametrically for a steel which was all pearlite (in (a)) or all bainite (in (b)) prior to tempering. (From J.H. Hollomon and L.D. Jaffe, *Trans. AIME,* Vol 162, p 223 (1945))

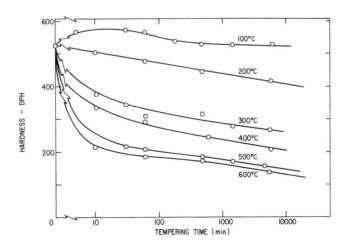

Fig. 5-32   Tempering curves for a 0.18% C steel. (From G.R. Speich, *Trans. AIME,* Vol 245, p 2553 (1969))

atoms only about three deep, so that effectively the chemical composition of the surface is obtained. Some data of the effect of P on the fracture surfaces in the untempered condition and in the tempered condition indicate that the presence of P *per se* at the prior austenite grain boundaries is not sufficient for the development of TME.

The other factor that enters into TME is the decomposition of retained austenite to carbides upon tempering. In some steels, thin sheets of retained austenite may be present after quenching, and this retained austenite can have a high carbon content (e.g., 1%). An example of a microstructure which originally contained thin layers of retained austenite between the martensite laths is shown in Fig. 5-55. Upon tempering, the retained austenite decomposed isothermally to ferrite and carbide, with the carbide forming as thin plates.

An example of retained austenite is shown in Fig. 5-55. The corresponding fractographs are shown in Fig. 5-56. Note that the sample tempered at 600°C had a relatively high impact energy (Fig. 5-55), but the fracture surface was predominantly intergranular. From this study, it was concluded that the minimum in the impact energy-temperature curve is due to the formation of thin carbides from retained austenite (see Fig. 5-57). Although the retained austenite decomposed into carbides and ferrite upon higher temperature tempering, coarser carbides form (Fig. 5-57) so that brittle fracture in these regions is not so likely.

In some low carbon steels, embrittlement is associated with peculiar carbide morphology which provides numerous sites for microcrack initiation, their growth by

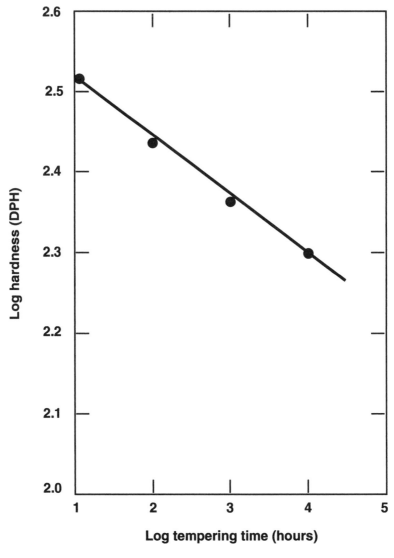

Fig. 5-33   Plot of log hardness versus log tempering time at 400 °C, from data in Fig. 2-32.

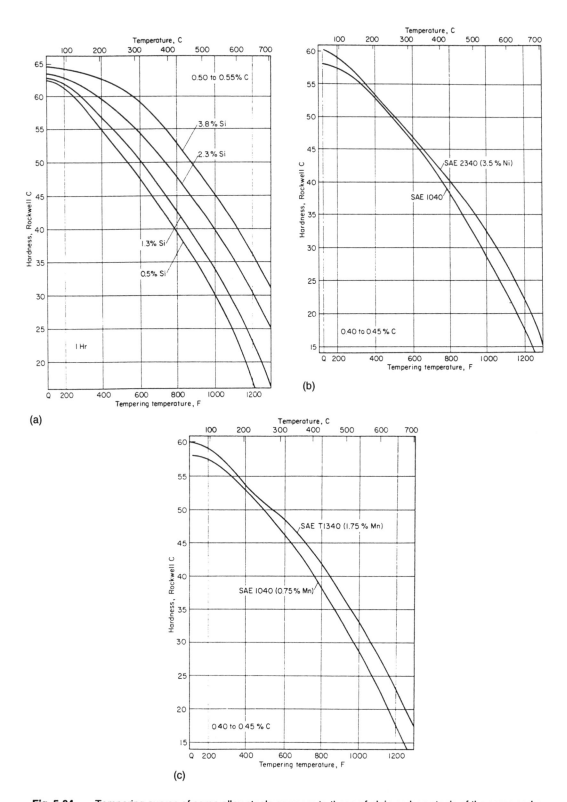

Fig. 5-34 Tempering curves of some alloy steels compare to those of plain carbon steels of the same carbon content. (a) Quenched 0.50 to 0.55% C steel as influenced by silicon content. (b) Quenched 0.40 to 0.45% C steels as influenced by about 3.5% Ni. (c) Quenched 0.40 to 0.45% C steels as influenced by an increase of manganese from about 0.75 to 1.75%. (From E.C. Bain and H.W. Paxton, *Alloying Elements in Steel,* 2nd ed., American Society for Metals, Metals Park, Ohio (1961))

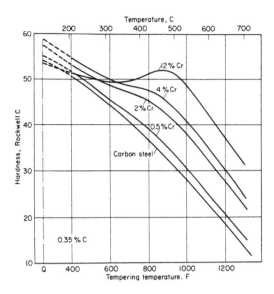

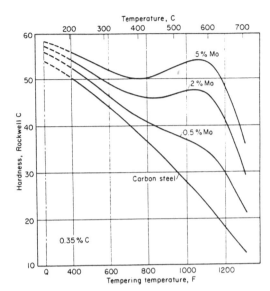

Fig. 5-35 Tempering curves for Cr steels containing 0.35% C, showing secondary hardening. (From same source as Fig. 5-34)

(a)

microvoid coalescence and then fracture with little gross plastic deformation. An example of the fracture surface for such cases is shown in Fig. 5-58, where dimples are shown along with some cleavage facets.

Once TME appears, there is no heat treatment to reverse the effect, other than to reaustenitize and quench the steel, then temper in a temperature range where TME does not occur.

Temper embrittlement

In studying embrittlement, it must be recognized that during tempering the ferrite-carbide structure of the tempered martensite is a function of tempering temperature. Thus to determine if there are other structural effects which are causing the embrittlement, it is necessary to establish a carbide-ferrite morphology which does not change while heating in the tempering range. Clearly this cannot be done with martensite. However, if the steel of interest is austenitized, quenched to form martensite, then tempered at a relatively high temperature, cooled to 25°C, then reheated (tempered again) to temperatures below the initial tempering temperature, the ferrite-carbide structures should remain relatively fixed. Embrittlement associated with this type of heat treatment is referred to as *temper embrittlement* (TE) or as *two step temper embrittlement* (TSTE) (see Fig. 5-59). This type of embrittlement is also caused by cooling too slowly through this temperature range.

Figure 5-60 shows the effect of aging on the hardness, impact energy (at 25°C) and the percentage of the fracture surface which was intergranular. Clearly, embrit-

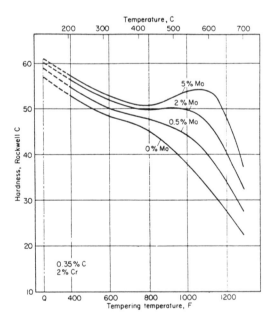

(b)

Fig. 5-36 Tempering curves for (a) Mo steels and (b) Mo-Cr steels, showing secondary hardening. (From same source as Fig. 5-34)

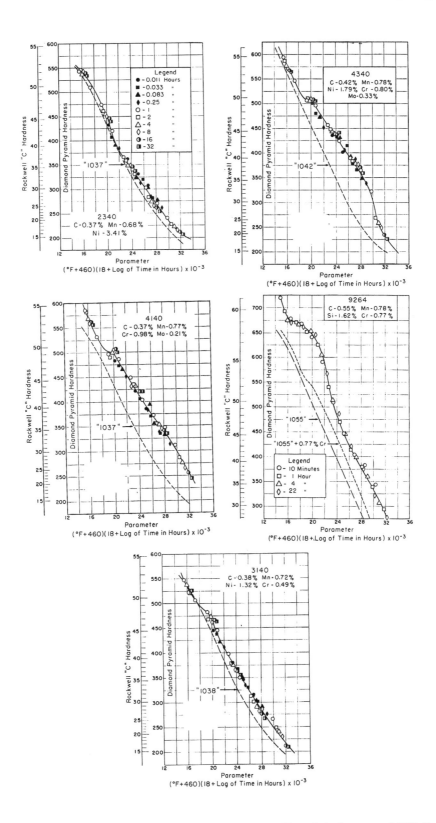

Fig. 5-37   Tempering data plotted parametrically for alloy steels. (From R.A. Grange and R.W. Baughman, *Trans. ASM,* Vol 48, p 165 (1956))

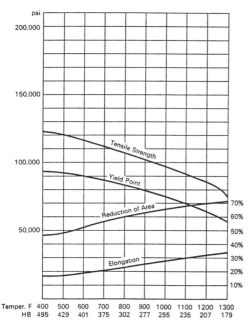

Water-quenched 1030

Treatment: Normalized at 1700 F; reheated to 1600 F; quenched in water.
1-in. Round Treated; .505-in. Round Tested.   As-quenched HB 514.

Temper, F	400	500	600	700	800	900	1000	1100	1200	1300
HB	495	429	401	375	302	277	255	235	207	179

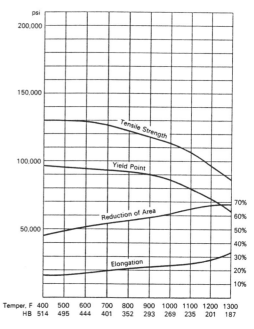

Water-quenched 1040

Treatment: Normalized at 1650 F; reheated to 1550 F; quenched in water.
1-in. Round Treated; .505-in. Round Tested.   As-quenched HB 534.

Temper, F	400	500	600	700	800	900	1000	1100	1200	1300
HB	514	495	444	401	352	293	269	235	201	187

Fig. 5-38   Tensile mechanical property data for the tempered condition of a 1040 (plain carbon) steel and a 4140 (alloy) steel. (From *Modern Steels and Their Properties*, Handbook 3310, Bethlehem Steel Corporation, Bethlehem, PA)

tlement is increasing with time at the aging temperature. Note that the hardness decreases only about 5% upon aging. Figure 5-61 shows for another steel the increase in the fracture appearance transition temperature (FATT) upon aging (second tempering).

Figure 5-62 shows impact energy-temperature curves for a 3140 steel which was martensitic, then initially tempered for one hour at 675°C, then tempered for various times at 500°C. The hardness following the initial tempering was 23 Rockwell C, and it decreased to only 20 Rockwell C after 240 h. Also shown on each curve is the percent of the fracture surface which was fibrous (ductile) as a function of the test temperature. This curve can also be used as an indication of the transition temperature. If the temperature at which the fracture is 100% fibrous is taken as a measure of this, then it is clear in Fig. 5-62 that increased tempering time increased the temper embrittlement. For this steel the effect of tempering temperature and time on the transition temperature is shown in Fig. 5-63. As noted above, the hardness, and thus the strength, was about constant during aging. However, clearly the impact curves have been shifted to higher temperatures the longer the tempering at 500°C.

From these data, curves can be obtained which relate the tempering temperature and time to the transition

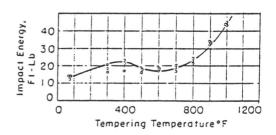

4340
Oil-Quenched
Tempered 1 hr.

Fig. 5-39   Impact energy (measured at 25 °C) for a 4340 steel as a function of tempering temperature. The tempering time was 15 min. (Adapted from L.J. Klingler, W.J. Barnett and R.P. Frohmberg, *Trans. ASM,* Vol. 46, p. 1557 (1954))

temperature, as shown in Fig. 5-64. (Note that this diagram is similar to an isothermal TTT diagram.) Following the initial tempering, the transition temperature was –83°C, indicating a tougher steel.

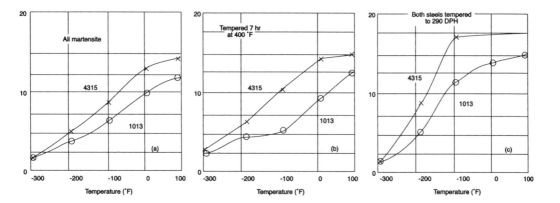

Fig. 5-40 Charpy V-notch impact energy-temperature curves for a plain carbon steel (1013) and an alloy steel (4315), for different tempering conditions. (The impact samples were 1/4 width of a standard sample.) (Adapted from R.H. Aborn, *Trans. ASM*, Vol. 48, p. 51 (1956))

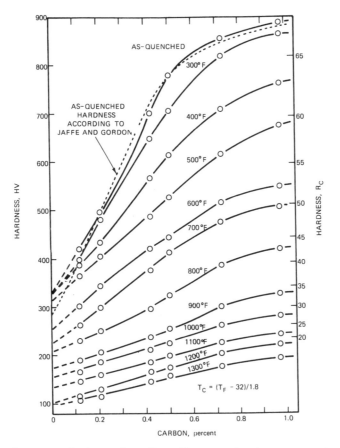

Fig. 5-41 Tempering curves for iron-carbon alloys. The tempering time was one hour, and the starting microstructure was martensite, except for the higher carbon steels which contained some retained austenite. (From R.A. Grange, C.R. Hribal, and L.F. Porter, *Met. Trans.*, Vol 8A, p 1775 (1977))

The fracture in TE is intergranular, occurring on the former austenite boundaries (now ferrite boundaries). Figure 5-65 shows fractographs of the fracture surface of impact samples for a quenched and tempered (unembrittled) steel and for the same steel after the second step aging; the latter clearly shows intergranular fracture. Its cause is segregation of impurities to the boundary, especially elements like Sb, Sn and P. Figure 5-66 shows the increase in the intergranular P content with aging time; the P was detected using Auger spectroscopy. Figure 5-67 shows the increase of P on the prior austenite grain boundaries with aging time and the correlation of this with the reduction in toughness.

It is to be noted that TSTE develops with aging time. It also can occur if the steel, at the end of the initial tempering time, is cooled too slowly through the temperature range in which TE occurs. This is illustrated by the data in Fig. 5-68. For this steel, the embrittlement was developed by either aging or by slow cooling. Figure 5-69 shows the effect of the cooling rate on the transition temperature. The embrittlement upon slow cooling from the tempering temperature is an important characteristic because steel components of large size (e.g., rotor forgings) cool very slowly from the tempering temperature, and thus may be quite susceptible to TE.

An important characteristic of TE is that, unlike TME, it is reversible. A steel which is embrittled can be heated to the temperature range of 600-700°C, still below the austenite region, and if not cooled too slowly from this range (see previous paragraph), the steel will have a toughness similar to that for the initial single tempering treatment. Thus in the higher temperature treatment, the deleterious segregants at the prior austenite grain boundaries are dispersed, and there is less intergranular fracture and a higher toughness. Subsequent aging will again develop TE. The de-embrittlement heat treatment is shown schematically in Fig. 5-70.

TE develops in relatively soft structures because of the high tempering temperature required to develop it. Also, it clearly is associated with the high angle ferrite

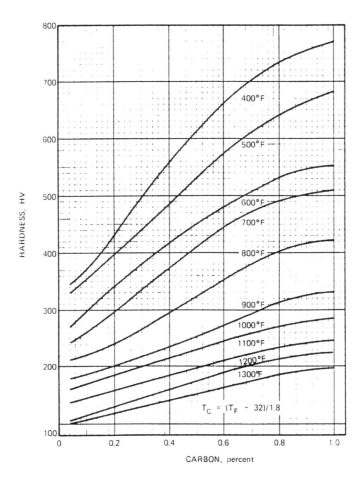

Fig. 5-42 Base tempering curves (one hour tempering time) from the data in Fig. 5-41. (From R.A. Grange, C.R. Hribal, and L.F. Porter, *Met. Trans.*, Vol 8A, p 1775 (1977))

grain boundaries, which are the former austenite grain boundaries. Thus, it is expected that austenite, which has the necessary concentration of segregants to allow development of TE when aging tempered martensite, will develop TE upon aging a bainitic structure (or pearlitic).

That this may occur is shown by the data in Fig. 5-71, which compares the influence of hardness (via the initial tempering treatment) on toughness and on the amount of P detected on the intergranular fracture surfaces. In Fig. 5-71a, the transition temperature is compared to that of

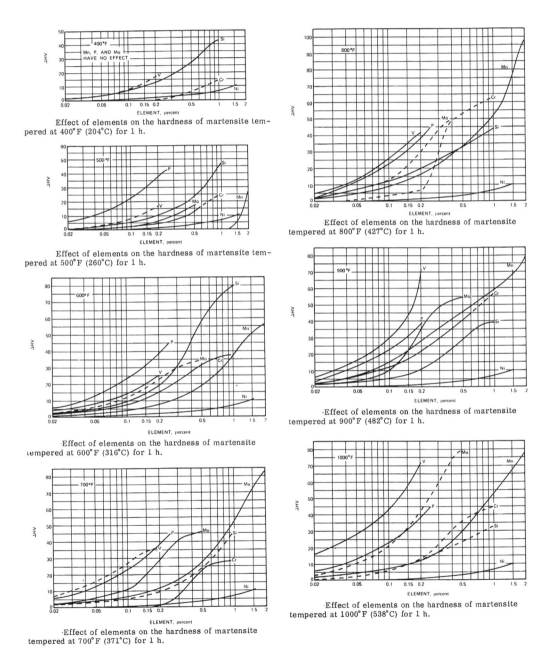

Effect of elements on the hardness of martensite tempered at 400°F (204°C) for 1 h.

Effect of elements on the hardness of martensite tempered at 500°F (260°C) for 1 h.

Effect of elements on the hardness of martensite tempered at 600°F (316°C) for 1 h.

Effect of elements on the hardness of martensite tempered at 700°F (371°C) for 1 h.

Effect of elements on the hardness of martensite tempered at 800°F (427°C) for 1 h.

·Effect of elements on the hardness of martensite tempered at 900°F (482°C) for 1 h.

·Effect of elements on the hardness of martensite tempered at 1000°F (538°C) for 1 h.

Fig. 5-43 Part 1 Effect of seven elements (chromium, manganese, molybdenum, nickel, phosphorus, silicon, and vanadium) on the hardness of martensite tempered (100°F) increments ranging from 205 to 705°C (400 to 1300°F), each for a 1-h duration. Note that manganese, molybdenum, and phosphorus have no effect on hardness at 205°C (400 °F) *(continued)*

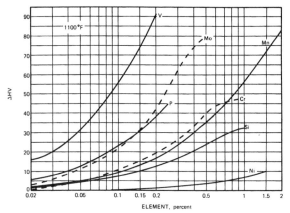

Effect of elements on the hardness of martensite tempered at 1100°F (592°C) for 1 h.

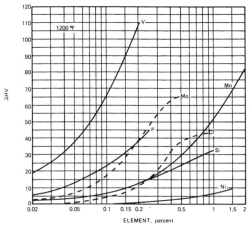

·Effect of elements on the hardness of martensite tempered at 1200°F (649°C) for 1 h.

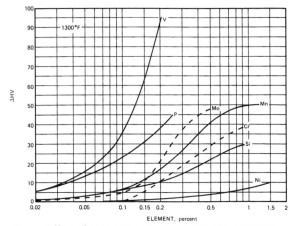

·Effect of elements on the hardness of martensite tempered at 1300°F (704°C) for 1 h.

Fig. 5-43 Part 2   (continued) Effect of seven elements (chromium, manganese, molybdenum, nickel, phosphorus, silicon, and vanadium) on the hardness of martensite tempered (100°F) increments ranging from 205 to 705°C (400 to 1300°F), each for a 1-h duration. Note that manganese, molybdenum, and phosphorus have no effect on hardness at 205°C (400 °F) (From same source as Fig. 5-41)

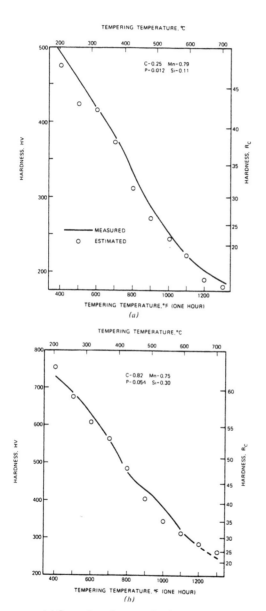

(a)

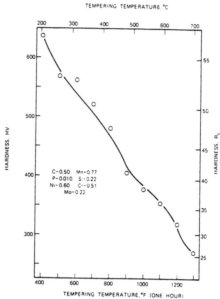

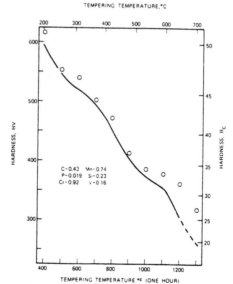

-Comparison of the measured (curve) and estimated (points) hardness of tempered martensite in an AISI 8650 steel.

(b)

(a) Comparison of measured and estimated hardness of tempered martensite in an AISI 1026 steel. (b) Comparison of measured and estimated hardness of tempered martensite in an AISI 1080 steel.

-Comparison of the measured and estimated hardness of tempered martensite in AISI 6145 steel.

Fig. 5-44 Comparison of measured and estimated hardness of tempered martensite. (From R.A. Grange, C.R. Hribal, and L.F. Porter, *Met. Trans.,* Vol 8A, p 1775 (1977))

the as-quenched, martensitic condition (FATT = 0°C). The curves marked "non-embrittled" refer to the properties of the steel after aging following the initial, single tempering treatment. Note that for a given hardness the embrittled condition has a considerably higher transition temperature, showing that the toughness is reduced. Also note that aging the bainitic structure reduces the toughness. However, this effect is less than it is for the tempered martensite structure. Also, there is less P segregated to the prior austenite grain boundaries in the aged bainite (Fig. 5-71b).

Given below is a list of relatively recent review papers which deal with embrittlement in tempered steels.

- C.J. McMahon, Jr., p 295 in *Fundamental Aspects of Structural Alloy Design*, R.I. Jaffee and B.A. Wilcox, editors, Plenum, New York (1975)
- C.J. McMahon, Jr., *Mat. Sci. and Engr.*, Vol 25, p 233 (1976)
- I. Olefjord, *Int. Metals Reviews*, Vol 23, p 149 (1978)
- C.L. Briant and S.K. Bainerji, *Int. Metals Reviews*, Vol 23, p 164 (1978)

- M. Guttmann, p 1 in *Advances in the Mechanics and Physics of Surfaces*, R.M. Latanision and R.J. Courtel, editors, Hardwood Academic Publishers, New York (1981)
- G.L. Eyre, B.C. Edwards and J.M. Titchmarsh, p 246, in *Advances in the Physical Metallurgy and Applications of Steels*, The Metals Society, London (1982)
- G. Krauss, p 101, in *Phase Transformations in Ferrous Alloys*, A.R. Marder and J.I. Goldstein, editors, The Metallurgical Society of AIME, Warrendale, PA (1984)
- G.F. Vander Voort, p 689, in *Metals Handbook*, 10th edition, Vol 1, *Properties and Selection: Irons, Steels and High-Performance Alloys*, ASM International, Materials Park, Ohio (1990)

Closure

The effects of the common alloying elements on the tempering of steel are summarized in Table 5-3. Comments about the influence of some of these elements on embrittlement caused by tempering are given.

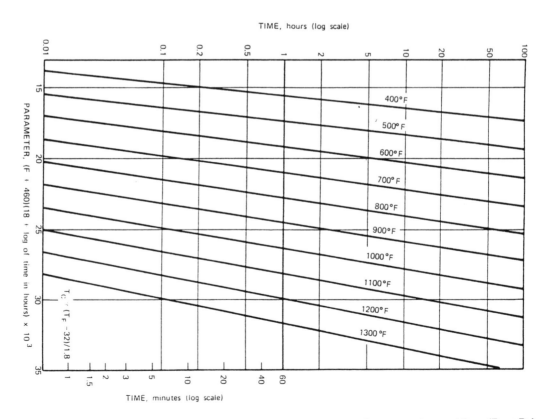

Fig. 5-45   Chart showing relationship of tempering parameter to tempering temperature and time. (From R.A. Grange, C.R. Hribal, and L.F. Porter, *Met. Trans.*, Vol 8A, p 1775 (1977))

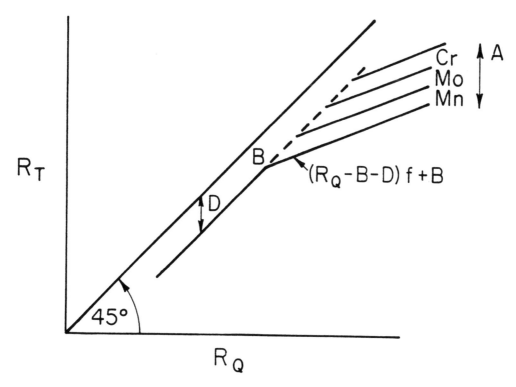

Fig. 5-46   Schematic illustration of the relation between the tempered hardness R_T, the quenched hardness R_Q and the parameters used in the Crafts and Lamont tempered hardness calculation. (Adapted from W. Crafts and J.L. Lamont, *Trans. AIME*, Vol 172, p. 222 (1947))

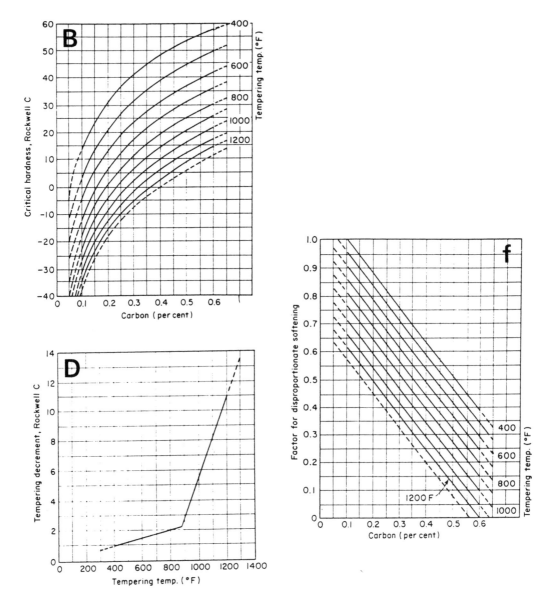

Fig. 5-47 The quantities B, D and f used in the Crafts and Lamont tempered hardness calculation. (Adapted from W. Crafts and J.L. Lamont, *Trans. AIME,* Vol 172, p 222 (1947))

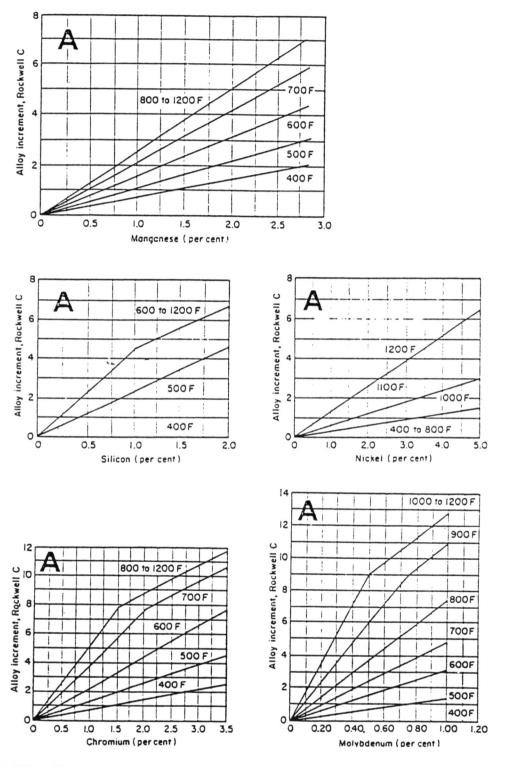

Fig. 5-48 The quantities A for correcting for alloy content in the Crafts and Lamont tempered hardness calculation. (Adapted from W. Crafts and J.L. Lamont, *Trans. AIME*, Vol 172, p 222 (1947))

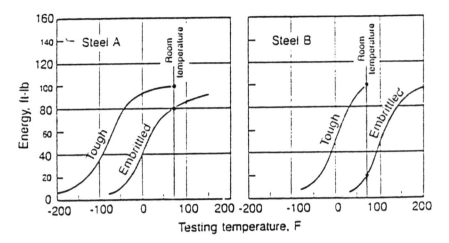

Fig. 5-49   Transition in fracture behavior for two hypothetical steels in the tough and embrittled conditions. (From G. Krauss, *Steels: Heat Treatment and Processing Principles,* ASM International, Materials Park, Ohio, p 230 (1989))

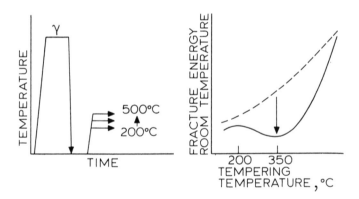

Fig. 5-50   Schematic illustration of the heat treatments involved in tempered martensite embrittlement (TME [or one-step temper embrittlement (OSTE)]. (From C.L. Briant and S.K. Banerji, *Int. Metals Reviews,* Vol 23, p 16 (1978))

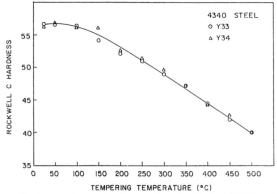

Hardness *vs* tempering temperature for the low (Y33) and high (Y34) phosphorus 4340 steels austenitized at 1143 K (870°C) and oil quenched and tempered 1 h at temperatures shown.

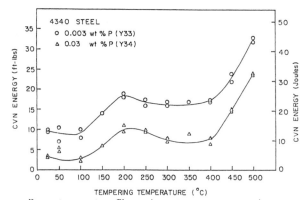

Room temperature Charpy impact energy *vs* tempering temperature for 4340 steel austenitized at 1143 K (870°C), oil quenched, and tempered 1 h at temperatures shown.

Fig. 5-51 Room-temperature Charpy impact energy versus tempering temperature for 4340 steel containing different amounts of phosphorus as shown. Specimens were austenitized at 870°C (1598°F), oil quenched, and tempered 1 h at temperatures shown (From J.P Materkowski and G. Krauss, *Met. Trans.*, Vol 10A, p 1643 (1979))

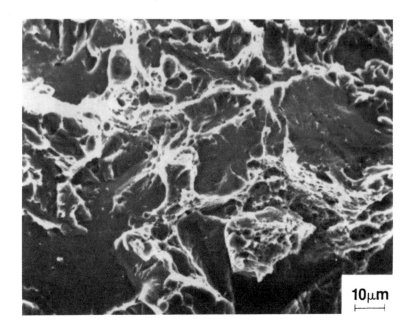

Flat cleavage facets in 4340 steel containing 0.003% phosphorus after tempering at 350 °C (662 °F). Specimen was broken by impact loading at room temperature.

Fig. 5-52   Flat cleavage facets in 4340 steel containing 0.003% phosphorus after tempering at 350 °C (662 °F). Specimen was broken by impact loading at room temperature. Fractograph of the fracture of an impact sample of a 4340 steel of low P content. (From J.P Materkowski and G. Krauss, *Met. Trans.*, Vol 10A, p 1643 (1979))

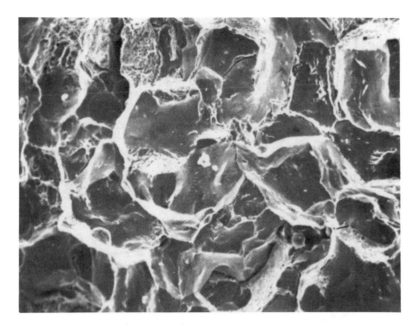

Intergranular fracture of 4340 steel containing 0.03% phosphorus after tempering at 400 °C (752 °F). Specimen was broken by impact loading at room temperature.

Fig. 5-53 Intergranular fracture of 4340 steel containing 0.03% phosphorus after tempering at 400°C (752°F). Specimen was broken by impact loading at room temperature. Fractobgraph of the fracture surface of an impact sample of a 4340 steel of a realtively high P content. (From G. Krauss, *Steels: Heat Treatment and Processing Principles,* ASM International, Materials Park, OH (1990))

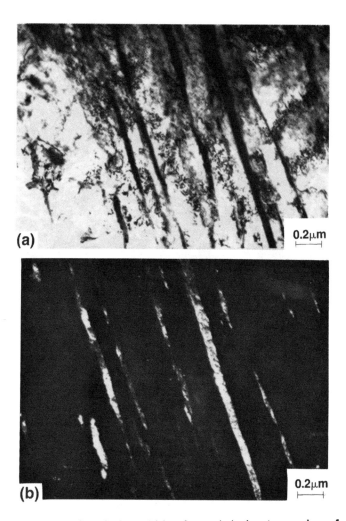

Interlath carbides formed during tempering of 4340 steel containing 0.003% phosphorus at 350 °C (662 °F). (a) Bright-field image and (b) dark-field image using a cementite diffracted beam for illumination. Transmission electron micrographs.

Fig. 5-54 Transmission electron micrographs showing retained austenite stringers between the martensite laths. (From J.P Materkowski and G. Krauss, *Met. Trans.,* Vol 10A, p 1643 (1979))

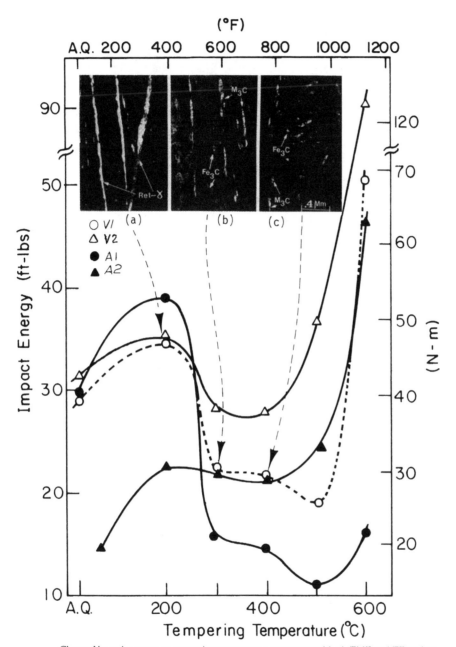

Charpy V-notch energy *vs* tempering temperature curves reveal both TME and TE regions
(1 h tempering). Inset micrographs of V1 alloy show the corresponding dark-field images: (*a*) retained
austenite, (*b*) interlath carbides, and (*c*) spheroidized intralath and interlath carbides in 2 Mn alloy.
Values for the air melted alloys of the same compositions are also plotted for comparison

Fig. 5-55   The effect of tempering temperature on the impact energy (measured at 25 °C) for four steels.
Transmission electron micrographs (dark field) are shown for one steel in which thin sheets of retained austenite
(light areas) in the martensite are revealed. (From M. Sarikaya, A.K. Jhingan, and G. Thomas, *Met Trans.*, Vol 14A,
p 1121 (1983))

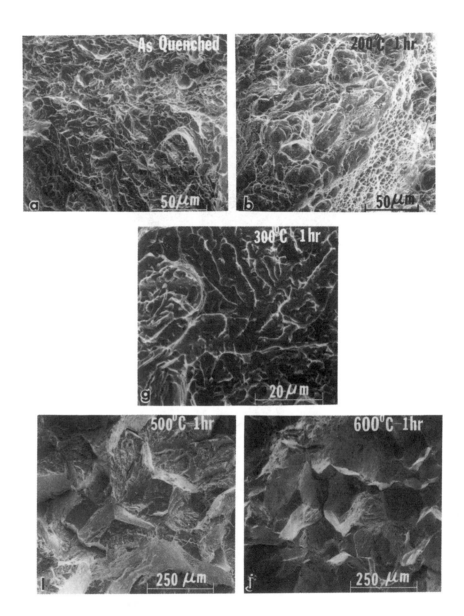

Fig. 5-56   Fractographs of the fracture surface of impact samples of some tempered steels. (From M. Sarikaya, A.K. Jhingan, and G. Thomas, *Met Trans.,* Vol 14A, p 1121 (1983))

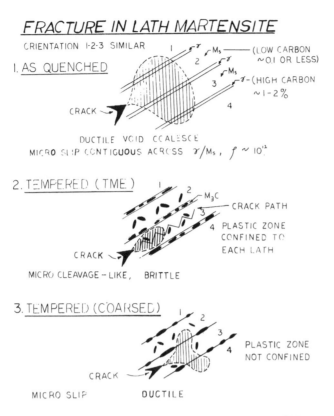

FRACTURE IN LATH MARTENSITE

ORIENTATION 1-2-3 SIMILAR

1. AS QUENCHED

CRACK

DUCTILE VOID COALESCE
MICRO SLIP CONTIGUOUS ACROSS γ/M_s, $\rho \sim 10^{12}$

M_s —— (LOW CARBON $\sim$0.1 OR LESS)

M_s — γ – (HIGH CARBON $\sim$1-2%

2. TEMPERED (TME.)

CRACK

MICRO CLEAVAGE – LIKE, BRITTLE

M_3C
CRACK PATH
PLASTIC ZONE CONFINED TO EACH LATH

3. TEMPERED (COARSED)

CRACK

MICRO SLIP   DUCTILE

PLASTIC ZONE NOT CONFINED

Fig. 5-57   Schematic diagram for a low carbon steel showing the microstructure of (a) martensite, (b) tempered martensite which is TME, and (c) tempered martensite tempered at too high a temperature to develop TME. (From M. Sarikaya, A.K. Jhingan, and G. Thomas, *Met Trans.*, Vol 14A, p 1121 (1983))

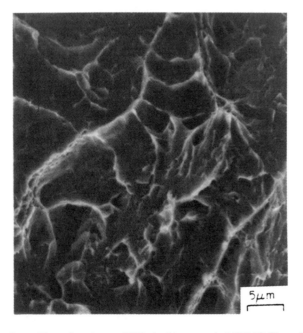

5μm

Fig. 5-58   Fracture surface of low-phosphorus 4130 steel tempered at 300 °C (From F. Zia-Ebrahimi and G. Krauss, *Met. Trans.*, Vol 14A, p 1109-1119 (1983))

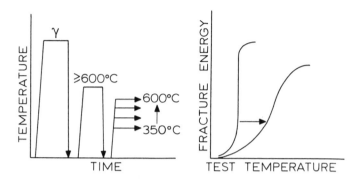

Fig. 5-59   Schematic illustration of the heat treatment involved in temper embrittlement (TE) [two-step temper embrittlement (TSTE)]. (From C.L. Briant and S.K. Banerji, *Int. Metals Reviews*, Vol 23, p 164 (1978))

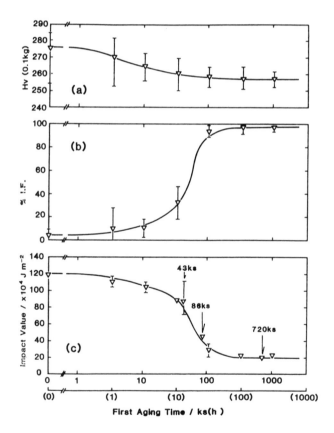

Fig. 5-60   The effect of aging time at 524 °C on the hardness, % intergranular fracture and impact energy. The steel contained 0.34% C, 0.49% Mn, 0.52% Ni, and 1.00% Cr. The samples were austenitized at 1100 °C for 20 min., oil quenched, tempered for one hour at 650 °C, then aged. (From T. Shinoda, Y. Mishima, A. Kobayashi and T. Suzuki, *Z. Metallkunde*, Vol 77, p 433 (1986))

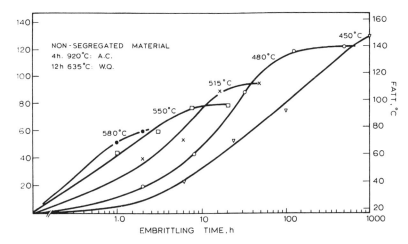

Fig. 5-61 The effect of aging time and temperature on the increase in the fracture appearance transition temperature. The steel contained 0.34% C, 0.89% Mn, 0.33% Si, 3.10% Cr, 0.18% Ni, and 0.59% Mo. The samples were austenitized at 920 °C, oil quenched, tempered for 12 hr at 635 °C, then aged at the temperatures shown. (From B.L. King and G. Wigmore, *Met. Trans.*, Vol 7A, p 1761 (1976))

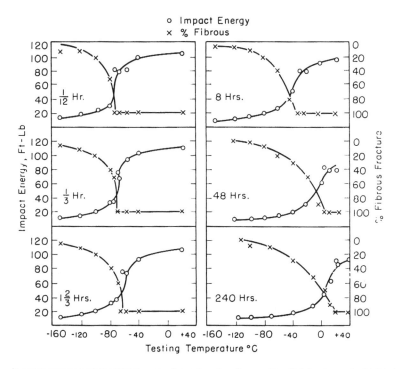

Fig. 5-62 Impact curves and % of fracture surface showing fibrous (ductile) fracture of a 3140 steel for different aging times at 500 °C. The samples were austenitized for one hour at 900 °C, water quenched, tempered for one hour at 675 °C, water quenched, then aged at 500 °C for the times shown. (From L.D. Jaffee and D.C. Buffum, *Trans. ASM,* Vol 42, p 604 (1950))

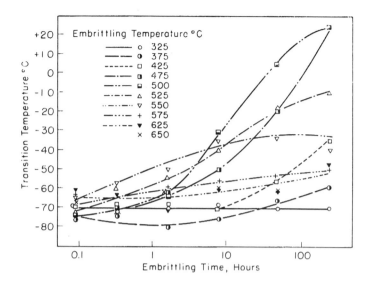

Fig. 5-63 The effect of aging temperature and time on the transition temperature of a 3140 steel, from data such as in Fig. 5-62. (From L.D. Jaffee and D.C. Buffum, *Trans. ASM,* Vol 42, p 604 (1959))

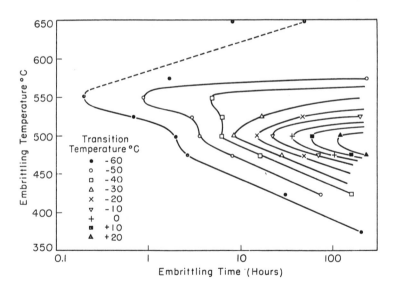

Fig. 5-64 The effect of aging temperature and time on the transition temperature of a 3140 steel, obtained from the data in Fig. 5-63. (From L.D. Jaffee and D.C. Buffum, *Trans. ASM,* Vol 42, p 604 (1959))

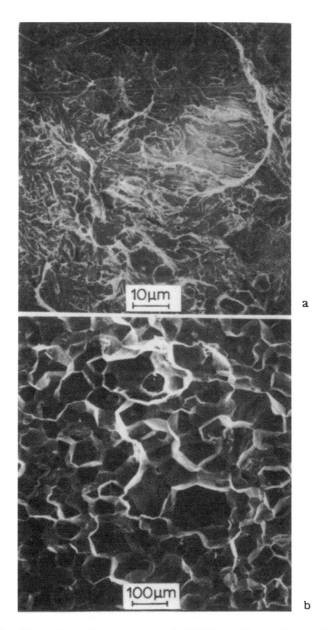

Fig. 5-65   Fractographs of the surface of impact samples of a HY130 steel for conditions of (a) quenched and tempered, and (b) quenched and tempered, then aged. (From same source as Fig. 5-5a)

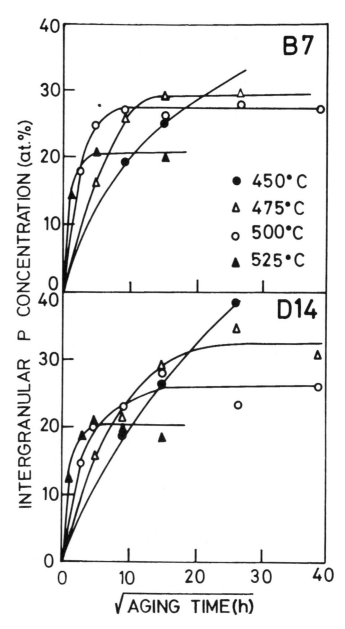

Fig. 5-66   The increase with aging time of the P concentration on the prior austenite grain boundaries for two steels. (From M. Guttmann, Ph. Dumoulin and M. Wayman, *Met. Trans.,* Vol 13A, p 1693 (1982))

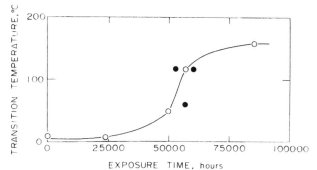

Effect of exposure time at 540 °C on the Charpy V-notch transition temperature of 2¹/₄ CrMoV steel bolts. Open points: uninterrupted exposure. Filled points: bolts retempered at 680 °C for 10 h after ~40,000 h exposure and returned to service for the remainder of the *total* time indicated.

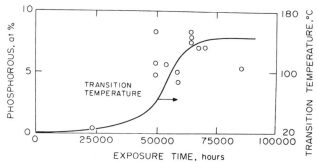

Effect of exposure time on the P concentration on fracture surfaces (points) compared with the effect on the transition temperature (curve).

Fig. 5-67   Effect of aging time on the transition temperature and on the concentration of P on the prior austenite grain boundaries as revealed by Auger analysis of the fracture surface of the impact samples (From Z. Qu and K.H. Kuo, *Met. Trans.*, Vol 6A, p 1333 (1981))

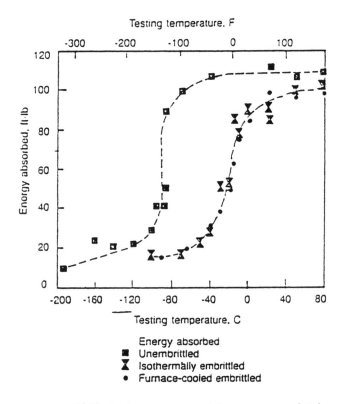

Energy absorbed
■ Unembrittled
⊠ Isothermally embrittled
● Furnace-cooled embrittled

Shift in impact transition curve to higher
temperature as a result of TE produced in SAE 3140
steel by isothermal holding and furnace cooling
through the critical range.

Fig. 5-68   The effect of isothermal aging or of cooling slowly on the development of TE in a 3140 steel. (From
same source as Fig. 5-49)

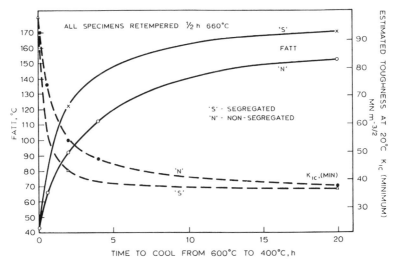

Fig. 5-69 The effect of cooling rate from the aging temperature on the increase in the fracture appearance transition temperature, see Fig. 5-7. (From same source as Fig. 5-62)

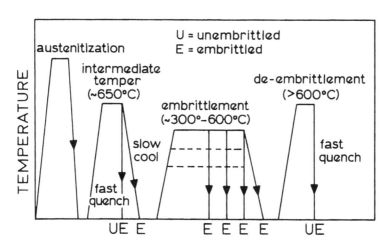

Fig. 5-70 Schematic diagram showing the heat treatments which will develop TE, and the reversal of TE by a de-embrittlement heat treatment. (From B.L. Eyre, B.C. Edwards, and J.M. Tichmarsh, p 246 in *Advances in Physical Metallurgy with Applications to Steels,* The Metals Society, London, (1982))

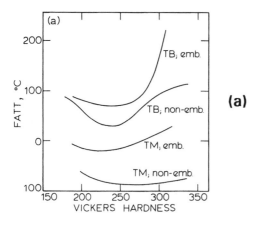

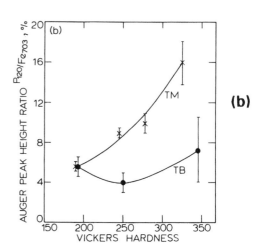

Fig. 5-71   Data showing the reversibility of TE for structures prior to aging of tempered martensite and of tempered bainite. (From B.L. Eyre, B.C. Edwards, and J.M. Tichmarsh, p 246 in *Advances in Physical Metallurgy with Applications to Steels,* The Metals Society, London (1982))

Table 5-3   The effects of alloying elements on tempering of steels. (From *Metals Handbook,* 10th edition, Vol 1, *Properties and Selection: Irons, Steels and High-Performance Alloys,* ASM International, Materials Park, Ohio (1990))

Manganese increases the hardness of tempered martensite by retarding the coalescence of carbides, which prevent grain growth in the ferrite matrix. These effects cause a substantial increase in the hardness of tempered martensite as the percentage of manganese in the steel increases.

Nickel has a relatively small effect on the hardness of tempered martensite, which is essentially the same at all tempering temperatures. Because nickel is not a carbide former, its influence is considered to be due to a weak solid-solution strengthening.

Copper is precipitated out when steel is heated to about 425-650°C (800-1200°F) and thus can provide a degree of precipitation hardening.

Silicon increases the hardness of tempered martensite at all tempering temperatures. Silicon also has a substantial retarding effect on softening at 316°C (600°F), and has been attributed to the inhibiting effect of silicon on the conversion of ε-carbide to cementite.
Molybdenum retards the softening of martensite at all tempering temperatures. Above 540°C (1000°F), molybdenum partitions to the carbide phase and thus keeps the carbide particles small and numerous. In addition, molybdenum reduces susceptibility to tempering embrittlement.

Chromium, like molybdenum, is a strong carbide-forming element that can be expected to retard the softening of martensite at all temperatures. Also, by substituting chromium for some of the iron in cementite, the coalescence of carbides is retarded.

Vanadium is a stronger carbide former than molybdenum and chromium and can therefore be expected to have a much more potent effect at equivalent alloy levels. The strong effect of vanadium is probably due to the formation of an alloy carbide that replaces cementite-type carbides at high tempering temperatures and persists as a fine dispersion up to the A_1 temperature.

Tungsten is also a carbide former and behaves like molybdenum in simple steels. Tungsten has been proposed as a substitute for molybdenum in reduced-activation ferritic steels for nuclear applications.

Titanium, niobium, and zirconium should behave like vanadium because they are strong carbide formers.

Boron has no effect on the tempering characteristics of martensite, but a detrimental effect on toughness can result from the transformation to nonmartensitic products.

Chapter 6

Austenitization of Steels

Introduction

Austenitization is the heat treatment of steel in the austenite region, and it is conducted for two reasons. One is to obtain austenite as a necessary precursor for heat treatment, and this is the main emphasis of the chapter. The other is to chemically homogenize the steel, so that concentration gradients formed during solidification upon casting are minimized. This treatment is usually accomplished at a much higher temperature than used for austenitizing for subsequent heat treatment. However, if it is improperly done, the structure may be affected in the subsequent austenitizing treatments. Therefore, a brief examination of austenitization for chemical homogenization is given before the main thrust of the chapter, which deals with austenitizing prior to heat treating.

Dendritic Segregation in Steels

Formation of dendrites

The process of solidification of steels involves the formation of crystals (or *grains*) in the liquid, and their growth. The crystals take on an irregular shape, called *dendrites*, as shown in Fig. 6-1. The crystals grow until they come into contact, then the remaining liquid between them freezes. Each crystal will have a different crystallographic orientation than that of its neighbor with which it comes into contact, which creates a grain boundary between them. As shown in Fig. 6-2, the shape of this boundary may not clearly reveal the actual shape of the dendrite as it grew during solidification.

In steels, the crystals can nucleate homogeneously inside the liquid, but usually they form around insoluble solid particles (e.g., high melting temperature oxides), and this point is examined later in this chapter. They also will tend to nucleate along the cold walls of the containing mold, as shown in Fig. 6-3, forming long *columnar grains*.

Process of dendritic segregation

In most alloys and in steels, as the crystals form and grow in the liquid, each layer of solid that forms on the surface has a different chemical composition than the previous layer. If the crystals have the dendritic morphology, this is called *dendritic segregation* or *coring*. Its origin is depicted using the following description.

Consider the system A-B having the phase diagram shown in Fig. 6-4. If an alloy containing 30% B is cooled sufficiently slowly from the liquid so that equilibrium is attained, then at any temperature the phases present and their chemical composition (%B) are given by the phase diagram. Thus freezing begins at temperature T_0, and the first crystal to form has a composition of 10% B. As cooling progresses and the crystal grows, its chemical composition will change. Thus at temperature T_1, the crystal will contain 20% B, and if equilibrium is attained, the crystal will have this composition uniformly. The liquid will contain 57% B. When freezing is complete, the crystal must have the composition of the alloy, 30% B. Thus at temperature T_2, the alloy is completely frozen, and the crystals will each contain 30% B and each will have the B atoms and A atoms dispersed randomly on the lattice sites to give locally everywhere 30% B. This process is depicted schematically in Fig. 6-5. Note that as each layer is frozen on the crystal, some of the B atoms must diffuse into the center of the crystal to maintain a composition at the value given by the phase boundary on the phase diagram.

Thus in Fig. 6-5, when the last liquid freezes, shown to contain about 70% B, the excess B atoms must diffuse in the crystal to the center to establish a uniform composition. This assumes equilibrium cooling. An important consideration here is whether the cooling rate which occurs in the solidification of commercial ingots is too rapid to allow equilibrium to be established at each temperature. If this cannot occur, the following description illustrates what will happen. Consider again a 30% B alloy cooled from the liquid, and let the first crystal to form have the composition 10% B (see Fig. 6-6). In Fig. 6-6a, the crystal is shown to develop side branches to simulate the dendritic morphology. (Only one half of the crystal is depicted.) Let the temperature decrease from T_0 to T_1, and assume that the layer that forms on the surface has the equilibrium composition of 20% B given by the phase diagram at T_1 (Fig. 6-6f). Also assume that cooling is so rapid that the center of the crystal does not change chemical composition, i.e., no solid state diffusion occurs. In the liquid, where diffusion is more rapid, the chemical composition is assumed to follow the phase diagram. When the temperature reaches T_2, under equilibrium conditions freezing would be complete. However, at T_2, the crystal has a composition gradient, being 10% B in the center and 30% B on the outside layer. Thus the average composition is less than that of the alloy, 30% B, and hence freezing cannot be complete. Thus layers increasingly richer (>30% B) continue to form on the crystal surface, until temperature T_3 is reached, at which the average composition of the crystal is 30% B. Note that the last layer to form contains 40% B, and the crystal has a composition gradient across it (Fig. 6-6e). This is *dendritic segregation*.

Figure 6-7 depicts the growth of two dendrites in which dendritic segregation is occurring. When freezing is complete, the two crystals have touched, and the den-

dritic shape of the crystals as they were growing in the liquid is not apparent from the geometry of the crystal boundary. However, the B rich (>30% B) and B poor (<30% B) regions are present in each crystal. If a sample of the material is polished and etched with a chemical which has a reaction rate which is sensitive to the amount of A and B present locally, then a variation in elevation is formed. Upon examining this polished and etched surface with a microscope, the amount of light reflected back to the observer depends on this topology, and hence dark and light regions are seen which are associated with the local chemical segregation. This is depicted in Fig. 6-8a, where the dendrite shape is revealed. The shape depends upon the plane of cut across the dendrites. The side arms of the dendrites may be revealed (Fig. 6-8a) or the cross-section of the dendrite arms (Fig. 6-8b). Figure 6-9 shows a typical microstructure. The dendritically segregated structure that is revealed is called a *cored* structure, and the process of dendritic segregation is sometimes called *coring*.

Dendritic segregation in steels

Figure 6-9 shows a microstructure exemplifying a cored structure in cast steels. In the case of carbon and alloy steels, the hardenability of local regions is dependent upon the degree of chemical segregation, and thus the

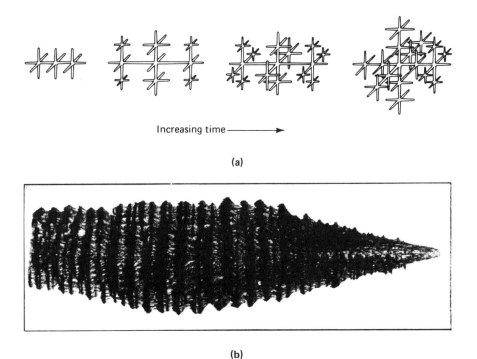

Increasing time ⟶

(a)

(b)

Fig. 6-1   (a) Schematic illustration of the growth of a dendritic crystal. (b) Photograph of a large, 9 inch long, dendrite which formed in a steel. (Photograph from A. Sauver, *The Metallography and Heat Treatment of Iron and Steel*, 4th edition, The University Press, Cambridge, London (1935))

microstructure formed will depend on this segregation and on the cooling rate after solidification as the austenite subsequently decomposes. For example, the amount of pearlite and primary ferrite formed will depend upon the carbon content. However, as will be discussed below, the high diffusion rate of carbon allows its easy dispersion during dendrite growth, so no chemical segregation of carbon occurs, but the heavier elements (e.g., Ni, Mn, Cr) will segregate, and this produces local regions with variation in hardenability. The effect on the microstructure which forms is depicted in Fig. 6-10 where regions high and low in pearlite are formed. The variation across dendrite arms of the amount of Mn, Si, and Cr in a cast steel is shown in Fig. 6-11, and the corresponding microstructure shows dark regions associated with higher amounts of pearlite.

Austenitization to Remove Coring

Dendritic segregation (coring) can be removed by heating a steel to the austenite region and holding for a

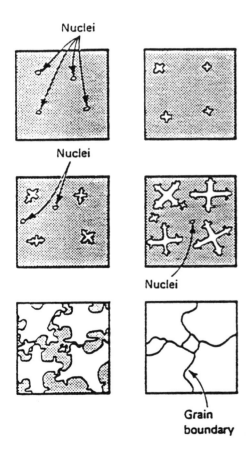

Fig. 6-2   Schematic illustration of the growth of dendritic crystals in a liquid. (C.R. Brooks, *Heat Treatment, Structure and Properties of Non-Ferrous Alloys*, American Society for Metals, Metals Park, Ohio (1986))

sufficient time for diffusion to occur. This is a *homogenization anneal* and is also called *soaking*. The relation between the time required and the distance over which diffusion must occur (e.g., the dendrite arm spacing) is given by a solution to Fick's diffusion equation. A simplified and useful form is

$$x \approx \sqrt{Dt}$$

where x is the diffusion distance, t is the time and D is the *diffusion coefficient* (chemical diffusivity) of the element of interest in austenite. Figure 6-12 shows a microstructure of a cored steel. The distance over which diffusion must occur to make the composition uniform is that from the region of low concentration to that of high concentration, which is the dendrite arm spacing. In Fig. 6-12, this is about 100 μm. Now if the steel with this microstructure is austenitized at 1100°C, and carbon is segregated, the approximate time to remove the segregation is

$$t \approx x^2/D = (0.01 \text{ cm})^2 / (8.8 \times 10^{-7} \text{ cm}^2/\text{sec.}) \approx 100 \text{ sec.}$$

Here the diffusion coefficient at 1100°C of carbon diffusion in austenite was used. Thus it is seen that if carbon is segregated, it becomes homogeneous at this temperature very quickly. This calculation actually shows that during solidification, which occurs in the range of 1500°C, carbon will not chemically segregate.

However, dendritic segregation will occur for the slower diffusing elements (e.g., Cr, Mo), since these elements have a much lower chemical diffusivity in austenite than does carbon. Thus to remove the type of segregation shown in Fig. 6-11, the calculation gives (using a D value for Ni diffusing in Fe at 1400°C)

$$t \approx x^2/D = (0.01 \text{ cm}) / (1.2 \times 10^{-9} \text{ cm}^2/\text{sec.}) \approx 23 \text{ h}$$

This shows that a heat treatment will be required to remove the coring associated with the heavy elements, and that it can be achieved in a practical time (e.g., a few hours).

Of particular importance in reducing the required austenitizing time for homogenization is a reduction in the diffusion distance upon hot working. The time to remove the coring is related to the distance "x." If an ingot having a dendritic arm spacing of 20 μm is hot rolled to a reduction of thickness of 80%, then the distance x is decreased by 80%, and the diffusion time is reduced by about a factor of 1/3, since the distance is squared in the relation.

If the dendritic segregation is not removed during the homogenization anneal of the ingot, then it may be retained even during hot rolling. This may lead to a *banded structure*, as shown in Fig. 6-13. An object having such a structure will have isotropic mechanical properties which may have to be taken into account during the design of the component.

Ingot Segregation

Chemical segregation in castings can also occur on a coarser scale than that of dendritic segregation. Its origin is depicted in Fig. 6-14. Consider a steel containing $X_0\%$ carbon. If during solidification the crystals nucleate on the walls of the cold mold, their initial chemical composition will be given by X_1. As they grow, this composition at the surface will remain at this value if diffusion in the solid is negligible. The chemical composition of the liquid at the liquid-solid interface is greater than X_0, as shown in Fig. 6-14. This creates a region of high carbon content in the liquid at the interface which travels ahead of the solid as the crystals grow. When the crystals growing from each side of the mold wall meet at the center of the ingot, the last liquid to freeze will have a carbon content above the value X_0. Hence the frozen ingot will have along the center line a high carbon content, and along the external surface a low carbon content.

The removal of the ingot segregation is not practical since the diffusion distance is usually too great. This can be shown by again using the diffusion equation $x \approx \sqrt{Dt}$. Taking a half-thickness of an ingot to be 20 cm, then at 1200°C the time for homogenization of carbon is

$$t \approx x^2/D = (20 \text{ cm}) / (3.3 \times 10^{-6} \text{ cm}^2 / \text{sec.} = 1.2 \times 10^8$$
$$\text{sec.} = 34,000 \text{ h}$$

Gross segregation of the slower diffusion elements (e.g., Cr, Mo) will also occur, and removal of their uneven distribution is also impractical.

Grain Growth

The boundary separating grains (crystals) in a polycrystalline material consists of a region of crystallographic mismatch, which has a higher energy than the bulk crystal. Thus a reduction in the amount of grain boundary area will reduce the energy of the material, which is the driving force for grain growth. Certain grain boundaries move, which is accomplished by atoms on one side of the boundary taking up the crystallographic

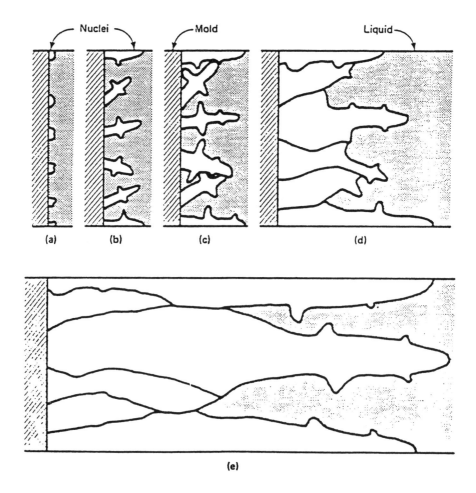

Fig. 6-3   Schematic illustration of the formation of columnar grains. (From same source as Fig. 6-2)

configuration of the atoms of the neighboring grain. The process is depicted in Fig. 6-15.

Figure 6-16 shows microstructures which illustrate the increase in grain size with annealing time. Figure 6-17 shows the effect of both austenitizing time and temperature on the austenite grain size in pure iron. Note that the higher the annealing temperature and the longer the time, the larger the grains.

The rate of grain growth is quite sensitive to the chemical composition, especially in pure materials. It also is sensitive to the presence of second phase particles, which usually retard grain growth. This is illustrated in Fig. 6-18, where the movement of the boundaries is restricted where they have encountered particles during their movement. This tends to stabilize the grain size.

Formation of Austenite

Austenite forms in the beginning microstructure by a nucleation and growth process. During its initial formation, the austenite has a chemical composition heterogeneity, since it forms from a two phase structure of low carbon ferrite and high carbon Fe₃C, which requires a finite time to disappear. Once the structure is all austenite, then the austenite grains grow, which occurs simultane-ously with the homogenization of the austenite. To introduce the process of austenite formation, its isothermal formation is described first. Then its formation during continuous heating to an austenitizing temperature is examined; this is the type of heating which actually occurs in heat treating practice.

Isothermal formation of austenite

The formation of austenite can be displayed as a time-temperature-transformation (TTT) diagram, just as in Chapter 2 the decomposition of austenite was described. An important difference is in the kinetics of the transformation. In the decomposition of austenite, as the temperature of transformation decreases the rate of formation of pearlite increases, but then decreases as the atom mobility becomes too restricted. In the decomposition of pearlite to austenite upon heating into the austenite region, increasing temperature continually favors an increasing atom mobility, so that the rate of formation of austenite shows a continuous increase with increasing transformation temperature.

Determining the TTT diagram for the formation of austenite can be carried out by heating samples very quickly to an austenitizing temperature, and monitoring the transformation at this temperature. This process is

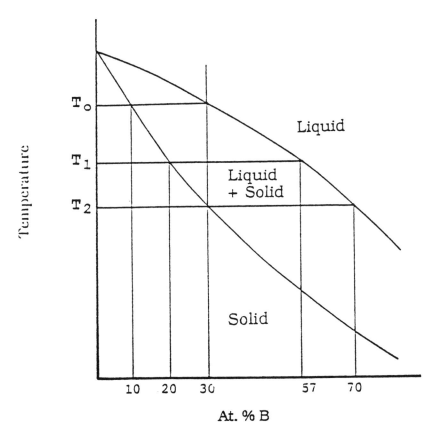

Fig. 6-4   Schematic illustration of the chemical composition of a crystal as freezing occurs. See text for details

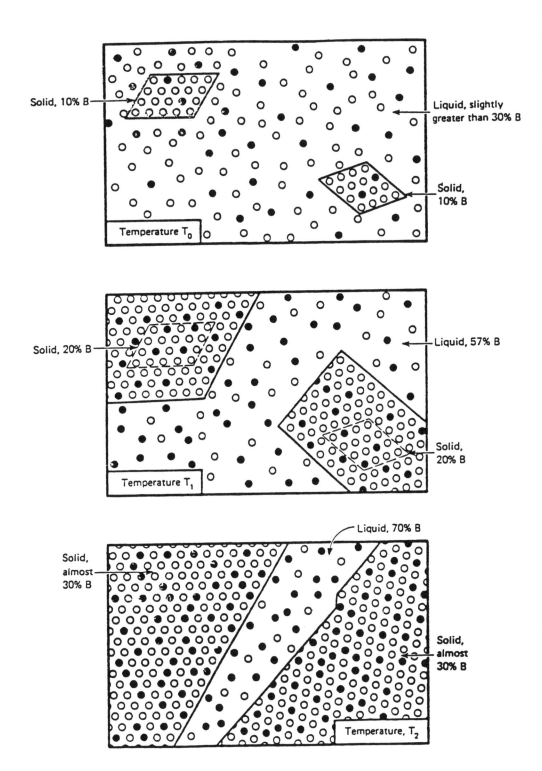

Fig. 6-5 Schematic illustration of the changes in chemical composition of crystals during equilibrium solidification. See text for details. (From same source as in Fig. 6-2)

then repeated at different temperatures. A microstructural method of determining the status of the formation of austenite is to quench samples from the austenitizing temperature at different times. If austenite has not begun to form, then the structure should be that of the beginning condition (e.g., pearlite). If the formation is complete, then the structure should be all martensite (austenite just before quenching). In between, the structure should be

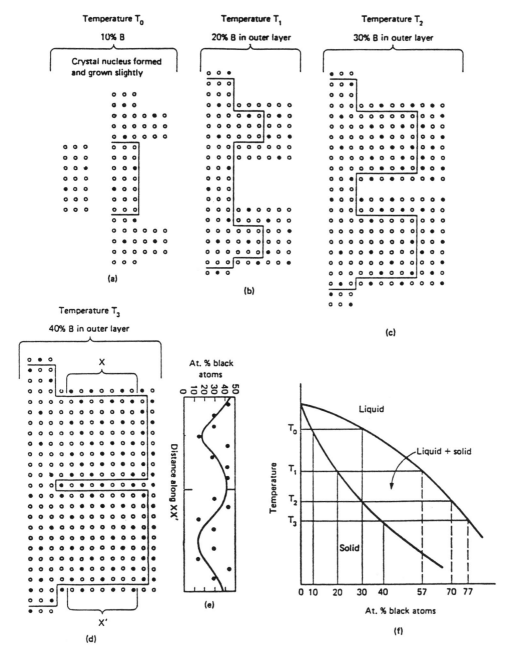

Fig. 6-6 Schematic illustration of the changes in chemical composition of a crystal during non-equilibrium solidification. See text for details. (From same source as in Fig. 6-2)

mixed. Figure 6-19 shows schematically how the TTT diagram is obtained from the microstructures where the beginning microstructure is pearlite.

Figure 6-20 shows the formation of austenite from pearlite. (The austenite formed upon heating has been converted to martensite by quenching to 25°C.) Note that the austenite (now martensite) regions have a mottled appearance. This is due to undissolved carbides. Eventu-

ally these carbides dissolve and chemically homogeneous austenite forms. Thus the TTT diagram in Fig. 6-21 shows a region during which the austenite contains undissolved carbides, then at longer time carbon inhomogeneities, then finally homogeneous austenite.

Figure 6-22 shows schematic TTT diagrams for three different carbon content steels. The beginning structure is pearlite (Fig. 6-22a), primary ferrite and pearlite (Fig.

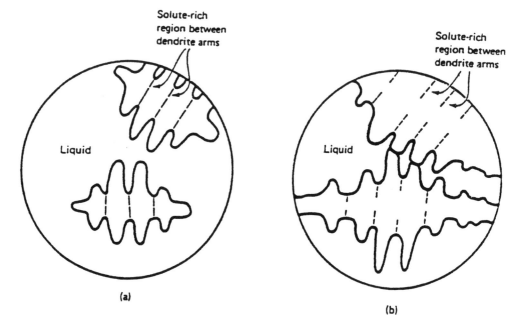

(a)

(b)

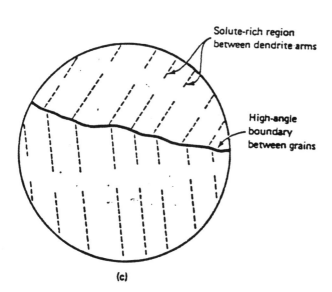

(c)

Fig. 6-7   Schematic illustration of the formation of a crystal boundary between two dendrites upon the completion of freezing. See text for details. (From same source as in Fig. 6-2)

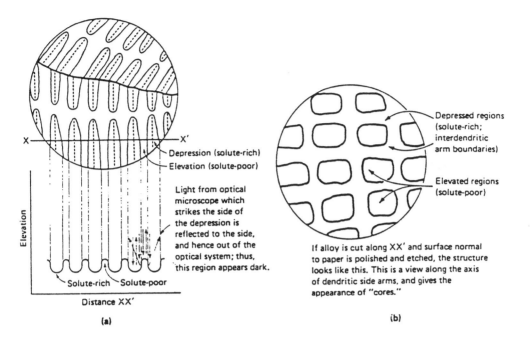

Fig. 6-8   Schematic illustration of the surface topology which develops upon etching an alloy in which dendritic segregation has occurred. See text for details. (From same source as in Fig. 6-2)

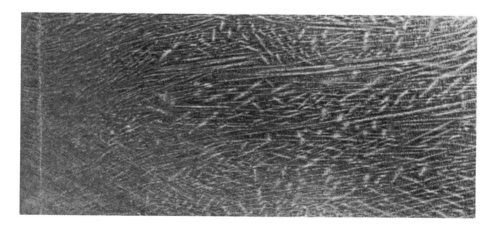

1017 steel, as strand cast. Macrostructure shows the outlines of the original columnar dendrites (light), which are oriented normal to the chill surface (left edge of macrograph). The vertical white line near the chill surface resulted from a disruption in solidification. Compare with   10% HNO₃ in H₂O. 4.75×. (J.R. Kilpatrick)

Fig. 6-9   Etched structure of a cast steel, showing dendrites. (B.L. Bramfitt, p 623, in *Metals Handbook*, 9th edition, Vol 9, *Metallography and Microstructure*, American Society for Metals, Metals Park, Ohio (1985))

6-22b) and primary Fe₃C and pearlite (Fig. 6-22c). The mechanism of the formation of austenite depends upon the starting structure. In pearlite, there are many sites for the reaction $\alpha + Fe_3C \rightarrow \gamma$ to begin. If the beginning structure consists of coarse carbides in ferrite, then the reaction will occur at the carbide-ferrite interface, as shown in Fig. 6-23.

Formation of austenite during continuous heating

The formation of austenite upon continuous heating is more complicated than upon isothermal transformation. The continuous rise in temperature produces an increasingly kinetically favorable situation for nucleation and growth of austenite and its homogenization. Upon

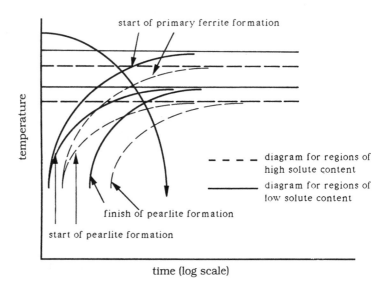

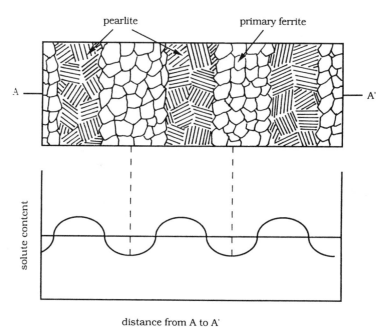

Fig. 6-10   Schematic illustration of the origin of microstructural bands due to chemical segregation. (C.R. Brooks, *Principles of the Austenitization of Steels*, Elsevier Applied Science, New York (1992))

heating slowly, the temperature at which austenite begins to form is given by the ferrite-austenite and Fe₃C-austenite phase boundaries. The temperature is shown on the Fe-C phase diagram in Fig. 6-24, and as indicated in Chapter 2, denoted by A_1 (eutectoid temperature), A_3 (ferrite-austenite boundary) and A_{cm} (iron carbide-austenite boundary). Upon cooling from austenite, these temperatures are depressed. They are denoted A_{r1}, A_{r3} and A_{rcm}; however, as indicated in

Chapter 2, they do not have fixed values but are dependent on the cooling rate.

These temperatures are also dependent on the heating rate. Figure 6-25 shows that for austenite forming from ferrite in pure iron, the effect is slight for heating rates up to 20,000°C/sec. However, the formation of austenite in steels is more sensitive to the heating rate. Figure 6-26 shows a continuous heating TTT diagram for the formation of austenite. Note that the more rapid heating rates

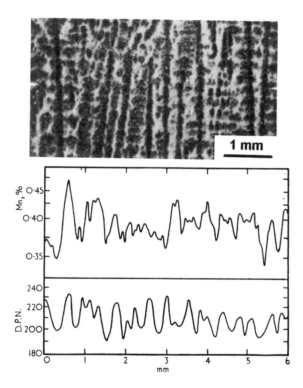

Fig. 6-11   Microstructure from a steel casting showing dendrites. The variation in the Mn content and microhardness (DPN) from a region along the mid-line of the micrograph is also shown. The dendritic segregation of Mn is revealed in the microstructure due to different amounts of primary α and pearlite present across the dendrites. (Adapted from R.G. Ward, *J. Iron and Steel Institute*, Vol 188, p 337 (1958))

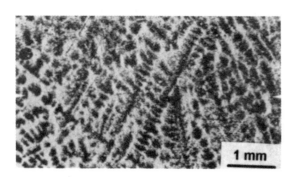

Fig. 6-12   Typical dendritic structure in a cast steel. (from same source as Fig. 6-11)

shift the temperature at which the transformations start to higher temperatures, but the effect is less for the heating curves corresponding to heating slowly. As for the case of isothermal formation of austenite, upon continuous heating when all austenite is present it is not initially chemically homogeneous, but eventually a high enough temperature (depending on the heating rate) is attained to homogenize it.

Austenite Grain Size: Austenite grain growth

When steels are austenitized, the austenite grain size when the structure is just completely austenite is usually between 0.06 and 0.02 mm (ASTM grain size number 5 and 8, respectively; see Appendix 17). This size range is rather irrespective of the steel composition and the starting microstructure, probably reflecting the numerous nucleation sites for austenite in all of these various microstructures.

After the beginning grain size is established, the grains should then grow. However, most steels while liquid are treated with additions to deoxidize the liquid steel, forming oxides (e.g., Al_2O_3). These steels are referred to as *deoxidized* or *killed*. These oxides form as very fine (e.g., 10 μm) particles which would normally rise in the liquid to the slag, but while small they remain suspended in the liquid. When the steel is cast into ingots, these particles are entrapped in the solid mass. After the ingot is homogenized, then rolled into usable shapes (e.g., 4 cm diameter rod), upon austenitization these particles are dispersed in the austenite which forms. The austenite grains begin to grow, but the particles inhibit their movement. Thus the grain size becomes stabilized.

In addition to the deoxidizers which serve as grain refiners, specific additions are also added to serve this purpose. These will form compounds (e.g., nitrides) which are stable at high austenitizing temperatures to retard grain growth.

The expected grain growth behavior is shown schematically in Fig. 6-27 for deoxidized 1080 steel. Figure 6-28 shows data for a specific steel. Note that grain coarsening does not begin until after 2 h at temperatures below 1000°C, and if austenitizing is carried out between 800 and 900°C, the grain size is constant for several hours. The behavior shown in Fig. 6-28 is found for most beginning microstructures, as shown in Fig. 6-29. The coarsening which eventually occurs is caused by either the particles dissolving in the austenite, or the coarsening of the particles so that they are too few to be effective in preventing grain growth.

The important point here is that deoxidized (killed) steel usually has an austenite grain size of between 6 and 8 ASTM number for common austenitizing temperatures and times. Thus when calculating hardenability (Chapter 3) an austenite grain size in this range can be comfortably used.

Effect of prior austenite grain size on mechanical properties

The prior austenite grain size can have a significant effect on some mechanical properties, especially toughness, even though the austenite has transformed on cooling to other structures. If samples of a steel are austenitized at a range of high temperatures to develop various austenite grain sizes, then all heat treated to give the same structure (e.g., martensite) and the same hardness, the toughness may be quite sensitive to the austenite grain size. This is illustrated in Fig. 6-30. It is seen that the toughness is lowered as the size of the prior austenite grains increases (smaller ASTM grain size number). Thus, a "fine" prior austenite grain size is desirable. However, for conventionally austenitized steels, this is

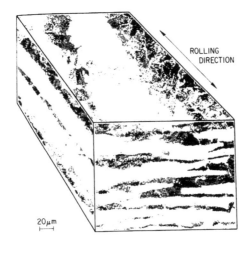

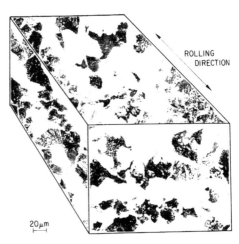

Fig. 6-13 Microstructures showing banding in two steels. The dark regions are pearlite and the white primary ferrite. (From R.A. Grange, *Met. Trans.*, Vol 2, p 417 (1971))

limited to between ASTM 6 and 8 (see previous paragraph).

Heating to the Austenite Region

In austenitizing steels, a finite time is required to attain the austenitizing temperature, and the process of the formation of the austenite will depend upon the heating rate. This was depicted in Fig. 6-26. These heating curves are for heating at an approximately constant heating rate. In actuality, the rate of heating decreases as the temperature of the steel part approaches the temperature of the furnace. The actual heating curve which is followed depends upon the heat transfer process, and the mechanisms described in Chapter 4 apply also to heating. However, austenitizing is usually carried out in air, so the heat transfer film coefficient "h" is not high compared to that of, say, water upon quenching. The methods to estimate

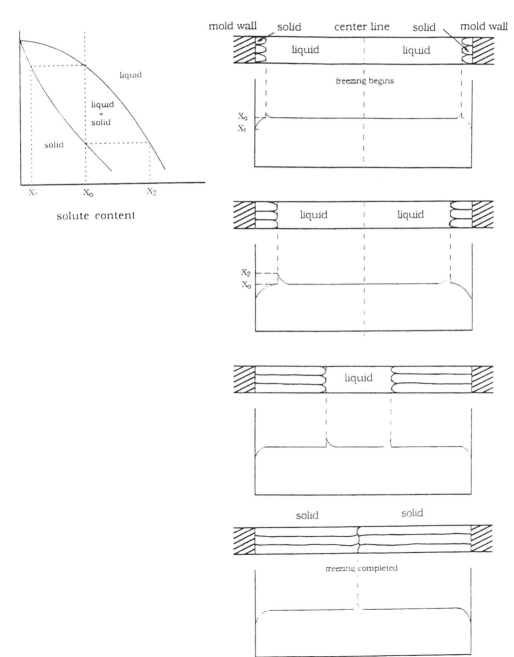

Fig. 6-14   Schematic illustration of the formation of ingot segregation. (From same source as Fig. 6-10)

the cooling curve described in Chapter 4 can be used to estimate the heating curve for a given severity of quench H value.

Figure 6-31 shows typical temperature-time heating curves. The marked change in the slope of the curve is associated with heat absorption upon the initial formation of austenite. The heating curves have the expected rela-

tive profile, with smaller steel parts and locations at and closer to the surface heating faster.

Heating curves can be placed on diagrams such as in Fig. 6-26 to estimate the austenitizing process. Although the TTT diagram for the formation of austenite for a specific steel should be used, the diagram in Fig. 6-26 and the heating curves in Fig. 6-31 will be used to demon-

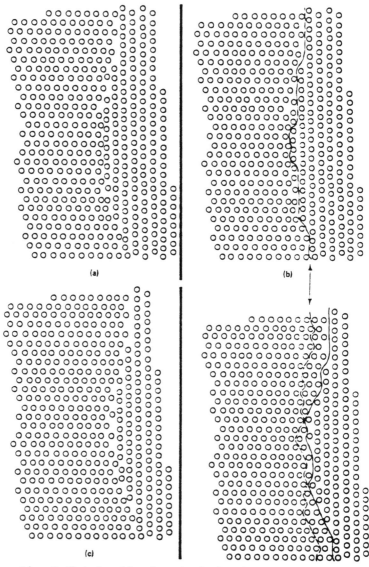

(a)

(b)

(c)

(d)

Schematic illustration of boundary migration in grain growth. (a) and (b) are the same, except that in (b) the boundary is marked. In (c) the boundary has moved to the right as atoms on the right of the boundary have taken up the orientation of the atoms of the grain on the left of the boundary. Thus, the boundary moves toward the right, and the grain on the left increases in size. In (d), the original boundary is shown dashed.

Fig. 6-15   Schematic illustration of a grain boundary, and the movement of atoms from one grain to the other corresponding to grain growth. (From same source as Fig. 6-2)

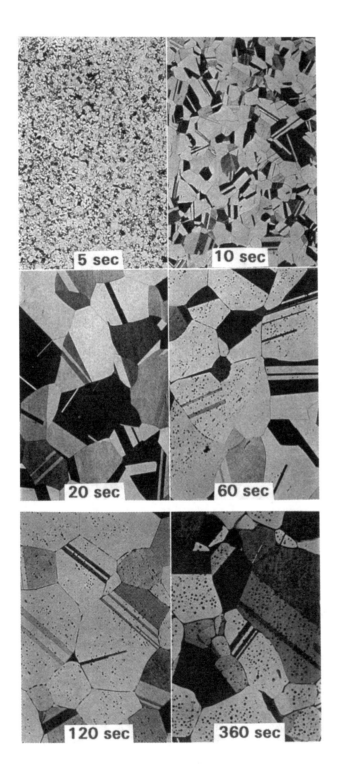

Fig. 6-16 Micrographs showing grain growth at 910°C in a Cu-30% Zn brass (single phase) alloy. (Adapted from J.M. Burke, *Trans. AIME*, Vol 180, p 73 (1949))

strate the expected austenitization process. Using the curves in Fig. 6-31 for the 50 mm diameter bars, homogeneous austenite has formed by the time the bars attain the furnace temperature of 1000°C (1830°F). Thus the determining factor in austenitizing is to ensure that the time is adequate for the steel to reach the furnace tem-

perature. At this time, homogeneous austenite will have formed during the heating in the austenite region. Also, as discussed above, for deoxidized steels the austenite grain size will be about ASTM 6-8 for up to several hours if the austenitizing temperature is not too high. Note in Fig. 6-31 that 0.5 to 2 hours is an adequate

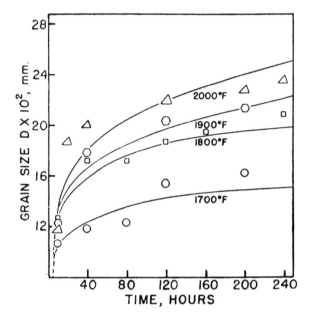

Fig. 6-17   Austenite grain size of pure iron as a function of austenitizing time and temperature. (H.B. Probst and M.J. Sinnott, *Trans. AIME*, Vol 203, p 215 (1955))

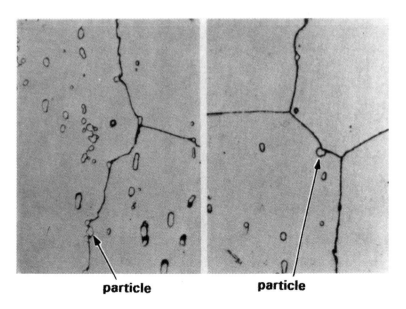

Fig. 6-18   Microstructures showing the retardation of grain boundary movement by particles. (T. Gladman, *Proc. Roy. Soc.*, Vol 294A, p 298 (1966))

austenitizing time for steels about 4 inches in thickness to attain a uniform temperature.

Practical Austenitizing Temperatures

The austenitizing temperatures used commercially are chosen to minimize the energy required to heat the furnace and the steel components and to minimize oxidation of the steel, which means using the lowest temperature and time. For the steel with the TTT diagram in Fig. 6-26, homogeneous austenite is achieved above about 860°C for heating times to attain this temperature of about 100 sec. or greater. It is clear in this case that there is no need to austenitize above about 860°C. Actual heating curves, for heating in air, such as those in Fig. 6-31, show that holding the steel component in the austenitizing furnace for about one hour will be sufficient to heat the steel to the austenitizing temperature and to establish a uniform temperature in the steel part.

This temperature depends upon the carbon and alloy content, which affect the equilibrium transformation temperatures. Low carbon (e.g., 0.2% C) steels require a higher austenitizing temperature than higher carbon steels. This is shown schematically in Fig. 6-32, where the range of austenitizing temperatures decreases as the carbon content increases. Note that above the eutectoid carbon content of 0.8% C, the recommended austenitizing temperature remains constant and in the two phase austenite + Fe₃C region. Thus for these high carbon steels, austenitizing is conducted in this two phase region and the microstructure to be heat treated contains carbides. The carbides are unaffected by the subsequent cooling, as only the austenite transforms.

Alloy content also affects the temperature of the equilibrium phase boundaries of the austenite region. If the element lowers the temperature of the boundaries, then a lower austenitizing temperature may be used. However, in some alloy steels alloy carbides (not Fe₃C) are present, and during austenitization these may be more difficult to dissolve and the elements more difficult to disperse (due to the lower diffusion rate compared to carbon) in the austenite to make it chemically homogeneous. Thus a higher austenitizing temperature may be required. Table 6-1 lists commonly used austenitizing temperatures for some plain carbon and alloy steels. Again, it is pointed out that the austenitizing time will be that required to ensure that the steel component attains this temperature; a time longer than this is not necessary.

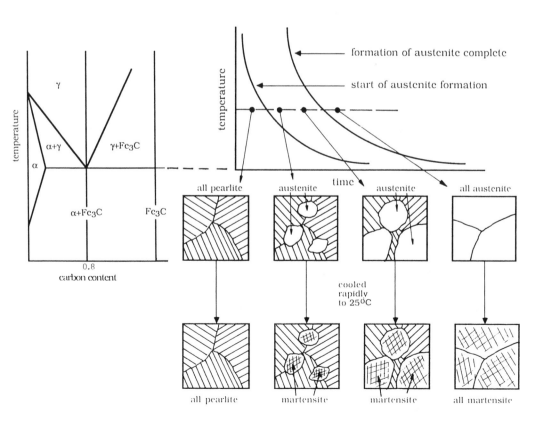

Fig. 6-19   Schematic illustration of the formation of austenite from pearlite. (Adapted from same source as Fig. 6-10)

Further Reading

Four books are listed which discuss the process of austenitization in more detail than presented in this chapter.

- K.E. Thelning, *Steel and Its Heat Treatment*, 2nd edition, Butterworths, Boston (1986)

- G. Krauss, *Steels: Heat Treatment and Processing Principles*, ASM International, Materials Park, Ohio (1990)
- A.K. Sinha, *Ferrous Physical Metallurgy*, Butterworths, Boston (1989)
- C.R. Brooks, *Principles of the Austenitization of Steels*, Elsevier Applied Science, London (1992)

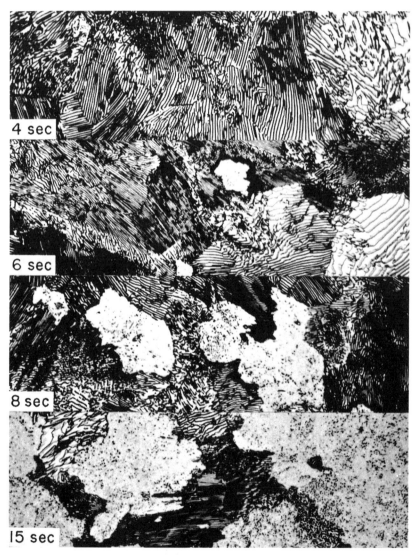

Fig. 34. Microstructures showing successive stages in formation of austenite from pearlite. 1000 ×. (Vilella)

Fig. 6-20   Microstructures showing the formation of austenite from pearlite. (Adapted from M.A. Grossmann and E.C. Bain, *Principles of Heat Treatment*, 5th edition, American Society for Metals, Metals Park, Ohio (1964))

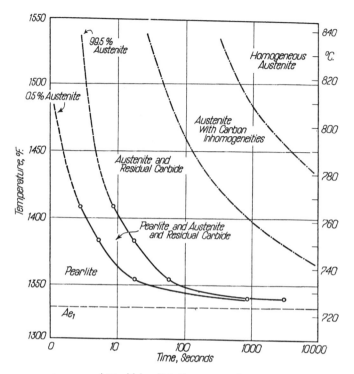

Austenitizing Rate-Temperature Curves for Commercial Simple-Carbon Eutectoid Steel. Prior Treatment—Normalized from 1610 Degrees Fahr. (875 Degrees Cent.). Initial Structure —Fine Pearlite. First Curve at Left Shows Beginning Disappearance of Pearlite. Second Curve Shows Final Disappearance of Pearlite. Third Curve Shows Final Disappearance of Carbide. Fourth Curve Shows Final Disappearance of Carbon Concentration Gradients.

Fig. 6-21 An isothermal TTT diagram for the formation of austenite. (From B.L. Bramfitt, *ASM Handbook*, Vol 4, p 42, *Heat Treating*, ASM International, Materials Park, Ohio (1991))

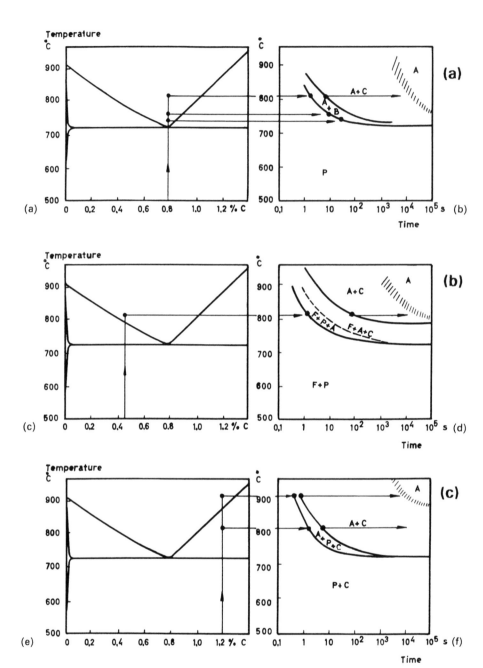

Structural transformations on heating steels containing: (a) 0·80% C; (b) 0·80% C; (c) 0·45% C; (d) 0·45% C; (e) 1·2% C; (f) 1·2% C. Schematic representation (after Rose and Strassburg[1])

A = austenite, B = bainite, C = cementite, F = ferrite, P = pearlite

Fig. 6-22 Schematic isothermal TTT diagrams for three different carbon content steels. (K.E. Thelning, *Ste and Its Heat Treatment*, Butterworths, London (1975))

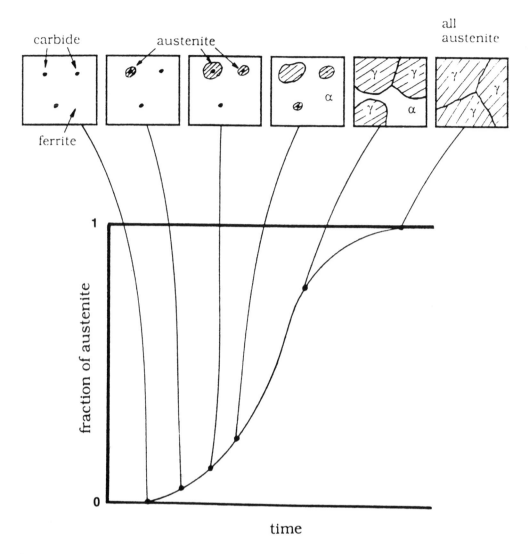

Fig. 6-23   Schematic illustration of the formation of austenite in a structure of carbides and ferrite. (From same source as Fig. 6-10)

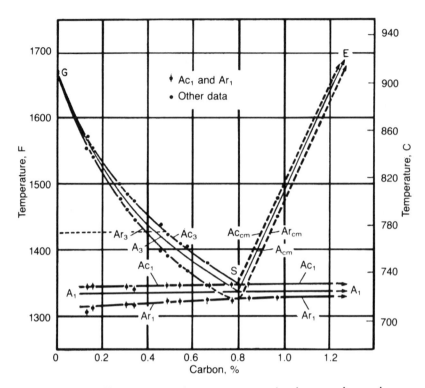

The transformation temperatures in the pure iron-carbon alloys as influenced by heating and cooling at 0.125° C per minute. The probable equilibrium temperatures for the several phases are also shown.

Fig. 6-24   Part of the Fe-C phase diagram showing the equilibrium phase boundaries and boundaries for phase transformations upon cooling (subscript r) and upon heating (subscript c). (Adapted from R.F. Mehl and C. Wells, *Metals Technology* (June 1937))

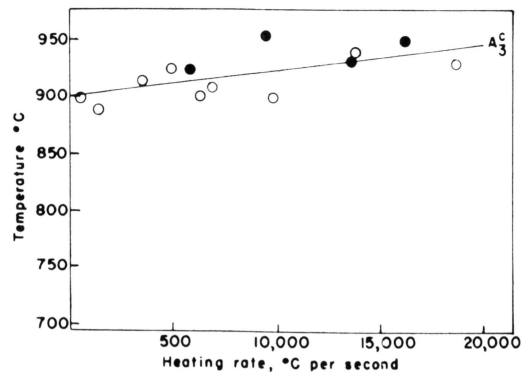

Fig. 6-25 The effect of heating rate on the temperature at which ferrite transforms to austenite in pure Fe. (Adapted from W.L. Haworth and J.G. Parr, *Trans. ASM*, Vol 58, p. 476 (1965))

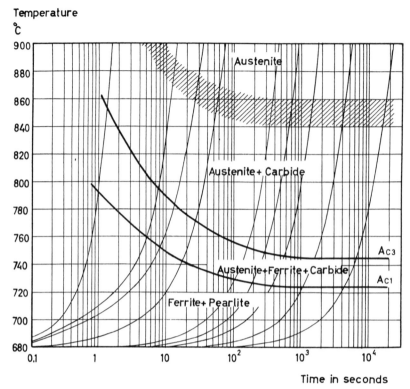

Temperature
°C

Transformation diagram for continuous heating. Dissolution of ferrite and lamellar pearlite in a 0·70% C steel

Fig. 6-26 The effect of heating rate on the formation of austenite for a steel of about 0.8% C, containing pearlite and a small amount of primary ferrite. (Adapted from A. Rose and V. Strassburg, *Stahl und Eisen*, Vol 76, p 976 (1956))

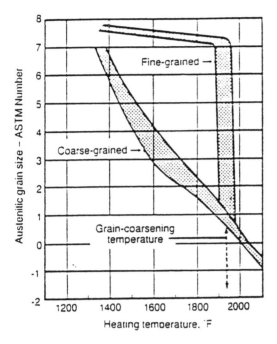

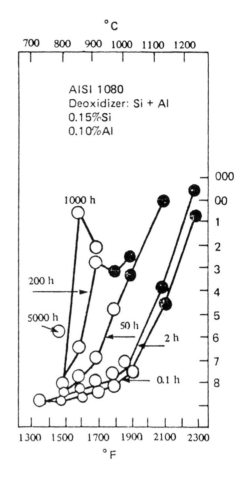

Fig. 6-27   Schematic illustration of the effect of austenitizing temperature on the austenite grain size for a deoxidized fine grained and a non-deoxidized steel. (G.F. Melloy, *Austenite Grain Size—Its Control and Effects*, Metals Engineering Institute, American Society for Metals, Metals Park, Ohio (1968))

Fig. 6-28   Effect of austenitizing time and temperature on the austenite grain size. (Adapted from O.O. Miller, *Trans. ASM*, Vol 43, p. 260 (1951))

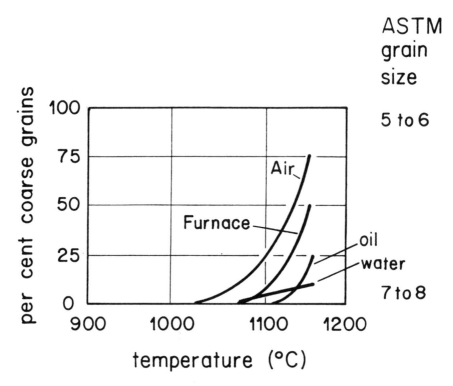

Fig. 6-29   The effect of temperature and prior heat treatment on the austenite grain size of 4615 steel. The austenitizing time was 8 hours. The different prior heat treatments produced different beginning microstructures (e.g., furnace cooling—primary ferrite and pearlite; water quenching—martensite). (Adapted from M.A. Grossmann, in *Grain Size Symposium*, American Society for Metals, Metals Park, Ohio (1954))

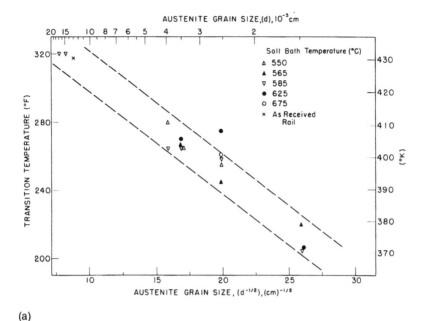

(a)

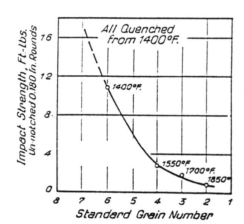

(b)

Fig. 6-30   (a) Effect of prior austenite grain size on toughness as measured by the transition temperature in pearlitic, eutectoid steels. (b) Impact energy (measured at 25°C) as a function of prior austenite grain size. ((a) J.M. Hyzak and I.M. Bernstein, *Met. Trans.*, Vol 7A, p 1217 (1976). (b) E.S. Davenport and E.C. Bain, *Trans. ASM*, Vol 22, p 879 (1934))

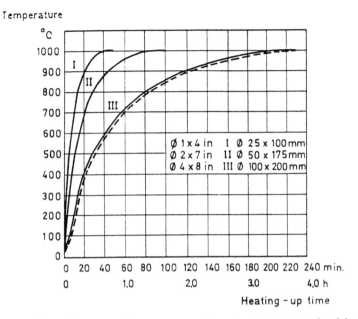

Time-temperature curves for steel bars packed in cast-iron chips, heated in a muffle furnace at 1000 °C. Full line: temperature at surface; Dashed line: temperature at centre.

Fig. 6-31   Heating curves for different size steel parts. (From same source as Fig. 6-22)

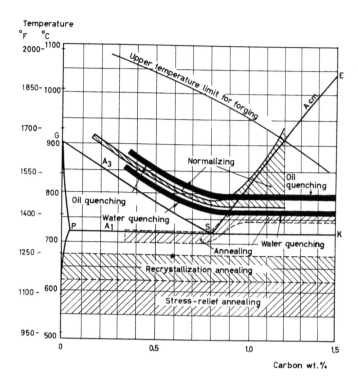

Fig. 6-32 Iron-carbon phase diagram showing temperature range for austenitizing for subsequent heat treatment. (From same source as Fig. 6-22)

Table 6-1 Recommended austenitizing temperatures for several steels. (From *ASM Handbook*, Vol 4, *Heat Treating*, ASM International, Materials Park, OH (1991))

Steel	Temperature °C	°F	Steel	Temperature °C	°F	Steel	Temperature °C	°F
			1146	800-845	1475-1550	50B60	800-845	1475-1550
Carbon steels			1151	800-845	1475-1550	5130	830-855	1525-1575
1025	855-900	1575-1650	1536	815-845	1500-1550	5132	830-855	1525-1575
1030	845-870	1550-1600	1541	815-845	1500-1550	5135	815-845	1500-1550
1035	830-855	1525-1575	1548	815-845	1500-1550	5140	815-845	1500-1550
1037	830-855	1525-1575	1552	815-845	1500-1550	5145	815-845	1500-1550
1038(a)	830-855	1525-1575	1566	855-885	1575-1625	5147	800-845	1475-1550
1039(a)	830-855	1525-1575				5150	800-845	1475-1550
1040(a)	830-855	1525-1575	**Alloy steels**			5155	800-845	1475-1550
1042	800-845	1475-1550	1330	830-855	1525-1575	5160	800-845	1475-1550
1043(a)	800-845	1475-1550	1335	815-845	1500-1550	51B60	800-845	1475-1550
1045(a)	800-845	1475-1550	1340	815-845	1500-1550	50100	775-800(c)	1425-1475(c)
1046(a)	800-845	1475-1550	1345	815-845	1500-1550	51100	775-800(c)	1425-1475(c)
1050(a)	800-845	1475-1550	3140	815-845	1500-1550	52100	775-800(c)	1425-1475(c)
1055	800-845	1475-1550	4037	830-855	1525-1575	6150	845-885	1550-1625
1060	800-845	1475-1550	4042	830-855	1525-1575	81B45	815-855	1500-1575
1065	800-845	1475-1550	4047	815-855	1500-1575	8630	830-870	1525-1600
1070	800-845	1475-1550	4063	800-845	1475-1550	8637	830-855	1525-1575
1074	800-845	1475-1550	4130	815-870	1500-1600	8640	830-855	1525-1575
1078	790-815	1450-1500	4135	845-870	1550-1600	8642	815-855	1500-1575
1080	790-815	1450-1500	4137	845-870	1550-1600	8645	815-855	1500-1575
1084	790-815	1450-1500	4140	845-870	1550-1600	86B45	815-855	1500-1575
1085	790-815	1450-1500	4142	845-870	1550-1600	8650	815-855	1500-1575
1086	790-815	1450-1500	4145	815-845	1500-1550	8655	800-845	1475-1550
1090	790-815	1450-1500	4147	815-845	1500-1550	8660	800-845	1475-1550
1095	790-815(a)	1450-1500(b)	4150	815-845	1500-1550	8740	830-855	1525-1575
			4161	815-845	1500-1550	8742	830-855	1525-1575
Free-cutting carbon steels			4337	815-845	1500-1550	9254	815-900	1500-1650
1137	830-855	1525-1575	4340	815-845	1500-1550	9255	815-900	1500-1650
1138	815-845	1500-1550	50B40	815-845	1500-1550	9260	815-900	1500-1650
1140	815-845	1500-1550	50B44	815-845	1500-1550	94B30	845-885	1550-1625
1141	800-845	1475-1550	5046	815-845	1500-1550	94B40	845-885	1550-1625
1144	800-845	1475-1550	50B46	815-845	1500-1550	9840	830-855	1525-1575
1145	800-845	1475-1550	50B50	800-845	1475-1550			

(a) Commonly used on parts where induction hardening is employed. All steels from SAE 1030 up may have induction hardening applications. (b) This temperature range may be employed for 1095 steel that is to be quenched in water, brine, or oil. For oil quenching, 1095 steel may alternatively be austenitized in the range 815 to 870°C (1500 to 1600°F). (c) This range is recommended for steel that is to be water quenched. For oil quenching, steel should be austenitized in the range 815 to 870°C (1500 to 1600°F)

Chapter 7

Annealing, Normalizing, Martempering and Austempering

Introduction

The previous chapters dealt with heat treating from the austenite region for hardening, whereby structures such as martensite formed. However, heat treatments which develop soft structures are sometimes required, such as for machining components prior to hardening. In this chapter, the heat treatments called annealing and normalizing are described, and the structures formed and the reasons for these treatments are examined. The chapter is concluded with a description of the special heat treatments martempering and austempering.

Annealing

In general, annealing can be considered heat treating to soften a metal or alloy, and this definition is applicable to steels. However, in heat treating steels there are different types of annealing, and care must be taken in distinguishing them. The common annealing processes for

steels are listed in Table 7-1, and are examined in the following sections.

Annealing of cold worked material

First, the general aspects of annealing a cold worked metal or alloy are reviewed. More detail is given in Chapter 8. When a metal or alloy is plastically deformed, and accompanying this deformation is an increase in strength, this is referred to as *work hardening* or *strain hardening*. The plastic deformation introduces lattice defects (e.g., dislocations) which produce an increase in the energy of the material, so that it is thermodynamically unstable. Thus, eventually the material will undergo structural changes to lower its energy. For most metals and alloys, for this to occur in a practical time (e.g., a few hours) requires heating the material above room temperature. The changes in hardness upon plastic deformation are exemplified by the curves in Fig. 7-1. If the 5% Zn alloy with 60% cold work (60% reduction in thickness in Fig. 7-1) is heated to 400°C, the change in hardness shown in Fig. 7-2 occurs. Note that the hardness de-

---

Table 7-1   Common types of annealing processes used on steels

- Annealing of cold worked material
    - Sometimes called recrystallization annealing
    - Heating is below eutectoid temperature (A_1)
- Stress relief annealing
    - Used to reduce residual stresses
    - Heating is below eutectoid temperature (A_1)
- Spheroidization annealing
    - Used to improve cold formability and machinability
    - May require several hours heating just below eutectoid temperature (A_1), or cycling just above and just below eutectoid temperature
- Full annealing
    - Used to produce material in soft condition
    - Heating to austenite, then cooling slowly (e.g., in a furnace, taking several hours)
    - Box annealing is full annealing in a special enclosure

creases drastically beginning at about 10 h, and that the hardness eventually reaches values similar to those before cold working. The heat treatment which produces such softening in cold worked materials is a common form of annealing.

The microstructural changes which occur during cold working are typified by the micrographs in Fig. 7-3. The grains (crystals) before cold working are *equiaxed*, each being about the same size. Cold working produces an elongation of the grains along the rolling direction. Also, in the etched microstructure striations begin to appear in the grains, which are *deformation bands* associated with the lattice defects which are forming.

Upon annealing, initially little change occurs in the microstructure as revealed by optical microscopy, or in the hardness, but some properties (e.g., electrical resistivity) show a change towards the value before cold working. This stage of annealing is called *recovery*. Eventually, small equiaxed, soft grains nucleate in the cold worked material (micrograph 2, Fig. 7-4), and this process is called *recrystallization*. With increased annealing time, these small grains grow (Fig. 7-4), consuming the cold worked matrix. Once recrystallization is complete,

there is no cold worked material remaining. The only continuing change is *grain growth* (see Chapter 6).

Figure 7-5 shows the microstructural changes upon annealing a low carbon steel in which the structure is almost all ferrite. In higher carbon steels, in which pearlite may be present, recrystallization occurs in the primary ferrite and also in the pearlitic ferrite.

In steels, annealing to produce recrystallization and accompanying softening is carried out below the eutectoid temperature, in the two phase ferrite + Fe₃C region, as shown in Fig. 7-6. The required time depends upon the steel (e.g., the amount of primary ferrite present), the annealing temperature, and the amount of cold work.

Stress relief annealing

In Chapter 4, the formation of residual thermal and transformation (e.g., formation of martensite) stresses was examined. Such stresses can also be due to cold working, machining and welding. These stresses can be reduced by heating in the two phase ferrite + Fe₃C region, a *stress relief annealing* treatment. The time and temperature used depend upon the steel, the magnitude of the stresses and the subsequent use of the steel component.

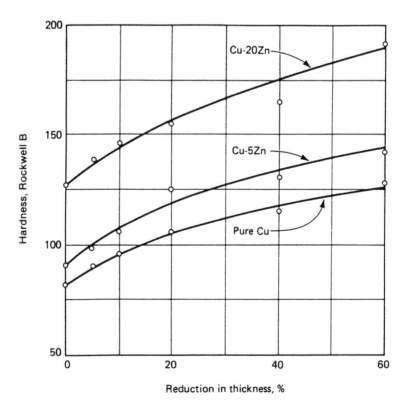

Fig. 7-1 Hardness as a function of reduction in thickness by rolling (at 20°C) for pure Cu and two Cu-Zn solid solution alloys. (From C.R. Brooks, *Heat Treatment, Structure and Properties of Non-Ferrous Alloys*, American Society for Metals, Metals Park, Ohio (1982))

Figure 7-7 shows an example of the reduction in residual stress upon annealing a steel.

Figure 7-6 shows the general range of temperatures used for stress relief annealing. Note that this is in the same range as used for tempering steels. It was shown in Chapter 5 that for many steels the effect of tempering time and temperature on tempered hardness can be represented parametrically by the relation T(c + log t), where T is the tempering temperature (in absolute temperature), t is the tempering time and c is a constant which depends upon the steel. Thus it is expected that the temperature and time for reduction in residual stress may be represented by a similar plot, as shown for a specific steel in Fig. 7-8. The response of this steel can also be represented by the curves in Fig. 7-9. As an example of the use of these curves, it is found from Fig. 7-9a that an anneal of one hour at 450°C results in about 50% stress relief. If the same level of stress relief is desired by using 400°C, the time required is obtained by drawing a vertical line from

the one hour/450°C point until the 400°C sloping curve is intersected, at which a time of 20 h is obtained.

It is pointed out that during a stress relief anneal, the structural changes which occur are those associated with tempering. Any martensite present will temper, and for other structures the carbides will spheroidize and coarsen.

Spheroidization anneal

For improved cold formability and machinability of steels, a *spheroidization anneal* is used, in which a structure of coarse carbides in ferrite is developed. A typical microstructure is shown in Fig. 7-10. The improvement of machinability by using a spheroidized structure is illustrated by the data in Fig. 7-11.

If the beginning microstructure is martensite, its decomposition precedes the coarsening which leads to the spheroidized structure. If the structure is bainite, then the fine carbides just spheroidize during the anneal. If the structure is pearlite, then the carbide plates spheroidize,

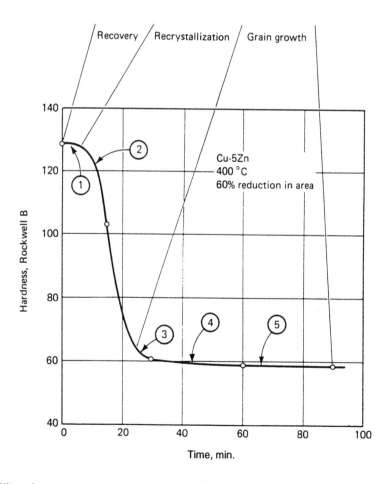

Fig. 7-2 Effect of annealing time at 400°C on the hardness of a Cu-5% Zn alloy cold worked 60%. (From same source as Fig. 7-1)

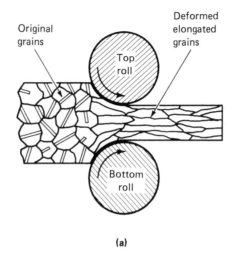

Original grains

Deformed elongated grains

Top roll

Bottom roll

(a)

0% cold work; 92 Rockwell B

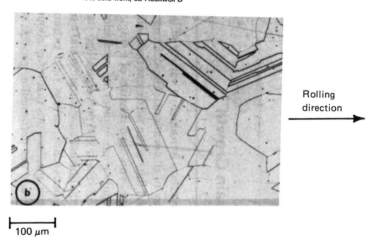

Rolling direction

⊢———⊣
100 μm

20% cold work; 120 Rockwell B

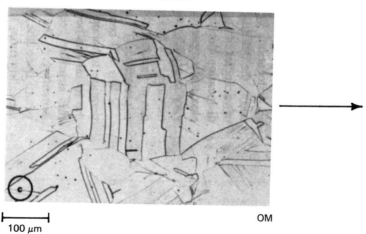

OM

⊢———⊣
100 μm

Fig. 7-3 Part 1 Microstructural changes associated with cold working a Cu-5% Zn alloy. (From same source as Fig. 7-1) *(continued)*

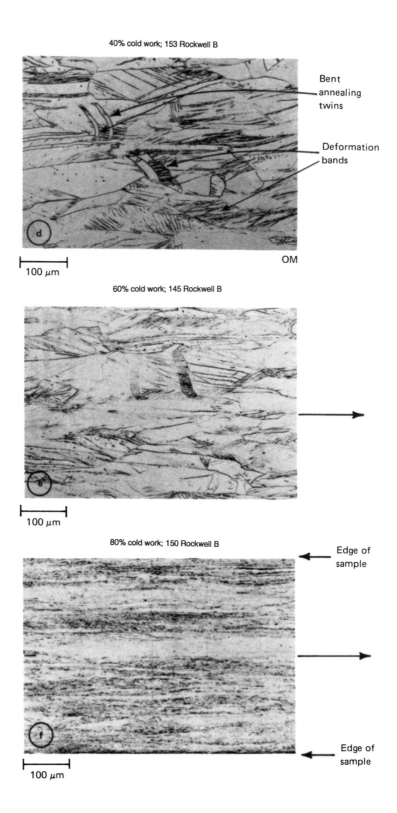

Fig. 7-3 Part 2 (continued) Microstructural changes associated with cold working a Cu-5% Zn alloy. (From same source as Fig. 7-1)

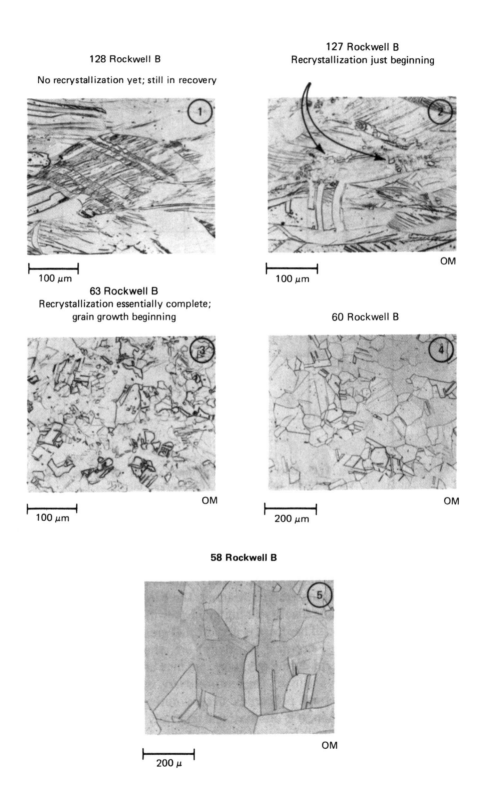

Fig. 7-4 Microstructural changes associated with annealing a 60% cold worked Cu-5% Zn alloy at 400°C. The numbers correspond to the times shown in Fig. 7-2. (From same source as Fig. 7-1)

then the structure coarsens. The development of a uniform distribution of coarse carbides in ferrite occurs more rapidly in a beginning structure of martensite than in one of primary ferrite and pearlite, as illustrated in Fig. 7-12.

The nucleation of the carbides in the martensite is uniform so initially a fine uniform distribution of carbide spheres in ferrite is formed, which then coarsens into a uniform distribution. However, in the primary ferrite-

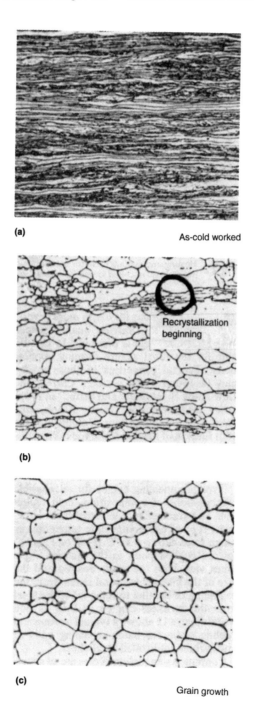

(a)

As-cold worked

(b)

(c)

Grain growth

Fig. 7-5 Microstructure of cold worked and annealed low carbon steel. A low-carbon sheet steel in the (a) as-cold rolled unannealed condition, (b) partially recrystallized annealed condition, and (c) fully recrystallized annealed condition. Marshall's etch. 1000× (Adapted from B.L. Bramfitt, Annealing of Steel, in *ASM Handbook*, Vol 4, *Heat Treating*, ASM International, Materials Park, Ohio (1991))

pearlite beginning microstructure, the carbide plates in the pearlite must first spheroidize in place, which forms a non-uniform distribution of carbides (see Fig. 7-12b). This then develops into a uniform dispersion.

The processes described above are for the development of a spheroidized structure upon reheating a steel from 25°C to the spheroidizing temperature, which is below the austenite region. However, a spheroidized structure can be formed from austenite if the steel is cooled sufficiently slowly or if it is isothermally transformed and held sufficiently long. The latter is called *isothermal annealing*, and depicted in Fig. 7-13. In some steels the spheroidization process is accelerated by cycling just above and just below the eutectoid temperature, as depicted in Fig. 7-14. This is especially useful in high carbon steels, and Fig. 7-6 shows this temperature range being used for hypereutectoid steels (marked "annealing" in the figure).

Full annealing

Heating a steel in the austenite region (for carbon contents less than 0.8%) or into the two phase austenite + Fe₃C region (for carbon contents greater than 0.8%), and then cooling slowly to 25°C, is the heat treatment of steels commonly associated with the term annealing. It is sometimes called *full annealing*. The rate of cooling is usually not specified, but "slowly" here usually means taking

several hours to cool to 25°C. In some cases, a box furnace is placed around the steel and it is heated slowly and cooled slowly from austenite, taking days to complete the process. This is called *box annealing*. These annealing treatments will form a microstructure predicted from the equilibrium diagram. This is primary ferrite and pearlite for hypoeutectoid steels, pearlite for eutectoid steels, and primary Fe₃C (cementite) and pearlite for hypereutectoid steels. Full annealing produces a structure which is soft and thus amenable to certain processing, such as forming and machining.

For high carbon steels (greater than the eutectoid carbon content), the presence of primary Fe₃C (cementite) in the prior austenite grain boundaries may be undesirable, since this produces a continuous network of the hard, brittle phase (see Fig. 2-7). This can be broken up by an anneal in the two phase austenite + Fe₃C region, so that it is not so detrimental.

In general, the austenitizing temperatures used for full annealing are the same as those for hardening, as shown in Fig. 7-6.

Normalizing

Normalizing is a heat treatment in which the steel is heated into the austenite region, somewhat above the range used for hardening (see Fig. 7-6), and cooled in air. It is to be understood that cooling common sizes (e.g., 2

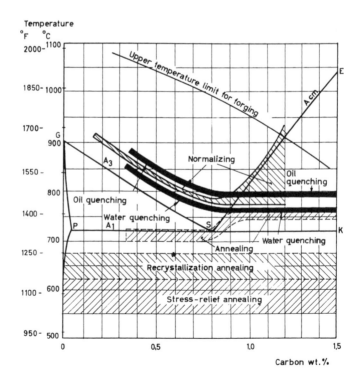

Fig. 7-6 Iron-carbon phase diagram with the approximate temperature ranges shown for various heat treatments. (From K.-E. Thelning, *Steel and Its Heat Treatment*, 2nd edition, Butterworths, London (1986))

inch diameter) in air will require of the order of minutes to cool to 25°C (Fig. 7-15), but for larger sizes cooling in air may be equivalent to annealing smaller sizes.

Normalizing is used to convert a heterogeneous structure, such as develops from a high austenitizing temperature treatment (e.g., during hot forging, see Fig. 7-6), to a finer and more uniform structure. The microstructures in Fig. 7-16 illustrate the effect. The annealed microstructure consists of coarse primary ferrite grains which have formed on the boundaries of large austenite grains. When the steel with this microstructure is reaustenitized in a lower temperature range, smaller austenite grains form (see Chapter 6), and a finer structure results upon air cooling (Fig. 7-16b).

In addition to the refinement of the prior austenite grains, there is a reduction in the size of the primary ferrite

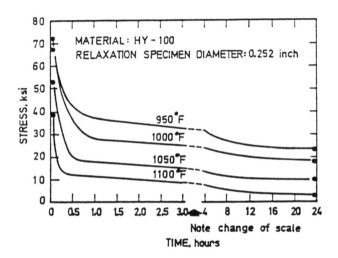

Fig. 7-7 Residual stress as a function of stress relief annealing temperature and time. (From A.H. Rosenstein, *J. Materials*, Vol 6, p 265 (1971))

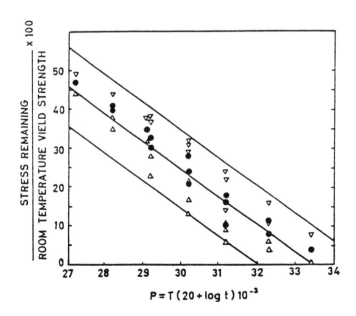

$$P = T (20 + \log t) \, 10^{-3}$$

Fig. 7-8 Residual stress as a function of a parameter of stress relief annealing time and temperature. T is temperature in Rankine and t is time in hours. (From same source as Fig. 7-7)

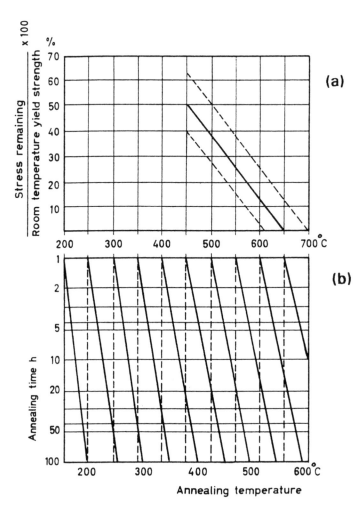

Fig. 7-9 Residual stress as a function of annealing time and temperature for the steel of the data in Fig. 7-8. (From same source as Fig. 7-7)

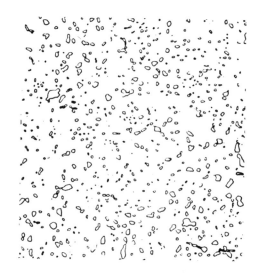

Fig. 7-10 The microstructure of a typical spheroidization annealed steel. (From same source as Fig. 7-5)

grains. This is due to the effect of the temperature of formation on the nucleation rate of these crystals. The nucleation rate of primary ferrite crystals formed isothermally is shown schematically in Fig. 7-17a. In the higher temperature range, the lower the transformation temperature, the higher the nucleation rate. Figure 7-17b shows that this produces finer ferrite grains on air cooling. In addition, the faster cooling allows less primary ferrite to form, so that more pearlite is present, as shown in Fig. 7-18. Also, since the pearlite forms in a lower temperature range, it will be finer and hence harder (see hardness data in Fig. 2-27). All of these factors make a normalized steel appreciably harder than the same steel in the annealed condition.

For normalizing, austenitizing is carried out in a temperature range slightly higher than that normally used for hardening for water quenching, to ensure a homogeneous austenite (see Fig. 7-6). In hypereutectoid steels, austenitizing may be carried out in the austenite region (above the two phase austenite + Fe_3C region; see Fig. 7-6) to completely dissolve the carbides.

Martempering and Austempering

The preceding heat treatments of annealing, normalizing and quenching dealt with cooling continuously and "smoothly" from the austenite region to 25°C. There are special heat treatments which can produce beneficial effects which involve interrupted cooling. The two heat treatments described here involve an isothermal hold at a temperature below the austenitizing temperature but above 25°C. The main disadvantage is that such heat treatments require removing the part from the austenitizing furnace, then placing it in another furnace for the isothermal treatment. The part must be cooled to the isothermal treatment temperature sufficiently rapidly to miss the "nose" of the TTT diagram, so that upon attaining the isothermal treatment temperature the part is still all austenite. This requires cooling much more rapidly than can be achieved in air, so the isothermal treatment furnace must consist of a molten metal (e.g., lead) or molten salt bath.

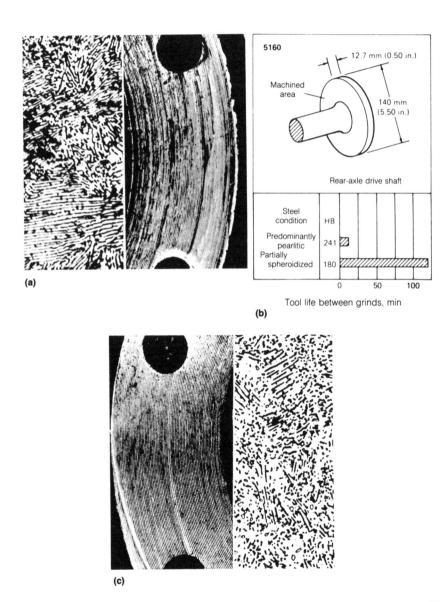

(a)

(b)

(c)

Fig. 7-11 An example of the improvement in machinability of a steel by using a spheroidized structure. (From *Metals Handbook*, 8th edition, Vol 2, *Heat Treating, Cleaning and Finishing*, American Society for Metals, Metals Park, Ohio (1964))

Martempering

In *martempering*, the steel part is quenched into a molten metal or salt bath which is at a temperature just above the M_s temperature (Fig. 7-19), and held for a few seconds. During this time, the temperature of the part becomes more uniform, and thermal residual stresses are relaxed. Then the part is quenched to 25°C before the bainite-start time is reached. This heat treatment minimizes transformation stresses and cracking associated with quenching. The part is commonly tempered after this heat treatment.

The term *marquenching* refers to a similar treatment for carburized steels, where the intermediate temperature is based on the M_s temperature of the high carbon case.

Austempering

In *austempering*, the part is cooled in a molten salt or metal bath at a temperature just above the M_s temperature, and held until the austenite transforms completely to bainite (Fig. 7-20). This treatment is based on the fact that lower bainite may have more favorable mechanical prop-

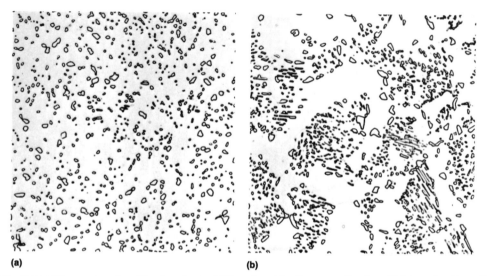

(a)   (b)

Fig. 7-12 Difference in spheroidization of a steel if the spheroidization anneal begins with (a) martensite and (b) primary ferrite and pearlite. (From same source as Fig. 7-5)

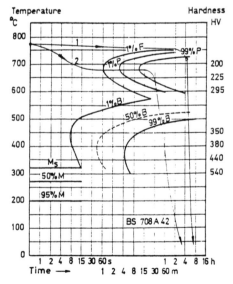

TTT diagram for steel B S 708A42 (Bofors RO 952).
Cooling curves shown represent full annealing (1)
and isothermal annealing (2).

Fig. 7-13 Illustration of isothermal annealing. (From same source as Fig. 7-6)

erties than a quenched (martensitic) and tempered structure of the same hardness. The treatment also reduces
residual thermal stress before the bainite forms. Table 7-2
compares the mechanical properties of a steel given this
treatment to that derived from a conventional quench-
and-temper process. Note that the hardness is the same for
the two processes, but that the austempering produced a
much tougher material.

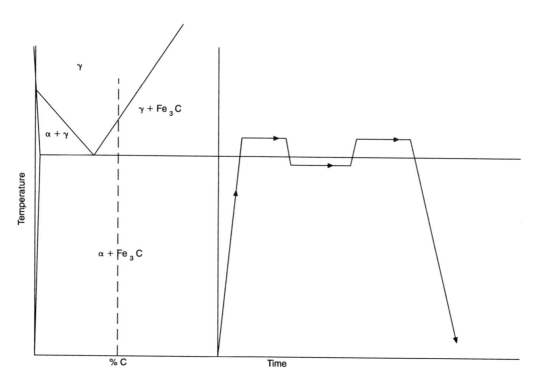

Fig. 7-14 Schematic illustration of the heat treatment used to produce a spheroidized structure by cycling the temperature of the part about the eutectoid temperature

Intercritical Heat Treatment

A critical limitation in taking advantage of the high strength of martensite is its lack of toughness. As described in Chapter 5, the common approach to alleviate this is to temper martensite, converting it to the tougher tempered martensite structure of fine carbide particles in ferrite, although this is accompanied by a loss in strength.

A method of taking advantage of the high strength of martensite and the better toughness of ferrite involves "austenitizing" in the two phase $\alpha + \gamma$ temperature range of the Fe-C phase diagram to produce a structure of α and γ. The steel is then quenched to convert the γ to martensite, and produce a mixture of ferrite and regions of martensite. Such a structure is sometimes referred to as dual phase. (Of course, most steels are multiphase struc-

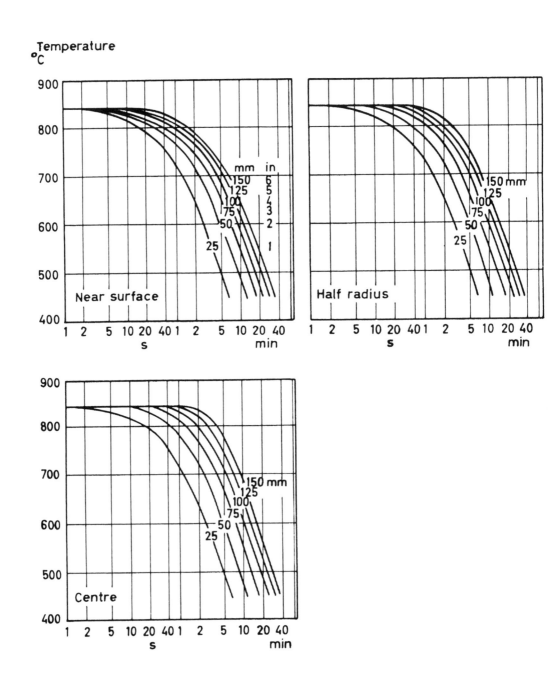

Fig. 7-15 Cooling curves for air cooled round bars. (From same source as Fig. 7-6)

tures, e.g., pearlite consists of α and Fe_3C.) The heat treatment to produce this dual phase structure is called intercritical annealing. The "austenitizing" temperature is sometimes referred to as the quenching temperature, but here the term austenitizing will be used.

Figure 7-21a shows the temperature range, between the A_1 and A_3, associated with intercritical annealing, and Fig. 7-21b shows a typical temperature-time history for this heat treatment. Note that the carbon content of the austenite increases as the austenitizing temperature is

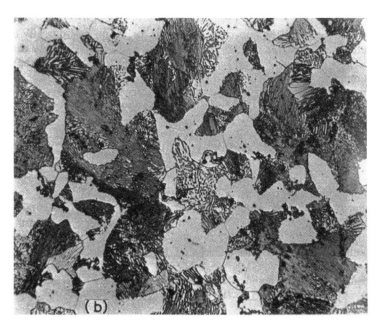

Fig. 7-16 Microstructures showing the refinement of the primary ferrite grains by normalizing in a 0.5% C steel. (a) Air cooled from hot working range (e.g., 1200°C). (b) Normalized after treatment in (a). (Adapted from same source as Fig. 7-6)

lowered (Fig. 7-21c). The amount of α and γ present at the austenitizing temperature can be calculated from a mass balance (lever rule) assuming that equilibrium has been attained. This is shown in Fig. 7-21d. Data for a specific steel are shown in Fig. 7-22. This curve differs from that in Fig. 7-21d because of the influence of alloy content on the amount of α and γ present.

Dual phase steels consist of a mixture of ferrite and martensite, which at the austenitizing temperature requires α and γ. For a given carbon content steel, the amount of these two phases present depends on the austenitizing temperature (see Fig. 7-21d). The temperature range in which two phases exist is reduced as the carbon content of the steel increases. To maintain flexibility in achieving a desired amount of α and γ, the dual phase steels are intrinsically limited to the lower carbon contents where the austenitizing temperature range is greater.

If the cooling rate is sufficiently high, the γ will be converted to martensite, so after quenching at 25°C the structure will be martensite and α. This is shown schematically in Fig. 7-23a. A typical microstructure is shown in Fig. 7-24. The amount of austenite present at the austenitizing temperature decreases as the temperature is lowered, and thus the amount of martensite which can form upon quenching is reduced. However, since the hardness of martensite increases with carbon content (Fig. 7-23b), the strength of the martensite formed increases with decreasing austenitizing temperature. But this is mitigated by the inability to convert all of the austenite to martensite upon quenching (Fig. 7-23c), so that some soft retained austenite is present. The amounts of phases present after quenching are shown in Fig. 7-23d.

Figure 7-25 shows data illustrating the formation of the two phase α + γ structure as a function of austenitizing time. In the microstructures in Fig. 7-25a the white regions are ferrite, and the darker regions represent γ at the austenitizing temperature. Figure 7-25b shows the amount of austenite formed as a function of time at different temperatures. For this steel, the A_3 temperature is approximately 890°C, so at and above this temperature the equilibrium structure is all austenite, which forms in about 2 minutes. At 780 and 740°C, the equilibrium amount of austenite forms at about 7,000 sec. (about 2 h). The kinetics of the formation of the α-γ structure dictates the required austenitizing time.

Figure 7-26 illustrates the marked effect the amount of martensite has on the strength. Figure 7-27 shows that the ductility decreases as the strength increases, but retains values above 10% due to the presence of the ductile ferrite.

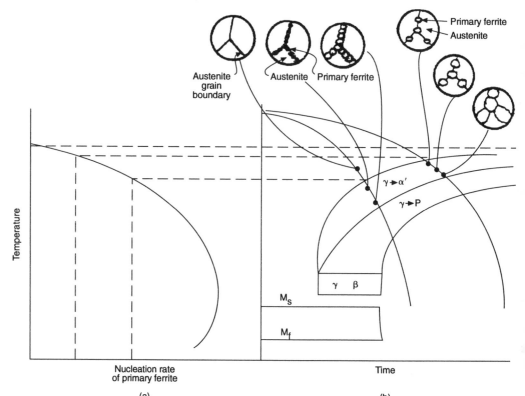

(a)   (b)

Fig. 7-17 (a) Schematic diagram showing the effect of the transformation temperature on the nucleation rate of primary ferrite at the grain boundaries of austenite. (b) Schematic diagram showing the effect of cooling rate from austenite on the grain size of the primary ferrite crystals

Figure 7-28 shows schematically the variation of the strength with austenitizing temperature. The strength increases as the temperature decreases because more martensite is present (see Fig. 7-23d) and also because it has a higher carbon content (see Fig. 7-21c). However, some reduction in strength at low austenitizing temperatures may occur due to the presence of retained γ.

The requirement that the austenite convert to martensite limits the application of dual phase steels of low carbon and low alloy content to components of relatively small sizes, such as plates. Thus the dual phase steels compete with high strength, low alloy steels (HSLA steels) which are covered in Chapter 8. These steels contain mainly primary ferrite (the remainder being pearlite), and strengthening is achieved by solid solution alloying of the ferrite (e.g., by Mn), by decreasing the primary ferrite grain size and by precipitation hardening of the ferrite. Figure 7-29 shows that the mechanical properties of dual phase steels can be more favorable than HSLA steels.

Further Reading

- G. Krauss, *Steels: Heat Treating and Processing Principles*, ASM International, Materials Park, Ohio (1990)
- K.-E. Thelning, *Steel and Its Heat Treatment*, 2nd edition, Butterworths, London (1986)
- *Metals Handbook*, Vol 4, *Heat Treating*, ASM International, Materials Park, Ohio (1991)
- W.C. Leslie, *The Physical Metallurgy of Steels*, Hemisphere Publishing Corporation/McGraw-Hill Book Company, New York (1981)
- A.K. Sinha, *Ferrous Physical Metallurgy*, Butterworths, Boston (1989)

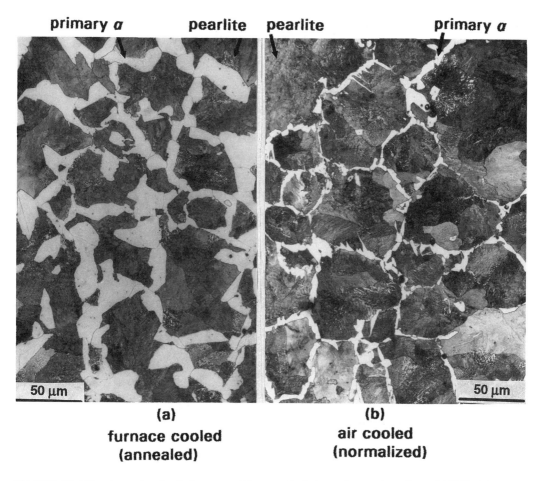

(a)
furnace cooled
(annealed)

(b)
air cooled
(normalized)

Fig. 7-18 Microstructures showing that more and finer pearlite is formed upon air cooling a 0.5% C, plain carbon steel

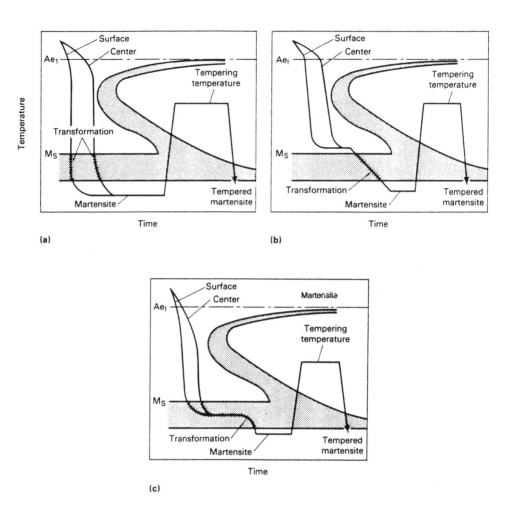

Fig. 7-19 Schematic isothermal TTT diagram showing the heat treatment of martempering. (Adapted from H. Webster and W.J. Laird, Jr., in *Metals Handbook*, Vol 4, p 137, *Heat Treating*, ASM International, Materials Park, Ohio (1991))

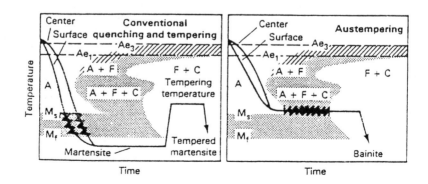

Fig. 7-20 Schematic isothermal TTT diagram showing the heat treatment of austempering. (From J.R. Keough, W.J. Laird, Jr., and A.D. Gooding, *Metals Handbook*, Vol 4, p 152, *Heat Treating*, American Society for Materials, Materials Park, Ohio (1991))

Table 7-2 Mechanical properties of a steel which was austempered and which was conventionally quenched and tempered. (From M.A. Grossmann and E.C. Bain, *Principles of Heat Treatment*, 5th edition, American Society for Metals, Metals Park, Ohio (1964))

Steel composition: 0.74C, 0.37Mn, 0.145Si, 0.039S, 0.044P

New Method, Direct from Austenite	Quench-and-Temper Method
Heat 5 min at 790°C (1450°F)	Heat 5 min at 790°C (1450°F)
Quench into lead alloy bath at 305°C (580°F)	Quench into oil at 21°C (70°F)
Let specimens remain in bath for 15 min	Temper immediately in lead alloy bath, 30 min at 315°C (600°F)
Quench into water	Quench into water

Mechanical Properties (Average of 6 tests)		Mechanical Properties (Average of 6 tests)	
Rockwell C hardness	50.4	Rockwell C hardness	50.2
Ultimate strength, ksi	282.7	Ultimate strength, ksi	246.7
Yield point, ksi	151.3	Yield point, ksi	121.7
Elongation, % in 6 inches	1.9	Elongation, % in 6 inches	0.3
Reduction of area, %	34.5	Reduction in area, %	0.7
Impact, ft-lb(a)	35.3	Impact, ft-lb(a)	2.9

(a) Foot-pounds absorbed in breaking 0.180-inch round, unnotched specimens

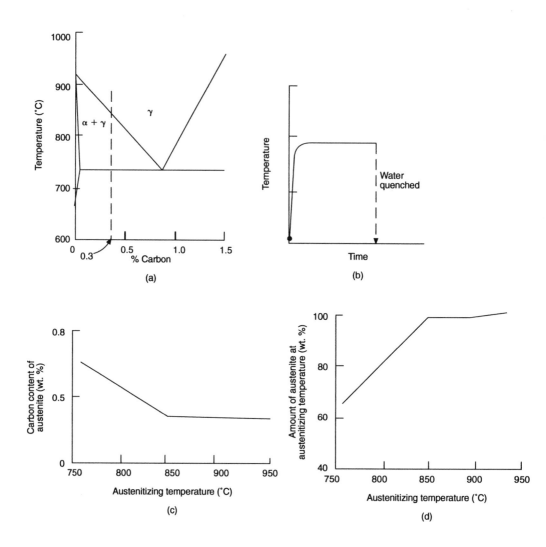

Fig. 7-21 (a) Illustration of the temperature range for austenitizing a dual phase steel containing 0.3% C. (b) Dual phase heat treatment. (c) Carbon content of austenite as a function of austenitizing temperature. (d) Equilibrium amount of austenite and ferrite as a function of austenitizing temperature

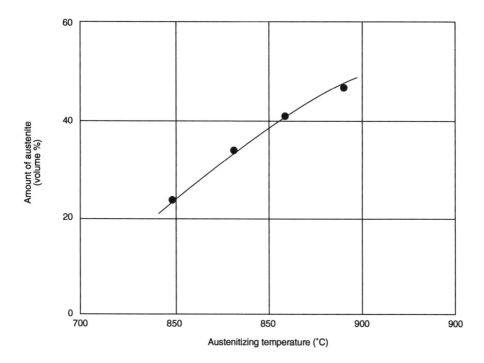

Fig. 7-22 Amount of austenite present at the austenitizing temperature for a 0.04% C, 2.2% Si, 1.8% Mn steel. The samples were austenitized for 1.4 h at each temperature. (Adapted from J.J. Yi, I.S. Kim, and H.S. Choi, *Metallurgical Transactions*, Vol 16A, p 1237 (1985))

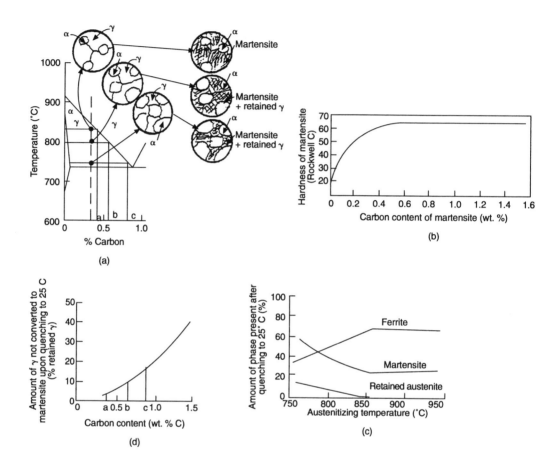

Fig. 7-23 Schematic illustration of the amount of phases present in a dual phase steel containing 0.3% C after quenching to 25°C

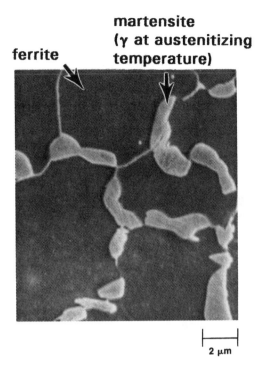

ferrite

martensite
(γ at austenitizing
temperature)

2 μm

Fig. 7-24 Microstructure typical of those of dual phase steels. The steel contained 0.06% C and 1.5% Mn and was water quenched from 760°C. (Adapted from G.R. Speich, in *Fundamentals of Dual-Phase Steels*, The Metallurgical Society, Warrendale, PA (1981))

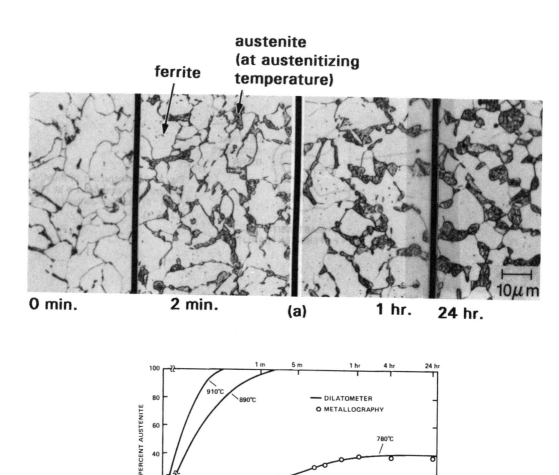

Fig. 7-25 (a) Microstructures of a 0.05% C, 1.5% Mn steel showing the development of the α-γ structure as a function of time at 740°C. (b) Amount of austenite formed as a function of time at four austenitizing temperatures. (Adapted from G.R. Speich, V.A. Demarest, and R.L. Miller, *Metallurgical Transactions*, Vol 1A, p 1419 (1981))

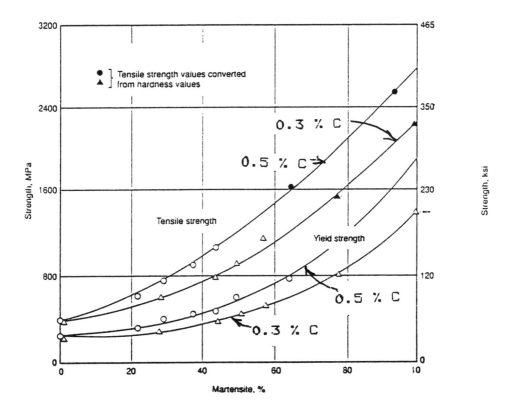

Fig. 7-26 Effect of the amount of martensite present on the tensile and yield strength of 1.5% Mn dual phase steels of two different carbon contents. (Adapted from G.R. Speich and R.L. Miller, in *Structure and Properties of Dual-Phase Steels*, AIME, Warrendale, PA (1979))

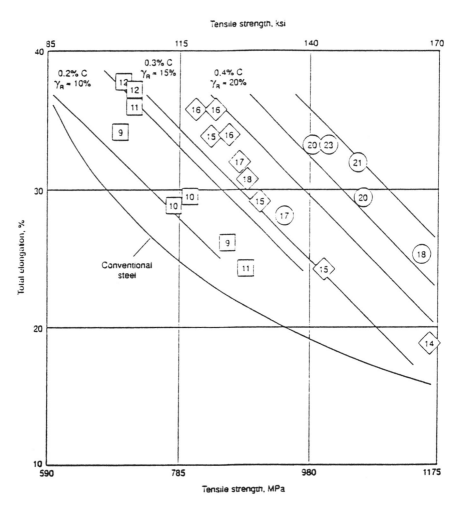

Fig. 7-27 Relation between the tensile ductility (% elongation at fracture) and tensile strength for several dual phase steels. (Adapted from S. Tasuhara, M. Osamu, H. Takechi, Y. Ishii, and M. Usada, in a paper presented at the 114th Iron and Steel Institute of Japan Meeting, Tokyo (1987), as reported by G.R. Speich, Dual-Phase Steels, in *Metals Handbook*, 10th edition, Vol 1, *Properties and Selection: Irons, Steels, and High-Performance Alloys*, ASM International, Materials Park, Ohio (1990))

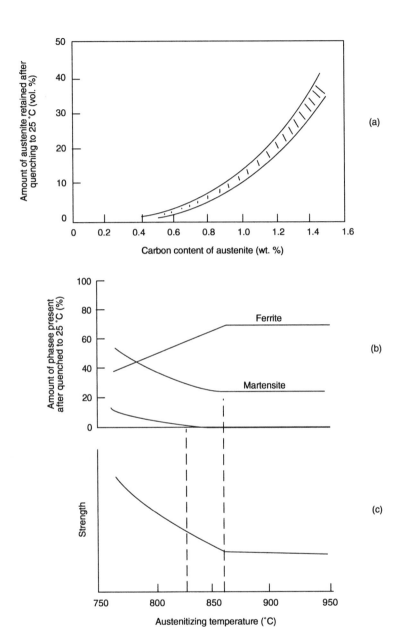

Fig. 7-28 Schematic illustration of the variation of strength with austenitizing temperature for dual phase steel containing 0.3% C

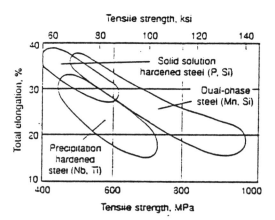

Fig. 7-29 Relation between ductility (% elongation at fracture) and tensile strength for three types of low carbon steels containing mainly primary ferrite. (Adapted from S. Hayami and T. Furakawa, in *Microalloying 75*, Union Carbide Corporation, New York (1977))

Chapter 8

Structural Steels

Introduction

For many applications of steels, adequate mechanical properties exist for a structure of primary ferrite and pearlite. Such steels cannot attain the strength levels of quenched and tempered steels, but their processing is simpler and the structure can be relatively easy to produce in large sizes (e.g., I-beams) which do not lend themselves to hardening unless the hardenability (and hence expense) is high.

These steels of primary ferrite-pearlite structure go by different names, reflecting different uses and processing methods. The term *structural steel* is generally used to denote low carbon (<0.25% C), low alloy steels which are used for components in structures, such as I-beams and automobile frames. Such steels are also referred to as *high strength, low alloy steels* (HSLA), although the strength level is considerably below that normally attained by quenching and low temperature tempering. The microstructure of these steels is usually primary ferrite and pearlite, and because of the low carbon content the amount of pearlite is low, and hence sometimes the term *pearlite-reduced* steels is used. They are also called *control-rolled steels* because the common method of developing a fine primary ferrite grain size is by control of the hot rolling process. They are sometimes referred to as *microalloyed steels,* because in many of these steels small alloying additions (e.g., <0.1% V) are made for control of the austenite grain size and the recrystallization process during hot working, and to allow the precipitation of very fine particles in the ferrite upon cooling, contributing to strengthening. Most of the components produced from these steels are made by a combination of heat treatment and plastic deformation, sometimes called *thermomechanical processing,* a term also used to describe this class of steels.

For the purpose of this chapter, attention is centered on processing such steels to attain a fine primary ferrite grain size to develop high strength. The structures do not involve the formation of martensite, and thus the strength levels being considered here do not approach those attainable with quenched and tempered steels. Increases in strength are brought about by a reduction in the primary ferrite grain size by microalloying and control of the hot rolling operation, solid solution strengthening of the ferrite by alloying additions, and the precipitation of very fine particles in the ferrite by microalloying.

Also very important in the development of structural steels has been the improvement of the toughness as the strength increases. Generally a higher strength material will be less tough. However, the formation of a microstructure of very fine primary ferrite grains will increase the strength and improve the toughness.

The primary characteristic of structural steels is processing to form a fine primary ferrite grain size. This is usually accomplished by the formation of a fine prior austenite grain size by controlling the recrystallization process during hot rolling. Thus, the first section in this chapter reviews the concepts and principles of recrystallization in plastically deformed metals.

Annealing of Plastically Deformed Metals to Effect Fine Grain Size

To examine how hot working can be used to control the austenite grain size, we will first review the concepts of annealing of cold worked metals. Then we will look at hot working and the grain size associated with it.

Effect of cold working on grain structure and mechanical properties

Plastically deforming a metal or alloy at sufficiently low temperatures (e.g., 25°C for Cu, below 25°C for Pb) increases the hardness, yield strength and tensile strength and lowers the ductility. An example is shown in Fig. 8-1. The strengthening is called *work hardening* or *strain hardening,* and *cold working* can be defined as plastic deformation which causes strain hardening. The strengthening is associated with the multiplication of dislocations and the restriction of their movement by interaction with

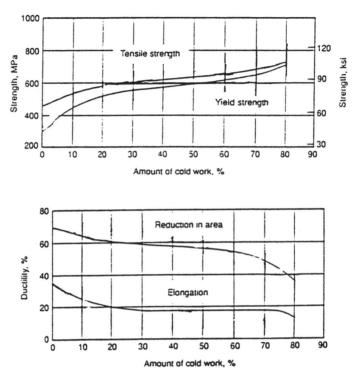

Fig. 8-1 Effect of the amount of plastic deformation (as measured by the percent reduction in thickness by rolling) on the tensile mechanical properties of 1016 annealed steel. (Adapted from *Metals Handbook*, Vol 1, *Properties and Selection: Irons and Steels*, American Society for Metals, Metals Park, Ohio (1978))

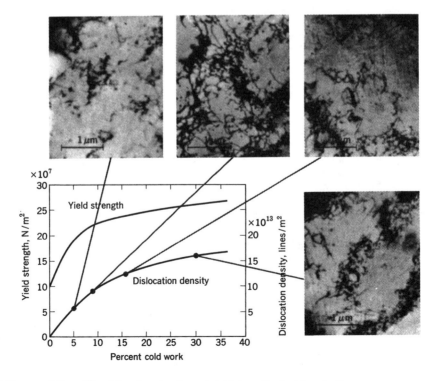

Fig. 8-2 The correlation of the dislocation density and yield strength of cold worked iron

each other and with grain boundaries, precipitates, etc. An example of the relation of the strength to the dislocation density is shown in Fig. 8-2.

The effect of cold working on the microstructure is shown in Fig. 8-3. The crystals of the metal take on the shape, on the average, of that of the sample, and the appearance of the grains depends upon the direction of viewing. If the metal is rolled, and then viewed normal to the rolling direction, the elongation of the grains is quite apparent, as shown in Fig. 8-3b. In the etched microstructure not only are the grain boundaries revealed, but striations are seen within the grains, sometimes called *deformation bands* (but not resolved in Fig. 8-3b). These are grooves caused by rapid etching where dislocations intersect the polished and etched surface.

Recovery, recrystallization and grain growth

The production of lattice defects during plastic deformation increases the internal energy of the metal, and thus it is thermodynamically unstable compared to the structure prior to deformation. Therefore, it should undergo changes to lower the energy by the removal of these defects. That such a process occurs is reflected in the change of hardness and mechanical properties if a cold worked metal is held sufficiently long at a given temperature. This is illustrated in Fig. 8-4 which shows hardness data as a function of time at 400°C for a Cu-5% Zn solid solution alloy (single phase structure) which had been cold rolled at 25°C to a reduction in thickness of 60%. The hardness remains approximately constant for about 2 h, then decreases drastically for about 30 h, then decreases more slowly.

Examination of microstructures associated with curves such as those in Fig. 8-4 reveal little change in the lower temperature (or shorter time) range in which the hardness remains approximately constant. However, when the hardness begins to decrease, the microstructure shows the formation of small, equiaxed grains; this process is called *recrystallization*. These small grains have a much lower defect concentration than the parent cold worked material from which they formed, and thus they are relatively soft. As the grains nucleate and grow, the cold worked matrix begins to disappear, as depicted in Fig. 8-5. Once recrystallization is complete and no more cold worked material remains, the structure consists of a relatively fine grained material. Further annealing allows some of these grains to grow at the expense of neighboring grains, so that the grain size increases. This process reduces the grain boundary area of the material and hence

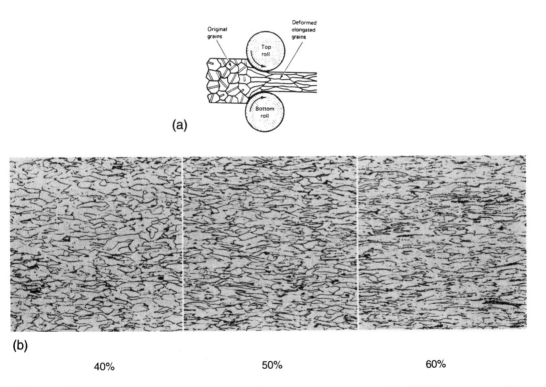

(a)

(b)

40%   50%   60%

Fig. 8-3 (a) Schematic diagram showing the plastic deformation of grains by cold rolling. (b) Microstructures of plastically deformed low carbon steel. The structure contains mostly primary ferrite and a small amount of pearlite. Note that the grains become longer and thinner with increasing plastic deformation. The amount of plastic deformation is the reduction in thickness. ((a) from C.R. Brooks, *Heat Treatment, Structure and Properties of Nonferrous Alloys*, American Society for Metals, Metals Park, Ohio, p 33 (1982). (b) adapted from *Metals Handbook*, 8th edition, Vol 7, *Atlas of Microstructures of Industrial Alloys*, American Society for Metals, Metals Park, Ohio, p 8 (1972))

its energy. Note that in this stage the hardness decreases, but not nearly as drastically as when recrystallization is occurring. Figure 8-6 shows microstructures of a cold worked and annealed alloy in which recrystallization and grain growth have occurred.

The heat treatment of cold worked metals and alloys to change their properties to values similar to those prior to cold working is called *annealing*. [Annealing has other meanings (Chapter 7), but in this chapter we restrict it to that just given.] It is common to present annealing data as properties as a function of annealing temperature for a specified annealing time (as shown in Fig. 8-5) instead of annealing time for a specified temperature (as shown in Fig. 8-4). The annealing process is usually separated into three regions. In the early stage the mechanical properties don't change much but other properties (e.g., electrical resistivity) may. This stage is called *recovery*. In the range in which the small, strain-free grains nucleate and grow and consume the cold worked matrix, the process is called *recrystallization*. After recrystallization is com-

plete, further annealing causes an increase in grain size, so this stage is called *grain growth*. Figure 8-7 shows these three stages, with the mechanism by which they occur and their effects.

Since obvious softening occurs when recrystallization commences, the temperature at which this occurs is of interest as an indicator of the required annealing temperature to produce softening. It is called the *recrystallization temperature*. It can be defined in several ways, such as the temperature of the inflection in the hardness-temperature curve or as the lowest temperature at which the hardness decrease is detected. Figure 8-8 shows annealing curves for Cu and two Cu-Zn solid solution (single phase) alloys, with the recrystallization temperature indicated for each. This temperature obviously depends upon the annealing time, as illustrated by the data in Fig. 8-9. Thus when quoting an annealing temperature an annealing time should be given. The recrystallization temperature also depends upon the amount (and type) of deformation, as shown in Fig. 8-10. Thus this information

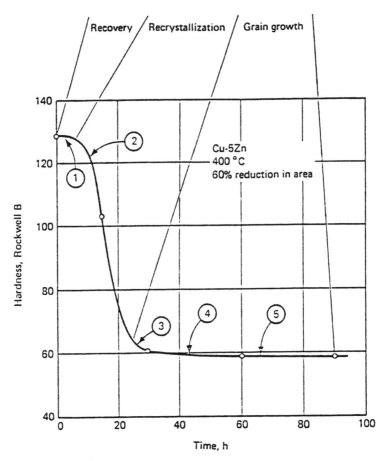

Effect of annealing time (at 400 °C) on the hardness of a Cu-5Zn solid solution alloy cold worked 60%.

Fig. 8-4 Effect of annealing time on the hardness of a cold worked Cu-5% Zn alloy. (From same source as Fig. 8-3a)

should be given when quoting a recrystallization temperature. There are several variables which affect the recrystallization temperature, and some are tabulated in Fig. 8-11.

The degree and type of deformation and the annealing temperature affect the kinetics of recovery and recrystallization, and indirectly affect the temperature and time at which grain growth begins. The rate of grain growth is

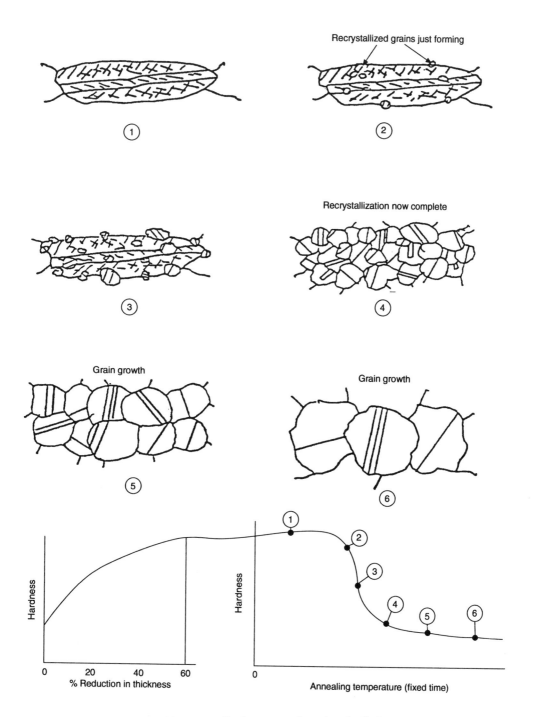

Fig. 8-5 Schematic illustration of the recrystallization process in a microstructure

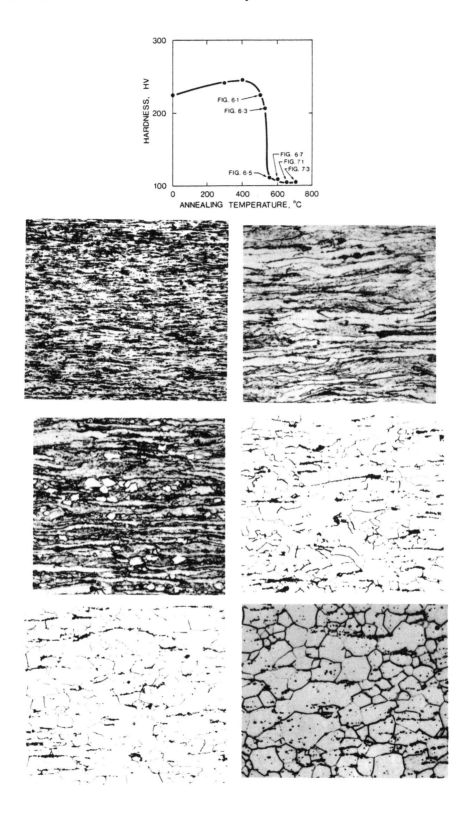

Fig. 8-6 Microstructures typical of those for a cold worked and annealed low carbon (0.1% C) steel. The approximate location of each microstructure is shown on the schematic hardness curve. (Micrographs from *Metals Handbook*, 9th edition, Vol 9, *Metallography and Microstructures*, American Society for Metals, Metals Park, Ohio (1985))

controlled by the factors discussed in Chapter 6 which dealt with grain growth of austenite.

Hot working

Recovery, recrystallization and grain growth are kinetic processes, and the rate of each will increase exponentially with temperature, following the expression [exp (−Q/RT)]. Here R is the ideal gas constant, T is the absolute temperature, and Q is the activation energy, which is different for each of the three processes. Using the values of Q, an estimation can be made of how fast these processes occur at a given temperature. Since the structural changes involve atom movement, Q is similar in magnitude to that for diffusion. In the case of Fe (or steels), by using values of Q for self-diffusion of Fe it is found that above 800°C recovery and recrystallization

occur typically in seconds. Thus if cold working such a metal is attempted in this temperature range (above the recrystallization temperature), recovery and recrystallization occur before the metal can be cooled to 25°C. Hence at 25°C it is soft. Plastic deformation under such conditions is hot working.

Thus hot working can be defined as plastic deformation such that work (strain) hardening does not occur. This is the opposite of the definition given earlier for cold working. Also hot working can be defined as plastic deformation above the recrystallization temperature. [Then cold working would be defined as plastic deformation below the recrystallization temperature.] However, as pointed out above, the recrystallization temperature depends on several variables. Thus it might be better to define hot working as plastic deformation such that recrystallization occurs almost instantly. [Note that the

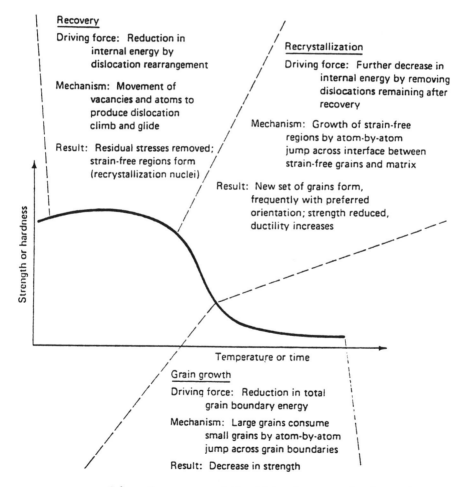

Schematic summary of the driving force, mechanism and result for recovery, recrystallization and grain growth. (Adapted, courtesy of Prof. E. E. Stansbury)

Fig. 8-7 Schematic illustration of the characteristics of recovery, recrystallization and grain growth. (From same source as Fig. 8-3a)

terms hot and cold working carry no implication about deformation at 25°C. For example, plastic deformation of Pb at 25°C is hot working, whereas plastic deformation of Mo at 800°C is cold working.]

Thus if a bar of a metal is plastically deformed by rolling at a sufficiently high temperature, the deformed grains, as they exit the rolls, very quickly undergo recovery and recrystallization, and also grain growth. This hot working effect is illustrated in Fig. 8-12. An important point here is that if it is desired to obtain a relatively fine grain size, the hot rolling should be carried out at a temperature just above the recrystallization temperature, so that little grain growth occurs as the bar cools to 25°C, or the bar must be cooled rapidly as it leaves the roll. Also, it is possible to obtain at low temperature, following cooling from the hot working temperature, a partially recrystallized structure.

Control of Primary Ferrite Grain Size

In structural steels, the microstructure is usually primary ferrite and pearlite. Strengthening in these steels relies mainly on reduction in the primary ferrite grain size, and the methods of doing this are reviewed in this section.

Effect of cooling rate from austenite

The ferrite grains nucleate mainly at the austenite grain boundaries, and hence it is the surface nucleation rate which is of importance. The nucleation rate depends on the temperature as shown in Fig. 8-13. If the ferrite nucleates at a high temperature, a larger grain size accrues than if it nucleates at a lower temperature (for temperatures above that of the maximum in the curve). This is shown in Fig. 8-14.

The heat treatments usually involve continuous cooling, not isothermal transformation, but we can apply the principle to the formation of primary ferrite on continuous cooling. We look at the general nucleation rate in the temperature range where primary ferrite forms. To obtain a relatively fine primary ferrite grain size upon continuous cooling, the cooling rate should be as high as feasible without forming other transformation products. The formation of primary ferrite on

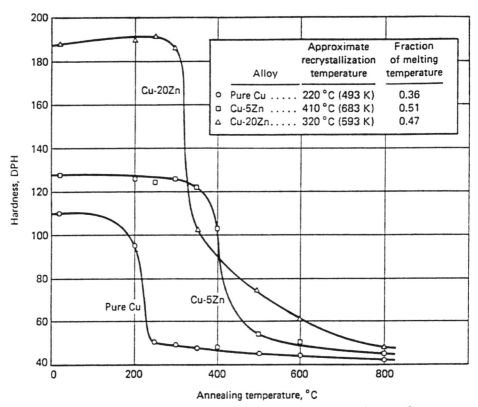

Hardness as a function of annealing temperature for 15-min annealing time. The alloys were originally rolled at 25 °C to a 60% reduction in thickness. The recrystallization temperatures listed are based on the inflection point.

Fig. 8-8 Annealing curves for Cu and two Cu-Zn alloys. The recrystallization temperature for each alloy is given. (From same source as Fig. 8-3a)

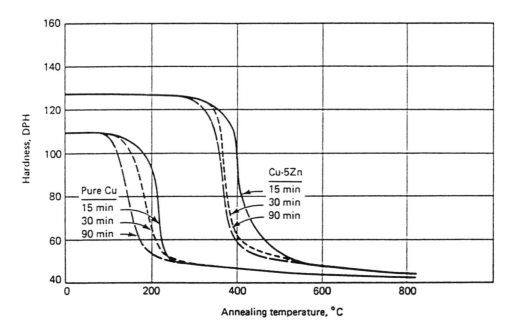

Hardness as a function of annealing temperature for pure Cu
and a Cu-5Zn alloy, using three different annealing times. Both materials were originally cold rolled at 25 °C to a 60% reduction in thickness.

Fig. 8-9 Effect of annealing time on the annealing curves of a Cu-5% Zn alloy. (From same source as Fig. 8-3a)

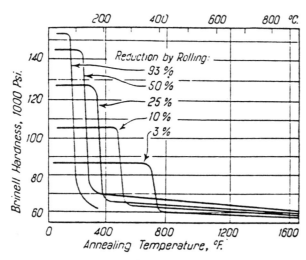

Curves for copper showing the effect of the amount of the
initial deformation of the annealing response. (From G. Sachs and
K. R. Van Horn, Practical Metallurgy, p 143, American Society for
Metals, Metals Park, Ohio, 1951)

Fig. 8-10 Effect of the amount of prior deformation on the annealing curves of Cu. (From same source as Fig. 8-3a)

continuous cooling is depicted in Fig. 8-15. The nucleation rate for the formation of primary ferrite is determined by the temperature range in which nucleation occurs. If this occurs in the higher temperature range, associated with relatively slow cooling, the nucleation rate is low, and primary ferrite forms with a large grain size. If the cooling rate is increased, then the formation of primary ferrite begins at a lower temperature, and hence with a higher nucleation rate. This produces a finer primary ferrite grain size. This effect is depicted in Fig. 8-16.

The microstructures in Fig. 8-17 illustrate the effect of cooling rate on the primary ferrite grain size. Faster cooling results in a finer grain size and a higher strength. Using the primary ferrite grain size and hardness values in Fig. 8-17, a plot of the hardness against the reciprocal of the grain size can be represented by a straight line (Fig. 8-18), which is a Hall-Petch relation.

Effect of austenite grain size

The prior austenite grain size influences the subsequent primary ferrite grain size since nucleation occurs on the austenite boundaries. The grain boundary nucleation rate N is given by

N_s = number of ferrite nuclei/austenite grain boundary area-time

Then the number of ferrite nuclei/time N is N_s times the austenite grain boundary area. Thus a decrease in the austenite grain size to increase the boundary area by a factor of ten increases the nucleation rate N by a factor of ten, and produces a finer primary ferrite grain size. This is illustrated in Fig. 8-19.

Also, during cooling, as the ferrite grows carbon is rejected into the decomposing austenite, until a level is reached where pearlite begins to form. The smaller the prior austenite grains size, the less distance the primary ferrite has to grow to initiate the formation of pearlite. Thus the final structure will consist of a higher density of primary ferrite grains and a smaller primary ferrite grain size. This effect is illustrated by the microstructures in Fig. 8-20. The yield strength will be controlled by the primary ferrite grain size, and it is expected that a Hall-Petch relation will be followed.

Effect of primary ferrite grain size on strength and toughness

To study the effect of the primary ferrite grain size on strength and toughness, a given steel can be processed to develop different austenite grain sizes and it can be cooled at different rates from austenite in forming the primary ferrite-pearlite structure. These methods were described in the preceding two sections.

The effect of reducing the primary ferrite grain size on the yield strength is illustrated by the data in Fig. 8-21. Note that in these cases the Hall-Petch relation is followed. Typically, a decrease in the primary ferrite grain size by a factor of two will increase the yield strength about 50%.

Generally, metals and alloys tested under conditions where brittle cracks are propagated will be tougher if there are microstructural features which divert these cracks. In body-centered cubic alloys, such cracks are cleavage cracks, propagating on the {100} planes. Thus when such a crack propagating inside a grain encounters a high angle boundary of a neighboring grain, the cleavage plane in this grain will have a very high probability

Variable	Effect on recrystallization temperature
Time at annealing temperature	Increasing time decreases temperature
Amount of plastic deformation by cold working	Increasing amount of cold work decreases temperature
Solute concentration in solid solution	Generally increases temperature; depends upon effect on melting temperature
Presence of second phases	Second-phase particles decrease temperature
Original grain size before cold working	Decreasing grain size decreases temperature
Rate of plastic deformation	Increasing rate decreases temperature
Temperature of cold working	Decreasing temperature of cold working decreases recrystallization temperature

Fig. 8-11 Some variables which affect the recrystallization temperature. (From same source as Fig. 8-3a)

of being at an angle to that on which propagation is occurring, and an increase in energy is required to propagate the crack into this neighboring grain. Thus in steels with a primary ferrite-pearlite microstructure, the smaller the primary ferrite grains, the tougher the steel.

This effect of smaller primary ferrite grains increasing the toughness is illustrated by the data in Fig. 8-22. Typically, for these steels if the primary ferrite grain size is decreased by a factor of two, the transition temperature is lowered by about 50°C.

The improvement in toughness by decreasing the primary ferrite grain size, along with the increase in strength, is the main factor that makes steels with a primary ferrite-pearlite microstructure used in applications in which toughness is important.

Development of Small Austenite Grain Size

There are two basic methods used to develop a small austenite grain size, and hence a small primary ferrite grain size. One is by microalloying with elements which form a fine dispersion of particles to retard austenite grain growth. The other is by control of the recrystallization process during hot working.

Control of austenite grain growth

As discussed in detail in Chapter 6, grain growth in austenite can be retarded by suitable additions of elements which will form a fine dispersion of particles. The elements used form compounds with carbon, oxygen and

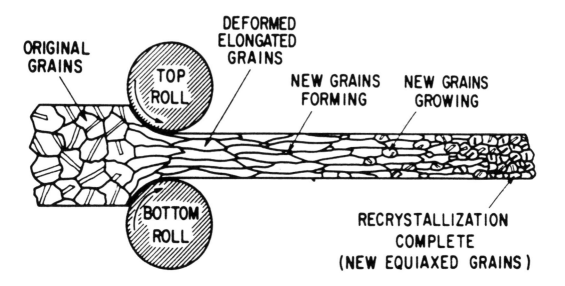

Schematic illustration of the change in grain structure upon hot rolling. (From R.A. Grange, in *Fundamentals of Deformation Processing,* ed. E.A. Backofen, J.J. Burke, L.F. Coffin, N.T. Reed and V. Weiss, Syracuse Univ. Press, Syracuse, N.Y., 1964, as adapted from J.M. Camp and C.B. Francis, *The Making, Shaping, and Treating of Steel,* 5th Ed., U.S. Steel Corp., Pittsburgh, 1940)

Fig. 8-12 Schematic illustration of the change in the grain structure during hot working

nitrogen. Their effectiveness depends upon their dispersion, their solubility with temperature, and the kinetics of their solution. To prevent austenite grain growth the particles must be small and there must be a high number of them.

The common microalloying elements added to effect austenite grain size control are Ti, Nb, V and Al (forming oxides, nitrides or carbides). However, the solubility must be examined to see in what temperature range these will be effective. Such information can be obtained from the appropriate phase diagram, but this entails examination of at least a quaternary diagram. Instead, the solubility product can be considered. For example, for the formation of NbN, the reaction

$$Nb + \underline{N} = NbN$$

is considered. Here $\underline{Nb}$ and $\underline{N}$ represent these elements dissolved in austenite. An equilibrium constant can be written in terms of the appropriate chemical activities for this reaction:

$$K = a_{NbN} / (a_{\underline{Nb}}) (a_{\underline{N}})$$

where K is temperature dependent. The NbN is a compound, so that its activity is fixed. Then this reaction can be written as

$$K' = 1 / [(W_{\underline{Nb}}) (W_{\underline{N}})]$$

where $W_{\underline{Nb}}$ and $W_{\underline{N}}$ are the weight percentages of Nb and N in the austenite. The product $[(W_{\underline{Nb}}) (W_{\underline{N}})]$ is termed the solubility product. Figure 8-23 shows schematically the dependence of this relation on temperature. Thus if a steel contains an amount of Nb and N in the austenite

corresponding to point A, then below temperature T_2 the product $[(W_{\underline{Nd}}) (W_{\underline{N}})]$ will be found to exceed the solubility product and hence the compound will form. However, at temperature T_1, it will not exceed the product, and thus some of the compound NbN will decompose (dissolve) to release Ti and N into the austenite.

Thus, it is desired for the solubility product to be as low as possible. Figure 8-24 shows some solubility product data as a function of temperature. If a structural steel contains 0.006 wt.% N and 0.08 wt.% Nb, the product of these is 4.8×10^{-4}. From Fig. 8-24 the solubility product at 1200, 1100 and 900°C is 10^{-3}, 4×10^{-4} and 10^{-5}, respectively. Thus NbN should precipitate at 900 and 1100°C, but dissolve at 1200°C. This points out the fact that Nb will not be effective for austenite grain refinement in the high temperature range of hot working. [However, as we will see, Nb is also added for another reason.] This effect is exemplified by the data in Fig. 8-25 where it is seen that below about 1100°C the austenite grain size varies only slightly with temperature, but above 1100°C there is a strong increase in the grain size.

Figure 8-26 shows the effect of the primary ferrite grain size on the yield strength of a plain carbon steel (same curve as in Fig. 8-21c) and of a steel of similar composition containing Nb. For both steels the Hall-Petch relation is followed. For the unalloyed steel, the primary ferrite grain size was varied by changing the austenite grain size by using different austenitizing temperatures and by using different cooling rates from austenite (see above). This curve is similar to that in Fig. 8-18.

The curve for the unalloyed steel can be extended by microalloying with Nb to retard austenite grain coarsening and hence produce an austenite grain size which is finer than that achievable with the unalloyed steel. This

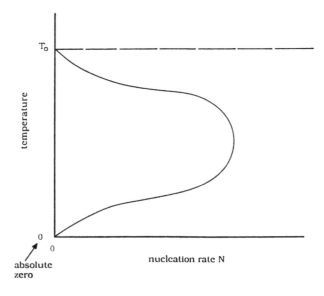

Fig. 8-13 Schematic diagram showing the general temperature dependence of the nucleation rate for a phase transformation occurring below the equilibrium temperature T_0

gives a finer primary ferrite grain size and hence the curve in Fig. 8-26 is an extension of and higher than the one for the unalloyed steel.

Control of austenite grain size in hot working

In structural steels, the primary method of effecting a very fine primary ferrite grain size is by controlling the hot working process so that a very fine austenite grain size is attained. The changes in the grain structure in hot working were depicted in Fig. 8-12. To retain the grain size developed by the hot working, the steel must be cooled and form primary ferrite before excessive austenite grain growth occurs. We will look at the methods used to attain this, but first we will examine the effect of hot working at relatively high temperature on the austenite grain size, and the effect of this on the primary ferrite grain size.

A method to determine the effect of hot working on the austenite grain size is to plastically deform the steel part at a given temperature, then immediately quench the part to 25°C. This minimizes additional grain growth following hot working, and the austenite grain size can be revealed by proper etching, even though following the quenching the structure is now martensite.

Figure 8-27 shows microstructures of a steel containing 0.03% Nb which has been heated to 1200°C, hot rolled in one pass at three different temperatures and for three different amounts of reduction in thickness, then quenched to 25°C. The structures are all martensite, but the prior austenite grain size is quite apparent. It is clear that the austenite grain size is reduced by increasing the amount of plastic deformation. This increases the nucleation rate of the recrystallizing grains, and produces the finer austenite grain size. Also plastic deformation at lower temperature produces a finer grain size. This is due to the lower rate of grain growth which occurs in the steel

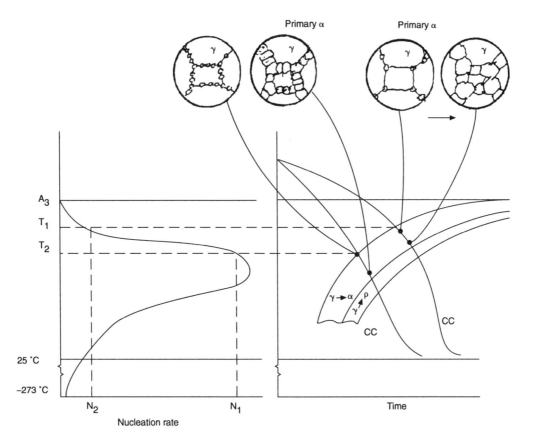

Fig. 8-14 Schematic diagram illustrating the effect of the isothermal transformation temperature on the primary ferrite grain size which nucleates at the austenite grain boundaries

after it exits the rolls. Such grain growth could not be prevented before quenching from the higher temperatures, but it was retarded by deforming at lower temperatures.

The microstructures in Fig. 8-28 show the effect of the processing on the primary ferrite grain structure. The structure after quenching from the austenitizing temperature is shown in (a), (e) and (i); all the other micrographs are for the steel after air cooling. If the steel is reheated to 1250°C then quenched (to form martensite), a coarse austenite grain size is revealed. If the steel is air cooled from this temperature a coarse primary ferrite structure is formed (b). Starting with a smaller austenite grain size (developed by hot working between 1050 and 1250°C), such as in (e) and (i), produces a finer primary ferrite grain

structure ((f) and (j)). These micrographs ((a), (b), (e), (f), (i) and (j)) illustrate dramatically the effect of prior austenite grain size on the primary ferrite grain size.

Further refinement of the primary ferrite structure can be achieved by low temperature hot rolling to obtain an even finer austenite grain size. For example, if this steel with the large austenite grain size (micrograph (a)) is cooled to 850°C, rolled 45% or 60% reduction in thickness, then air cooled, a much finer primary ferrite structure is obtained ((c) and (d)). If the finest austenite grain size structure (i) is rolled 60% at 850°C, the finest primary ferrite structure is obtained (l).

As seen in Fig. 8-28, the recrystallized grain size depends upon the deformation temperature. This dependence is also illustrated by the data in Fig. 8-29 and the

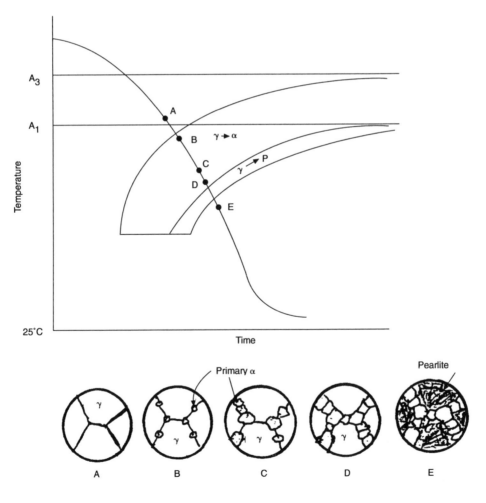

Fig. 8-15 Schematic diagram illustrating the formation of primary ferrite in austenite during continuous cooling. The ferrite nucleated along the austenite grain boundaries

microstructures in Fig. 8-30. It also depends upon the strain rate and the amount of deformation per pass, as illustrated by the data in Fig. 8-31.

In one study, Cuddy found empirically that the recrystallized austenite grain size could be related to the flow stress by the relation

$$d = [623/\sigma]^{2.9}$$

where d is the recrystallized grain size (in mm) and σ is the maximum stress (in MPa) to which the steel is subjected during multipass reductions. The flow stress enters into the relation through its dependence on the strain, the strain rate and the temperature. If a typical flow stress which was used in these experiments is inserted in this relation, the smallest recrystallized austenite grain size is

about 20 μm. This is too large to attain the toughness required for some applications. However, this grain size can be reduced by rolling at a sufficiently low temperature so that the austenite does not recrystallize before forming primary ferrite. Taking this approach, Cuddy obtained for the final primary ferrite grain size the relation

$$d = [1/2] [1.17 - R] [623/\sigma]^{2.9}$$

where R is the total finishing reduction (fraction reduction in thickness). Thus if R = 0.5 and σ = 250 MPa (a typical value used in the experiments), the primary ferrite grain size is about 2 μm.

Thus the possibility of forming primary ferrite from a fine-grained, deformed austenite that has not recrystallized is an important consideration. To develop such

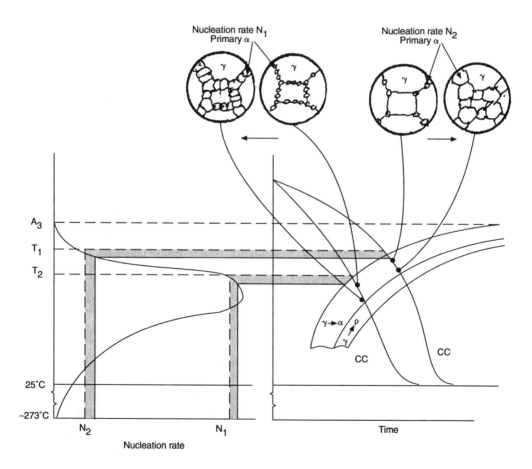

Fig. 8-16 Schematic diagram illustrating the effect of the cooling rate from austenite on the size of the primary ferrite grains which nucleate on the austenite grain boundaries

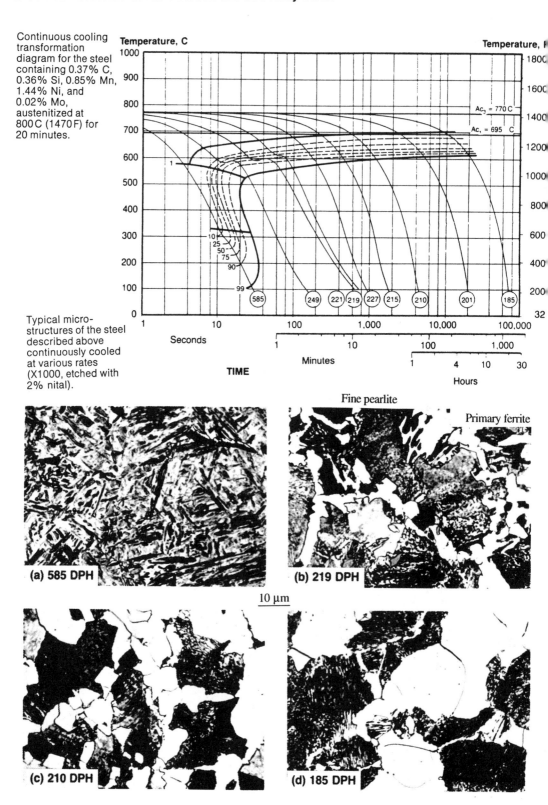

Continuous cooling transformation diagram for the steel containing 0.37% C, 0.36% Si, 0.85% Mn, 1.44% Ni, and 0.02% Mo, austenitized at 800 C (1470 F) for 20 minutes.

Typical microstructures of the steel described above continuously cooled at various rates (X1000, etched with 2% nital).

(a) 585 DPH

(b) 219 DPH

Fine pearlite

Primary ferrite

10 μm

(c) 210 DPH

(d) 185 DPH

Fig. 8-17   Microstructures showing the effect of cooling from austenite on the primary ferrite grain size. (From W.W. Cias, *Phase Transformation Kinetics and Hardenability of Medium-Carbon Alloy Steels,* Climax Molybdenum Co., Greenwich, CT (1972))

structures requires intrinsically a low deformation temperature. The types of structure that may be formed are summarized schematically in Fig. 8-32. Deformation at high temperature gives rise to the structures already discussed (see Fig. 8-27 and 8-28). Deformation at lower temperatures will allow the primary ferrite to form before beginning or completion of recrystallization in the austenite. Microstructures illustrating these effects are shown in Fig. 8-33.

The kinetics of the recrystallization of deformed austenite has been studied in detail for many structural steels. The diagram in Fig. 8-34 shows the effect of rolling temperature and of the reduction in thickness on recrystallization for a specific steel. These data are for one rolling pass at the temperatures indicated. Note that the higher the amount of reduction in thickness, the lower the temperature at which recrystallization is complete. Also note that the greater the amount of deformation at a given

rolling temperature, the *smaller* the recrystallized grain size.

Figure 8-35 compares the primary ferrite grain size developed when deforming the austenite above the transformation temperature and *below* the transformation temperature. [The temperature used depended upon the steels used.] Deformation below the transformation temperature resulted in the formation of ferrite during the deformation, and hence some recrystallization of the ferrite may have occurred. Note that the finest structure was obtained by deforming below the transformation temperature.

Figure 8-36 shows schematically the relation between the kinetics of recrystallization of deformed austenite and that of the formation of primary ferrite. The continuous cooling TTT diagram is for deformed austenite, which will be displaced to shorter times than for underformed austenite. A cooling curve is shown along

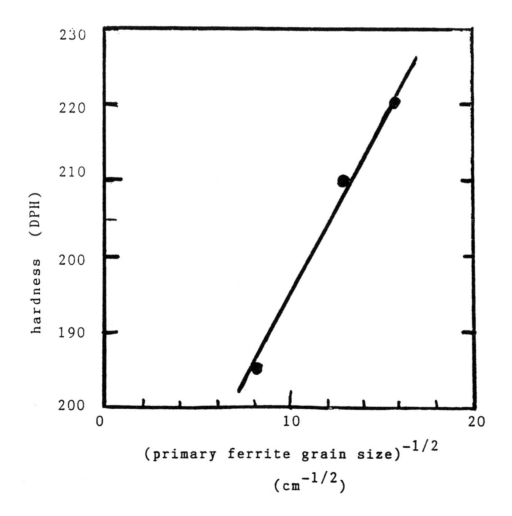

Fig. 8-18 Plot of hardness versus estimates of primary ferrite grain size from data in Fig. 8-17, showing that the Hall-Petch relation is followed

which the regions in which deformation is carried out are noted. In the case shown there, deformation in the austenite is carried out along points 1 to 2, and in this temperature range the rate of recrystallization is sufficiently rapid that hot working is occurring. This is shown by the recrystallization curve being located at shorter times than the cooling curve. However, if deformation of the austenite is carried out in the lower temperature range (from points 3 to 4), then cooling is faster than recrystallization can occur, and primary ferrite begins to form in deformed austenite (at point 4). In the case depicted in the figure, deformation continues from point 4 to 5, which means that the primary ferrite is being deformed as it forms. Thus the final primary ferrite structure will consist of ferrite that has formed from deformed austenite, and which itself has undergone plastic deformation. This deformed ferrite may recrystallize before the steel cools to a low temperature, but in the figure there is no curve that shows this information.

Figure 8-37 shows the continuous cooling TTT diagram for the region of primary ferrite formation for two steels of different Nb content, and illustrates the above concepts. For the lower Nb content steel, the temperature-time curve shows that for this type of deformation, austenite recrystallized on cooling to temperatures of about 1550°F (point 1). Below this temperature the steel was cooling faster than it could recrystallize. Thus primary ferrite began to form at about the same temperature at which recrystallization of the deformed austenite ceased. Deformation was continued during the formation of primary ferrite (from points 1 to 3), but the ferrite only recrystallized in the higher temperature range (from points 1 to 2). Below about 1300°F, the steel was cooling faster than the deformed ferrite could recrystallize, as depicted by the solid line marked "ferrite recryst." The formation of primary ferrite was completed at about 1100°F (point 4), and thus the final primary ferrite structure consisted of ferrite which all formed in deformed austenite but some of which had recrystallized.

In Fig. 8-37b is shown a similar diagram for the same steel but containing more Nb. Note that the higher Nb content has displaced the austenite recrystallization curve to longer times; that is, the Nb has retarded the rate of recrystallization of the deformed austenite. However, the additional Nb had little effect on the recrystallization of ferrite. The effect of the increased Nb content on the kinetics of the formation of the primary ferrite in the deformed austenite was slight.

The effect of the finishing process on the primary ferrite grain size is illustrated by the microstructures in Fig. 8-38. Here the final deformation was carried out *below* the transformation temperature, and during and following the formation of primary ferrite. Thus recrystallization of the primary ferrite occurred. The effect of

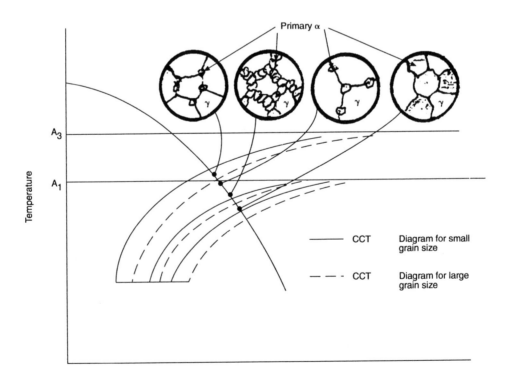

Fig. 8-19 Schematic diagram illustrating the effect of austenite grain size on the primary ferrite grain size. The ferrite nucleated on the austenite grain boundaries

the amount of deformation at 600°C on the yield strength and the toughness is shown in Fig. 8-39. Note the significant increases in strength with the amount of reduction in thickness. Note also that there is a difference in the strength measured in the longitudinal (L) and transverse (T) directions. As mentioned earlier, it is expected that the toughness would increase with a decrease in the primary ferrite grain size. However, for small amounts of deformation the toughness decreases. In the Nb-containing steel it does improve for higher amounts of deformation. The discrepancy of these toughness data has been blamed on the appearance of fissures due to the low rolling temperature.

Precipitation Hardening of the Ferrite

Elements such as Nb and V are useful grain refiners because they form compounds which retard austenite grain growth. They also retard the growth of recrystallized austenite grains, either as particles present or as a solute effect. In addition, some of these elements, especially Nb, have been found to have a strengthening effect above that associated with the effect on the primary ferrite

grain size. This is shown by the curves in Fig. 8-40. If such a steel is austenitized at 1100°C, then air cooled at different rates, the curve marked with this temperature is obtained. Note that this curve is considerably above that for austenitizing at 950°C. If the steel is austenitized at 1250°C, the curve is even higher. Note that for both the 1250 and the 1100°C curves no data exist along the dashed lines. This is because in this high temperature range the austenite grain growth cannot be prevented.

To make clear the importance of the effect of the austenitizing temperature on the strength, we compare the strength for the different temperatures for a primary ferrite grain size of ASTM 8 (at heavy line in Fig. 8-40). The plain carbon steel has a strength of about 17 tons/in.^{2}. Austenitizing at 1100°C gives a value of about 21, and austenitizing at 1250°C a value of about 29. Since the primary ferrite grain size is the same, the strengthening must be due to another factor, which is the precipitation of Nb carbonitrides *in the ferrite* upon cooling. That is, the ferrite is precipitation hardened. Using a higher austenitizing temperature dissolves more of the carbonitrides (thus reducing the effectiveness in refining the grain size of the austenite), and hence on subsequent

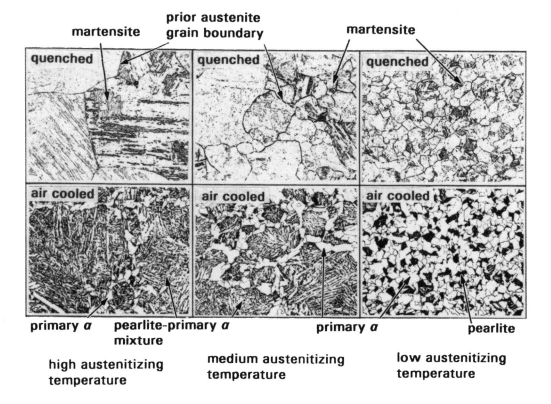

Fig. 8-20 Microstructures illustrating the effect of prior austenite grain size on the primary ferrite grain size. The microstructures (a), (b) and (c) show the initial austenite grain size. The structure here is martensite, in samples quenched after austenitizing at increasingly higher temperatures. The microstructures below each of these are those obtained by air cooling from the austenitizing temperature to produce primary ferrite and pearlite. (Adapted from I. Kozasu, C. Ouchi, T. Sampei, and T. Okita, in *MicroAlloying 75*, p 120, Union Carbide Corporation, New York (1977))

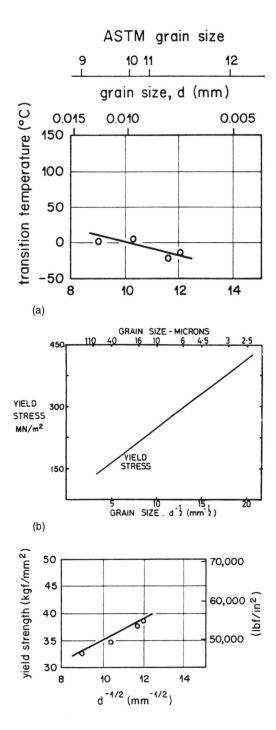

(a)

(b)

cooling more carbonitrides precipitate in the ferrite, giving a higher strength.

The carbonitrides are very fine, as shown by the microstructure in Fig. 8-41. The particles (white) are about 20 atoms across [0.01 μm (note marker in micrograph), or about 100 Å].

As pointed out with regard to Fig. 8-40, at the high austenitizing temperatures grain growth of austenite cannot be prevented. Thus the advantage of dissolving the Nb carbonitrides to achieve subsequent precipitation hardening in the primary ferrite is somewhat offset by the larger primary ferrite grain size. However, the data in Fig. 8-40 were for underformed austenite. Thus if the Nb-containing steel is heated to 1250°C, to dissolve the Nb carbonitrides, then hot worked upon cooling to develop a fine austenite grain size and a subsequent fine primary ferrite grain size, the strength can be increased. This is depicted in Fig. 8-42. Note that the lower the finishing temperature (e.g., 850°C), the smaller the primary ferrite grain size and hence the higher the strength. Also note that fast cooling following the final (finish) rolling gives the

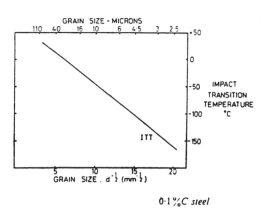

0.1 %C steel

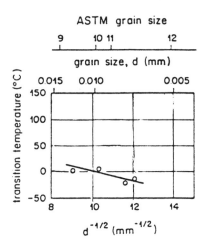

Fig. 8-21 The effect of primary ferrite grain size on the yield strength of some steels. ((a) from I. Kozasu and T. Osuka, *Processing and Properties of Low Carbon Steels*, J.M. Gray, editor, The Metallurgical Society, Warrendale, PA (1973). (b) from F.B. Pickering, *Physical Metallurgy and the Design of Steels*, Applied Science Publishers, London (1978). (c) from K.J. Irvine, *J. Iron and Steel Institute*, Vol 207, p 837 (1969))

Fig. 8-22 Effect of primary ferrite grain size on the impact transition temperature of two steels. ((a) from same source as Fig. 8-21a. (b) from same source as Fig. 8-21b))

highest strength. This is because the fast cooling minimizes precipitation of the Nb carbonitrides in the austenite during cooling, and hence maximizes the subsequent precipitation hardening effect in the primary ferrite.

Some Thermomechanical Processing Treatments of Structural Steels

With the background given in the preceding sections, we are now in a position to examine some commercial thermomechanical processes used on structural steels. Two aspects are involved: hot deformation and controlled cooling. The hot deformation of austenite is used to achieve a fine austenite grain size, and in some cases the hot deformation extends to that of the ferrite which has formed from the austenite. This type of hot working develops a fine primary ferrite grain size. The controlled cooling is used to cool the steel properly to control the recrystallization process (e.g., in some cases to prevent it) and to control the precipitation of the carbonitrides in the ferrite. The major commercial development has been to combine these aspects into a continuous deformation process, such as in a hot rolling strip mill.

The general idea is depicted schematically in Fig. 8-43. This shows the change in the austenite grain size as a steel plate is hot worked during cooling. The width of the cross-hatched area is an indication of the plate thickness. The abrupt change in the cooling rate below the A_{r1} temperature is designed to allow the precipitation of carbonitrides in the primary ferrite.

An example of the transformation for a specific steel is shown in Fig. 8-44. Shown on the continuous cooling TTT diagram are five cooling curves. At the end of each curve is the as-cooled hardness (Rockwell B), and the primary ferrite grain size. [The other numbers on the curves are the percentages of primary ferrite and pearlite.] The dashed line shows a typical cooling curve for a thermomechanically processed plate. At about 550°C, the sheet left the final roll, and if the sheet cooled in air, the dashed curve marked "plate cooling" is followed. However, more precipitation of carbonitrides in the ferrite occurs if the cooling rate is reduced. This can be achieved by the slower cooling when the sheet is coiled, as noted by the curve marked "coil cooling." Thus in this process, the controlled rolling develops the small primary ferrite grain size, and the controlled cooling, to allow precipitation hardening of the ferrite, is achieved during cooling of

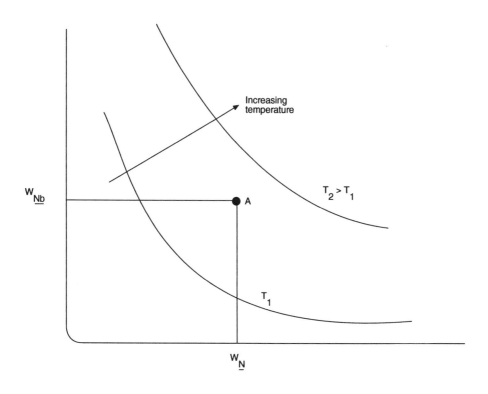

Fig. 8-23 Schematic illustration of the relation between the Nb and N content of austenite if they react to form NbN and at two temperatures

the sheet in the coil. The process is depicted schematically in Fig. 8-45.

Effect of Carbon and Manganese Content on Properties

Two important compositional variables which we now examine are carbon and manganese content. The strength, especially the tensile strength, of structural steels is increased by increasing the carbon content since this increases the amount of pearlite (Fig. 8-46). This contribution is essentially linear with carbon content. The addition of Mn increases the strength through its effect of solid solution hardening, and this contribution is essentially linear with Mn content. Also the Mn content lowers the eutectoid carbon content, giving more pearlite (for a fixed carbon content) with increasing Mn content. The contribution to the tensile strength from these effects is depicted in Fig. 8-47.

In these steels there also is a contribution from solid solution strengthening of the ferrite by silicon and free nitrogen. The magnitude increases with an increase in the amount of these, but the variation is slight, and thus the contribution is shown as a constant value in Fig. 8-47b. [A contribution due to these two elements is not shown in Fig. 8-47a.]

There is the important additional contribution from the primary ferrite grain size and from precipitation hardening. These are also shown in Fig. 8-47 for a fixed processing procedure and fixed amount of element which causes precipitation hardening (e.g., Nb). Also note in this figure that the contribution from primary ferrite grain size increases slightly with the Mn and the C content. This is due to the effect that increasing amounts of each has on shifting the continuous cooling TTT diagram to longer times, so that for a given cooling rate, the primary ferrite begins to form at a lower temperature, giving a smaller primary ferrite grain size.

The effects of alloying elements on toughness are somewhat more difficult to assess. In general, increasing strength means a less tough steel, unless the strength increase is caused by a finer primary ferrite grain size. The effects of microstructural variables and chemical composition are summarized in Fig. 8-48. Note that of the microstructural parameters only ferrite grain refinement lowers the transition temperature. Mn and Al lower it also, but indirectly through their effect on the primary ferrite grain size or on removal of nitrogen from solid solution.

Figure 8-49 summarizes schematically the general combinations of yield strength and toughness available in primary ferrite-pearlite structural steels. Mathematical re-

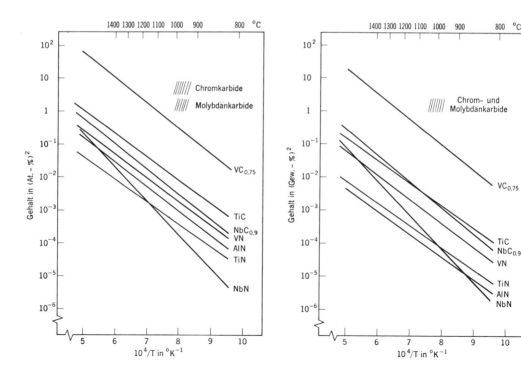

Fig. 8-24 Solubility product for various carbides and nitrides in austenite. (From B. Aronsson, in *Steel Strengthening Mechanisms*, p 77, Climax Molybdenum Co., Greenwich, CT (1969))

lations relating mechanical properties to structural characteristics (e.g., primary ferrite grain size) for steels of primary ferrite-pearlite structure are given in Chapter 9.

Some References on Structural Steels

- K.J. Irvine, "The Physical Metallurgy of Steel," *J. Iron and Steel Institute*, Vol 207, p 854 (1969)
- W.E. Duckworth and J.D. Baird, "Mild Steels," *J. Iron and Steel Institute*, Vol 207, p 854 (1969)
- J.M. Gray, "Technology of Microalloyed Steel for Large Diameter Pipe," *Int. J. Pressure Vessels and Piping*, Vol 2, p 95 (1974)
- *MicroAlloying 75*, Union Carbide Corporation, New York (1977)
- L. Meyer and H. de Boer, "HSLA Plant Metallurgy: Alloying, Normalizing, Controlled Rolling," *J. Metals*, p 17 (Jan 1977)
- *Hot Deformation of Austenite*, J.B. Ballance, editor, The Metallurgical Society, Warrendale, PA (1977)

- F.B. Pickering, *Physical Metallurgy and the Design of Steels*, Applied Science Publishers, London (1978)
- L.J. Cuddy, "Thermomechanical Treatment of Steels: Controlled Rolling," *J. Educational Modules for Materials Science and Engineering*, Vol 1, p 739 (1979)
- T. Tanaka, "Controlled Rolling of Steel Plate and Strip," *Int. Metals Reviews*, p 185 (No. 4, 1981)
- W.C. Leslie, *The Physical Metallurgy of Steels*, Hemisphere Publishing Corporation/McGraw-Hill Book Company, New York (1981)
- L.F. Porter and P.E. Repas, "The Evolution of HSLA Steels," *J. Metals*, p 14 (April 1982)
- *HSLA—Steels Technology and Applications*, American Society for Metals, Metals Park, Ohio (1984)
- R.S. Cline, W.E. Heitmann, and D. Bhattacharya, "Microalloyed Steel Bars and Forgings," *J. Metals*, p 26 (May 1986)
- *HSLA Steels: Metallurgy and Applications*, J.M. Gray, T. Ko, Z. Shouhua, W. Baorong, and X.

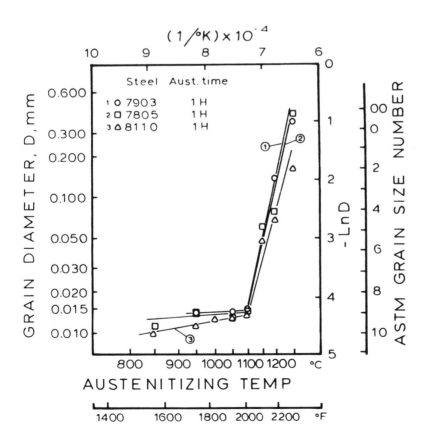

Fig. 8-25 The effect of austenitizing temperature on the austenite grain size for steels containing about 0.8% C and about 0.8% Nb. (From R. Coladas, J. Masounave, J.-P. Bailon, in *The Hot Deformation of Austenite*, p 341, J.B. Ballace, editor, The Metallurgical Society, Warrendale, PA (1977))

Xishan, editors, ASM International, Materials Park, Ohio (1986)

• High-Strength Structural and High-Strength Low-Alloy Steels, p 389-423, *Metals Handbook*, Vol 1,

Properties and Selection: Irons, Steels and High-Performance Alloys, ASM International, Materials Park, Ohio (1990)

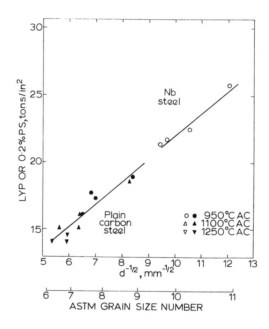

Fig. 8-26 Effect of primary ferrite grain size on the yield strength of plain carbon structural steels and such steels containing niobium. (Adapted from K.J. Irvine, *J. Iron and Steel Institute*, Vol 207, p 837 (1969))

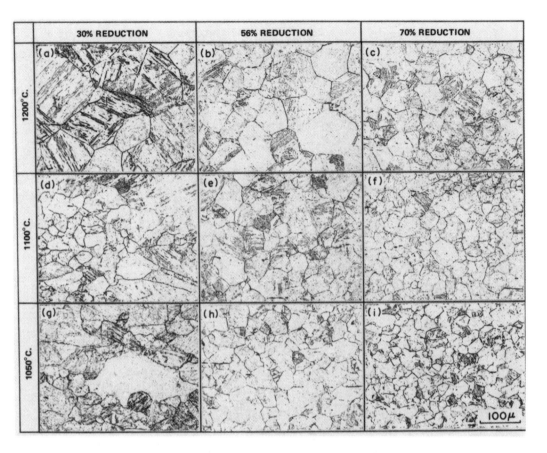

Fig. 8-27 The effect of different processing conditions on the austenite grain size of a 0.03% Nb steel that was reheated to 1250°C, rolled in one pass, then quenched to form martensite. (From I. Kozasu, C. Ouchi, T. Sampei, and T. Okita, in *MicroAlloying 75*, p 120, Union Carbide Corporation, New York (1977))

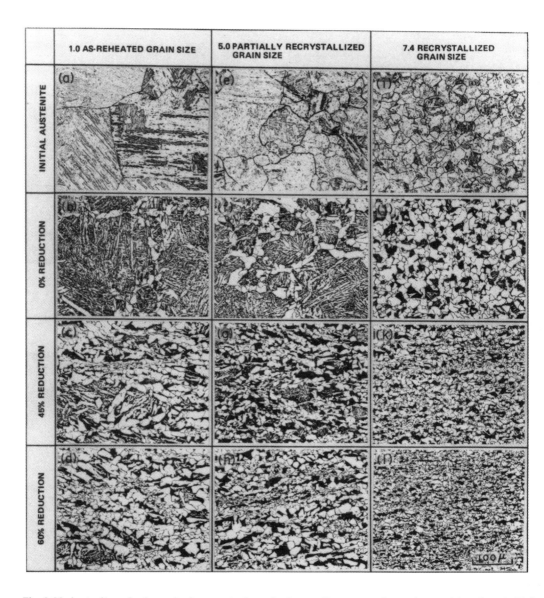

Fig. 8-28 Austenite grain size and subsequent primary ferrite-pearlite structure for steels containing about 0.4% C and 0.03% Nb. The austenite grain size was varied by rolling above 1050°C. The final rolling was carried out at 850°C, followed by air cooling. In the top row of micrographs, the samples were water quenched to produce all martensite. This reveals the prior austenite grain size for the other treatments shown. All other samples were air cooled after the final rolling to produce primary ferrite-pearlite mixture. (From same source as Fig. 8-27)

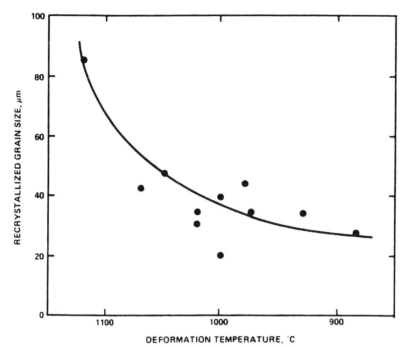

Effect on recrystallized grain size of the deformation temperature within the complete-recrystallization range. Total reduction 40 to 60 pct in 5 passes, 0.05 Nb-N steel.

Fig. 8-29 Effect of deformation temperature on the recrystallized austenite grain size. The steel contained about 0.1% C and 0.05% Nb. (From L.J. Cuddy, *Met. Trans.*, Vol 12A, p 1313 (1981))

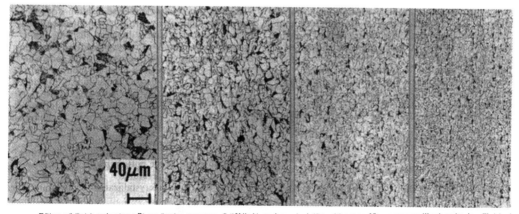

Effect of finish reduction (R) on ferrite structure. 0.05Nb-N steel roughed 40 to 60 pct to 30 μm recrystallized grain size. Finished in four to six passes between 880 and 820 °C. Transformed at 650 °C, 2 min. Magnification 190 times. Recrystallized austenite, 30 μm (extreme left); four passes, 880 to 820 °C, R = 49 pct (center left); four passes, 880 to 820 °C, R = 67 pct (center right); six passes, 880 to 820 °C, R = 90 pct (extreme right).

Fig. 8-30 Microstructures illustrating the effect of finishing temperature and the amount of reduction on the primary ferrite grain size. (From same source as Fig. 8-29)

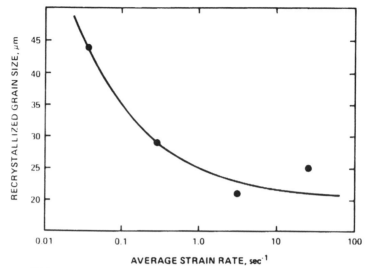

Effect of strain-rate on recrystallized grain size of the 0.05
Nb-N steel reduced ~70 pct in a single pass at 1050 °C.

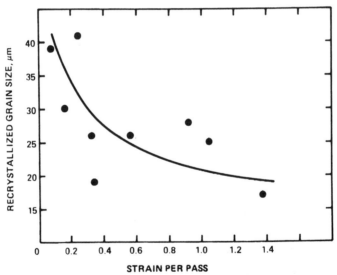

Effect of strain per pass on recrystallized grain size in the 0.05
Nb-N steel reduced 65-75 pct between 1060 and 980 °C.

Fig. 8-31 The effect of the strain rate and the reduction per pass on the recrystallized austenite grain size. (From same source as Fig. 8-29)

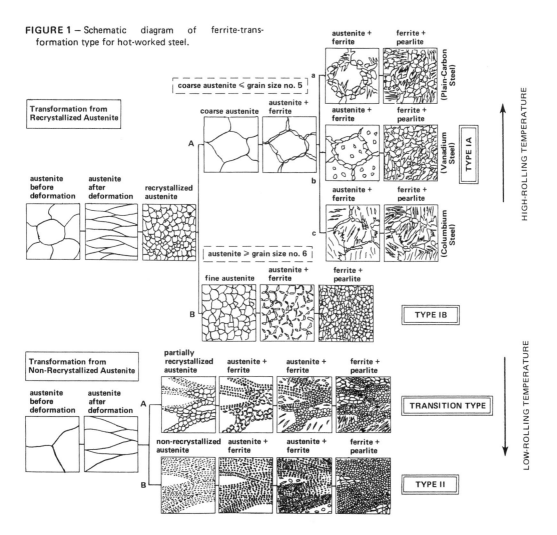

FIGURE 1 — Schematic diagram of ferrite-transformation type for hot-worked steel.

Fig. 8-32 Schematic diagram of the effect of thermomechanical processing on the austenite grain size and on the subsequent primary ferrite grain size. (From M. Fukuda, T. Hashimoto, and K. Kunishige, in *MicroAlloying 75*, p 136, Union Carbide Corporation, New York (1977))

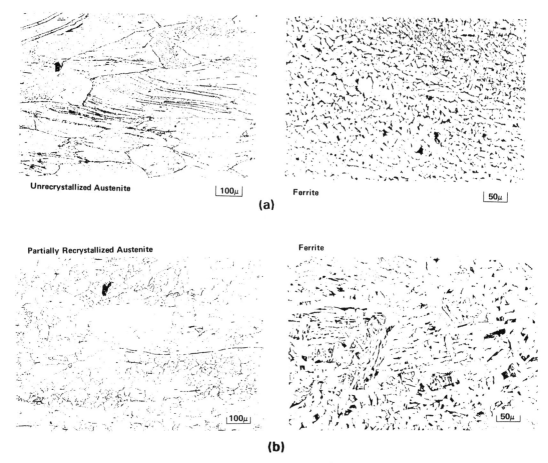

Fig. 8-33 Microstructures illustrating the effect on the primary ferrite grain size of forming primary ferrite and pearlite from an austenite that is (a) unrecrystallized and (b) partially recrystallized. The micrographs on the left are for the samples water quenched to form martensite, thus allowing revelation of the austenite grain structure. The micrographs on the right are for the samples air cooled following deformation, allowing the austenite structure shown at the left to form primary ferrite and pearlite. (From T.M. Hoogendoorn and M.J. Spanraft, in *MicroAlloying 75*, p 75, Union Carbide Corporation, New York (1977))

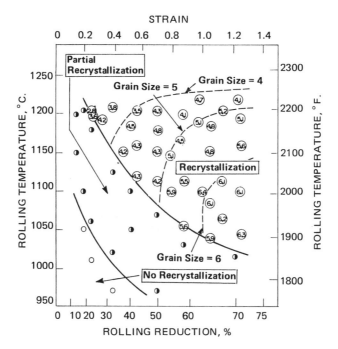

Austenite recrystallization and resulting grain size as a function of rolling temperature and reduction for 0.03% columbium steel. The steel was reheated to 1250°C. for 20 minutes, rolled with one pass, and quenched. The initial grain-size number was 1.0.

Fig. 8-34 Diagram showing for a structural steel the recrystallization process as a function of the reduction in thickness by rolling and the rolling temperature. The numbers in the circles are ASTM grain size values. (From same source as Fig. 8-27)

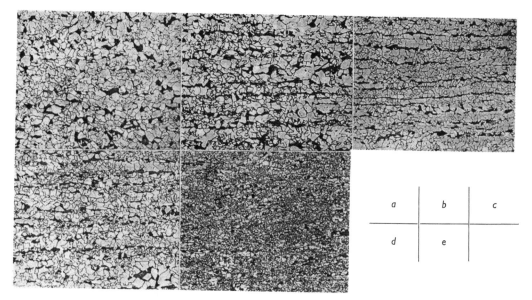

a 0% reduction; *b* 40% reduction, finished above transformation; *c* 65% reduction, finished above transformation; *d* 40% reduction, finished below transformation; *e* 65% reduction, finished below transformation
Metallographic structures of vermiculite cooled Nb steel × 120

Fig. 8-35 Microstructures illustrating the effect on the primary ferrite grain size of plastically deforming the austenite below the transformation temperature. (From R. Priestner and E. de los Rios, in *Heat Treatment '76*, p 129, The Metals Society, London (1976))

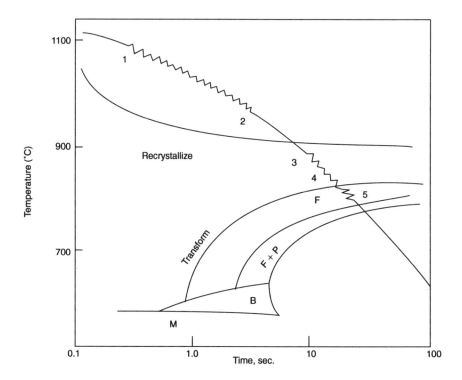

Fig. 8-36 Schematic illustration of the relationship of the recrystallization of deformed austenite and the formation of primary ferrite. (Adapted from L.J. Cuddy, *J. Mats. Ed.*, Vol 1, p 739 (1979))

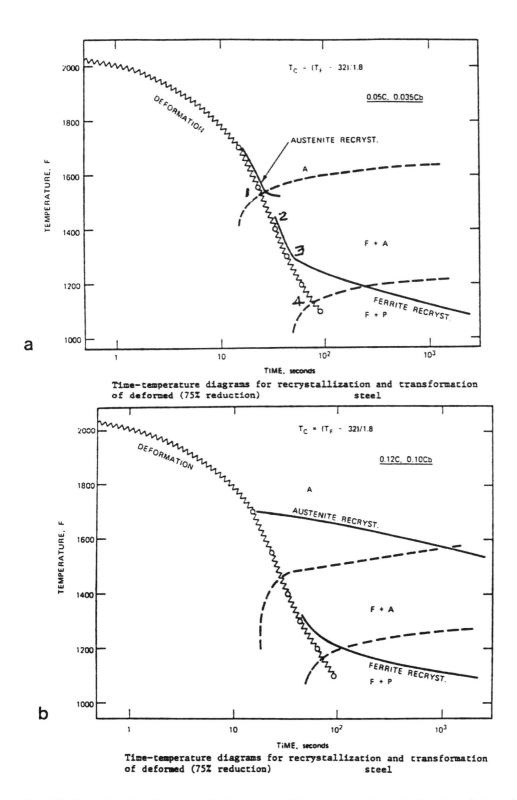

Fig. 8-37 The relationship of the recrystallization process of deformed austenite and the formation of primary ferrite for two Nb-containing steels. (From L.J. Cuddy, in *The Hot Deformation of Austenite*, p 169, J.B. Ballace, editor, The Metallurgical Society, Warrendale, PA (1977))

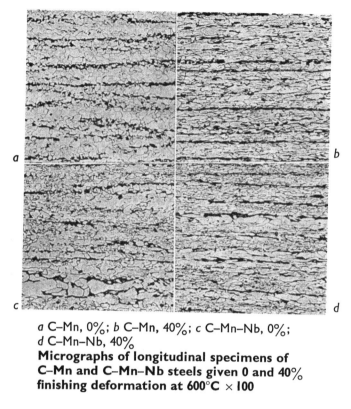

a C–Mn, 0%; *b* C–Mn, 40%; *c* C–Mn–Nb, 0%;
d C–Mn–Nb, 40%
**Micrographs of longitudinal specimens of
C–Mn and C–Mn–Nb steels given 0 and 40%
finishing deformation at 600°C × 100**

Fig. 8-38 The effect of the amount of plastic deformation, when deformed below the transformation temperature, on the primary ferrite grain structure. (From W.B. Morrison and B. Mintz, *Heat Treatment '76*, p 135, The Metals Society, London (1976))

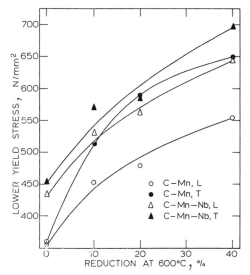

Influence of finishing deformation on lower yield strength

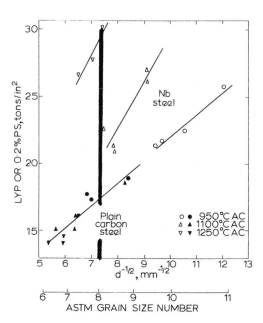

Fig. 8-40 The effect of austenitizing temperature on the relation between the yield strength and the primary ferrite grain size in Nb-containing steels. (Adapted from K.J. Irvine, *J. Iron and Steel Institute*, Vol 207, p 837 (1969))

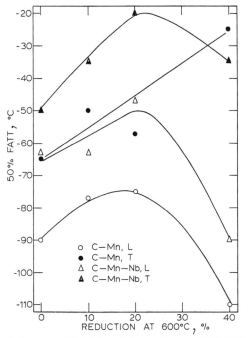

Influence of finishing deformation on 50% FATT

Fig. 8-39 The effect of the amount of deformation on the yield strength and the toughness of some structural steels. (From same source as Fig. 8-35)

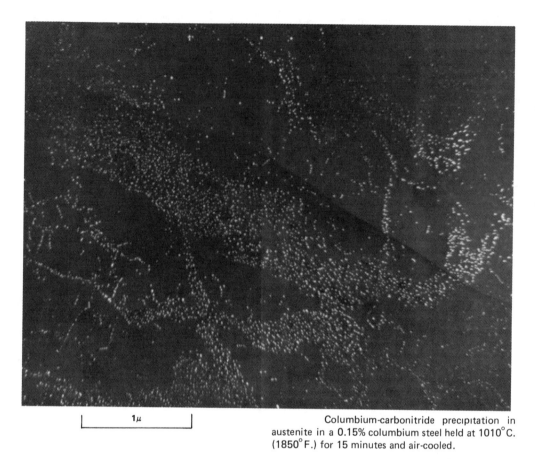

1μ

Columbium-carbonitride precipitation in austenite in a 0.15% columbium steel held at 1010°C. (1850°F.) for 15 minutes and air-cooled.

Fig. 8-41 Transmission electron micrograph (dark field) showing fine Nb carbonitrides (white) in a 0.15% Nb steel. (From G. Gauthier and A.B. LeBon, *MicroAlloying 75,* Union Carbide Corporation, New York, p 73 (1975))

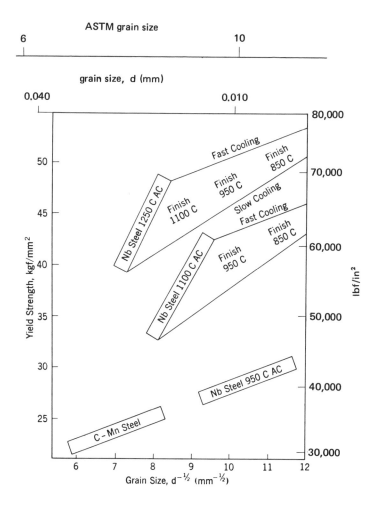

Fig. 8-42 The influence of hot rolling variables on the effect of primary ferrite grain size on the yield strength of Nb-containing steels. (Adapted from K.J. Irvine, A Comparison of the Bainite Transformation with Other Strengthening Mechanisms in High-Strength Structural Steel, *Steel-Strengthening Mechanisms*, p 55, Climax Molybdenum Company, Ann Arbor, MI (1969))

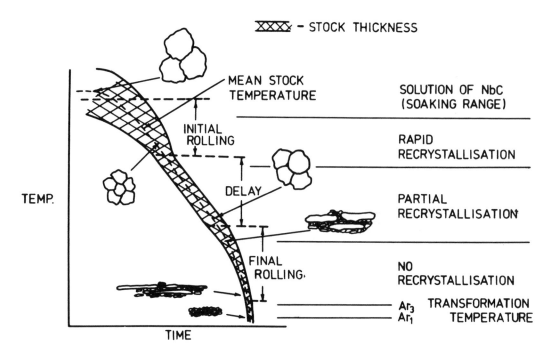

Fig. 8-43 Schematic illustration of the hot rolling process used for structural steels. The width of the cross-hatched area is an indication of the plate thickness. (Adapted from J.K. Baird and R.R. Preston, in *Processing and Properties of Low Carbon Steel*, The Metallurgical Society, Warrendale, PA (1973))

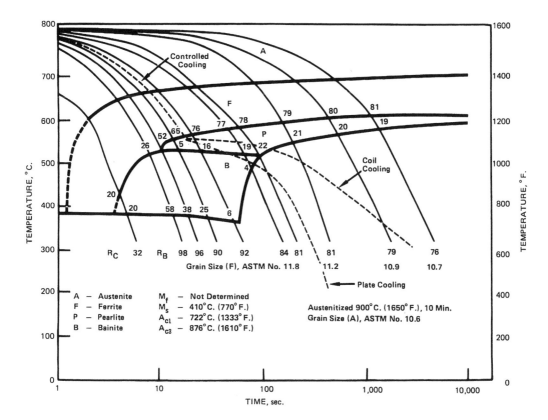

Continuous-cooling transformation diagrams for a vanadium-nitrogen microalloyed steel. Cooling paths for controlled-cooled coils and plates, are superimposed on this diagram. This steel analyzed 0.16% carbon, 1.40% manganese, 0.004% phosphorus, 0.012% sulfur, 0.40% silicon, 0.04% aluminum, 0.11% vanadium, and 0.018% nitrogen.

Fig. 8-44 A continuous cooling TTT diagram for a structural steel, showing a cooling curve typically used in making sheet material. (From J.D. Grozier, in *MicroAlloying 75*, p 241, Union Carbide Corp., New York (1977))

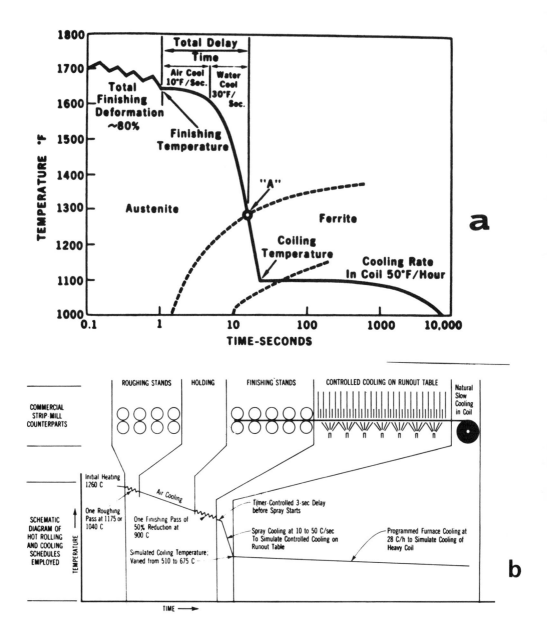

Fig. 8-45 Illustrations of the process for development of fine-grained primary ferrite-pearlite structure in structural steels. ((a) adapted from M. Korchynsky and H. Stuart, in *Low Alloy, High Strength Steels*, Metallurg Co., Dusseldorf (1970). (b) from A.P. Coldren, R.L. Cryderman, and M. Semchyshen, in *Steel Strengthening Mechanisms*, p 17, Climax Molybdenum, Ann Arbor, MI (1969))

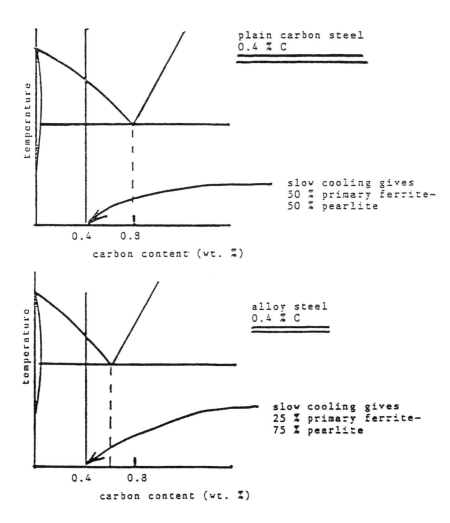

plain carbon steel
0.4 % C

slow cooling gives
50 % primary ferrite-
50 % pearlite

alloy steel
0.4 % C

slow cooling gives
25 % primary ferrite-
75 % pearlite

Fig. 8-46 Schematic illustration of the effect of alloying elements shifting the carbon content of the eutectoid point and hence allowing more pearlite to form upon slow cooling

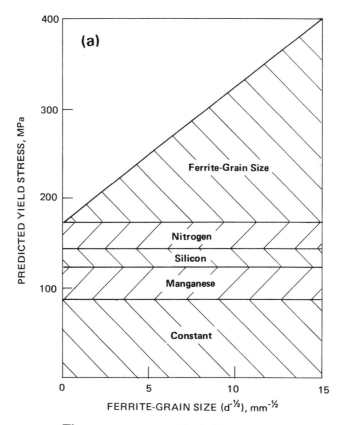

The components of yield stress for
an air-cooled carbon-manganese steel
containing 1.0 % manganese, 0.25 %
silicon and 0.01 % nitrogen.

Fig. 8-47 Factors affecting (a) the tensile strength and (b) the yield strength of structural steels with a primary ferrite-pearlite microstructure. (From T. Gladman, D. Dulieu, and I.D. McIvor, in *MicroAlloying 75*, p 32, Union Carbide Corporation, New York (1977)) *(continued)*

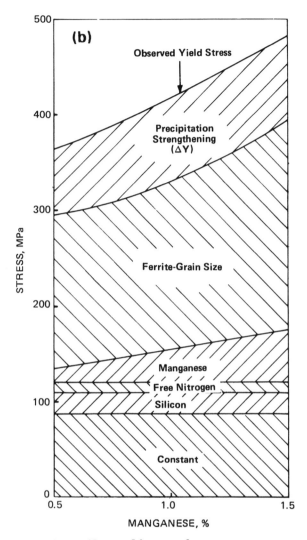

The effect of increasing manganese content on the components of the yield stress of steels containing 0.02 % carbon, 0.2 % silicon, 0.15 % vanadium and 0.015 % nitrogen, normalized from 900 °C.

Fig. 8-47 (continued) Factors affecting (a) the tensile strength and (b) the yield strength of structural steels with a primary ferrite-pearlite microstructure. (From T. Gladman, D. Dulieu, and I.D. McIvor, in *MicroAlloying 75*, p 32, Union Carbide Corporation, New York (1977))

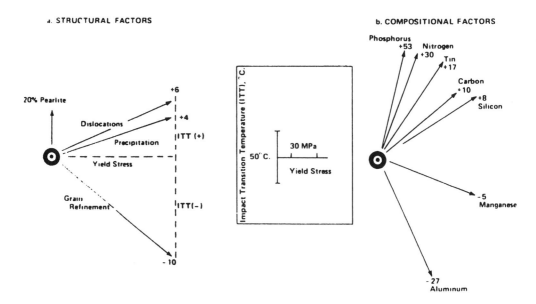

Fig. 8-48 Factors affecting the yield strength and toughness in structural steels with a primary ferrite-pearlite microstructure. (From F.B. Pickering, *Physical Metallurgy and the Design of Steels*, Applied Science Publishers, London (1978))

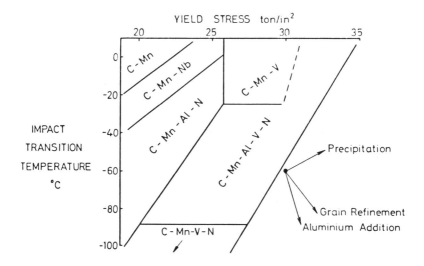

Fig. 8-49 Schematic illustration of the general combinations of yield strength and toughness available in structural steels with a primary ferrite-pearlite microstructure. (From same source as Fig. 8-45a)

Modeling and Use of Correlations in Heat Treatment

Introduction

If the fundamental principles governing the behavior of steels were sufficiently understood, the necessary processing to provide desired properties could be predicted and used in practice. This understanding, of course, is not available at this level. Instead, theories are used where valid, and where not reliance is placed on correlations connecting processing and the resulting properties.

For example, the microstructure at locations in hardened steel components can be predicted, in principle, if the cooling curves at the various locations and the kinetics of the transformation of austenite to the various microconstituents are known. This is illustrated schematically in Fig. 9-1. The cooling curve can be determined using fairly well developed heat transfer calculation methods. But modeling from first principles (e.g., nucleation and growth theory) the kinetics of the formation of the microconstituents (e.g., pearlite, primary ferrite, bainite) is difficult. Another approach, in order to predict the microstructure, is to calculate the continuous cooling transformation (CCT) diagram from an empirical approach, using many predetermined CCT diagrams to determine expressions relating the key times and temperatures of the decomposition of austenite to the chemical composition and the austenite grain size. This approach is similar to that used to calculate the Jominy curve (see Chapter 3).

If the microstructure is known at various locations in the component, the mechanical properties can be estimated, since they depend on the microstructure. This requires knowledge of the properties of the individual microconstituents and the amount of each constituent. However, the properties of each microconstituent depend on the characteristics of the microconstituent; for example, the hardness of pearlite depends on the interlamellar spacing.

Some approaches to estimating properties of heat treated steels have been described in previous chapters. For example, an empirical approach to estimate the Jominy curve, which correlated the hardness with the cooling rate from austenite, was described in Chapter 3, and correlations to calculate tempered hardness were described in Chapter 5. Other methods will be covered in this chapter.

The bases for some of the models and correlations covered in this chapter are too detailed and complicated to cover here. However, references to original work are given in which the details can be found. It is also useful to remember that these approaches only provide information to serve as guidelines for establishing processing and for predicting expected properties. For all of the models and correlations, it is prudent to keep in mind restrictions which limit their applicability.

Calculation of Cooling Curves

The general characteristics of the heat transfer upon cooling steels from the austenite region were outlined in Chapter 4. As shown in Fig. 4-3, the temperature is not a simple function of time. These data show that the highest heat transfer rate occurs at intermediate temperatures (stage 2, nucleate boiling, see Chapter 4) and for hardening it is desirable that this corresponds to the temperature range in which the transformation rate is highest (i.e., the "nose" of the TTT diagram). However, the data in Fig. 4-2 show that this may not always occur. Thus it is of interest to know the effect of quenchant and of the geometry and size of the steel component on the entire temperature-time curve at various locations in the component.

There are features of quenching steels that complicate calculation of a temperature-time curve. One is that the appropriate heat transfer properties (thermal conductivity and thermal diffusivity of the steel and heat transfer film coefficient of the quenchant) are temperature de-

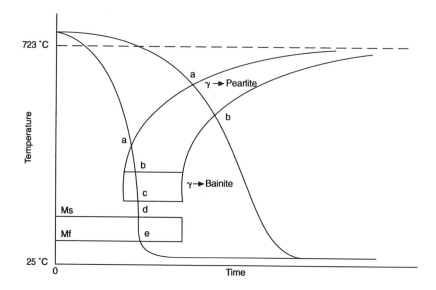

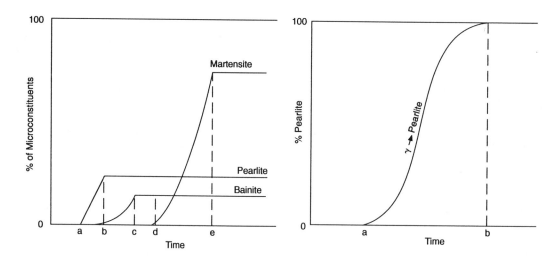

Fig 9-1 Schematic illustration of the effect of the decomposition of austenite during cooling on the transformation products present after quenching

pendent. This is illustrated in Fig. 9-2 and 9-3. However, the thermal properties of steels are not very temperature sensitive in the temperature range where cooling is im-

portant in hardening. For example, Fig. 9-2 shows that the thermal diffusivity of austenite is about 0.008 at 900°C but only decreases to about 0.007 at 700°C; the diffusivity

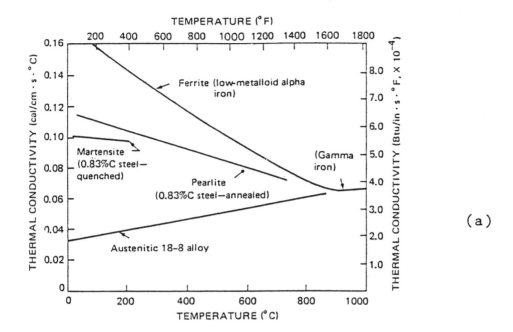

(a)

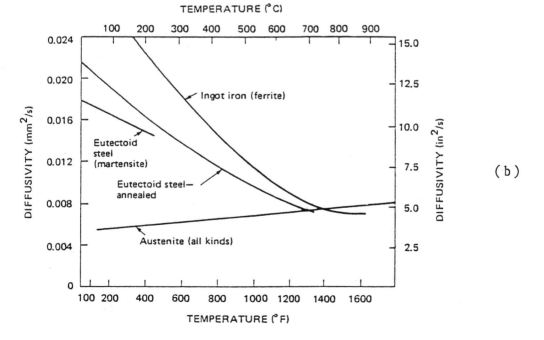

(b)

Fig 9-2 (a) The thermal conductivity and (b) thermal diffusivity of steels as a function of temperature. (From J.B. Austin, *Flow of Heat in Metals*, American Society for Metals, Metals Park, Ohio (1942))

of pearlite (annealed eutectoid steel) is about the same. The thermal conductivity of austenite is about 0.07 at 900°C, but increases to about 0.09 at 700°C, and that of pearlite at this temperature is about 0.07. These quantities are also not very sensitive to the chemical composition of the steel.

The film coefficient is much more sensitive to temperature. This is shown in Table 9-1. Figure 9-3 shows that for water the film coefficient is about one around 900°C, but around 700°C (about 200°C lower), which is in the nucleate boiling regime (stage 2, see Chapter 4), the value has increased to about 1000. The film coefficient is very sensitive to the quenchant and the relative velocity of the steel part and the quenchant, as shown in Table 9-1. As discussed in Chapter 4, choosing a quenchant is the most common method of controlling the cooling rate in quenching. Note in Table 9-1 that the data are also given in terms of the Grossmann number, or H value of the quenchant (see Chapter 4).

Another complication in calculating the cooling curve is that the curve is perturbed by the heat of transformation. This is shown in Fig. 9-4. This means that to be rigorous in calculating the cooling curve, the kinetics of the decomposition of austenite and the accompanying heat release must be accounted for. This is not usually taken into account in film coefficient data since they are usually measured using a material which has no phase transformation (e.g., a solid solution alloy or nickel).

The basic mathematical expressions to use in calculating the temperature-time curves were given in Chapter 4. The usual approach is to use an average value of the conductivity, thermal diffusivity and film coefficient, and the perturbation in the cooling curve from the heat of transformation is neglected.

Solutions to the heat transfer in simple shapes, such as cylinders and plates, have been obtained. However, the results are not usually given in terms of temperature-time curves, but in reduced and dimensionless parameters, from which the cooling curves can be determined. Further, many of these solutions are for special cases, such as the cooling (or heating) of thin plates or small diameter cylinders where the temperatures at the center and the surface are assumed to be identical. Thus many of the treatments may not be amenable to obtaining the cooling curves of interest in quenching steels.

Also, many of the treatments do not deal with the case of high film coefficients, but are more applicable to cases such as heating or cooling in air. Figure 9-5 shows such a case. The results are shown in dimensionless form, with the parameters defined in the figure. The parameter on the curve is the inverse of the Biot number B_i, where $B_i = h/k$. For a 2.54 cm radius cylinder quenched into still water, with a film coefficient of about 5000 W/m$^2 \cdot$ K, $B_i = 2.4$

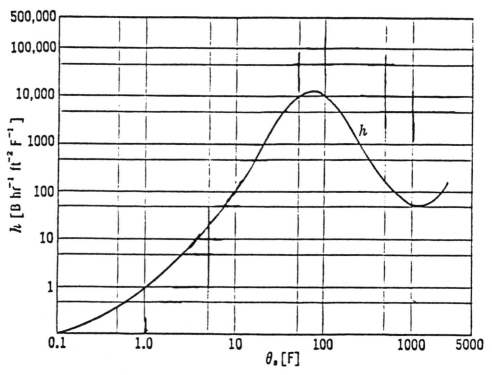

Fig 9-3   Film heat transfer coefficient as a function of temperature for water cooling a Chromel C wire. (Adapted from E.A. Farber and R.L. Scorah, *Trans. Am. Soc. Mech. Engrs.*, Vol 70, p 369 (1948))

This places the region of interest in the upper left hand corner where it is difficult to read the reduced temperature-reduced time values.

Results based on the relations presented in Chapter 4, which do cover the range which can be used for calculations for quenching, are given in Table 9-2. For a cylinder of 2.54 cm radius and a film coefficient of 5000, $B_i = 2.4$; this is HL in the tables. If the initial temperature of the cylinder is 980°C and the quenchant temperature is 25°C, then the time for the temperature to decrease to about 200°C can be determined. These temperatures correspond to a value of $U = 0.2$, and the appropriate table gives $\tau = 0.7$ for the center of the cylinder ($x/L = 0$). $\tau = \alpha t/r^2 = 0.02t = 0.7$, which gives $t = 30$ sec. This procedure can be repeated to obtain the cooling curve at any diametrical location.

Calculation of Heating Curves

The calculation of heating curves, of importance in austenitizing and tempering, is approached in the same manner as that of cooling curves, as discussed in the previous section. The main difference is that usually heating is in air, which has a low film coefficient (see Table 9-1), although some treatments are carried out in molten salts and molten metals. The data in Table 9-2 can be used to calculate the heating curves. These results have the same assumptions built in as described in the previous section: constant thermal conductivity and thermal diffusivity of the steel, constant film coefficient, and neglect

of the heat absorption upon the decomposition of the microconstituents to austenite.

The effect of sample size on the time to heat the center of cylinders in air from 25°C to a temperature of 900°C was calculated and the result is shown in Fig. 9-6. The film coefficient for still air was taken as 200 W/m² · K (Table 9-1). It is seen that a 2.5 cm (1 inch) radius cylinder takes about 20 minutes for the center to become within about 5°C of 900°C, and for a 1.3 cm (0.5 inch) radius cylinder it takes about 10 minutes.

Estimating Austenitizing Time

As pointed out in Chapter 6, for proper austenitizing, the time *in the furnace* must allow the center of the component, which heats most slowly, to attain homogeneous austenite. The required time at the furnace temperature depends on the kinetics of the decomposition of austenite from the precursor structure (e.g., pearlite, tempered martensite). Such data can be represented as a continuous heating time-temperature-transformation diagram for the formation of austenite, such as shown in Fig. 9-7, which shows that the time depends upon the heating rate. This diagram is for a specific steel having a specific starting microstructure (in this case pearlite with a small amount of primary ferrite).

The intersection of a given heating curve with the kinetic curves in Fig. 9-7 shows the progress of austenitization along the heating curve. The upper shaded curve is the one which represents the attainment of homogeneous austenite, and can be represented by the solid line. If a

Table 9-1   Severity of quench values (H) and film coefficients for several quenchants. (From C.E. Bates, Predicting Properties and Minimizing Residual Stress in Quenched Steel Parts, *Journal of Heat Treating*, Vol 6, p 27-45 (1988))

Quenchant	Quenchant temperature		Quenchant velocity		Grossmann number,	Effective film coefficient	
	°C	°F	m/s	ft/min	(H = h/2k)	W/m² · K	Btu/ft² · h · °F
Water	32	90	0.00	0	1.1	5000	880
			0.25	50	2.1	9000	1600
			0.51	100	2.7	12000	2100
			0.76	150	2.8	12000	2100
	55	130	0.00	0	0.2	1000	180
			0.25	50	0.6	2500	440
			0.51	100	1.5	6500	1100
			0.76	150	2.4	10500	1850
Fast oil	60	140	0.00	0	0.5	2000	350
			0.25	50	1.0	4500	790
			0.51	100	1.1	5000	880
			0.76	150	1.5	6500	1200
25% polyvinyl pyrrolidone	43	110	0.00	0	0.8	3500	620
			0.25	50	1.3	6000	1100
			0.51	100	1.5	6500	1200
			0.76	150	1.8	7500	1300
Conventional oil	65	150	0.51	100	0.7	3000	530
Martempering oil	150	300	0.51	100	1.2	5000	880
Air	27	80	0.00	0	0.05	200	35
			2.54	500	0.06	250	44
			5.08	1000	0.08	350	62

SAE 1040 Steel

Composition: 0.39% C - 0.72% Mn - 0.23% Si - 0.010% P - 0.018% S Grain size: 7-8

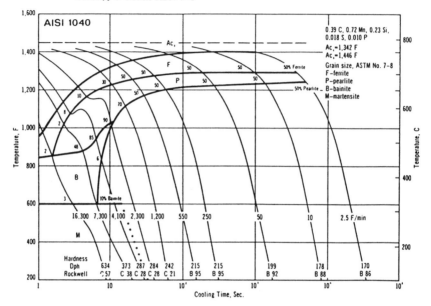

SAE 1541 Steel

Composition: 0.39% C - 1.56% Mn - 0.21% Si - 0.010% P - 0.024% S Grain size: 8

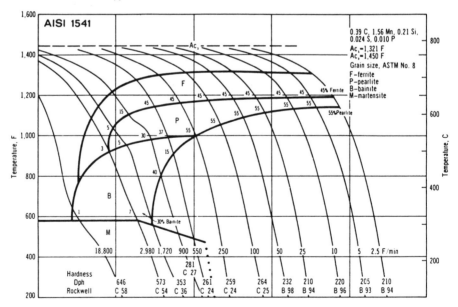

Fig 9-4 Cooling curves imposed on continuous cooling transformation diagrams, showing at the arrows the perturbation in the cooling curves from heat release associated with the decomposition of austenite. (From *Atlas of Time-Temperature Diagrams for Irons and Steels*, G.F. Vander Voort, editor, p 535, ASM International, Materials Park, Ohio (1991))

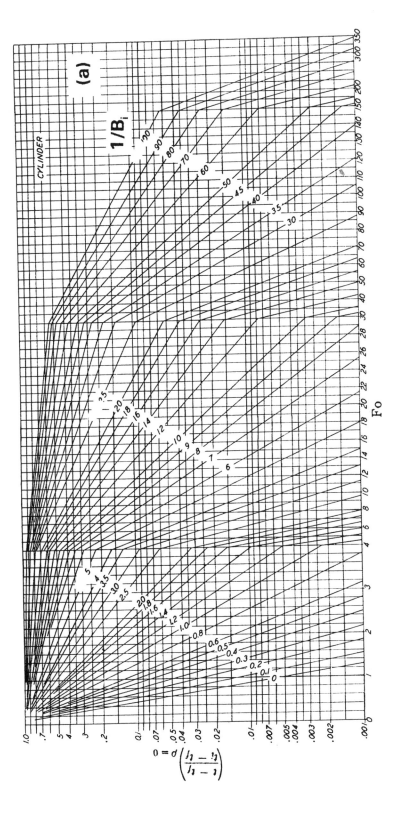

Fig. 9-5 Charts by which temperature-time curves can be determined for long cylinders. The curves in (a) are for the center of the cylinders, and the curves in (b) are corrections to the curves in (a) to obtain values from which to calculate curves at different diameter locations. (from M.P. Heislet, *Trans. ASME*, Vol 69, p 227-236 (1947)) *(continued)*

mathematical expression is known for a heating curve and for the time-temperature dependence of the formation of homogeneous austenite (the solid line in Fig. 9-7), then the intersection of these two curves gives the required austenitization time and temperature. To illustrate this, the heating curve for the center of the 1.3 cm radius cylinder is represented by $T = 85 + 5.4t - 0.012t^2 + 8.1 \times 10^{-6}t^3$ (time t is in seconds and T is in °C), and is shown as the thick heating curve in Fig. 9-7. It is seen that the homogeneous curve is essentially constant at about 850°C. Equating this temperature to the expression for the heating curve yields a minimum austenitizing time of about 770 sec., at the intersection of the two curves in Fig. 9-7.

The point is that once an expression is obtained for the temperature-time relation for the formation of homogeneous austenite upon continuous heating, it can be combined with the heating curves calculated from the

heat transfer relations (e.g., Table 9-2) to obtain guidelines for choosing austenitizing times and temperatures.

The equilibrium transformation temperatures are designated A_1 and A_3, as shown in Fig. 9-8. If heating is sufficiently rapid, the transformations will occur at higher temperatures, designated as A_{c1} and A_{c3}, as labeled in Fig. 9-8. If a steel is heated relatively slowly, taking several minutes to attain the austenitizing temperature, then the temperature at which the austenite disappears is close to the equilibrium temperatures. For example, in Fig. 9-7, if the time to heat to the A_1 temperature of 723°C is greater than about 400 sec. (about 7 minutes), then the A_{c1} and A_1 temperatures coincide as well as do the A_{c3} and A_3 temperatures.

The kinetics of the formation of austenite, such as depicted in Fig. 9-7, depends upon the beginning microstructure, and hence such curves are needed for each microstructure present. However, a method to estimate

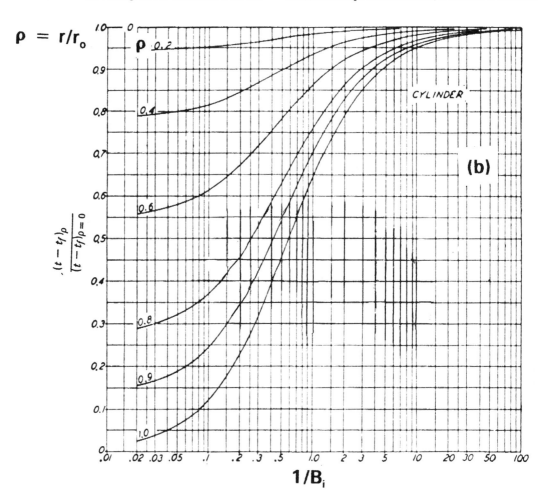

Fig 9-5 (continued) Charts by which temperature-time curves can be determined for long cylinders. The curves in (a) are for the center of the cylinders, and the curves in (b) are corrections to the curves in (a) to obtain values from which to calculate curves at different diameter locations. (From M.P. Heislet, *Trans. ASME*, Vol 69, p 227-236 (1947))

Table 9-2   Tables for calculating the temperature distribution in steels as a function of time during heating and cooling. (From J.B. Austin, *The Flow of Heat in Metals*, American Society for Metals, Metals Park, Ohio (1942))

These tables, taken from Russell (First Report of the Alloy Steels Research Committee, Special Report 24, of the Iron and Steel Institute 1936) are used to calculate the rate of change of temperature or the temperature distribution within an infinite plate or slab and within an infinite cylinder or rod. The data are presented in terms of four generalized variables:

(1) A surface coefficient, HL, which characterizes the rate of heat transfer across the surface of the body. It is composed of two factors: L, which is the radius or half-thickness of the body, and H, a coefficient which represents, in effect, the rate at which heat is supplied to the surface of the rod or slab. The value of H depends on the particular metal under consideration and on the particular type of heating or cooling used, but once determined for a given combination of metal and method of heating or cooling, the value can be used for all sizes or shapes. For example, in heating slabs in a particular furnace, H was found to be $0.10 \ in.^{-1}$, hence, for a 6-inch slab $HL = 0.10 \times 3 = 0.30$.

(2) A relative temperature, U, which is the fraction of the total temperature ultimately to be achieved which remains to be accomplished at a given instant. Thus,

$$U = \frac{\text{Temperature at given time} - \text{Final uniform temperature}}{\text{Initial uniform temperature} - \text{Final uniform temperature}}$$

Hence, at the start of heating or cooling, when all the temperature change remains to be accomplished, U is unity whereas at final equilibrium U is zero.

(3) A relative position (x/L) which expresses the location of any point within a body in terms of its relation to the center or central axis of the piece and is given numerically by the ratio of the distance of the point from the center (x) to the total distance between surface and center (L). For example, on the central axis of a cylinder $x/L = 0$, at a point midway between the axis and the surface $x/L = 0.50$, and at the surface $x/L = 1$.

(4) A relative time ratio, τ, which is equal to $\frac{a^2 t}{L^2}$, where a is the thermal diffusivity of the material, L is the radius or half-thickness, and t is the elapsed time since the beginning of heating or cooling. This time ratio therefore takes account of differences in size and in diffusivity.

As an illustration of the use of the Tables suppose that a steel cylinder 4 inches in diameter and 4 feet long, initially at 70 °F, is to be heated in a furnace held at 2200 °F (1205 °C), the diffusivity of the steel is $1.0 \ in.^2/min$, and H has a value of $0.05 \ in.^{-1}$. How long will it take the center of the rod to come to 2000 °F (1095 °C)? The coefficient HL has a value of $0.05 \times 2 = 0.10$, hence, we use the Table headed HL = 0.10. The value of U is $\frac{2000 - 2200}{70 - 2200} = 0.094$, and since we are interested in the center, $x/L = 0$. Now looking down the column for $x/L = 0$, it is found that when $U = 0.094$, τ has a value of about 12, hence $\frac{a\ t}{L^2} = 12$, or $t = \frac{12.0 \times 22}{1.0} = 48$ minutes.

If the rate of change of temperature at any location within a slab or rod being heated or cooled is determined, the value of H can be determined by reversing the procedure just described.

Heat flow tables for infinite plate or slab (after Russell)

The designation N.E. indicates that in the calculation the standard procedure of using eight terms in the summation was not enough to give a value precise to five significant figures.

| | | | | Plate, HL = 0.2 | | | |
| | | | | Value of U when x/L is | | | |
τ	0.0	0.5	0.6	0.7	0.8	0.9	1.0
0.02	N.E.	0.99983	0.99932	0.99770	0.99349	0.98334	0.96885
0.04	N.E.	0.99829	0.99606	0.99173	0.98447	0.97240	0.95641
0.05	0.99995	0.99699	0.99396	0.98871	0.98040	0.96782	0.95147
0.06	0.99984	0.99551	0.99171	0.98567	0.97660	0.96362	0.94703
0.08	0.99938	0.99216	0.98713	0.97981	0.96965	0.95610	0.93923
0.10	0.99846	0.98859	0.98257	0.97431	0.96338	0.94944	0.93244
0.20	0.98826	0.97015	0.96155	0.95097	0.93831	0.92349	0.90646
0.30	0.97298	0.95204	0.94264	0.93142	0.91834	0.90340	0.88659
0.40	0.95601	0.93434	0.92478	0.91345	0.90039	0.88557	0.86905
0.50	0.93865	0.91699	0.90748	0.89626	0.88334	0.86876	0.85252
0.60	0.92138	0.89996	0.89059	0.87953	0.86683	0.85250	0.83656
0.70	0.90432	0.88326	0.87404	0.86318	0.85069	0.83663	0.82098
0.80	0.88756	0.86686	0.85780	0.84715	0.83490	0.82108	0.80572
0.90	0.87109	0.85077	0.84188	0.83141	0.81939	0.80583	0.79076
1.0	0.85493	0.83498	0.82626	0.81598	0.80418	0.79087	0.77608
1.5	0.77848	0.76032	0.75237	0.74302	0.73227	0.72015	0.70668
2.0	0.70886	0.69233	0.68509	0.67657	0.66679	0.65575	0.64349
3.0	0.58776	0.57404	0.56805	0.56098	0.55287	0.54372	0.53355
4.0	0.48734	0.47597	0.47100	0.46514	0.45841	0.45083	0.44240
5.0	0.40408	0.39465	0.39053	0.38567	0.38009	0.37380	0.36681
6.0	0.33504	0.32723	0.32381	0.31978	0.31516	0.30994	0.30414
7.0	0.27780	0.27132	0.26848	0.26515	0.26131	0.25698	0.25218

(continued)

Table 9-2 (Continued)

τ	Plate, HL = 0.2 Value of U when x/L is						
	0.0	0.5	0.6	0.7	0.8	0.9	1.0
8.0	0.23034	0.22445	0.22261	0.21985	0.21667	0.21308	0.20910
9.0	0.19099	0.18653	0.18458	0.18229	0.17965	0.17668	0.17337
10.0	0.15836	0.15466	0.15305	0.15114	0.14930	0.14649	0.14375
11.0	0.13130	0.12824	0.12690	0.12532	0.12351	0.12146	0.11919
12.0	0.10887	0.10633	0.10522	0.10391	0.10241	0.10071	0.09883
16.0	0.05146						0.04671
20.0	0.02432						0.02208
24.0	0.01150						0.01043
28.0	0.00544						0.00493
32.0	0.00257						0.00233

τ	Plate, HL = 0.5 Value of U when x/L is						
	0.0	0.5	0.6	0.7	0.8	0.9	1.0
0.02	N.E.	0.99960	0.99826	0.99424	0.98400	0.96200	0.92503
0.04	0.99992	0.99580	0.99044	0.98023	0.96267	0.93493	0.89645
0.05	0.99983	0.99273	0.98542	0.97292	0.95326	0.92404	0.88537
0.06	0.99959	0.98919	0.98014	0.96578	0.94394	0.91427	0.87551
0.08	0.99846	0.98131	0.96942	0.95222	0.92852	0.89718	0.85845
0.10	0.99630	0.97298	0.95892	0.93970	0.91448	0.88242	0.84387
0.15	0.98663	0.95190	0.93434	0.91210	0.88478	0.85203	0.81411
0.20	0.97257	0.93134	0.91196	0.88829	0.86012	0.82734	0.79013
0.30	0.93812	0.89197	0.87143	0.84703	0.81878	0.78671	0.75099
0.40	0.90103	0.85456	0.83420	0.81024	0.78274	0.75180	0.71754
0.50	0.86409	0.81880	0.79907	0.77591	0.74942	0.71970	0.68686
0.60	0.82823	0.78457	0.76555	0.74334	0.71790	0.68940	0.65793
0.70	0.79371	0.75179	0.73356	0.71773	0.68784	0.66051	0.63036
0.80	0.76058	0.72038	0.70291	0.68245	0.65907	0.63289	0.60400
0.90	0.72881	0.69028	0.67354	0.65393	0.63153	0.60644	0.57876
1.00	0.69837	0.66144	0.64540	0.62661	0.60514	0.58110	0.55457
2.00	0.45577	0.43167	0.42120	0.40894	0.39493	0.37923	0.36192
3.00	0.29744	0.28171	0.27488	0.26688	0.25774	0.24750	0.23620
4.00	0.19412	0.18385	0.17939	0.17417	0.16820	0.16152	0.15415
5.00	0.12668	0.11998	0.11707	0.11367	0.10977	0.10541	0.10060
6.00	0.08268	0.07830	0.07641	0.07418	0.07164	0.06879	0.06565
7.00	0.05396	0.05110	0.04986	0.04841	0.04675	0.04490	0.04285
8.00	0.03521	0.03335	0.03254	0.03159	0.03051	0.02930	0.02796
9.00	0.02298	0.02177	0.02124	0.02062	0.01991	0.01912	0.01825
10.00	0.01500	0.01420	0.01386	0.01346	0.01300	0.01248	0.01191
12.00	0.00639						0.00507
14.00	0.00272						0.00216
15.00	0.00178						0.00141

τ	Plate, HL = 1 Value of U when x/L is						
	0.0	0.5	0.6	0.7	0.8	0.9	1.0
0.05	0.99994	0.98654	0.97338	0.94963	0.91333	0.86080	0.79062
0.10	0.99332	0.95073	0.92539	0.89106	0.84643	0.79074	0.72384
0.20	0.94864	0.87950	0.84637	0.80627	0.75904	0.70481	0.64365
0.30	0.89202	0.81550	0.78183	0.74215	0.69663	0.64552	0.58912
0.40	0.83119	0.75696	0.72478	0.68718	0.64439	0.59670	0.54444
0.50	0.77455	0.70285	0.67269	0.63755	0.59765	0.55328	0.50479
0.60	0.71793	0.65269	0.62459	0.59188	0.55478	0.51356	0.46853
0.70	0.66681	0.60612	0.57999	0.54961	0.51513	0.47685	0.43500
0.80	0.61929	0.56290	0.53863	0.51039	0.47837	0.44282	0.40398
1.0	0.53411	0.48547	0.46454	0.44018	0.41257	0.38190	0.34841
1.5	0.36895	0.33535	0.32090	0.30407	0.28499	0.26380	0.24068
2.0	0.25487	0.23166	0.22167	0.21005	0.19687	0.18223	0.16625
3.0	0.12162	0.11054	0.10578	0.10023	0.09394	0.08696	0.07933
4.0	0.05803	0.05275	0.05047	0.04783	0.04483	0.04150	0.03786
5.0	0.02769	0.02517	0.02408	0.02282	0.02139	0.01980	0.01806
6.0	0.01321						0.00862

(continued)

Table 9-2   (Continued)

| | Plate, HL = 1 | | | | | | |
| | | | Value of U when x/L is | | | | |
τ	0.0	0.5	0.6	0.7	0.8	0.9	1.0
7.0	0.00630						0.00411
8.0	0.00301						0.00196
9.0	0.00144						0.00094

| | Plate, HL = 2 | | | | | | |
| | | | Value of U when x/L is | | | | |
τ	0.0	0.5	0.6	0.7	0.8	0.9	1.0
0.02	0.99999	0.99860	0.99403	0.97973	0.94373	0.87000	0.74655
0.04	0.99990	0.98552	0.96732	0.93327	0.87606	0.78943	0.66956
0.05	0.99954	0.97533	0.95117	0.91058	0.84811	0.75954	0.64380
0.06	0.99867	0.96395	0.93476	0.88925	0.82324	0.73390	0.62091
0.08	0.99485	0.93979	0.90294	0.85073	0.78067	0.69135	0.58350
0.10	0.98779	0.91543	0.87334	0.81710	0.74524	0.65717	0.55361
0.15	0.95813	0.85809	0.80921	0.74884	0.67655	0.59262	0.49795
0.20	0.91789	0.80643	0.75574	0.69517	0.62488	0.54541	0.45765
0.30	0.83661	0.71549	0.66699	0.61041	0.54632	0.47537	0.39841
0.40	0.74225	0.63652	0.59358	0.54128	0.48381	0.42059	0.35235
0.50	0.66025	0.56664	0.52709	0.48141	0.43012	0.37382	0.31314
0.60	0.58775	0.50455	0.46927	0.42854	0.38284	0.33269	0.27868
0.70	0.52335	0.44929	0.41785	0.38157	0.34087	0.29622	0.24812
0.80	0.46603	0.40009	0.37209	0.33978	0.30353	0.26376	0.22094
0.90	0.41500	0.35629	0.33135	0.30257	0.27029	0.23488	0.19675
1.00	0.36956	0.31654	0.29507	0.26944	0.24070	0.20916	0.17522
1.20	0.29306	0.25159	0.23399	0.21367	0.19087	0.16588	0.13899
1.40	0.23187	0.19952	0.18555	0.16905	0.15136	0.13154	0.11018
1.50	0.20695	0.17767	0.16524	0.15089	0.13479	0.11713	0.09812
1.60	0.18429	0.15822	0.14714	0.13437	0.12003	0.10431	0.08737
1.80	0.14615	0.12547	0.11669	0.10655	0.09519	0.08272	0.06929
2.00	0.11589	0.09950	0.09253	0.08450	0.07548	0.06559	0.05495
3.00	0.03634						0.01723
4.00	0.01140						0.00540
5.00	0.00357						0.00169
6.00	0.00112						0.00053

| | Plate, HL = 3 | | | | | | |
| | | | Value of U when x/L is | | | | |
τ	0.0	0.5	0.6	0.7	0.8	0.9	1.0
0.02	N.E.	N.E.	0.99159	0.98748	0.92183	0.82292	0.65643
0.04	0.99981	0.98165	0.95531	0.92181	0.83343	0.72154	0.56786
0.05	0.99929	0.96739	0.93398	0.88107	0.79830	0.68554	0.53766
0.06	0.99810	0.95207	0.91273	0.85347	0.76771	0.65533	0.51263
0.08	0.99289	0.92049	0.87239	0.80562	0.71666	0.60665	0.47287
0.10	0.98350	0.88967	0.83586	0.76492	0.67536	0.56850	0.44208
0.15	0.94503	0.81967	0.75937	0.68558	0.59828	0.50126	0.38702
0.20	0.89480	0.75872	0.69777	0.62552	0.54258	0.45102	0.34885
0.30	0.78624	0.65488	0.59869	0.53368	0.45765	0.38161	0.29473
0.40	0.68153	0.56731	0.51779	0.46085	0.39726	0.32887	0.25384
0.50	0.59422	0.49193	0.44879	0.39927	0.34405	0.28466	0.21953
0.60	0.51559	0.42667	0.38922	0.34623	0.29832	0.24681	0.19051
0.70	0.44728	0.37011	0.33762	0.30031	0.25875	0.21369	0.16524
0.80	0.38800	0.32105	0.29286	0.26050	0.22444	0.18611	0.14331
0.90	0.33657	0.27850	0.25404	0.22597	0.19469	0.16107	0.12433
1.0	0.29196	0.24158	0.22037	0.19647	0.16888	0.13972	0.10785
1.2	0.21969	0.18179	0.16582	0.14750	0.12708	0.10513	0.08115
1.4	0.16531	0.13679	0.12478	0.11099	0.09563	0.07911	0.06107
1.5	0.14340	0.11866	0.10799	0.09628	0.08295	0.06863	0.05297
1.6	0.12411	0.10293	0.09389	0.08352	0.07196	0.05953	0.04595
1.8	0.09360	0.07745	0.07065	0.06284	0.05415	0.04480	0.03458
2.0	0.07044	0.05825	0.05316	0.04729	0.04074	0.03371	0.02602
3.0	0.01699						0.00628
4.0	0.00410						0.00152
5.0	0.00099						0.00037

(continued)

Table 9-2 (Continued)

	Plate, HL = 4						
				Value of U when x/L is			
τ	0.0	0.5	0.6	0.7	0.8	0.9	1.0
0.02	N.E.	0.99554	0.98860	0.96445	0.90289	0.78040	0.58354
0.04	0.99975	0.97393	0.93491	0.88837	0.79900	0.66522	0.48925
0.05	0.99917	0.95774	0.91940	0.85563	0.75906	0.62586	0.45839
0.06	0.99773	0.94016	0.89464	0.82461	0.72483	0.59339	0.43330
0.08	0.99138	0.90410	0.84844	0.77093	0.66887	0.54325	0.39440
0.10	0.98013	0.86924	0.80743	0.72632	0.62463	0.50406	0.36499
0.15	0.93529	0.78157	0.72370	0.64119	0.54431	0.43514	0.31383
0.20	0.87786	0.72534	0.65786	0.57843	0.48784	0.38818	0.27941
0.30	0.75740	0.61464	0.55406	0.48435	0.40646	0.32224	0.23160
0.40	0.64744	0.52306	0.47078	0.41094	0.34442	0.27280	0.19599
0.50	0.55218	0.44559	0.40092	0.34982	0.29310	0.23210	0.16672
0.60	0.47067	0.37970	0.34160	0.29804	0.24969	0.19772	0.14201
0.70	0.40113	0.32358	0.29110	0.25397	0.21276	0.16847	0.12102
0.80	0.34185	0.27576	0.24808	0.21643	0.18132	0.14358	0.10313
0.90	0.29133	0.23501	0.21142	0.18445	0.15452	0.12236	0.08789
1.00	0.24828	0.20028	0.18017	0.15719	0.13169	0.10427	0.07490
1.20	0.18032	0.14546	0.13085	0.11416	0.09564	0.07573	0.05451
1.40	0.13096	0.10564	0.09503	0.08291	0.06946	0.05500	0.03967
1.50	0.11160	0.09003	0.08099	0.07066	0.05919	0.04687	0.03381
2.0	0.05012	0.04047	0.03641	0.03176	0.02660	0.02107	0.01520
2.5	0.02255	0.01819	0.01637	0.01428	0.01196	0.00947	0.00681
3.0	0.01014						0.00306
4.0	0.00205						0.00062

	Plate, HL = 4.8						
				Value of U when x/L is			
τ	0.0	0.5	0.6	0.7	0.8	0.9	1.0
0.02	N.E.	N.E.	0.99540	0.96625	0.88998	0.74562	0.52177
0.04	N.E.	0.97244	0.93971	0.87785	0.77588	0.62819	0.43506
0.05	0.99969	0.95406	0.91074	0.83992	0.73334	0.58873	0.40594
0.06	0.99767	0.93439	0.88357	0.80620	0.69724	0.55430	0.38219
0.08	0.99039	0.89481	0.83352	0.74899	0.63898	0.50370	0.34540
0.10	0.97784	0.85715	0.78984	0.70221	0.59352	0.46463	0.31790
0.15	0.92890	0.77538	0.70213	0.61448	0.51346	0.39708	0.27086
0.20	0.86723	0.70545	0.63423	0.55077	0.45617	0.35182	0.23963
0.30	0.74008	0.59126	0.52840	0.45626	0.37602	0.28894	0.19661
0.40	0.62598	0.49791	0.44433	0.38313	0.31539	0.24213	0.16472
0.50	0.52818	0.41977	0.37447	0.32279	0.26564	0.20390	0.13870
0.60	0.44551	0.35398	0.31576	0.27216	0.22395	0.17189	0.11692
0.70	0.37574	0.29852	0.26628	0.22951	0.18885	0.14495	0.09860
0.80	0.31688	0.25175	0.22457	0.19356	0.15927	0.12224	0.08315
0.90	0.26724	0.21281	0.18939	0.16324	0.13431	0.10309	0.07013
1.0	0.22537	0.17906	0.15972	0.13766	0.11327	0.08694	0.05914
1.2	0.16030	0.12735	0.11360	0.09791	0.08057	0.06184	0.04206
1.4	0.11401	0.09058	0.08080	0.06980	0.05730	0.04398	0.02992
1.5	0.09615	0.07639	0.06814	0.05873	0.04832	0.03709	0.02522
1.6	0.08109	0.06442	0.05747	0.04953	0.04075	0.03128	0.02128
1.8	0.05767	0.04582	0.04087	0.03523	0.02899	0.02225	0.01513
2.0	0.04102	0.03259	0.02907	0.02506	0.02062	0.01582	0.01076
2.5	0.01750						0.00459
3.0	0.00746						0.00196
3.5	0.00318						0.00084
4.0	0.00136						0.00036

	Plate, HL = 6						
				Value of U when x/L is			
τ	0.0	0.5	0.6	0.7	0.8	0.9	1.0
0.02	0.99989	0.99638	0.98579	0.95262	0.87257	0.71286	0.47260
0.04	0.99976	0.96973	0.92937	0.85976	0.74707	0.58697	0.37845
0.05	0.99891	0.94905	0.89849	0.81923	0.70199	0.54518	0.34946
0.06	0.99602	0.92723	0.86884	0.78316	0.66403	0.51137	0.32654
0.08	0.98893	0.88346	0.81532	0.72268	0.60364	0.45944	0.29200
0.10	0.97496	0.84264	0.76873	0.67390	0.55732	0.42081	0.26675

(continued)

Table 9-2 (Continued)

	Plate, HL = 6 Value of U when x/L is						
τ	0.0	0.5	0.6	0.7	0.8	0.9	1.0
0.15	0.92114	0.74498	0.68716	0.58402	0.47619	0.35557	0.22455
0.20	0.85467	0.68276	0.60748	0.51983	0.42101	0.31280	0.19713
0.30	0.72031	0.56530	0.50012	0.42560	0.34305	0.25391	0.15981
0.40	0.60184	0.47047	0.41538	0.35332	0.28447	0.21038	0.13237
0.50	0.50190	0.39201	0.34621	0.29422	0.23684	0.17512	0.11017
0.60	0.41840	0.32670	0.28857	0.24518	0.19735	0.14591	0.09179
0.70	0.34873	0.27231	0.24052	0.20435	0.16448	0.12161	0.07651
0.80	0.29067	0.22469	0.20047	0.17032	0.13713	0.10136	0.06377
0.90	0.24227	0.18917	0.16709	0.14197	0.11426	0.08448	0.05310
1.00	0.20193	0.15768	0.13927	0.11833	0.09511	0.07042	0.04430
1.20	0.14028	0.10954	0.09675	0.08220	0.06617	0.04892	0.03078
1.40	0.09746	0.07610	0.06721	0.05711	0.04597	0.03398	0.02138
1.50	0.08123	0.06343	0.05602	0.04760	0.03831	0.02833	0.01782
2.0	0.03268	0.02551	0.02360	0.01915	0.01541	0.01139	0.00717
2.5	0.01314	0.01026	0.00949	0.00788	0.00620	0.00458	0.00288
3.0	0.00529						0.00116
3.5	0.00213						0.00047

	Plate, HL = 7.5 Value of U when x/L is						
τ	0.0	0.5	0.6	0.7	0.8	0.9	1.0
0.02	N.E.	0.99590	0.98327	0.94527	0.85554	0.67962	0.41207
0.04	0.99974	0.96350	0.92024	0.84283	0.71994	0.54403	0.32161
0.05	0.99875	0.94082	0.88648	0.79925	0.67251	0.50161	0.29483
0.06	0.99664	0.91710	0.85443	0.76095	0.63294	0.46798	0.27398
0.08	0.98753	0.87045	0.79719	0.69780	0.57110	0.41736	0.24303
0.10	0.97205	0.82738	0.74858	0.64754	0.52444	0.38038	0.22077
0.15	0.91369	0.73623	0.65436	0.55657	0.44414	0.31884	0.18420
0.20	0.84293	0.66205	0.58358	0.49251	0.39026	0.27890	0.16078
0.30	0.70245	0.54242	0.47547	0.39915	0.31488	0.22424	0.12908
0.40	0.58062	0.44676	0.39117	0.32802	0.25851	0.18397	0.10586
0.50	0.47911	0.36839	0.32246	0.27034	0.21300	0.15157	0.08722
0.60	0.39522	0.30383	0.26595	0.22294	0.17525	0.12499	0.07191
0.70	0.32593	0.25117	0.21935	0.18388	0.14488	0.10309	0.05931
0.80	0.26887	0.20669	0.18092	0.15167	0.11949	0.08503	0.04892
0.90	0.22177	0.17009	0.14922	0.12510	0.09856	0.07013	0.04035
1.0	0.18292	0.14062	0.12308	0.10318	0.08129	0.05784	0.03328
1.2	0.12431	0.09566	0.08373	0.07019	0.05530	0.03935	0.02264
1.4	0.08466	0.06508	0.05696	0.04775	0.03762	0.02677	0.01540
1.5	0.06983	0.05368	0.04698	0.03943	0.03103	0.02208	0.01270
1.6	0.05759	0.04427	0.03875	0.03256	0.02560	0.01821	0.01048
1.8	0.03918	0.03012	0.02636	0.02210	0.01741	0.01239	0.00713
2.0	0.02665	0.02049	0.01794	0.01503	0.01185	0.00843	0.00485
2.5	0.01017						0.00185
3.0	0.00389						0.00071
3.5	0.00148						0.00027

	Plate, HL = 8 Value of U when x/L is						
τ	0.0	0.5	0.6	0.7	0.8	0.9	1.0
0.02	N.E.	0.99581	0.98416	0.94308	0.84881	0.66905	0.39421
0.04	0.99973	0.96226	0.91872	0.83798	0.71082	0.53225	0.30596
0.05	0.99871	0.93895	0.88398	0.79360	0.66257	0.48987	0.27997
0.06	0.99648	0.91464	0.85117	0.75485	0.62289	0.45688	0.25979
0.08	0.98714	0.86709	0.79280	0.69092	0.56107	0.40619	0.22998
0.10	0.97101	0.82337	0.74348	0.64037	0.51464	0.36973	0.20862
0.15	0.91163	0.73125	0.64840	0.54925	0.43502	0.30924	0.17368
0.20	0.83971	0.65656	0.57732	0.48531	0.38182	0.27012	0.15138
0.30	0.69769	0.53642	0.46905	0.39228	0.30724	0.21664	0.12124
0.40	0.57503	0.44162	0.38484	0.32150	0.25157	0.17727	0.09917
0.50	0.47318	0.36231	0.31637	0.26425	0.20673	0.14566	0.08148
0.60	0.38923	0.29797	0.26019	0.21731	0.17000	0.11977	0.06700

(continued)

Table 9-2   (Continued)

τ	0.0	0.5	0.6	0.7	0.8	0.9	1.0
				Plate, HL = 8			
				Value of U when x/L is			
0.70	0.32015	0.24509	0.21401	0.17874	0.13983	0.09851	0.05511
0.80	0.26333	0.20160	0.17603	0.14702	0.11501	0.08103	0.04533
0.90	0.21660	0.16582	0.14445	0.12093	0.09460	0.06664	0.03728
1.0	0.17825	0.13639	0.11909	0.09946	0.07781	0.05482	0.03067
1.5	0.06707	0.05135	0.04483	0.03744	0.02929	0.02064	0.01154
2.0	0.02525	0.01933	0.01684	0.01409	0.01102	0.00776	0.00435
2.5	0.00951						0.00164
3.0	0.00358						0.00062
3.5	0.00135						0.00023

τ	0.0	0.5	0.6	0.7	0.8	0.9	1.0
				Plate, HL = 10			
				Value of U when x/L is			
0.02	N.E.	0.99502	0.97971	0.93536	0.83007	0.63234	0.33641
0.04	0.99970	0.95774	0.90844	0.82257	0.68464	0.49340	0.25538
0.05	0.99856	0.93241	0.87118	0.77531	0.63497	0.45157	0.23230
0.06	0.99609	0.90630	0.83664	0.73464	0.59462	0.41895	0.21462
0.08	0.98573	0.85715	0.77587	0.66864	0.53259	0.37063	0.18880
0.10	0.96842	0.81016	0.72516	0.61727	0.48656	0.33597	0.17057
0.15	0.90476	0.71520	0.62863	0.52602	0.40869	0.27924	0.14110
0.20	0.82925	0.63905	0.55716	0.46268	0.35717	0.24289	0.12248
0.30	0.68246	0.51755	0.44888	0.37093	0.28514	0.19331	0.09735
0.40	0.55742	0.42142	0.36515	0.30145	0.23254	0.15724	0.07897
0.50	0.45464	0.34351	0.29557	0.24563	0.18863	0.12789	0.06432
0.60	0.37071	0.28005	0.24259	0.20023	0.15376	0.10416	0.05242
0.70	0.30225	0.22834	0.19779	0.16325	0.12537	0.08493	0.04275
0.80	0.24643	0.18617	0.16127	0.13310	0.10221	0.06924	0.03486
0.90	0.20092	0.15179	0.13148	0.10852	0.08333	0.05646	0.02842
1.0	0.16382	0.12404	0.10720	0.08847	0.06795	0.04603	0.02317
1.2	0.10890	0.08227	0.07126	0.05882	0.04517	0.03053	0.01540
1.4	0.07239	0.05469	0.04737	0.03910	0.03003	0.02029	0.01024
1.5	0.05902	0.04459	0.03862	0.03188	0.02448	0.01659	0.00835
1.6	0.04812	0.03635	0.03149	0.02599	0.01996	0.01353	0.00680
1.8	0.03199	0.02417	0.02094	0.01728	0.01326	0.00899	0.00453
2.0	0.02126	0.01606	0.01392	0.01149	0.00882	0.00598	0.00301
2.5	0.00766						0.00108
3.0	0.00276						0.00039
3.5	0.00099						0.00014

τ	0.0	0.5	0.6	0.7	0.8	0.9	1.0
				Plate, HL = 13			
				Value of U when x/L is			
0.02	N.E.	0.99430	0.97708	0.92684	0.80968	0.58904	0.27382
0.04	0.99985	0.95272	0.89836	0.80536	0.65688	0.45219	0.20362
0.05	0.99855	0.92522	0.85870	0.75424	0.60625	0.41177	0.18421
0.06	0.99570	0.89722	0.82209	0.71242	0.56511	0.38057	0.16949
0.08	0.98429	0.84402	0.76883	0.64530	0.50393	0.33488	0.14831
0.10	0.96549	0.79642	0.70678	0.59364	0.45876	0.30249	0.13350
0.15	0.89761	0.69897	0.60908	0.50295	0.38321	0.25008	0.10984
0.20	0.81855	0.62165	0.53743	0.44054	0.33361	0.21673	0.09501
0.30	0.66730	0.49913	0.42942	0.35039	0.26433	0.17124	0.07497
0.40	0.54018	0.40295	0.34636	0.28238	0.21287	0.13783	0.06033
0.50	0.43672	0.32561	0.27983	0.22812	0.17194	0.11132	0.04872
0.60	0.35300	0.26317	0.22616	0.18436	0.13895	0.08996	0.03937
0.70	0.28532	0.21271	0.18280	0.14901	0.11231	0.07271	0.03182
0.80	0.23061	0.17192	0.14774	0.12016	0.09078	0.05877	0.02572
0.90	0.18639	0.13896	0.11942	0.09734	0.07337	0.04750	0.02079
1.00	0.15065	0.11231	0.09652	0.07868	0.05930	0.03839	0.01680
1.20	0.09840	0.07337	0.06305	0.05140	0.03874	0.02508	0.01097
1.40	0.06430	0.04793	0.04119	0.03358	0.02531	0.01638	0.00717
1.50	0.05197	0.03874	0.03329	0.02714	0.02046	0.01324	0.00580
1.60	0.04200	0.03131	0.02691	0.02194	0.01653	0.01070	0.00468

(continued)

Table 9-2 (Continued)

| | | | Plate, HL = 13 | | | | |
| | | | Value of *U* when x/L is | | | | |
	0.0	0.5	0.6	0.7	0.8	0.9	1.0
1.80	0.02744	0.02546	0.01758	0.01433	0.01080	0.00699	0.00306
2.0	0.01793	0.01336	0.01148	0.00936	0.00705	0.00457	0.00200
2.50	0.00618						0.00069
3.00	0.00213						0.00024

| | | | Plate, HL = 14 | | | | |
| | | | Value of *U* when x/L is | | | | |
	0.0	0.5	0.6	0.7	0.8	0.9	1.0
0.02	0.99996	0.99402	0.97613	0.92370	0.80263	0.58054	0.25691
0.04	0.99959	0.95128	0.89561	0.79844	0.64823	0.44197	0.19034
0.05	0.99826	0.92322	0.85530	0.74884	0.59748	0.40185	0.17205
0.06	0.99535	0.89476	0.81825	0.70674	0.55690	0.37102	0.15820
0.08	0.98371	0.84085	0.75440	0.63936	0.49547	0.32604	0.13827
0.10	0.96452	0.79282	0.70206	0.58767	0.45061	0.29426	0.12464
0.15	0.89563	0.69480	0.60413	0.49721	0.37586	0.24295	0.10224
0.20	0.81572	0.61725	0.53249	0.43506	0.32687	0.21035	0.08836
0.30	0.66582	0.49454	0.42459	0.34534	0.28548	0.16589	0.06960
0.40	0.53619	0.39838	0.34174	0.27773	0.20774	0.13326	0.05589
0.50	0.43233	0.32123	0.27551	0.22387	0.16743	0.10729	0.04504
0.60	0.34866	0.25906	0.22219	0.18054	0.13502	0.08660	0.03632
0.70	0.28120	0.20894	0.17919	0.14561	0.10889	0.06984	0.02929
0.80	0.22679	0.16851	0.14452	0.11743	0.08782	0.05633	0.02363
0.90	0.18291	0.13590	0.11656	0.09471	0.07083	0.04543	0.01905
1.00	0.14751	0.10961	0.09400	0.07639	0.05713	0.03664	0.01537
1.20	0.09595	0.07129	0.06115	0.04968	0.03716	0.02383	0.00999
1.40	0.06241	0.04637	0.03977	0.03232	0.02417	0.01550	0.00650
1.50	0.05034	0.03740	0.03208	0.02606	0.01949	0.01250	0.00524
1.60	0.04060	0.03016	0.02587	0.02102	0.01572	0.01008	0.00423
1.80	0.02641	0.01962	0.01683	0.01367	0.01023	0.00656	0.00275
2.0	0.01718	0.01276	0.01095	0.00889	0.00665	0.00427	0.00179
2.5	0.00586						0.00061
3.0	0.00200						0.00021

| | | | Plate, HL = 17 | | | | |
| | | | Value of *U* when x/L is | | | | |
τ	0.0	0.5	0.6	0.7	0.8	0.9	1.0
0.02	0.99997	0.99339	0.97385	0.91726	0.78791	0.55350	0.21814
0.04	0.99955	0.94777	0.88873	0.78653	0.62982	0.41667	0.15953
0.05	0.99811	0.91836	0.84694	0.73578	0.57889	0.37779	0.14375
0.06	0.99500	0.88880	0.80885	0.69327	0.53845	0.34808	0.13188
0.08	0.98262	0.83330	0.74371	0.62552	0.47768	0.30505	0.11494
0.10	0.96248	0.78427	0.69077	0.57361	0.43362	0.27483	0.10322
0.15	0.89108	0.68503	0.59249	0.48369	0.36062	0.22630	0.08462
0.20	0.80913	0.60696	0.51657	0.42226	0.31296	0.19562	0.07300
0.30	0.65441	0.48387	0.41279	0.33367	0.24642	0.15359	0.05726
0.40	0.52580	0.38783	0.33099	0.26703	0.19707	0.12278	0.04577
0.50	0.42202	0.31113	0.26556	0.21416	0.15805	0.09845	0.03670
0.60	0.33863	0.24964	0.21307	0.17183	0.12680	0.07899	0.02944
0.70	0.27172	0.20031	0.17097	0.13787	0.10175	0.06338	0.02363
0.80	0.21803	0.16073	0.13719	0.11063	0.08164	0.05086	0.01896
0.90	0.17495	0.12897	0.11008	0.08877	0.06551	0.04081	0.01521
1.0	0.14038	0.10349	0.08833	0.07123	0.05256	0.03274	0.01221
1.2	0.09038	0.06663	0.05687	0.04586	0.03384	0.02108	0.00786
1.4	0.05819	0.04290	0.03662	0.02953	0.02179	0.01357	0.00506
1.5	0.04669	0.03442	0.02938	0.02369	0.01748	0.01089	0.00406
1.6	0.03747	0.02762	0.02357	0.01901	0.01403	0.00874	0.00326
1.8	0.02412	0.01778	0.01518	0.01224	0.00903	0.00563	0.00210
2.0	0.01553	0.01145	0.00977	0.00788	0.00582	0.00362	0.00135
2.2	0.01000						0.00087
2.4	0.00644						0.00056
2.6	0.00415						0.00036
2.8	0.00267						0.00023

(continued)

Table 9-2   (Continued)

τ	0.0	0.5	0.6	Plate, HL = 17 Value of U when x/L is 0.7	0.8	0.9	1.0
3.0	0.00172						0.00015

τ	0.0	0.5	0.6	Plate, HL = 20 Value of U when x/L is 0.7	0.8	0.9	1.0
0.02	N.E.	0.99305	0.97178	0.91204	0.77812	0.53165	N.E.
0.04	0.99986	0.94516	0.88336	0.77712	0.61562	0.39720	0.13618
0.05	0.99831	0.91470	0.84046	0.72563	0.56458	0.35941	0.12272
0.06	0.99498	0.88428	0.80160	0.68250	0.52436	0.33071	0.11234
0.08	0.98203	0.82760	0.73564	0.62445	0.46432	0.28931	0.09786
0.10	0.96112	0.77789	0.68235	0.56493	0.42000	0.26038	0.08787
0.15	0.88778	0.67787	0.58396	0.47383	0.34957	0.21409	0.07204
0.20	0.80434	0.59948	0.51226	0.41303	0.30298	0.18480	0.06212
0.30	0.64788	0.47621	0.40538	0.32533	0.23766	0.14472	0.04861
0.40	0.51858	0.38030	0.32350	0.25944	0.18958	0.11530	0.03873
0.50	0.41466	0.30398	0.25854	0.20733	0.15148	0.09212	0.03094
0.60	0.33152	0.24300	0.20668	0.16573	0.12109	0.07364	0.02473
0.70	0.26503	0.19427	0.16523	0.13249	0.09680	0.05887	0.01977
0.80	0.21187	0.15531	0.13209	0.10592	0.07739	0.04706	0.01581
0.90	0.16938	0.12390	0.10560	0.08468	0.06187	0.03762	0.01264
1.00	0.13541	0.09926	0.08442	0.06769	0.04946	0.03008	0.01010
1.20	0.08654	0.06343	0.05395	0.04327	0.03161	0.01922	0.00645
1.40	0.05531	0.04054	0.03448	0.02765	0.02020	0.01228	0.00413
1.60	0.03535	0.02591	0.02204	0.01769	0.01291	0.00785	0.00264
1.80	0.02259	0.01656	0.01408	0.01129	0.00825	0.00502	0.00168
2.0	0.01444	0.01058	0.00900	0.00722	0.00528	0.00321	0.00108
2.2	0.00930						0.00069
2.4	0.00590						0.00044
2.6	0.00377						0.00028
2.8	0.00241						0.00018

τ	0.0	0.5	0.6	Plate, HL = 32 Value of U when x/L is 0.7	0.8	0.9	1.0
0.02	0.99998	0.99152	0.96716	0.89865	0.74697	0.48303	0.12180
0.04	0.99943	0.93824	0.87049	0.75568	0.58353	0.35516	0.08711
0.05	0.99767	0.90556	0.82536	0.70283	0.53316	0.32025	0.07809
0.06	0.99397	0.87341	0.78505	0.65909	0.49380	0.29394	0.07140
0.08	0.97972	0.81444	0.71753	0.59094	0.43557	0.25633	0.06196
0.10	0.95720	0.76338	0.66367	0.53989	0.39393	0.23022	0.05548
0.15	0.87976	0.66192	0.56518	0.45241	0.32578	0.18866	0.04530
0.20	0.79322	0.58295	0.49424	0.39299	0.28147	0.16241	0.03893
0.30	0.63327	0.45941	0.38793	0.30731	0.21943	0.12635	0.03026
0.40	0.50267	0.36394	0.30710	0.24314	0.17353	0.09989	0.02392
0.50	0.39865	0.28853	0.24345	0.19272	0.13753	0.07917	0.01896
0.60	0.31611	0.22878	0.19303	0.15281	0.10905	0.06277	0.01503
0.70	0.25065	0.18140	0.15306	0.12117	0.08677	0.04977	0.01192
0.80	0.19875	0.14384	0.12136	0.09608	0.06856	0.03946	0.00945
0.90	0.15759	0.11405	0.09623	0.07618	0.05437	0.03129	0.00749
1.00	0.12496	0.09044	0.07631	0.06041	0.04311	0.02481	0.00594
1.20	0.07857	0.05686	0.04798	0.03798	0.02711	0.01560	0.00374
1.40	0.04940	0.03575	0.03016	0.02388	0.01704	0.00981	0.00235
1.50	0.03917	0.02835	0.02392	0.01893	0.01351	0.00778	0.00186
1.60	0.03106	0.02248	0.01897	0.01501	0.01071	0.00617	0.00148
1.80	0.01953	0.01413	0.01192	0.00944	0.00674	0.00388	0.00093
2.00	0.01228	0.00889	0.00750	0.00748	0.00423	0.00244	0.00058
2.20	0.00772						0.00037
2.40	0.00485						0.00023
2.60	0.00305						0.00015
2.80	0.00192						0.00009

(continued)

Table 9-2   (Continued)

	Plate, HL = 44 Value of U when x/L is						
τ	0.0	0.5	0.6	0.7	0.8	0.9	1.0
0.02	0.99998	0.99069	0.96440	0.89130	0.73350	0.45777	0.08952
0.04	0.99938	0.93461	0.86377	0.74464	0.56749	0.33453	0.06372
0.05	0.99752	0.90084	0.81761	0.69130	0.51762	0.30125	0.05705
0.06	0.99358	0.86789	0.77668	0.64744	0.47882	0.27625	0.05212
0.08	0.97865	0.80789	0.70859	0.57945	0.42171	0.24060	0.04519
0.10	0.95528	0.75627	0.65456	0.52878	0.38102	0.21593	0.04044
0.15	0.87584	0.65422	0.55630	0.44228	0.31462	0.17675	0.03299
0.20	0.78784	0.57511	0.48559	0.38360	0.27147	0.15199	0.02833
0.30	0.62634	0.45154	0.37978	0.29896	0.21096	0.11788	0.02196
0.40	0.49520	0.35634	0.29953	0.23566	0.16621	0.09286	0.01728
0.50	0.39120	0.28142	0.23653	0.18607	0.13124	0.07331	0.01365
0.60	0.30900	0.22228	0.18682	0.14696	0.10365	0.05790	0.01078
0.70	0.24407	0.17557	0.14756	0.11608	0.08187	0.04573	0.00851
0.80	0.19278	0.13867	0.11655	0.09169	0.06468	0.03613	0.00673
0.90	0.15227	0.10953	0.09206	0.07242	0.05107	0.02853	0.00531
1.00	0.12027	0.08651	0.07271	0.05720	0.04034	0.02254	0.00420
1.20	0.07503	0.05397	0.04536	0.03569	0.02517	0.01406	0.00262
1.40	0.04681	0.03367	0.02830	0.02226	0.01570	0.00877	0.00163
1.50	0.03698	0.02660	0.02235	0.01759	0.01240	0.00693	0.00129
1.60	0.02920	0.02103	0.01766	0.01389	0.00980	0.00547	0.00102
1.80	0.01822	0.01311	0.01102	0.00867	0.00611	0.00341	0.00064
2.00	0.01137	0.00818	0.00687	0.00541	0.00381	0.00213	0.00040
2.20	0.00709						0.00025
2.40	0.00443						0.00015
2.60	0.00276						0.00010
2.80	0.00172						0.00006

	Plate, HL = 60 Value of U when x/L is						
τ	0.0	0.5	0.6	0.7	0.8	0.9	1.0
0.02	0.99973	0.99003	0.96214	0.86081	0.72314	0.43942	0.06601
0.04	0.99933	0.93180	0.85861	0.73577	0.55561	0.31948	0.04685
0.05	0.99732	0.89697	0.81177	0.67270	0.49614	0.28748	0.04193
0.06	0.99328	0.86371	0.77041	0.63881	0.46785	0.26339	0.03837
0.08	0.97775	0.80299	0.70196	0.57103	0.41160	0.22925	0.03317
0.10	0.95379	0.75100	0.64787	0.52067	0.37166	0.20564	0.02968
0.15	0.87320	0.64861	0.54981	0.43494	0.30656	0.16822	0.02420
0.20	0.78386	0.56941	0.47933	0.37683	0.26428	0.14452	0.02076
0.30	0.62127	0.44586	0.37392	0.29296	0.20490	0.11185	0.01607
0.40	0.48978	0.35086	0.29409	0.23030	0.16101	0.08784	0.01262
0.50	0.38582	0.27632	0.23159	0.18134	0.12677	0.06917	0.00993
0.60	0.30389	0.21763	0.18240	0.14282	0.09984	0.05448	0.00782
0.70	0.23936	0.17142	0.14367	0.11249	0.07864	0.04291	0.00616
0.80	0.18853	0.13501	0.11316	0.08860	0.06194	0.03380	0.00486
0.90	0.14849	0.10634	0.08913	0.06979	0.04878	0.02662	0.00382
1.0	0.11696	0.08376	0.07183	0.05497	0.03842	0.02096	0.00301
1.2	0.07256	0.05196	0.04355	0.03410	0.02384	0.01301	0.00186
1.4	0.04501	0.03224	0.02702	0.02115	0.01479	0.00807	0.00116
1.5	0.03546	0.02539	0.02128	0.01666	0.01165	0.00636	0.00091
1.6	0.02792	0.02000	0.01676	0.01312	0.00917	0.00501	0.00072
1.8	0.01732	0.01241	0.01040	0.00814	0.00569	0.00311	0.00044
2.0	0.01074	0.00770	0.00645	0.00505	0.00353	0.00193	0.00028
2.2	0.00667						0.00017
2.4	0.00414						0.00011
2.6	0.00257						0.00007

	Plate, HL = ∞ Value of U when x/L is						
τ	0.0	0.5	0.6	0.7	0.8	0.9	1.0
0.02	0.99967	0.98750	0.95432	0.86763	0.60871	0.38318	0
0.04	0.99915	0.92286	0.84271	0.71116	0.49894	0.27686	0
0.05	0.99695	0.88614	0.79409	0.65722	0.46127	0.24818	0

(continued)

Table 9-2   (Continued)

| | Plate, HL = ∞ | | | | | | |
| | | | Value of U when x/L is | | | | |
τ	0.0	0.5	0.6	0.7	0.8	0.9	1.0
0.06	0.99221	0.85108	0.75174	0.61354	0.42991	0.22706	0
0.08	0.97516	0.78853	0.68007	0.54673	0.38108	0.19741	0
0.10	0.94931	0.73565	0.62756	0.49751	0.34469	0.17692	0
0.15	0.86429	0.63252	0.53099	0.41424	0.28402	0.14447	0
0.20	0.77231	0.55318	0.46154	0.35783	0.24424	0.12387	0
0.30	0.60680	0.42984	0.35749	0.27627	0.18812	0.09526	0
0.40	0.47440	0.33559	0.27898	0.21550	0.14669	0.07410	0
0.50	0.37078	0.26218	0.21794	0.16833	0.11458	0.05800	0
0.60	0.28971	0.20486	0.17029	0.13152	0.08953	0.04532	0
0.70	0.22636	0.16006	0.13305	0.10277	0.06995	0.03541	0
0.80	0.17687	0.12506	0.10396	0.08030	0.05466	0.02767	0
0.90	0.13819	0.09772	0.08123	0.06274	0.04271	0.02162	0
1.0	0.10798	0.07635	0.06347	0.04902	0.03337	0.01689	0
1.2	0.06592	0.04661	0.03875	0.02993	0.02037	0.01031	0
1.4	0.04024	0.02846	0.02365	0.01827	0.02144		0
1.5	0.03144	0.02223	0.01844	0.01428			0
2.0	0.00925	0.00647	0.00538				0
2.5	0.00267	0.00189	0.00157				0
3.0	0.00078						0

Tables for infinite cylinder or rod (after Russell)
Heat flow

| | Cylinder, HL = 0.05 | | | | | | |
| | | | Value of U when x/L is | | | | |
τ	0.0	0.5	0.6	0.7	0.8	0.9	1.0
0.08	0.99941	0.99680	0.99520	0.99301	0.98987	0.98640	0.98189
0.10	0.99866	0.99522	0.99333	0.99089	0.98753	0.98393	0.97940
0.20	0.99172	0.98624	0.98374	0.98076	0.97699	0.97317	0.96859
0.30	0.93264	0.97673	0.97411	0.97103	0.96721	0.96335	0.95880
0.40	0.97313	0.96717	0.96455	0.96147	0.95765	0.95383	0.94932
0.50	0.96360	0.95767	0.95507	0.95201	0.94823	0.94444	0.93997
0.60	0.95415	0.94826	0.94568	0.94265	0.93891	0.93516	0.93073
0.80	0.93548	0.92972	0.92719	0.92422	0.92055	0.91687	0.91253
1.00	0.91719	0.91153	0.90905	0.90614	0.90254	0.89893	0.89468
1.20	0.89925	0.89371	0.89127	0.88842	0.88489	0.88135	0.87718
1.60	0.86442	0.85909	0.85675	0.85400	0.85061	0.84721	0.84320
2.00	0.83093	0.82581	0.82357	0.82093	0.81767	0.81440	0.81054
2.8	0.76781	0.76308	0.76100	0.75856	0.75555	0.75253	0.74897
3.0	0.75280	0.74815	0.74612	0.74373	0.74077	0.73781	0.73432
4.0	0.68200	0.67780	0.67595	0.67379	0.67111	0.66843	0.66527
5.0	0.61787	0.61406	0.61239	0.61042	0.60800	0.60557	0.60270
5.6	0.58232	0.57873	0.57715	0.57530	0.57302	0.57073	0.56803
6.0	0.55976	0.55631	0.55480	0.55302	0.55097	0.54862	0.54603
7.0	0.50712	0.50400	0.50262	0.50101	0.49902	0.49703	0.49468
8.0	0.45943	0.45660	0.45536	0.45390	0.45210	0.45029	0.44816
10.0	0.37708	0.37476	0.37374	0.37254	0.37106	0.36958	0.36783
12.0	0.30950	0.30759	0.30675	0.30577	0.30456	0.30334	0.30190
14.0	0.25402	0.25246	0.25177	0.25096	0.24997	0.24897	0.24779
16.0	0.20849	0.20721	0.20664	0.20598	0.20516	0.20434	0.20338
18.0	0.17112	0.17007	0.16961	0.16906	0.16839	0.16772	0.16692
20.0	0.14045	0.13959	0.13921	0.13876	0.13821	0.13766	0.13701
25	0.08572						0.08362
30	0.05231						0.05103
40	0.01949						0.01901
50	0.00726						0.00708
60	0.00270						0.00264

(continued)

Table 9-2   (Continued)

	Cylinder, HL = 0.1 Value of U when x/L is						
τ	0.0	0.5	0.6	0.7	0.8	0.9	1.0
0.1	0.99722	0.98946	0.98671	0.98313	0.97515	0.96920	0.95930
0.2	0.98356	0.97191	0.96796	0.96336	0.95467	0.94832	0.93847
0.3	0.96584	0.95344	0.94932	0.94455	0.93585	0.92951	0.91982
0.4	0.94747	0.93513	0.93099	0.92625	0.91768	0.91144	0.90192
0.5	0.92923	0.91709	0.91300	0.90834	0.89993	0.89380	0.88447
0.6	0.91129	0.89936	0.89536	0.89079	0.88254	0.87653	0.86738
0.8	0.87641	0.86494	0.86109	0.85670	0.84876	0.84298	0.83418
1.0	0.84287	0.83184	0.82814	0.82391	0.81628	0.81072	0.80225
1.5	0.76453	0.75452	0.75116	0.74733	0.74040	0.73520	0.72769
2.0	0.69346	0.68439	0.68134	0.67786	0.67159	0.66686	0.66005
3.0	0.57054	0.56307	0.56057	0.55770	0.55254	0.54865	0.54304
4.0	0.46940	0.46326	0.46120	0.45884	0.45459	0.45140	0.44678
5.0	0.38620	0.38114	0.37945	0.37751	0.37401	0.37138	0.36759
6.0	0.31774	0.31430	0.31219	0.31059	0.30771	0.30555	0.30243
8.0	0.21508	0.21226	0.21132	0.21024	0.20829	0.20678	0.20471
10.0	0.14559	0.14335	0.14304	0.14231	0.14099	0.13997	0.13857
12.0	0.09855	0.09726	0.09683	0.09633	0.09544	0.09496	0.09380
14.0	0.06671	0.06583	0.06554	0.06521	0.06460	0.06428	0.06349
16.0	0.04515	0.04456	0.04437	0.04414	0.04373	0.04351	0.04298
18.0	0.03056	0.03016	0.03003	0.02988	0.02960	0.02945	0.02909
20.0	0.02069	0.02042	0.02033	0.02022	0.02004	0.01994	0.01969
25.0	0.00780						0.00742
30.0	0.00294						0.00280
35.0	0.00111						0.00106

	Cylinder, HL = 0.2 Value of U when x/L is						
τ	0.0	0.5	0.6	0.7	0.8	0.9	1.0
0.1	0.99381	0.98051	0.97330	0.96374	0.95199	0.93750	0.92333
0.2	0.96731	0.94674	0.93743	0.92624	0.91326	0.89836	0.88446
0.3	0.93358	0.91200	0.90252	0.89191	0.87844	0.86390	0.85047
0.4	0.89923	0.87807	0.86884	0.85795	0.84548	0.83144	0.81849
0.5	0.86577	0.84531	0.83639	0.82589	0.81386	0.80034	0.78787
0.6	0.83346	0.81375	0.80516	0.79504	0.78347	0.77044	0.75844
0.7	0.80234	0.78336	0.77509	0.76535	0.75421	0.74167	0.73011
0.8	0.77238	0.75410	0.74614	0.73677	0.72604	0.71397	0.70285
0.9	0.74353	0.72594	0.71827	0.70925	0.69892	0.68731	0.67660
1.0	0.71576	0.69883	0.69142	0.68276	0.67282	0.66164	0.65133
1.5	0.59167	0.57771	0.57158	0.56443	0.55621	0.54697	0.53844
2.0	0.48916	0.47758	0.47252	0.46661	0.45981	0.45217	0.44512
3.0	0.33429	0.32638	0.32292	0.31888	0.31423	0.30901	0.30419
4.0	0.22845	0.22304	0.22068	0.21792	0.21474	0.21117	0.20788
5.0	0.15612	0.15243	0.15081	0.14892	0.14675	0.14431	0.14207
6.0	0.10669	0.10417	0.10306	0.10177	0.10029	0.09862	0.09708
7.0	0.07291	0.07119	0.07043	0.06955	0.06854	0.06739	0.06635
8.0	0.04983	0.04865	0.04813	0.04753	0.04684	0.04606	0.04534
9.0	0.03405	0.03325	0.03289	0.03248	0.03201	0.03148	0.03099
10.0	0.02327	0.02272	0.02248	0.02220	0.02187	0.02151	0.02118
11.0	0.01590	0.01553	0.01536	0.01517	0.01495	0.01470	0.01447
12.0	0.01087	0.01061	0.01050	0.01037	0.01022	0.01005	0.00989
14.0	0.00508						0.00462
16.0	0.00237						0.00216
18.0	0.00111						0.00101

	Cylinder, HL = 0.4 Value of U when x/L is						
τ	0.0	0.5	0.6	0.7	0.8	0.9	1.0
0.05	N.E.	0.99114	0.98380	0.97135	0.95516	0.92842	0.89654
0.1	0.99032	0.96454	0.95073	0.93278	0.91051	0.88324	0.85163
0.2	0.94009	0.90201	0.88492	0.86456	0.84093	0.81412	0.78428
0.3	0.87856	0.84005	0.82325	0.80354	0.78099	0.75573	0.72788
0.4	0.81810	0.78163	0.76582	0.74731	0.72621	0.70264	0.67673
0.5	0.76120	0.72712	0.71237	0.69511	0.67546	0.65353	0.62942

(continued)

Table 9-2   (Continued)

| | Cylinder, HL = 0.4 | | | | | | |
| | | | Value of U when x/L is | | | | |
τ	0.0	0.5	0.6	0.7	0.8	0.9	1.0
0.6	0.70811	0.67639	0.66265	0.64660	0.62831	0.60790	0.58547
0.7	0.65869	0.62918	0.61640	0.60147	0.58446	0.56548	0.54461
0.8	0.61272	0.58527	0.57338	0.55949	0.54367	0.52601	0.50543
0.9	0.56996	0.54442	0.53336	0.52044	0.50572	0.48817	0.47124
1.0	0.53018	0.50642	0.49614	0.48412	0.47042	0.45514	0.43835
1.2	0.45875	0.43819	0.42831	0.41890	0.40705	0.39383	0.37929
1.4	0.39695	0.37916	0.37146	0.36247	0.35221	0.34077	0.32820
1.6	0.34347	0.32808	0.32142	0.31363	0.30476	0.29487	0.28398
1.8	0.29720	0.28389	0.27812	0.27138	0.26371	0.25514	0.24573
2.0	0.25705	0.24564	0.24065	0.23482	0.22818	0.22077	0.21262
3.0	0.12474						0.10314
4.0	0.06050						0.05003
5.0	0.02935						0.02426
6.0	0.01424						0.01177
7.0	0.00691						0.00571
8.0	0.00335						0.00277
9.0	0.00162						0.00134

| | Cylinder, HL = 0.6 | | | | | | |
| | | | Value of U when x/L is | | | | |
τ	0.0	0.5	0.6	0.7	0.8	0.9	1.0
0.05	0.99935	0.98691	0.97603	0.95849	0.93264	0.89687	0.85088
0.10	0.98566	0.94888	0.92908	0.90362	0.87202	0.83389	0.78955
0.20	0.91429	0.86146	0.83791	0.80991	0.77770	0.74150	0.70109
0.30	0.82959	0.77782	0.75540	0.72915	0.69936	0.66616	0.62986
0.40	0.74897	0.70145	0.68099	0.65711	0.63011	0.60009	0.56738
0.50	0.67540	0.63240	0.61390	0.59233	0.56796	0.54089	0.51139
0.60	0.60892	0.57011	0.55342	0.53397	0.51199	0.48758	0.46098
0.70	0.54895	0.51394	0.49890	0.48136	0.46155	0.43954	0.41557
0.80	0.49486	0.46331	0.44975	0.43394	0.41608	0.39624	0.37463
0.90	0.44611	0.41767	0.40544	0.39119	0.37509	0.35721	0.33772
1.00	0.40216	0.37652	0.36550	0.35265	0.33814	0.32201	0.30445
1.20	0.32682	0.30599	0.29703	0.28659	0.27480	0.26169	0.24742
1.40	0.26560	0.24867	0.24139	0.23290	0.22332	0.21267	0.20107
1.60	0.21584	0.20208	0.19617	0.18927	0.18149	0.17283	0.16340
1.80	0.17541	0.16423	0.15942	0.15382	0.14749	0.14045	0.13279
2.00	0.14255	0.13346	0.12956	0.12500	0.11986	0.11414	0.10792
2.5	0.08487						0.06425
3.0	0.05053						0.03825
4.0	0.01791						0.01356
5.0	0.00635						0.00480
6.0	0.00225						0.00170

| | Cylinder, HL = 0.80 | | | | | | |
| | | | Value of U when x/L is | | | | |
τ	0.0	0.5	0.6	0.7	0.8	0.9	1.0
0.02	N.E.	0.99904	0.99649	0.99127	0.97118	0.93551	0.87713
0.04	N.E.	0.99048	0.97971	0.96129	0.93128	0.88732	0.82836
0.05	0.99933	0.98314	0.96877	0.94648	0.91323	0.86756	0.80902
0.06	0.99784	0.97558	0.95673	0.93190	0.89633	0.84960	0.79167
0.08	0.99167	0.95525	0.93320	0.90378	0.86538	0.81770	0.76114
0.10	0.98119	0.93432	0.90917	0.87725	0.83742	0.78973	0.73451
0.15	0.94123	0.87989	0.85127	0.81685	0.77633	0.73001	0.67828
0.20	0.89142	0.82595	0.79678	0.76270	0.72341	0.67934	0.63090
0.30	0.78755	0.72522	0.69829	0.66721	0.63194	0.59289	0.55043
0.40	0.69145	0.63585	0.61194	0.58451	0.55343	0.51912	0.48191
0.50	0.60624	0.55731	0.53631	0.51221	0.48494	0.45486	0.42225
0.60	0.53136	0.48845	0.47002	0.44890	0.42499	0.39862	0.37004
0.70	0.46569	0.42808	0.41193	0.39342	0.37246	0.34935	0.32430
0.80	0.40814	0.37517	0.36102	0.34479	0.32643	0.30617	0.28422
0.90	0.35769	0.32880	0.31640	0.30218	0.28608	0.26833	0.24909
1.00	0.31348	0.28816	0.27729	0.26483	0.25072	0.23517	0.21831

(continued)

Table 9-2 (Continued)

τ	0.0	0.5	0.6	0.7	0.8	0.9	1.0
			Cylinder, HL = 0.80				
			Value of U when x/L is				
1.20	0.24078	0.22133	0.21298	0.20341	0.19258	0.18063	0.16768
1.40	0.18494	0.17000	0.16359	0.15624	0.14792	0.13874	0.12879
1.50	0.16208	0.14899	0.14338	0.13693	0.12963	0.12159	0.11287
1.60	0.14205	0.13058	0.12565	0.12001	0.11309	0.10656	0.09892
1.80	0.10911	0.10029	0.09651	0.09217	0.08719	0.08185	0.07598
2.00	0.08381	0.07703	0.07413	0.07080	0.06703	0.06287	0.05836
3.00	0.02240						0.01560
4.00	0.00599						0.00417
5.00	0.00160						0.00111

τ	0.0	0.5	0.6	0.7	0.8	0.9	1.0
			Cylinder, HL = 1				
			Value of U when x/L is				
0.04	N.E.	0.99013	0.97748	0.97638	0.91801	0.86467	0.79388
0.05	N.E.	0.98114	0.96416	0.93687	0.89640	0.84128	0.77338
0.06	0.99937	0.97070	0.95209	0.91929	0.87630	0.82022	0.75133
0.08	0.99179	0.94737	0.92134	0.88353	0.83982	0.78312	0.71637
0.10	0.97904	0.92337	0.89278	0.85423	0.80716	0.75080	0.68635
0.20	0.87208	0.79536	0.76197	0.72227	0.67709	0.62659	0.57162
0.30	0.75176	0.68071	0.65064	0.61545	0.57598	0.53242	0.48553
0.40	0.64340	0.58167	0.55568	0.52539	0.48151	0.45423	0.41491
0.50	0.54977	0.49686	0.47461	0.44868	0.41971	0.38786	0.35366
0.60	0.46963	0.42438	0.40537	0.38321	0.35846	0.33125	0.30204
0.70	0.40111	0.36246	0.34623	0.32731	0.30616	0.28292	0.25797
0.80	0.34259	0.30958	0.29572	0.27955	0.26150	0.24164	0.22034
0.90	0.29261	0.26442	0.25257	0.23877	0.22855	0.20639	0.18819
1.0	0.24992	0.22584	0.21424	0.20393	0.19032	0.17628	0.16073
1.2	0.18231	0.16475	0.15737	0.14877	0.13916	0.12860	0.11726
1.4	0.13300	0.12018	0.11480	0.10853	0.10152	0.09381	0.08554
1.6	0.09702	0.08767	0.08375	0.07917	0.07406	0.06843	0.06237
1.8	0.07078	0.06396	0.06109	0.05910	0.05402	0.04992	0.04550
2.0	0.05163	0.04666	0.04457	0.04213	0.03941	0.03642	0.03319
3.0	0.01067						0.00686
4.0	0.00220						0.00142

τ	0.0	0.5	0.6	0.7	0.8	0.9	1.0
			Cylinder, HL = 2				
			Value of U when x/L is				
0.04	0.99616	0.97812	0.95515	0.91569	0.85210	0.76204	0.64513
0.05	0.99748	0.96246	0.93229	0.88603	0.81709	0.72597	0.61304
0.06	0.99419	0.94464	0.90894	0.85695	0.78545	0.69450	0.58536
0.08	0.98101	0.90584	0.86198	0.80403	0.73165	0.64121	0.53906
0.10	0.95921	0.86560	0.81725	0.75655	0.68264	0.59691	0.50099
0.15	0.88075	0.76738	0.71627	0.65592	0.58664	0.50980	0.42687
0.2	0.78992	0.67738	0.62902	0.57321	0.51064	0.44152	0.37016
0.3	0.61929	0.52557	0.48753	0.44183	0.39255	0.33956	0.28383
0.4	0.48072	0.40711	0.37651	0.34178	0.30350	0.26244	0.21921
0.5	0.37240	0.31525	0.29150	0.26336	0.23493	0.20312	0.16974
0.6	0.28838	0.24409	0.22570	0.20485	0.18230	0.15762	0.13142
0.7	0.22329	0.18900	0.17436	0.15861	0.14083	0.12176	0.10176
0.8	0.17289	0.14634	0.13531	0.12281	0.10904	0.09428	0.07879
0.9	0.13387	0.11331	0.10472	0.09509	0.08442	0.07300	0.06101
1.0	0.10365	0.08773	0.08112	0.07363	0.06537	0.05652	0.04724
1.5	0.02884	0.02441	0.02255	0.02049	0.01823	0.01372	0.01315
2.0	0.00803	0.00679	0.00628	0.00570	0.00506	0.00438	0.00366
2.2	0.00481						0.00219
2.4	0.00289						0.00131
2.6	0.00173						0.00079

(continued)

Table 9-2 (Continued)

τ	Cylinder, HL = 2.4 Value of U when x/L is						
	0.0	0.5	0.6	0.7	0.8	0.9	1.0
0.02	N.E.	0.99677	0.99072	0.97074	0.92295	0.83355	0.69204
0.04	0.99940	0.97474	0.94821	0.90230	0.82989	0.72883	0.59799
0.05	0.99760	0.95681	0.92230	0.86866	0.79108	0.68950	0.56409
0.06	0.99374	0.93660	0.89579	0.83677	0.75634	0.65557	0.53518
0.08	0.97591	0.89300	0.84370	0.77859	0.69623	0.59889	0.48746
0.10	0.95358	0.84830	0.79449	0.72704	0.64550	0.55248	0.44884
0.15	0.86579	0.74100	0.69529	0.61971	0.54472	0.46299	0.37512
0.20	0.76618	0.64459	0.59282	0.53327	0.46667	0.39543	0.32000
0.30	0.58385	0.48584	0.44521	0.39914	0.34828	0.29453	0.23816
0.40	0.44036	0.36566	0.33484	0.29998	0.26160	0.22115	0.17879
0.50	0.33147	0.27512	0.25189	0.22563	0.19676	0.16632	0.13445
0.60	0.24941	0.20699	0.18951	0.16975	0.14802	0.12511	0.10115
0.70	0.18764	0.15572	0.14258	0.12771	0.11136	0.09413	0.07610
0.80	0.14117	0.11716	0.10727	0.09608	0.08378	0.07082	0.05725
0.90	0.10621	0.08814	0.08070	0.07229	0.06303	0.05328	0.04307
1.0	0.07991	0.06631	0.06071	0.05439	0.04742	0.04008	0.03241
1.2	0.04523	0.03754	0.03437	0.03078	0.02684	0.02269	0.01834
1.4	0.02560	0.02125	0.01945	0.01742	0.01519	0.01284	0.01038
1.5	0.01926	0.01598	0.01463	0.01311	0.01143	0.00966	0.00781
1.6	0.01449	0.01203	0.01101	0.00986	0.00860	0.00727	0.00588
1.8	0.00820	0.00680	0.00623	0.00558	0.00487	0.00411	0.00332
2.0	0.00464	0.00385	0.00353	0.00316	0.00276	0.00233	0.00188
2.2	0.00263						0.00107
2.4	0.00149						0.00060

τ	Cylinder, HL = 4 Value of U when x/L is						
	0.0	0.5	0.6	0.7	0.8	0.9	1.0
0.02	0.99931	0.99266	0.98504	0.95586	0.88710	0.75858	0.56290
0.04	0.99786	0.96237	0.92472	0.87053	0.76224	0.62607	0.45661
0.05	0.99532	0.93744	0.88942	0.81611	0.71299	0.57968	0.42098
0.06	0.98970	0.90998	0.85430	0.77522	0.66896	0.54095	0.39164
0.08	0.96823	0.85385	0.78760	0.70336	0.59923	0.47986	0.34523
0.10	0.93439	0.79640	0.72701	0.64204	0.54232	0.43031	0.30937
0.15	0.82047	0.66635	0.59923	0.52163	0.43513	0.34202	0.24503
0.20	0.69869	0.55632	0.49709	0.43006	0.35686	0.27943	0.19988
0.30	0.49164	0.38697	0.34445	0.30063	0.24560	0.19188	0.13713
0.40	0.34242	0.26898	0.23927	0.20612	0.17041	0.13307	0.09509
0.50	0.23806	0.18695	0.16627	0.14322	0.11840	0.09275	0.06606
0.60	0.16547	0.12993	0.11556	0.09953	0.08228	0.06425	0.04591
0.70	0.11500	0.09030	0.08031	0.06918	0.05718	0.04465	0.03190
0.80	0.07992	0.06275	0.05582	0.04808	0.03974	0.03103	0.02217
0.90	0.05555	0.04361	0.03879	0.03341	0.02762	0.02157	0.01541
1.00	0.03860	0.03031	0.02696	0.02322	0.01920	0.01499	0.01071
1.20	0.01865	0.01464	0.01302	0.01122	0.00927	0.00724	0.00517
1.40	0.00900	0.00707	0.00629	0.00542	0.00448	0.00350	0.00250
1.50	0.00626	0.00491	0.00437	0.00377	0.00311	0.00243	0.00174
1.60	0.00435						0.00121
1.80	0.00210						0.00058

τ	Cylinder, HL = 6 Value of U when x/L is						
	0.0	0.5	0.6	0.7	0.8	0.9	1.0
0.02	N.E.	0.99563	0.97961	0.94155	0.85177	0.68957	0.45024
0.04	0.99886	0.95236	0.90426	0.82415	0.70338	0.53841	0.34566
0.05	0.99533	0.92124	0.86149	0.77195	0.64826	0.49100	0.31283
0.06	0.98805	0.88792	0.81994	0.72512	0.60172	0.45226	0.28659
0.08	0.96084	0.82027	0.74336	0.64526	0.52677	0.39172	0.24654
0.10	0.91835	0.75542	0.67591	0.57958	0.46824	0.34563	0.21673
0.15	0.78602	0.61289	0.53792	0.45493	0.36257	0.26496	0.16543
0.20	0.65034	0.49689	0.43421	0.36409	0.28861	0.21007	0.13093
0.30	0.43206	0.32655	0.28432	0.23759	0.18821	0.13637	0.08492

(continued)

Table 9-2   (Continued)

τ	Cylinder, HL = 6 Value of U when x/L is						
	0.0	0.5	0.6	0.7	0.8	0.9	1.0
0.40	0.28441	0.21460	0.18675	0.15597	0.12322	0.08945	0.05568
0.50	0.18696	0.14103	0.12271	0.10248	0.08095	0.05876	0.03659
0.60	0.12286	0.09268	0.08064	0.06735	0.05320	0.03862	0.02405
0.70	0.08073	0.06091	0.05300	0.04426	0.03496	0.02538	0.01580
0.80	0.05306	0.04003	0.03491	0.02908	0.02297	0.01668	0.01036
0.90	0.03487	0.02630	0.02289	0.01911	0.01510	0.01096	0.00681
1.00	0.02291	0.01729	0.01504	0.01256	0.00992	0.00720	0.00447
1.2	0.00900	0.00747	0.00649	0.00543	0.00428	0.00311	0.00193
1.4	0.00427	0.00322	0.00280	0.00234	0.00185	0.00134	0.00084
1.5	0.00281	0.00212	0.00184	0.00154	0.00121	0.00088	0.00055
1.6	0.00185						0.00036

τ	Cylinder, HL = 7 Value of U when x/L is						
	0.0	0.5	0.6	0.7	0.8	0.9	1.0
0.02	0.99959	0.99324	0.97615	0.93826	0.83762	0.66188	0.40756
0.04	0.99747	0.94693	0.89518	0.81035	0.68124	0.51031	0.30659
0.05	0.99372	0.91373	0.84974	0.75520	0.62446	0.46815	0.27570
0.06	0.98581	0.87840	0.80602	0.70636	0.57698	0.42246	0.25126
0.08	0.95655	0.80906	0.72660	0.62423	0.50140	0.36249	0.21442
0.10	0.91251	0.74063	0.65733	0.55758	0.44308	0.31780	0.18736
0.15	0.77284	0.59423	0.51868	0.43284	0.33921	0.24084	0.14135
0.20	0.63320	0.47709	0.41371	0.34310	0.26744	0.18913	0.11082
0.25	0.51239	0.38315	0.33033	0.27419	0.21329	0.15070	0.08819
0.30	0.41272	0.30772	0.26560	0.21982	0.17085	0.12057	0.07058
0.35	0.33186	0.24717	0.21342	0.17644	0.13710	0.09640	0.05662
0.40	0.26670	0.19853	0.17145	0.14167	0.11008	0.07765	0.04545
0.45	0.21423	0.15947	0.13773	0.11378	0.08840	0.06215	0.03650
0.50	0.17209	0.12809	0.11063	0.09139	0.07100	0.05009	0.02932
0.60	0.11103	0.08264	0.07137	0.05896	0.04581	0.03232	0.01891
0.70	0.07163	0.05332	0.04605	0.03804	0.02955	0.02085	0.01220
0.80	0.04622	0.03440	0.02971	0.02454	0.01907	0.01345	0.00787
0.90	0.02982	0.02219	0.01917	0.01583	0.01230	0.00868	0.00508
1.0	0.01924	0.01432	0.01237	0.01022	0.00794	0.00560	0.00328
1.2	0.00801						0.00136
1.4	0.00333						0.00057
1.5	0.00215						0.00037

τ	Cylinder, HL = 10 Value of U when x/L is						
	0.0	0.5	0.6	0.7	0.8	0.9	1.0
0.02	N.E.	0.99176	0.97753	0.91991	0.80419	0.60102	0.31398
0.04	0.99758	0.93678	0.88088	0.77742	0.63307	0.44568	0.22635
0.05	0.99280	0.89879	0.83028	0.71805	0.57391	0.39830	0.20094
0.06	0.98335	0.85918	0.78199	0.66643	0.52551	0.36100	0.18125
0.08	0.94931	0.78149	0.69637	0.58135	0.45027	0.30530	0.15239
0.10	0.89935	0.70956	0.62362	0.51380	0.39354	0.26471	0.13165
0.15	0.74686	0.55776	0.48176	0.39044	0.29492	0.19641	0.09723
0.20	0.59981	0.43926	0.37704	0.30364	0.22828	0.15049	0.07485
0.30	0.37361	0.27301	0.23362	0.18765	0.14068	0.09318	0.04601
0.40	0.23430	0.16977	0.14522	0.11660	0.08740	0.05787	0.02858
0.50	0.14574	0.10559	0.09031	0.07251	0.05434	0.03598	0.01777
0.60	0.09064	0.06567	0.05617	0.04510	0.03380	0.02238	0.01105
0.70	0.05637	0.04084	0.03493	0.02805	0.02102	0.01392	0.00687
0.80	0.03506	0.02540	0.02173	0.01744	0.01307	0.00866	0.00427
0.90	0.02180	0.01580	0.01351	0.01085	0.00813	0.00539	0.00266
1.00	0.01356	0.00982	0.00840	0.00675	0.00506	0.00335	0.00165
1.20	0.00524	0.00380	0.00325	0.00261	0.00196	0.00130	0.00064
1.40	0.00203	0.00147	0.00126	0.00101	0.00076	0.00050	0.00025
1.50	0.00126	0.00092	0.00078	0.00063	0.00047	0.00031	0.00015

(continued)

Table 9-2 (Continued)

| | Cylinder, HL = 15 | | | | | |
| | | | Value of U when x/L is | | | |
τ	0.0	0.5	0.6	0.7	0.8	0.9	1.0
0.02	N.E.	0.99043	0.98119	0.90815	0.76901	0.53639	0.22266
0.04	0.99810	0.92769	0.85927	0.74714	0.58703	0.38429	0.15520
0.05	0.99202	0.88494	0.80285	0.68398	0.52708	0.33969	0.13628
0.06	0.98104	0.84133	0.75125	0.63009	0.47892	0.30549	0.12200
0.08	0.94255	0.75779	0.66183	0.54325	0.40559	0.25528	0.10136
0.10	0.88723	0.68210	0.58744	0.47597	0.35137	0.21938	0.08684
0.15	0.72387	0.52651	0.44557	0.35520	0.25893	0.16006	0.06311
0.20	0.57119	0.40740	0.34310	0.25995	0.19730	0.12162	0.04790
0.25	0.44581	0.31623	0.26560	0.20080	0.15223	0.09372	0.03688
0.30	0.34668	0.24545	0.20596	0.15562	0.11792	0.07256	0.02852
0.35	0.26927	0.19052	0.15982	0.12069	0.09146	0.05627	0.02214
0.40	0.20906	0.14788	0.12403	0.09808	0.07097	0.04365	0.01718
0.45	0.16224	0.11479	0.09628	0.07613	0.05509	0.03389	0.01334
0.50	0.12654	0.08910	0.07473	0.05909	0.04276	0.02631	0.01035
0.55	0.09777	0.06916	0.05801	0.04587	0.03319	0.02042	0.00803
0.60	0.07589	0.05368	0.04502	0.03560	0.02576	0.01585	0.00623
0.70	0.04571						0.00376
0.80	0.02754						0.00226
0.90	0.01659						0.00136
1.00	0.01000						0.00082
1.20	0.00363						0.00030
1.40	0.00132						0.00011

| | Cylinder, HL = 30 | | | | | |
| | | | Value of U when x/L is | | | |
τ	0.0	0.5	0.6	0.7	0.8	0.9	1.0
0.02	N.E.	N.E.	N.E.	N.E.	N.E.	N.E.	N.E.
0.04	0.99839	0.91186	0.83102	0.70461	0.52909	0.31430	0.07575
0.05	0.99134	0.86397	0.77077	0.63922	0.47062	0.27539	0.06625
0.06	0.97798	0.82559	0.71642	0.58468	0.42457	0.24589	0.05915
0.08	0.93394	0.72980	0.62416	0.49867	0.35575	0.20329	0.04904
0.10	0.87109	0.64907	0.54908	0.43305	0.30571	0.17331	0.04193
0.15	0.69563	0.49139	0.40889	0.31470	0.22158	0.12442	0.03023
0.20	0.54186	0.37398	0.30956	0.23959	0.16628	0.09310	0.02265
0.25	0.41263	0.28513	0.23562	0.18615	0.12621	0.07059	0.01719
0.30	0.31547	0.21751	0.17964	0.13863	0.09614	0.05376	0.01308
0.35	0.24074	0.16596	0.13703	0.10574	0.07333	0.04099	0.00998
0.40	0.18369	0.12663	0.10456	0.08067	0.05594	0.03127	0.00762
0.45	0.14017	0.09662	0.07975	0.06156	0.04268	0.02386	0.00581
0.50	0.10695	0.07373	0.06088	0.04697	0.03257	0.01821	0.00443
0.60	0.06227	0.04292	0.03545	0.02735	0.01896	0.01060	0.00258
0.70	0.03626	0.02499	0.02064	0.01592	0.01104	0.00617	0.00150
0.80	0.02111	0.01455	0.01202	0.00927	0.00643	0.00359	0.00088
0.90	0.01229	0.00847	0.00700	0.00540	0.00357	0.00209	0.00051
1.00	0.00716						0.00030
1.20	0.00243						0.00010

| | Cylinder, HL = ∞ | | | | | |
| | | | Value of U when x/L is | | | |
τ	0.0	0.5	0.6	0.7	0.8	0.9	1.0
0.02	N.E.	0.98429	0.94081	0.83942	0.63713	0.34802	0
0.04	0.99628	0.88906	0.79433	0.65141	0.46025	0.23473	0
0.05	0.98434	0.83555	0.73000	0.58562	0.40630	0.20449	0
0.06	0.97054	0.78396	0.67357	0.53191	0.36437	0.18181	0
0.08	0.91776	0.69061	0.58016	0.44887	0.30249	0.14938	0
0.10	0.84836	0.61025	0.50576	0.38661	0.25805	0.12669	0
0.15	0.66183	0.45262	0.32229	0.27866	0.18402	0.08974	0
0.20	0.50150	0.33797	0.27467	0.20633	0.13582	0.06611	0
0.30	0.28271	0.18934	0.15362	0.11523	0.07576	0.03684	0
0.40	0.15850	0.10618	0.08613	0.06460	0.04246	0.02065	0
0.50	0.08889	0.05955	0.04831	0.03623	0.02382	0.01158	0
0.60	0.04985	0.03340	0.02709	0.02032	0.01336	0.00649	0

(continued)

Table 9-2   (Continued)

τ	Cylinder, HL = ∞ Value of U when x/L is						
	0.0	0.5	0.6	0.7	0.8	0.9	1.0
0.70	0.02796	0.01874	0.01519	0.01140	0.00749	0.00364	0
0.80	0.01568	0.01051	0.00852	0.00639	0.00420	0.00205	0
0.90	0.00880	0.00589	0.00478	0.00358	0.00236	0.00115	0
1.00	0.00494	0.00331	0.00268	0.00201	0.00132	0.00064	0
1.20	0.00155	0.00104	0.00084	0.00063	0.00042	0.00020	0

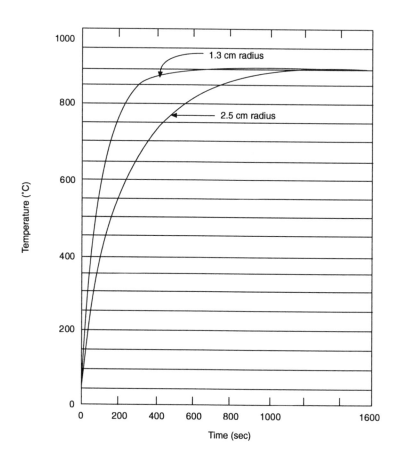

Fig 9-6   Calculated heating curves for the center of 1.3 cm and 2.5 cm radius cylinders when heated in still air

the effect is given by Gergely, Somogyi, Reti, and Konkoly (Computerized Properties Prediction and Technology Planning in Heat Treatment of Steels, in *ASM Handbook*, Vol 4, p 638-658, *Heat Treating*, ASM International, Materials Park, Ohio (1991)). They give a relation for the A_{c3} temperature to be

$$A_{c3} = A_3 + Av^{1/3}$$

where v is the rate of heating at the A_3 temperature. (See Fig. 9-9.) The temperatures are in °C and v is in °C/sec. The quantity A depends upon the microstructure, and values are given in terms of the prior structure or heat treatment: 3 for martensite, 5 for quenched and tempered, 10 for normalized and 15 for annealed. Note that the A_{c3} temperature is higher for the coarser beginning structures. Presumably the finer structures have higher nucleation rates for the formation of austenite grains.

To illustrate the calculation, assume that the steel contains about 0.7% C and is in the annealed condition. This would correspond approximately to the structure for the curves in Fig. 9-7 (pearlite with a small amount of primary ferrite). From the phase diagram (Fig. 2-4), the A_3 temperature is found to be about 745°C. For a heating rate of about 0.3°C/sec. at this temperature, the A_{c3} temperature is about 750°C. The curve marked in Fig. 9-7 corresponds to approximately this heating rate, and the calculated value agrees well with the A_{c3} curve.

It is pointed out that the data in Fig. 9-7 show residual carbides present above the A_{c3} temperature, which means that their complete solution in the austenite which has formed is not taken into account in the defined A_{c3} in Fig. 9-7. To attain homogeneous austenite, the steel must be heated about 100°C above the calculated A_{c3}.

Transformation of Austenite

The rate of the decomposition of austenite to pearlite, bainite, primary ferrite and primary iron carbide is controlled by the nucleation and growth rates of the constituents. These rates are strongly temperature dependent. The models developed are too detailed and numerous to review here. It is useful, however, to get a feeling of the principles involved, and the general ideas and approaches taken, and what follows is a qualitative description designed to illustrate these. For convenience, the description will be given in terms of the formation of pearlite from austenite.

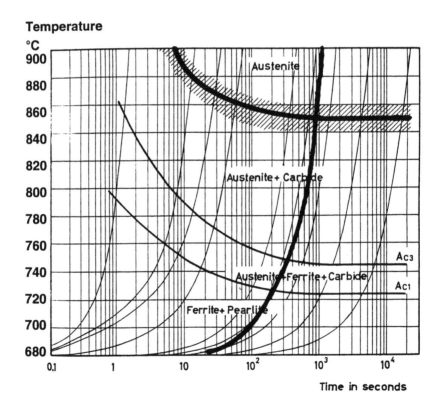

Fig 9-7   The formation of austenite from an initial structure of pearlite and a small amount of primary ferrite in a steel containing about 0.8% C, upon heating at different rates characterized by the heating curves shown. (Adapted from A. Rose and V. Strassburg, *Stahl und Eisen*, Vol 76, p 976 (1956))

Nucleation rate

The formation of pearlite begins by the nucleation of small regions of the lamellar structure. The exact atomistic mechanism is difficult to determine, but it is not necessary to know this to examine the development for the rate of nucleation. The thermodynamic instability of austenite (or the stability of the product structure, pearlite), is reflected in the difference in the Gibbs free energy of the pearlite and the parent austenite, ΔG. The temperature dependence of the free energy difference is shown schematically in Fig. 9-10.

Now consider a volume of austenite V^γ at some temperature below the eutectoid temperature, 996 K (723°C). The free energy per volume of austenite is g_v^γ so the free energy of this volume G_i is

$$G_i = g_v^\gamma V^\gamma$$

Now let a sphere of pearlite of volume V^P form in the initial volume of austenite. The free energy of the system should decrease as the more stable pearlite forms. However, there is a surface formed between the ferrite and the carbide in the pearlite and the austenite, which *increases* the energy of the system. Let the average surface energy be E_s and the surface area be A_s. Then the free energy G_f at this stage is

$$G_f = g_v^\gamma (V^\gamma - V^P) + g_v^P V^P + A_s E_s$$

and the change in free energy is

$$\Delta G = (g_v^\gamma(V^\gamma - V^P) + g_v^P + A_s E_s) - (g_v^\gamma V^\gamma)$$

$$= (g_v^P - g_v^\gamma)V^P + A_s E_s$$

$$= \Delta g_v V^P + A_s E_s$$

where Δg_v is the free energy change per volume for γ changing to pearlite at the temperature of interest. This is the volumetric or chemical free energy change. The surface area is $4\pi r^2$, and the volume of pearlite is $\frac{4}{3}\pi r^3$, which gives

$$\Delta G = \frac{4}{3}\pi r^3 (\Delta g_v) + 4\pi r^2 E_s$$

Thus, the free energy change of the system as the transformation progresses (the sphere of pearlite grows into γ)

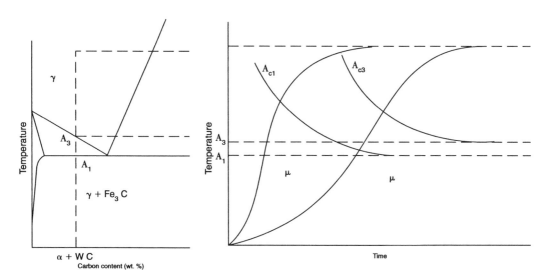

Fig 9-8   Schematic continuous heating time-temperature-transformation diagram for the formation of austenite from a specific microstructure, showing the relation between the equilibrium transformation temperatures A₁ and A₃ and the corresponding non-equilibrium transformation temperatures Ac1 and Ac3

is dependent on the radius. Note that the volumetric free energy change Δg_v is negative, since the pearlite is stable at the temperature of consideration and hence g_v^P is less than g_v^γ. However, E_s is positive as a surface is formed which requires energy. The dependency of ΔG on radius is shown schematically in Fig. 9-11. It is seen that as the radius increases the free energy of the system increases, then passes through a maximum, and decreases.

Nucleation theory assumes that the sphere of pearlite becomes stable when it attains the radius of the maximum ΔG (critical radius r_c). If a few atoms are removed from a sphere of radius r_c, the free energy decreases, so it appears that the sphere would never grow beyond the critical radius. However, if a few atoms of γ at the pearlite $-\gamma$ interface take up the arrangement of pearlite, then the sphere *grows* beyond radius r_c, and the free energy also decreases. However, for a given incremental change in r_c, there is a larger decrease in ΔG if the sphere increases in size. Thus, once the critical size is attained, there is a greater probability that it will grow in size than decrease. Hence this size is considered to be that of a stable nucleus.

Differentiation of the equation for ΔG gives for the critical free energy change

$$\Delta G_c = (16/3)\,\pi \left[\frac{E_s^3}{(\Delta g_v)^2}\right]$$

The free energy change is given by

$$\Delta g_v = \Delta h_v - T\Delta s_v$$

where Δh_v is the enthalpy change and Δs_v the entropy change. At the eutectoid temperature (723°C (996 K)), the free energy of the pearlite and the γ is equal, so $\Delta g_v = 0$, and hence

$$\Delta s_v = \Delta h_v / 996$$

If the enthalpy of the transformation is assumed to be independent of temperature (which means that the difference in the heat capacity of the pearlite and the γ is negligible), then

$$\Delta g_v = \Delta h_v[1 - (T/996)]$$

$$= \Delta h_v\left[\frac{996 - T}{996}\right]$$

$$= \Delta h_v\left[\frac{\Delta T}{996}\right]$$

where ΔT is the degree of undercooling below the eutectoid temperature of 996 K.

The barrier for the formation of a stable pearlite nucleus is taken as the critical free energy change ΔG_c (Fig. 9-11). Substituting Δg_v, the expression for ΔG_c is

$$\Delta G_c = (16/3)\,(996)^2 \left[E_s^3/(\Delta h_v)^2\,(\Delta T)^2\right]$$

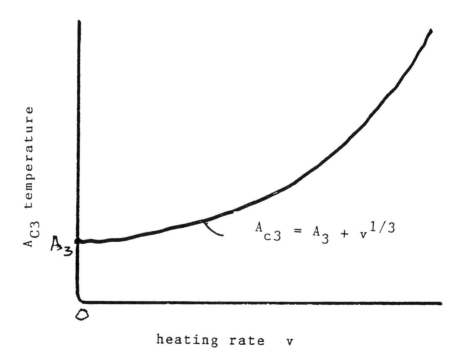

heating rate v

Fig 9-9 Schematic illustration of the variation of the A_{c3} temperature with heating rate v

The temperature dependence of ΔG_c is shown in Fig. 9-12. Note that the critical free energy for attaining the critical radius decreases with temperature. This implies that nucleation of pearlite is easier the greater the undercooling below 723°C.

However, the kinetic aspect of atom movement must be considered. For example, the critical free energy for nucleation (ΔG_c) is a minimum (maximum driving force) at absolute zero, but atom exchange cannot occur, so the rate of nucleation must be zero at this temperature.

It is assumed that the rate of growth of a nucleus is proportional to an Arrhenius type expression, exp($-\Delta G_b/RT$), where ΔG_b is taken as the free energy barrier for atoms at the pearlite-γ interface to move from the γ configuration. This also depends upon the frequency of vibration v of the atoms, the probability P_1 that an atom vibrates towards the interface, and the probability P_2 that it will remain in the pearlite configuration. Thus, the number of atoms adding to the interface per time is

$$dn/dt = vP_1 P_2 \exp (-\Delta G_b/RT)$$

This is for one nucleus. The total number of stable nuclei is taken as

$$n = N_T \exp (\Delta G_c/RT)$$

where N_T is the total number of atoms. The nucleation rate N is the product of these two equations

$$N = vP_1 P_2 \exp (\Delta G_b/RT) \exp (-\Delta G_c/RT)$$

It is assumed that only ΔG_c is temperature dependent, so that

$$N = K \exp (\Delta G_c/RT) \exp (-\Delta G_b/RT)$$

where K is a constant. The temperature dependence of the first exponential term involves that of ΔG_c, as shown in Fig. 9-12. However, the division by temperature causes N to approach zero as temperature decreases. This is also true for the second exponential term. Thus, the nucleation rate varies with temperature as shown in Fig. 9-13.

The nucleation described in the preceding treatment refers to *homogeneous nucleation*, where the nuclei form inside the parent phase. However, in most cases the phase forms at the interface between the parent phase and another surface. For example, in freezing of a material in

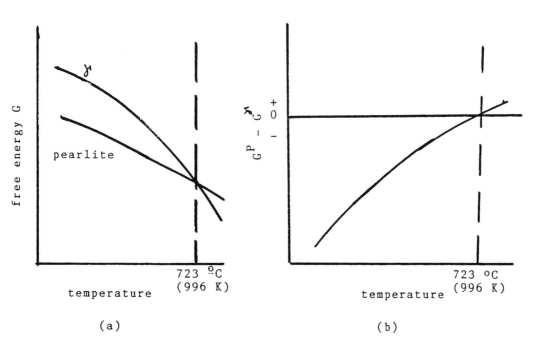

(a)

(b)

Fig 9-10 Schematic illustration of (a) the Gibbs free energy of austenite (γ) and pearlite as a function of temperature for a 0.8% C plain carbon eutectoid steel, and of (b) the difference in the free energy of these two constituents

a mold, the crystals may nucleate at the mold wall. In the solidification of steels, fine particles (e.g., Al_2O_3), formed from the reaction of dissolved gases with deoxidizers added, serve as these sites. Such nucleation is called *heterogeneous nucleation*. In the decomposition of austenite, nucleation of the microconstituents (e.g., pear-

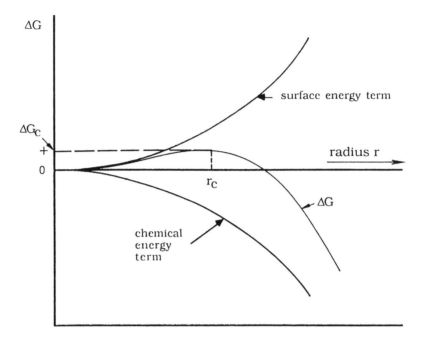

Fig 9-11   Schematic illustration of the dependence of ΔG on the radius of the sphere of pearlite forming in γ. The critical radius is r_c, and the corresponding critical free energy change is ΔG_c

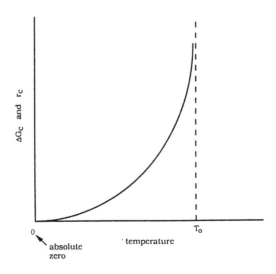

Fig 9-12   Schematic illustration of the temperature dependence of the critical free energy change ΔG_c

lite) frequently occurs at the austenite grain boundaries. Another important factor neglected here for solid-state transformation is the strain generated by the volume difference (density difference) between the two phases. Modeling these two effects gives relations more complex than those derived above, but does not change the basic temperature dependence of the nucleation rate depicted in Fig. 9-13.

Growth rate

The growth of a stable pearlite nucleus involves the movement of carbon and iron atoms at the pearlite-α interface. Two things occur here. One is that the iron atoms in the γ at the interface change from the face-centered cubic γ arrangement to the structure of either the body-centered cubic ferrite or the iron carbide. In addition, the carbon in the γ ahead of the advancing pearlite interface moves towards the regions which are becoming iron carbide (high carbon content) and away from regions which are becoming ferrite (low carbon content). This is depicted schematically in Fig. 9-14.

It is assumed that the growth rate of pearlite is controlled by the diffusion rate of carbon in the austenite. The carbon distribution is complicated, but Fig. 9-14 shows how the carbon gradient is involved. Using Fick's first law of diffusion, the flux can be approximated by

J = number of carbon atoms crossing a unit area surface perpendicular to their movement per unit time

$$= - D [dC/dX]$$

$$\approx - D [(\Delta C) / (\Delta X)]$$

where D is the diffusion coefficient of carbon in γ, C is the concentration of carbon in γ and X is the distance (see Fig. 9-14). Figure 9-14 shows how the concentration difference ΔC increases with decreasing temperature, which corresponds to a higher gradient and hence a higher flux. However, the diffusion coefficient is quite temperature dependent, given by an Arrhenius type equation as

$$D = D_0 \exp (-Q/RT)$$

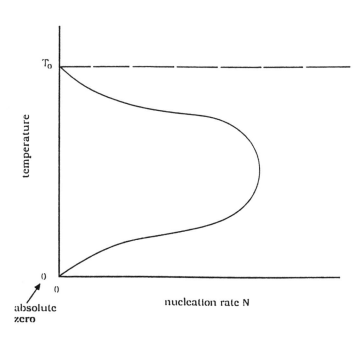

Fig 9-13   Schematic illustration of the temperature dependence of the nucleation rate

where D_0 is a constant, Q is the activation energy for diffusion of carbon in γ (a constant), R is the ideal gas constant, and T is the absolute temperature. This gives for the flux

$$J \approx - D_0 \, [exp \, (-Q/RT)] \, [(\Delta C) / (\Delta X)]$$

the rate of growth G of the pearlite is taken to be proportional to the flux, so that

$$G = A \, [exp \, (-Q/RT)] \, [(\Delta C)]$$

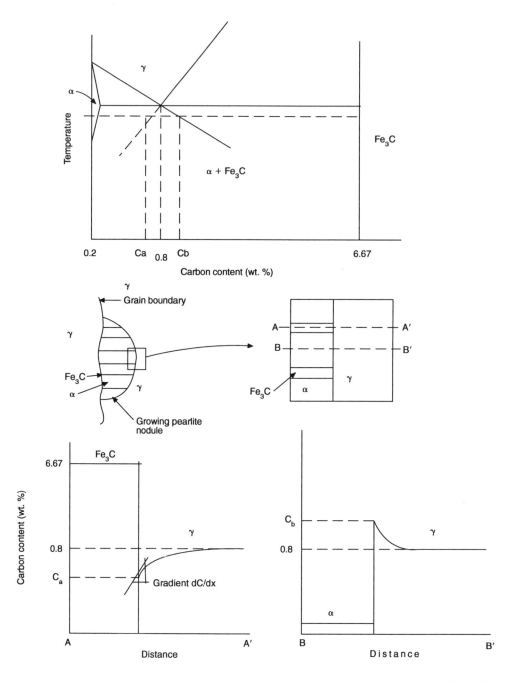

Fig 9-14 Schematic illustration of the profile of the carbon content in austenite at and ahead of an advancing pearlite interface

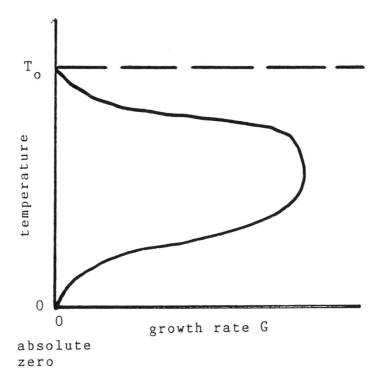

Fig 9-15   Schematic illustration of the temperature dependence of the growth rate

where A is a constant. This gives the temperature depend-ence shown in Fig. 9-15, similar to that found for the nucleation rate (Fig. 9-13).

The simplified analysis above is a useful basis for qualitatively seeing the general ideas about the kinetics of the decomposition of austenite. There are a number of problems with the analysis. A fundamental one is whether the kinetics are given by the model described. Another is that there must be a separate relation for each microcon-stituent which forms (i.e., pearlite, bainite, etc.), and experimental data of primary quantities (e.g., activation energy Q) and of the constants must be obtained.

Rate of decomposition of austenite

An important fundamental consideration is how to connect the nucleation rate and the growth rate to the overall rate of decomposition of austenite. These are two independent events, but the amount of transformation product depends on each. A very applicable approach which was developed is to assume random nucleation and constant nucleation and growth rates (at a given temperature). Correction has to be made for the disap-pearance of the parent phase since nucleation can only occur in the remaining parent phase. The decomposition product is assumed to form and grow as spheres. A result

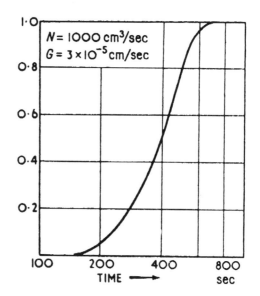

Fig 9-16   The calculated amount of transformation product formed isothermally as a function of time, using the values of the nucleation rate N and the growth rate G noted. (From R.F. Mehl and W.C. Hagel, in *Progress in Metal Physics*, Vol 6, B. Chalmers and R. King, editors, Pergamon Press, Oxford, UK (1956))

is that the fraction f(t) of the product constituent formed as a function of time t is

$$f(t) = 1 - \exp[(\pi/3) \, N \, G^3 t^4]$$

This relation predicts the correct general shape of the kinetics curve, as shown in Fig. 9-16.

For convenience, the treatment just given for the nucleation rate and the growth rate was couched in terms of the formation of pearlite from austenite. The prediction that the nucleation rate is a maximum at an intermediate temperature was confirmed by experimental data of pearlite formation (Fig. 9-17), and this means that the time for the beginning of the formation of pearlite will be a minimum at an intermediate temperature. This is confirmed by the isothermal TTT diagram in Fig. 9-18a. The maxi-

mum in the growth rate at an intermediate temperature (Fig. 9-17), along with the temperature dependence of the nucleation rate, predicts from the equation above that the finish of the formation of pearlite will be a minimum at an intermediate temperature, which is confirmed by the TTT diagram in Fig. 9-18a.

It is seen in Fig. 9-17 that the experimental data for N and G do not extend below about 550°C. This is because in this lower temperature range the formation of bainite is kinetically more favored than pearlite formation. Careful study shows that there is a narrow temperature range in which both products form. Also the time for the beginning and end of the formation of bainite is a minimum at an intermediate temperature. These effects are best seen in alloy steels, where the pearlite and bainite formation curves are better separated, as shown in Fig. 9-18(b).

Table 9-3 The cooling rate (velocities) in °C/h to obtain the given microstructure (from J.S. Kirkaldy, Quantitative Prediction of Transformation Hardening in Steels, *ASM Handbook*, Vol 4, p 20-32, Heat Treating, ASM International, Materials Park, Ohio (1991))

$\log V_1 = 9.81-4.62C-1.05Mn-0.54Ni-0.5Cr-0.66Mo-0.00183P_a$
$\log V_1(10) = 8.76-4.04C-0.96Mn-0.49Ni-0.58Cr-0.97Mo-0.0010P_a$
$\log V_1(50) = 8.50-4.13C-0.86Mn-0.57Ni-0.41Cr-0.94Mo-0.012P_a$
$\log V_2 = 10.17-3.80C-1.07Mn-0.70Ni-0.57Cr-1.58Mo-0.0032P_a$
$\log V_2(90) = 10.55-3.65C-1.08Mn-0.77Ni-0.61Cr-1.49Mo-0.0040P_a$
$\log V_2(50) = 8.74-2.23C-0.86Mn-0.56Ni-0.59Cr-1.60Mo-0.0032P_a$
$\log V_3(90) = 7.51-1.38C-0.35Mn-0.93Ni-0.11Cr-2.31Mo-0.0033P_a$
$\log V_3 = 6.36-0.43C-0.49Mn-0.78Ni-0.26Cr-0.38Mo-0.0019P_a - 2\sqrt{Mo}$

where the smallest rate for the formation of 100% martensite is V_1; the rate for 90% martensite-10% bainite is $V_1(90)$; the rate for 50% martensite-50% bainite is $V_1(50)$; the smallest rate for no ferrite-pearlite is V_2; the rate for 90% bainite-10% ferrite-pearlite is $V_2(90)$; the rate for 50% bainite-50% ferrite-pearlite is $V_2(50)$; the rate for 90% ferrite-pearlite-10% bainite is $V_3(90)$; and the largest rate for 100% ferrite-pearlite is V_3. These relations are based on the following range of composition (wt.%): 0.2-0.5% C; <1% Si; <2% Mn; <4% Ni; <3% Cr; <1% Mo; <0.2% V.

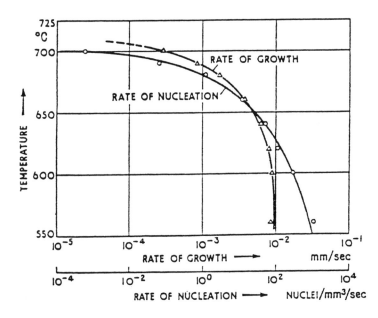

Fig 9-17 Experimental values of the nucleation rate N and the growth rate G as a function of transformation temperature for the formation of pearlite in an 0.8% C eutectoid steel. (From same source as Fig. 9-16)

Estimation of transformation products of austenite

If the nucleation rate and growth rate for the formation of each transformation product (e.g., pearlite, bainite) are constant at a given temperature, and if their temperature dependence is known, then the progress of the transformation of austenite upon cooling for a known temperature-time curve can be calculated. Both N and G

Type: 1035 Mod.
Composition: Fe - 0.35% C - 0.37% Mn Grain size: 75% 2-3, 25% 7-8 Austenitized at 843° C (1550°F)

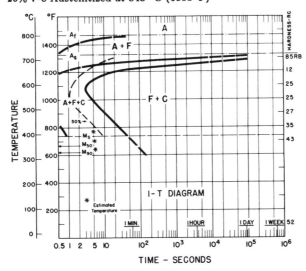

Type: 4340
Composition: Fe - 0.42% C - 0.78% Mn - 1.79% Ni - 0.80% Cr - 0.33% Mo Grain size: 7-8 Austenitized at 843°C (1550°F)

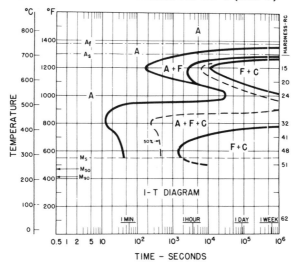

Fig 9-18 Isothermal time-temperature-transformation diagrams for (a) a plain carbon steel and for (b) an alloy steel. (From *Isothermal Transformation Diagrams of Austenite in a Wide Variety of Steels*, United States Steel Corporation (1963))

depend upon the chemical composition of the steel, and since nucleation of the products usually occurs at the austenite grain boundaries, N depends on the austenite grain size. Thus to determine the type and amount of the transformation products requires an immense quantity of experimental data of N and G. In addition, there are concerns about the applicability of isothermal data to

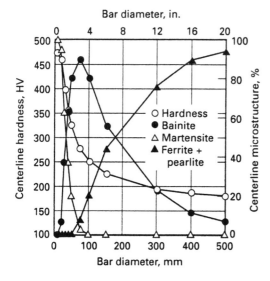

Fig 9-19 Hardness and microstructure along the center line of a water quenched 8620-type steel cylinder as predicted by the Creusot-Loire method. The composition of the steel was 0.2% C, 1% Mn, 0.5% Ni, 0.5% Cr and 0.2% Mo. (From J.S. Kirkaldy, in *ASM Handbook*, Vol 4, p 20, *Heat Treating*, ASM International, Materials Park, Ohio (1991))

transformation during cooling. For example, the nucleation of bainite may be influenced by the presence of pearlite which has formed before the bainite appears. Therefore, a different approach to determine the transformation products of austenite must be used.

Models have been developed to estimate the isothermal TTT diagram, but the continuous cooling TTT (CCT) diagram is of more practical interest. Although this diagram, coupled with the cooling curve of a location in a steel component, would allow prediction of the constituents in the final microstructure, the diagram by itself doesn't give the relative amounts, which is required to estimate strength. However, from the location of the "nose" of the CCT diagram, which can be estimated, the critical cooling velocity can be estimated. This is the cooling rate which must be equaled or exceeded to produce all martensite to give complete hardening.

The Creusot-Loire method is one approach. It is based on fitting a great quantity of experimental data to obtain the cooling rate (velocity) to obtain a specified amount of mixtures of transformation products. The equations are given in Table 9-3. All but V_2 give a unique volume fraction of the three designated constituents. In the case of V_2 it is easy to interpolate the volume percents of bainite at log V_2 from log V_2 (90) and log V_1 (50), yielding an estimate of the bainite and martensite phase fractions at log V_2. Note that the first equation gives the critical cooling rate for the formation of all martensite. The parameter P_a is related to the austenitizing temperature T and time t by the relation

$$P_a = \{[1/T] - [0.000042 \, (\log t)]\}^{-1} - 273$$

where T is in K and t in hours.

These relations can be coupled with cooling rate data to estimate the final microstructure. Figure 9-19 shows the predicted microstructure at the center of cylinders of different diameter after quenching into water. The hardness can be estimated by knowing the hardness of the

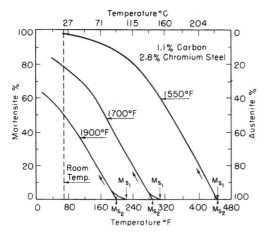

Fig 9-20 The amount of martensite formed as a function of the temperature below the M$_s$ temperature, for a 1.1% C-2.8% Cr steel austenitized at 1550°F. (From M. Cohen, *Trans. ASM*, Vol 41, p 35 (1949))

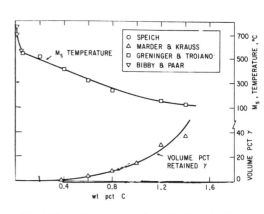

Fig 9-21 The amount of retained austenite upon quenching to 25°C as a function of carbon content of the austenite. Also shown is the M$_s$ temperature. (Adapted from G.R. Speich and W.C. Leslie, *Met Trans.*, Vol 3, p 1043 (1972))

individual constituents and their relative amounts (additive rule), which is discussed later in this chapter.

Calculation of Amount of Martensite and Retained Austenite

Austenite begins to decompose to martensite upon reaching the martensite start temperature, M_S. However, the amount of martensite formed with the degree of cooling below M_S is not linear, but instead there is increasing difficulty in forming martensite. This is illustrated in Fig. 9-20. Note that the temperature of the completion of the formation of martensite, M_f, is difficult to establish. Also note that, for this steel, upon quenching to 25°C there will be present some untransformed austenite, referred to as *retained austenite*. The amount of retained austenite at 25°C is dependent on the carbon content of the austenite, as shown in Fig. 9-21.

Figure 9-22 shows that the M_S temperature is dependent on the alloy content (e.g., amount of Mn, Ni). Thus the curves in Fig. 9-21 are also dependent upon the alloy content. Based on experimental data, relations have been derived from which the M_S can be estimated. These are summarized in Table 9-4. However, of more use is a method to estimate the amount of retained austenite as a function of chemical composition of the austenite and of the temperature to which the steel is quenched. Two relations have been derived, and are given in terms of the temperature difference between M_S and the quench temperature. The graphical result is shown in Fig. 9-23. The equations representing the data are shown in the figure. For these equations M_S can be calculated via the equations in Table 9-4. (In the normal range of austenite grain size (e.g., ASTM 6 to 8), the M_S is not significantly affected by the austenite grain size.)

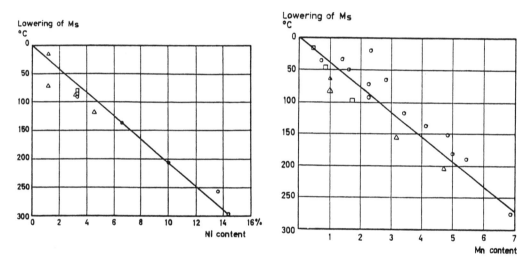

Lowering of M_S
°C

NI content

Lowering of M_S
°C

Mn content

Fig 9-22 Effect of Mn and Ni content of austenite on the M_S temperature. (Adapted from K.E. Thelning, *Steel and Its Heat Treatment*, Butterworths, London (1975))

Table 9-4 Formulas for calculation of the M_S temperature from the composition of the steel. (From sources cited)

Investigators	Date	Equation
Payson and Savage	1944	M_S (°F) = 930 − 570C − 60Mn − 50Cr − 30Ni − 20Si − 20Mo − 20W
Carapella	1944	M_S (°F) = 925 × (1 − 0.620C)(1 − 0.092Mn)(1 − 0.033Si)(1 − 0.045Ni)(1 − 0.070Cr)(1 − 0.029Mo)(1 − 0.018W)(1 + 0.120Co)
Rowland and Lyle	1946	M_S (°F) = 930 − 600C − 60Mn − 50Cr − 30Ni − 20Si − 20Mo − 20W
Grange and Stewart	1946	M_S (°F) = 1000 − 650C − 70Mn − 70Cr − 35Ni − 50Mo
Nehrenberg	1946	M_S (°F) = 930 − 540C − 60Mn − 40Cr − 30Ni − 20Si − 20Mo
Steven and Haynes	1956	M_S (°C) = 561 − 474C − 33Mn − 17Cr − 17Ni − 21Mo
Andrews (linear)	1965	M_S (°C) = 539 − 423C − 30.4Mn − 12.1Cr − 17.7Ni − 7.5Mo
Andrews (product)	1965	M_S (°C) = 512 − 453C − 16.9Ni + 15Cr − 9.5Mo + 217(C)^2 − 71.5(C)(Mn) − 67.6(C)(Cr)

Sources: P. Payson and C.H. Savage, Martensite Reactions in Alloys Steels, *Trans. ASM*, Vol 33, p 261-275 (1944); L.A. Carapella, Computing A[11] or M_S (Transformation Temperature on Quenching) from Analysis, *Metal Progress*, Vol 46, p 108 (1944); E.S. Rowland and S.R. Lyle, The Application of M_S Points to Case Depth Measurement, *Trans. ASM*, Vol 37, p 27-47 (1946); R.A. Grange and H.M. Stewart, The Temperature Range of Martensite Formation, *Trans. AIME*, Vol 167, p 467-490 (1946); A.E. Nehrenberg, *Trans. AIME*, Vol 167, p 494-498 (1946); W. Steven and A.G. Haynes, The Temperature of Formation of Martensite and Bainite in Low-Alloy Steel, *JISI*, Vol 183, p 349-359 (1956); and K.W. Andrews, Empirical Formulae for the Calculation of Some Transformation Temperatures, *JISI*, Vol 203, p 721-727 (1965)

To illustrate the effect of chemical composition, the M_s temperature and the amount of retained austenite after quenching to 25°C was calculated for three steels using the correlation by Payson and Savage and by Andrews in Table 9-4. The composition used for each steel is shown in Table 9-5, along with the calculated values. Note that

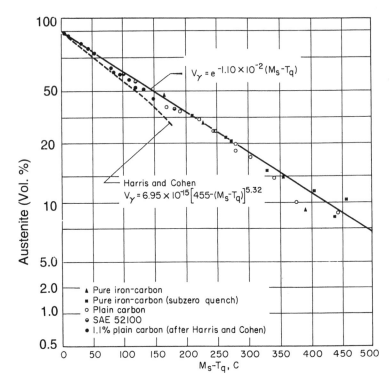

$$V_\gamma = e^{-1.10 \times 10^{-2}(M_s-T_q)}$$

Harris and Cohen
$$V_\gamma = 6.95 \times 10^{-15}[455-(M_s-T_q)]^{5.32}$$

▲ Pure iron-carbon
■ Pure iron-carbon (subzero quench)
○ Plain carbon
◉ SAE 52100
● 1.1% plain carbon (after Harris and Cohen)

Austenite (Vol. %)

M_s-T_q, C

Fig 9-23 The amount of retained austenite as a function of the martensite start temperature M_s and the temperature T_q to which the steel is quenched. (From D.P. Koistinen and R.E. Marburger, *Acta Metallurgica*, Vol 7 p 59-60 (1959))

Table 9-5 Calculated M_s temperatures and amount of retained austenite after quenching to 25°C for four steels

Steel	C	Mn	Si	Cr	Ni	Mo
			Composition (wt.%)			
1040	0.40	0.85	0.20	0	0	0
4140	0.40	0.85	0.20	0.80	0	0.15
4118	0.20	0.85	0.20	0.60	0	0.15
4340	0.40	0.70	0.20	0.80	1.80	0.25

Steel	M_s (°C)	
	(Payson and Savage)	(Andrews)
1040	348	272
4140	320	237
4118	386	382
4340	294	210

Steel	Amount of retained austenite at 25°C (volume %)	
	(Payson and Savage)	(Andrews)
1040	3	6
4140	4	10
4118	2	2
4340	5	13

the relation of Payson and Savage gives less retained austenite than does that of Andrews. It is important to recognize that these relations predict in these three steels some retained austenite present after quenching to 25°C, although the lower the carbon and alloy content the less the amount of retained austenite. Even for the plain car-

bon 1040 steel, the amount of retained austenite is calculated to be 3 or 6%, which is consistent with the data in Fig. 9-21.

The M_s and M_f temperatures can be useful in estimating the magnitude of residual stresses which form upon quenching. A high M_s temperature allows any martensite formed to *auto-temper* upon cooling to 25°C, and hence reduce the residual stresses associated with the formation of martensite. The amount of retained austenite present after quenching to 25°C is an important characteristic of carburized steels and of tool steels. The relations noted here can be used to determine the effect of carbon and alloy content on the amount of retained austenite.

Hardenability Calculations

The calculation of measures of hardenability is central to estimating properties of steels hardened by quenching. The most useful approach is to use correlations to calculate the Jominy curve, which then can be coupled with cooling curves to estimate the hardness at locations in quenched components. The hardness can then be related to tensile and fatigue strength by the correlations described later in this chapter. The methods of calculating hardenability were described in detail in Chapter 3, and hence are not repeated here.

Tempering

Models for tempering of steels have been reviewed by Kirkaldy (Quantitative Prediction of Transformation Hardening in Steels, in *ASM Handbook*, Vol 4, p 20-32, *Heat Treating*, ASM International, Materials Park, Ohio (1991)) and details and references can be found there. In this section, the treatment in Chapter 5 is extended to examine the effect on the tempered hardness of the time required to heat up a component to the tempering temperature.

The effects of tempering temperature and time on the hardness of steels were described in Chapter 5. There the relationship which was emphasized to connect hardness to temperature and time was that developed by Holloman and Jaffe. This related the absolute temperature T and time t to give the same hardness by the relation [t exp (B/T)] were B is a constant. (See Chapter 5.) From this approach, for a given steel all the tempered hardness data

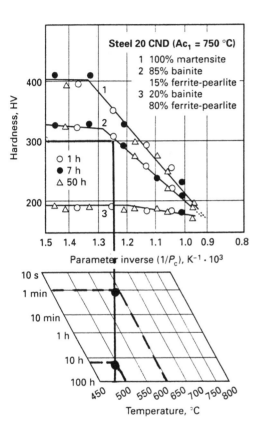

Fig 9-24 Hardness versus inverse tempering parameter for a steel containing 0.2% C, 1% Mn, 0.5% Ni, 0.5% Cr and 0.2% Mo, for three different beginning microstructures. (Adapted from J.S. Kirkaldy, *Quantitative Prediction of Transformation Hardening in Steels*, in *ASM Handbook*, Vol 4, p 20, *Heat Treating*, ASM International, Materials Park, Ohio (1991))

Table 9-6 Hardness of tempered structures given by the Creusot-Loire system. (From the same source as Table 9-3)

$$HV_M = -74 - 434 - 368Si + 25Mn + 37Ni - 335Mo - 223V + \frac{10^3}{P_c}(260 + 616C + 321Si - 21Mn - 35Ni - 11Cr + 352Mo + 2345V)$$

$$HV_B = 262 + 163C - 349Si - 64Mn - 6Ni - 186Cr - 458Mo - 857V + \frac{10^3}{P_c}(-149 + 43C + 446Si + 79Mn + 16Ni + 196Cr + 498Mo + 1094V)$$

$$HV_{F-P} = 152 - 493C - 10Mn - 19Mo + \frac{10^3}{P_c}(-37 + 726C + 14Mn + 17Mo)$$

$10^3/P_c = 1.365 - (0.205C + 0.233Mo + 0.135V)$

The composition of the elements is in weight percent. The hardness is Vickers.
The tempering temperature (T in K) and time (t in hours) are taken into account by
$P_c = [(1/T) - 7.96 \times 10^{-5} \log t] \%Mo < 0.04$
$P_c = [(1/T) - 4.58 \times 10^{-5} \log t] \%Mo > 0.04$

were fitted well to a common curve if plotted against a parameter T(C + log t). [Other models are available, but the analysis by Murphy and Woodhead in 1972 (*Metallurgical Transactions*, Vol 3, p 727-735 (1972)) con-

cluded that the Holloman-Jaffe parameter is the most useful.]

This information in Chapter 5 was presented in terms of hardness versus tempering parameter plots, but each

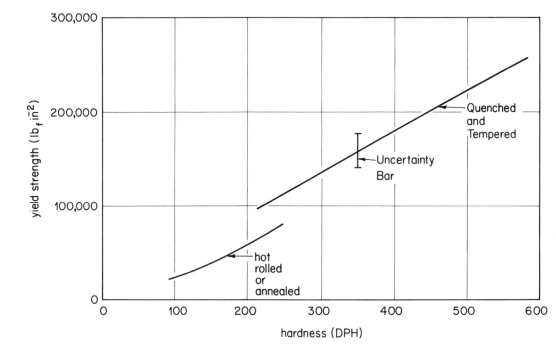

Fig 9-25 Relation between the yield strength and the hardness for steels. (Adapted from *Metals Handbook*, 8th edition, Vol 2, American Society for Metals, Metals Park, Ohio; W.G. Patton, *Metals Progress*, Vol 43, p 726 (1943))

plot has to be obtained for a given composition steel. The Creusot-Loire system uses a Holloman-Jaffe parameter with which experimental data have been used to obtain the tempered hardness versus the tempering parameter. The parameter is defined by

$$P_c = \left[\frac{1}{T} - \frac{nR}{H_a} \cdot \log \frac{t}{t_0} \right]^{-1}$$

for the process and t_0 is 1 hour, T is in K, t is in hours, and n is 2.303. The constants were determined for steels of a given composition range from tempering data. $H_a =$ 57,500 cal/mole for %Mo < 0.04% and 100,000 for %Mo >0.04.

Figure 9-24 shows typical data for one of the steels studied. The hardness remains constant to a parameter value called the deflection point, then decreases linearly. The value of P_c at the deflection was found to be a function of the C, Mo and V content (Table 9-6). For values of the tempering parameter less than this calcu-

lated value of P_c, there is no change in the as-quenched hardness.

The method reports the tempered hardness as a function of the deflection tempering parameter P_c and the composition for three beginning microstructures: martensite, bainite and primary ferrite-pearlite. The relations are given in Table 9-6. These relations can be used to estimate the hardness of mixtures of these microconstituents by assuming that the hardness is the sum of the product of the hardness of each constituent and its volume fraction (rule of mixtures). A disadvantage of the Creusot-Loire method is that knowledge is required of the amount of the starting microconstituents. This can be estimated by the methods described earlier in this chapter.

The nomograph below the tempering curves in Fig. 9-24 can be used to obtain the combination of temperature and time to give the same hardness. (This is the same type of diagram as discussed in Chapter 5 with reference to Fig. 5-45.) For example, if the hardness is 300 HV, then the line at this level is extended to the hardness curve and at the intersection is continued to the nomograph, as

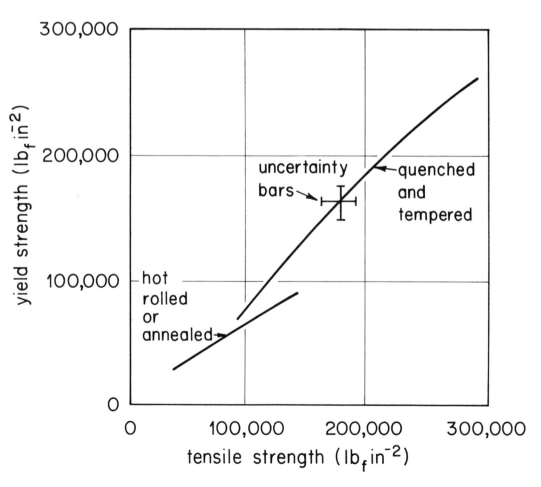

Fig 9-26   Relation between yield strength and the tensile strength for steels. (From same source as Fig. 9-25)

shown in Fig. 9-24. Any temperature-time point on this line will give the same hardness. Note that the line is different for the three different beginning microstructures. For a microstructure of 85% bainite-15% primary ferrite: pearlite, a hardness of 300 HV will be obtained by tempering for 24 h at 500°C and tempering for 1 min at 600°C (see Fig. 9-24). Note that this monograph is only valid for this specific steel.

This section is concluded by examining a method to estimate the amount of softening which occurs during heating to the tempering temperature. The temperature-time relation for the heating curve is needed, which can be estimated by the methods described earlier in this chapter. Also a known heating curve can be fitted to an analytical expression. For example, heating curves such as those in Fig. 6-31 can be approximated by the relation

$$T = T_t - A \exp (Bt + C')$$

where T is temperature, time is t, T_t is the tempering temperature to which the steel is to be heated, and A, B and C' are constants. An analytical relation between the hardness and the tempering temperature and time is needed, and is given through the tempering parameter P. The tempered hardness decreases approximately linearly with the tempering parameter (see Fig 5-28, 5-29, 5-30, 5-31, and 9-24), so the hardness can be represented by

$$H = D + C\,P$$

D is a constant and P is the tempering parameter, given by [(C) (T) (E + log t)], where T is absolute temperature (see Chapter 5). C and E are constants which are derived from experimental data for each given steel.

Hardness (at 25 °C) is obtained as a function of time during heating by substituting the temperature = f(t) relation for the heating curve for the temperature in the tempered hardness expression. The expression is valid only for the heating curve specified. The additional softening which occurs as a function of time after attaining the tempering temperature can be determined from the tempering parameter. An example of a calculation of the softening which occurs during heating is given in Chapter 10.

Estimation of Mechanical Properties

Correlation of hardness and strength properties

Because the measurement of hardness is simple and is essentially nondestructive (leaving only a small impression on the surface), many heat treating correlations are presented in terms of predicting hardness. However in design it is the tensile mechanical properties that are usually desired. Fortunately, for steels there exist work

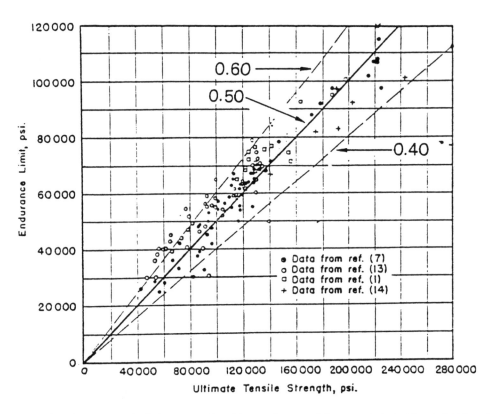

Fig 9-27 Relation between the fatigue strength and the tensile strength for several steels. The straight lines have the slope shown. (Adapted from a compilation of T.J. Dola and C.S. Yen, *Proc. ASTM*, Vol 48, p 664 (1948))

able empirical relations between hardness and some of these properties. Figure 9-25 shows curves of yield strength as a function of hardness based on measurements on many steels. From tensile tests, an approximate relation has been obtained between the yield strength and the tensile strength, and Fig. 9-26 shows an example. In both Fig. 9-25 and 9-26 there are uncertainty bars on the curves, which are based on the general spread of the data used to obtain the curves.

In the design of many machine components, fatigue is a crucial consideration. Fortunately, for steels there also exists a usable correlation between fatigue strength (or fatigue limit or endurance limit) and tensile strength, which is illustrated by the data in Fig. 9-27. This allows construction of a plot of fatigue strength versus yield strength, as shown in Fig. 9-28, and using the curves in Fig. 9-25 a plot of fatigue strength versus hardness can be obtained. However, Fig. 9-29 shows that there can be a large scatter in the data for high strength levels. This is the reason for the spread in the correlation at high hardness levels shown in Fig. 9-30.

Primary ferrite-pearlite structures

The common structure of normalized steels, annealed steels and of high strength low alloy (and low carbon) steels is a mixture of primary ferrite and pearlite. The strength and hardness levels are determined primarily by the alloy and carbon content and the primary ferrite grain size. (Although in the high strength low alloys steels, other factors such as precipitation hardening in the ferrite are important. See Chapter 8.) The alloy content provides solid solution strengthening of the primary ferrite. It also affects the eutectoid carbon content, and hence the amount of pearlite and primary ferrite present (see Chapter 8), which affects the strength. Nitrogen is a small element and dissolves interstitially in the iron lattice. Hence it behaves similarly to carbon in affecting properties, and in some relations it appears as a factor to consider. Other factors may be involved. Table 9-7 lists factors affecting the strength properties of steels with a primary ferrite-pearlite structure.

In single phase alloys, for a given purity the strength is usually controlled by the grain size ("diameter" of the

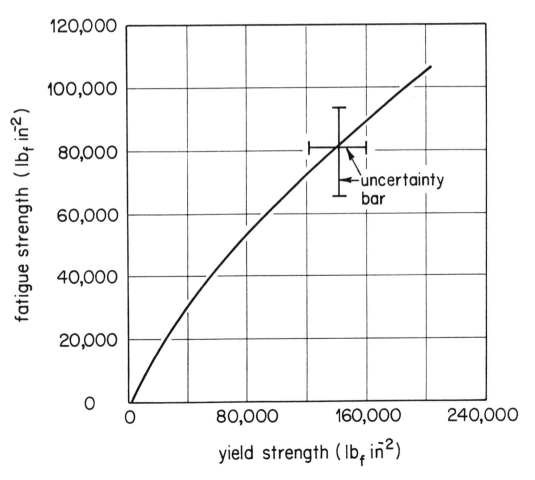

Fig 9-28 The fatigue strength as a function of yield strength for steels. (From C.R. Brooks, *The Heat Treatment of Ferrous Alloys*, Hemisphere Publishing Corporation/McGraw-Hill Book Company, New York (1979))

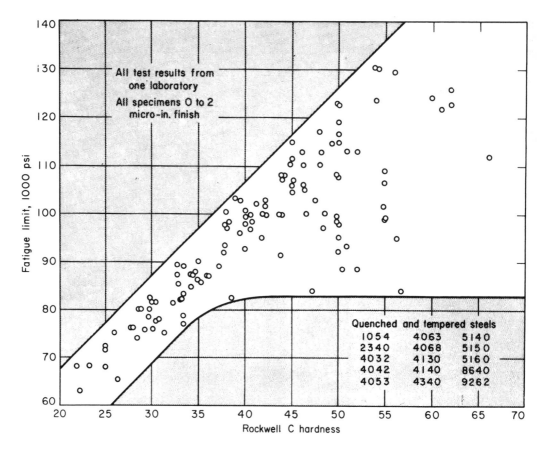

Fig 9-29 The fatigue limit as a function of hardness based on quenched and tempered steels. (From *Metals Handbook*, 8th edition, Vol 1, p 217, American Society for Metals, Metals Park, Ohio (1961))

grains). This usually can be represented by the Hall-Petch relation, in which the strength is inversely linear with the grain size "d."

$$\text{strength} = A + Bd^{-1/2}$$

where A and B are constants. For multiphase structures, a similar relation may be valid where the "d" must be properly identified. In pearlite, it is the interlamellar spacing.

In steels with a structure of primary ferrite and pearlite, one can take the strength to be an additive relation of the amount of primary ferrite and pearlite each times the strength of the microconstituent. Thus one may have

$$\text{strength} = (A + Bd^{-1/2})$$
$$\text{(fraction of primary ferrite present)}$$

$$+ (C + D S_0^{-1/2}) \text{ (fraction of pearlite present)}$$

where d is the primary ferrite grain size and S_0 is the pearlite spacing (the distance between adjacent carbide

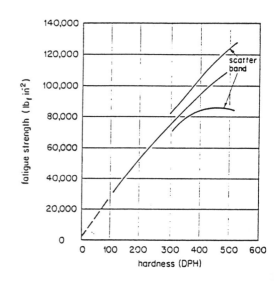

Fig 9-30 The fatigue strength as a function of hardness for quenched and tempered steels. (From same source as Fig. 9-28)

Table 9-7 Factors affecting the mechanical properties of steels with a primary ferrite-pearlite structure

Structural factors

Primary ferrite grain size
Amount of pearlite and primary ferrite
Pearlite interlamellar spacing

Chemical factors

Carbon content (affects amount of pearlite and primary ferrite)
Alloy content (affects amount of pearlite and primary ferrite)
Alloy content (affects solid solution strengthening of primary ferrite)

lamellae). A practical problem with such an approach is that, whereas it is relatively easy to measure the primary ferrite grain size, determining the pearlite spacing is quite difficult, since it is very small. But this relation can be useful to estimate the effect of the structure on the strength.

The amount of pearlite and primary ferrite present depends especially upon the carbon content, but it also depends on the alloy content since alloying elements shift the eutectoid carbon content and hence the amount of the two microconstituents which form. (This was discussed in Chapter 8.) Because it is difficult to model these

Table 9-8 Relations for primary ferrite-pearlite steels which give some mechanical properties as a function of composition and microstructural parameters

(T. Gladman, D. Dulieu, and I.D. McIvor, Structure-Property Relationships in High-Strength Microalloyed Steels, *MicroAlloying 75*, p 32-58, Union Carbide Corporation, New York (1977))

$$\text{Yield strength (MPa)} = K + 37(\%Mn) + 83(\%Si) + (\pm 31 \text{ MPa}) 2918(\%N) + 15.1(d^{-1/2})$$

$K = 88$ MPa for an air cooled material and 62 MPa for a furnace-cooled material, the variation being caused by effects of the cooling rate on the distribution of cementite. The grain size, d, is defined as the mean linear intercept of the polygonal-ferrite grains expressed in mm. f_p is the fraction pearlite for steels with less than 30% pearlite.

$$\text{ITT (°C)} = 19 + 44(\%Si) + 700(\%N)^{1/2} + (\pm 30°C) 220 f_p - 11.5 (d^{-1/2})$$

(H.J. Kouwenhoven, *Trans. ASM*, Vol 62, p 437 (1969))

All-pearlite structure.

$$\sigma_{ys} \text{ (ksi)} = 3.16 \times 10^{-1} (S^{-1/2}) - 5.79 \times 10^{-2} (P^{-1/2}) - 4.17 \times 10^{-1} (d^{-1/2}) + 7.58$$

$$\text{T.T. (°F)} = -8.25 \times 10^{-2} (S^{-1/2}) - 1.22(P^{-1/2}) - 5.55(d^{-1/2}) + 4.35 \times 10^2$$

d is the prior austenite grain size, S is the pearlite spacing and P is the pearlite colony size, all in cm. T.T. is the Charpy impact test temperature at which the energy absorbed divided by the fracture area $= 13.5 \times 10^4$ N/m (71 ft · lb/in^2)
(F.B. Pickering, *Physical Metallurgy and the Design of Steels*, Applied Science Publishers, London (1978))

$$\text{Yield stress (MN/m}^2) = 15.4[3.5 + 2.1(\%Mn) + 5.4(\%Si) + 23(\%N) + 1.13d^{-1/2}]$$

$$\text{Tensile strength (MN/m}^2) = 15.4[19.1 + 1.8(\%Mn) + 5.4(\%Si) + 2500 f_p + 0.5d^{-1/2}]$$

$$\text{Impact transition temperature (°C)} = -19 + 44(\%Si) + 700\sqrt{(\%N)} + 220 f_p - 1.5d^{-1/2}$$

These relations are for low carbon manganese steels.

$$\text{Yield stress (MN/m}^2) = 15.4 f_\alpha^{1/3} [2.3 + 3.8(\%Mn) + 1.13d^{-1/2}] + (1 - f_\alpha^{1/3}) [11.6 + 0.25S_0^{-1/2}] + 4.1(\%Si) + 27.6\sqrt{(\%N)}$$

$$\text{Tensile strength (MN/m}^2) = 15.4\{f_\alpha^{1/3}[16 + 74.2\sqrt{(\%N)} + 1.18d^{-1/2}] + (1 - f_\alpha^{1/3})[46.7 + 0.23S_0^{-1/2}] + 6.3(\%Si)\}$$

$$\text{I (°C)} = [-46 - 11.5d^{-1/2}S_0^{-1/2} - 13.3S_p^{-1/2} + 3.48 \times 10^6 t] + 48.7(\%Si) + 762\sqrt{(\%N)}$$

S_0 is the pearlite spacing in mm, S_p is the pearlite colony size in mm, and t is the pearlite-cementite plate thickness in mm. These relations are for the range of pearlite up to the eutectoid composition.
(F.B. Pickering and T. Gladman, in *Iron and Steel Institute Special Report 81*, Iron and Steel Institute, London (1961))

$$\text{Yield strength (N/mm}^2) = 53.9 + 32.3(\%Mn) + 83.2(\%Si) + 354(\%N) + 17.4d^{-1/2}$$

$$\text{Tensile strength (N/mm}^2) = 294 + 27.7(\%Mn) + 83.2(\%Si) + 385f_p + 7.7d^{-1/2}$$

(W.E. Duckworth and J.D. Baird, *Journal of the Iron and Steel Institute*, Vol 207 (1969))

Fracture appearance transition temperature (FATT)

$$\text{FATT(°C) (85\% cleavage)} = 36 + \frac{690 - 190d^{-1/2}}{3.5(100f_p)}$$

factors, an empirical approach is usually taken. Some of the equations developed are listed in Table 9-8. They all contain the primary ferrite grain size as a parameter. However, there is no convenient method of relating this to the chemistry of the steel or its heat treatment.

The toughness of steels is an important mechanical property and it can be defined in several ways. One method is based on the impact test, which is depicted in Fig. 5-7a. The energy absorbed in impact fracturing a specimen of a specified size and with a specified notch in it is measured at various temperatures. This produces the impact curve depicted in Fig. 5-7b. One definition of toughness is the impact energy at a specified temperature. Another is the temperature where the impact energy has a specified toughness. This latter definition is called the *impact transition temperature* (ITT). Another definition is based on the appearance of the fracture surface. The

fracture surface usually shows a central region and a shear lip on the sides; the tougher the steel, the greater the fraction of the surface covered by the shear lip region. Thus the toughness is sometimes defined as the temperature at which a given amount of the fracture surface is covered by the two types of appearance. This is illustrated in Fig. 5-7c. In primary ferrite-pearlite structures, the toughness is especially sensitive to the primary ferrite grain size (see Chapter 8). Table 9-8 gives some relations from which to predict toughness.

Structures containing mostly pearlite

As the amount of pearlite increases in a steel, the influence of the amount of the primary ferrite on properties is diminished. An important structure factor becomes the pearlite spacing, the distance between adjacent carbide plates in the pearlite. This quantity appears in some

Table 9-9   Relations for structures containing a high amount of pearlite which give some mechanical properties as a function of composition and microstructural parameters

(T. Gladman, E.D. McIvor, and F.B. Pickering, *Journal of the Iron and Steel Institute*, Vol 210 (1972))

$$\text{Yield strength (N/mm}^2) = f_\alpha^{1/3}\,[35 + 58.5(\%\text{Mn}) + 17.4\,d^{-1/2}] + (1 - f_\alpha^{1/3})[178 + 3.85S\,\bar{o}^{1/2}] + 63.1(\%\text{Si}) + 426\sqrt{(\%\text{N})}$$

$$\text{Tensile strength (N/mm}^2) = f_\alpha^{1/3}\,[247 + 1146\sqrt{(\%\text{N})} + 18.2\,d^{-1/2}] + (1 - f_\alpha^{1/3})[721 + 3.55S_0^{1/2}] + 97.3(\%\text{Si})$$

$$27\ \text{J ITT (°C)} = f_\alpha[-46 - 11.5d^{-1/2}] + (1 - f_\alpha)[-335 + 5.6S_0^{1/2} - 13.3S_p^{-1/2} + 3.48 \times 10S_0] + 48.7(\%\text{Si}) + 762\sqrt{(\%\text{N})}$$

S_p is the pearlite colony size (mm).
(J.M. Hyzak and I.M. Bernstein, *Met. Trans. A*, Vol 7A (1976))

All-pearlite structure.

$$\sigma_{ys}\ (\text{Ksi}) = 3.16 \times 10^{-1}\left(S^{-1/2}\right) - 5.79 \times 10^{-2}\left(P^{-1/2}\right) - 4.17 \times 10^{-1}(d^{-1/2}) + 7.58$$

$$\text{T.T. (°F)} = -8.25 \times 10^{-2}\,(S^{-1/2}) - 1.22\,(P^{1/2}) - 5.55(d^{-1/2}) + 4.35 \times 10^2$$

d is the prior austenite grain size, S is the pearlite spacing and P is the pearlite colony size, all in cm. T.T. is the Charpy impact test temperature at which the energy absorbed divided by the fracture area $= 13.5 \times 10^4$ N/m (71 ft · lb/in.^{2})

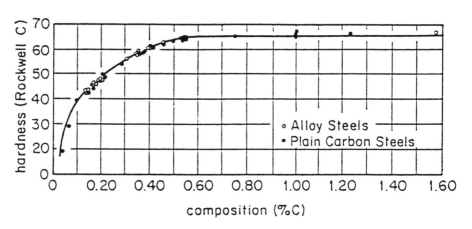

Fig 9-31   The hardness of martensite as a function of the carbon content of the martensite. The data for both the plain carbon steels and the alloy steels are fitted by a single curve, showing that the hardness of martensite is not very sensitive to the alloy content. (From C.R. Brooks, *Heat Treatment of Ferrous Alloys*, Hemisphere Publishing Corporation/McGraw-Hill Book Company, New York (1979))

of the equations in Table 9-8 for relations that are valid up to high amounts of pearlite. Specific relations for pearlitic structures are given in Table 9-9. Note that these relations contain the pearlite spacing as a parameter. As noted above, this is difficult to measure due to its small size.

Tempered martensite

Methods to estimate the hardness of tempered martensite were described in Chapter 5. From the as-quenched hardness (the structure need not be all martensite) the hardness after tempering for a given time at a given temperature can be estimated from the carbon and alloy content. Then the hardness correlations for tempered martensite, such as in Fig. 9-25, can be used to estimate the yield strength, then from the correlation in Fig. 9-26 the tensile strength can be obtained. Correlations such as in Fig. 9-28 to 9-30 can be used to estimate the fatigue strength.

Hardness of Martensite

The hardness of martensite is considered mainly to be a function of carbon content, and not very sensitive to alloy content or prior austenite grain size. This was assumed to be valid in the treatment of hardenability in Chapter 3. Figure 9-31 shows data for both plain carbon and alloy steels with all-martensite structures, for which a single curve can well represent all the data. Figure 9-32 shows similar data. It is emphasized that these data are for structures of 100% martensite in which all the carbon is in solution in the martensite (and hence was in solution in the parent austenite).

Points from the dashed curve in Fig. 9-32 were fitted to polynomials to obtain equations of hardness of martensite as a function of carbon content. The equation given with the figure is an excellent fit to the curve, as evidenced by the calculated points located on the curve. Hardnesses of structures of essentially 100% martensite were also given in Table 3-2. These data are plotted in Fig. 9-33, and a polynomial which fits the data well is given with the figure. These equations can be used in analytical treatments where a relation for the hardness of martensite as a function of carbon content of the martensite is needed.

Blondeau et al. have obtained an expression for the hardness of martensite which includes the effect of alloy content and of the cooling rate from austenite. This is

$$H \text{ (Vickers)} = 127 + 949(\%C) + 27(\%Si) + 11(\%Mn) + 8(\%Ni) + 16(\%Cr) + 21 \log V$$

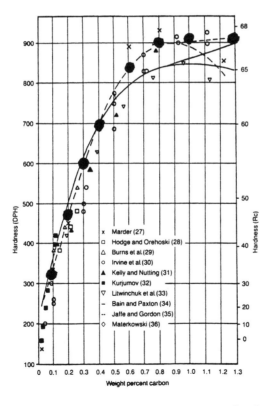

x Marder (27)
□ Hodge and Orehoski (28)
△ Burns et al. (29)
○ Irvine et al. (30)
▲ Kelly and Nutting (31)
■ Kurjumov (32)
▽ Litwinchuk et al. (33)
– Bain and Paxton (34)
·· Jaffe and Gordon (35)
◇ Materkowski (36)

Fig 9-32 The hardness of martensite as a function of carbon content, taken from several sources. Points from the dashed curve were fitted to obtain the equation given, and the prominent points were calculated from this equation. (Adapted from G. Krauss, Martensitic Transformation, Structure and Properties in Hardenable Steels, *Hardenability Concepts with Applications to Steel*, p 235, D.V. Doane and J.S. Kirkaldy, editors, The Metallurgical Society, Warrendale, PA (1978))

V is the cooling rate in °C/h. This expression is based on steels with the following composition (wt.%): 0.1 < %C < 0.5; <1% Si; <2% Mn; <4% Ni; <3% Cr; <1% Mo; (%Mn + %Ni + %Cr + %Mo) < 5%. Although this equation shows a dependency of the martensite hardness on alloy content and cooling rate, if values of carbon and alloy content over the range of validity of the expression are used to calculate the hardness for cooling rates of 500 and 50°C/sec., the data fall within the scatter of the curves shown in Fig. 9-32. For example, for 0.5% C, the calculated hardness ranges from about 700 to 760 Vickers, which is within the data in Fig. 9-32. It thus appears that the equations given with Fig. 9-32 and 9-33 are adequate for representing the hardness of martensite for alloy steels and the cooling rate need not be taken into account.

Residual Stresses

The formation of residual stresses is an important by-product of heat treating. They may cause fine cracking and gross fracture, but they may be beneficial for components having certain stress distributions and under certain loading conditions. In hardening steels, the uneven contraction associated with the quenching process and the volume changes associated with the decomposition of austenite are the primary factors controlling the formation of residual stresses. These two factors are clearly related to the cooling rate and to the kinetics of the decomposition of austenite to the transformation products. In Chapter 4, a qualitative description of the formation of residual stresses was given. In this section, factors to consider to be able to calculate the residual stresses are described. Although the calculations are complicated and subject to uncertainty, such information is important in locating regimes in heat treating parameters (e.g., severity of quench of quenchant, quenching temperature) which may be exploited to develop favorable stresses, or which should be avoided to minimize unfavorable stresses.

The book *Handbook of Quenchants and Quenching Technology* by G.E. Totten, C.E. Bates, and N.A. Clinton

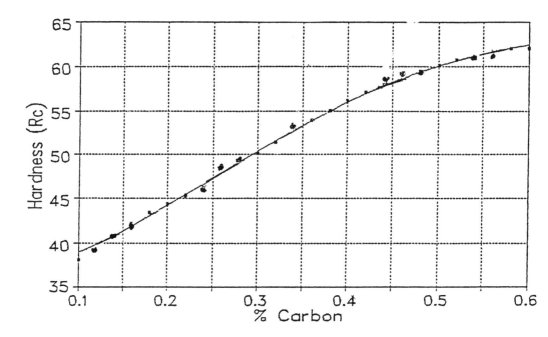

$$\text{Hardness (Rc)} = 31 + \left[\frac{34}{1 + \exp\left[\dfrac{0.263 - (\%C)}{0.137} \right]} \right]$$

Fig 9-33 The hardness of steels containing 99.9% martensite as a function of carbon content, plotted from the data in Table 3-3. The data in the table were fitted to obtain the equation shown, and the prominent points on the curve were calculated from this equation

(ASM International, Materials Park, Ohio (1993)) contains a chapter which discusses in detail the formation of residual stresses in quenched steels. The October 1985 issue of *Materials Science and Technology* (Vol 10, No. 1) is devoted to the proceedings of the conference "Calculation of Internal Stresses in Heat Treatment of Metallic Materials," and contains papers relevant to quenching of steels. Several of these papers describe quantitative models used to calculate residual stresses. They will not be detailed here, but instead factors are referred to which are important in developing the models. Three references are given here in which the models are presented in detail. One is B. Hildenwall, "Prediction of the Residual Stresses Created during Quenching," Ph.D. dissertation No. 39, Department of Mechanical Engineering, Division of En-

gineering Materials, Linkoping University, Linkoping, Sweden (1979). Another is T. Inoue and B. Raniecki, "Determination of Thermal-Hardening Stress in Steels by Use of Thermoplastic Theory," *Journal of Mechanics and Physics of Solids*, Vol 26, p 187-212 (1978). The third, from which some of the information given below is taken, is S. Denis, S. Sjostrom, and A. Simon, "Coupled Temperature, Stress, Phase Transformation Calculation Model Numerical Illustration of the Internal Stresses Evolution during Cooling of a Eutectoid Carbon Steel Cylinder," *Met. Trans.*, Vol 18A, p 1203-1212 (1987).

The calculation of residual stresses in steels is complicated due to several factors. The temperature-time curves at locations in the component must be determined. But these can be calculated by methods described in the section "Calculation of Cooling Curves" in this chapter, although limitations in this were pointed out there. The kinetics of the decomposition of austenite must be known, and as pointed out in the section "Transformation of Austenite" in this chapter, this is a very difficult problem. To be realistic, the effect of the elastic and plastic deformation which occurs in the component during cooling upon the decomposition of austenite to the microconstituents such as pearlite and on the M_S temperature should be included in the analysis. For example, Fig. 9-34 shows that the shift of the time for the beginning and completion of austenite decomposition at a fixed temperature can be significant.

In addition to the complications associated with the heat transfer and the kinetics of the decomposition of austenite, the factors listed in Table 9-10 should be considered. The mechanical properties and the volumetric coefficient of thermal expansion of the microconstituents must be known as a function of temperature. These determine the mechanical response of the steel component to the attempted contraction of the austenite and the microconstituents during cooling and to the volume increase associated with the decomposition of austenite to the microconstituents. Elastic equations can be used to determine the elastic stresses, but since the yield strength will be exceeded (see Chapter 4), the plastic response must be known to determine the dimensional changes which occur. The plastic response is dictated by the stress-strain curve in the plastic range and is temperature and composition dependent. In addition, creep and stress relaxation,

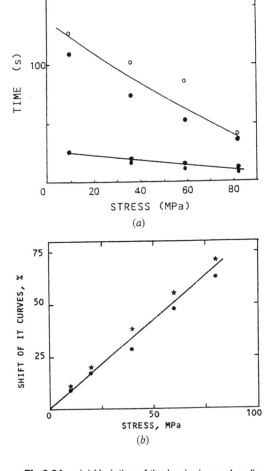

Fig 9-34   (a) Variation of the beginning and ending times of the decomposition of austenite at 663°C with applied tensile stress. (b) Shift of the isothermal transformation curves as a function of the applied stress. (From E. Gautier, A. Simon, and G. Beck, in *Proc. ICOMAT*, Nara, Japan (Aug 1986))

Table 9-10   Some factors which are unique to a rigorous calculation of residual stresses in quenched steels

1.	Temperature dependence of mechanical properties
2.	Plastic behavior of microconstituents and their temperature dependence
3.	Stress relaxation and creep during cooling
4.	Effect of residual stresses developed during cooling on the kinetics of the decomposition of austenite and on the M_s temperature
5.	Coefficient of thermal expansion of austenite and products of decomposition of austenite

which are temperature and composition dependent, should be included in the calculations.

Figure 9-35 shows the temperature dependence of the elastic modulus for austenite and pearlite for a given steel. This property must be known for all microconstituents which form during quenching. Note that there is about a 40% difference in the modulus of austenite and pearlite,

and that the modulus of pearlite changes by about a factor of two from 600 to 25°C. The yield strength as a function of temperature is shown in Fig. 9-36. It is noted that these data are based on tensile tests made during cooling, but the tests were relatively rapid so that each data point corresponds to an approximately constant temperature. Thus these data include the effect of stress on the decom-

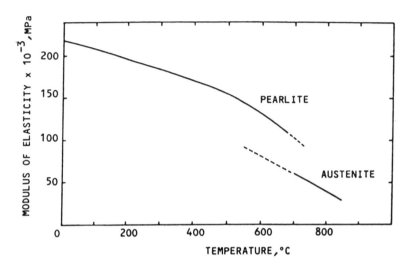

Fig 9-35   Modulus of elasticity of pearlite and austenite as a function of temperature. (From S. Denis, S. Sjostrom, and A. Simon, *Met. Trans., Vol 18A, p 1203-1212 (1987)*)

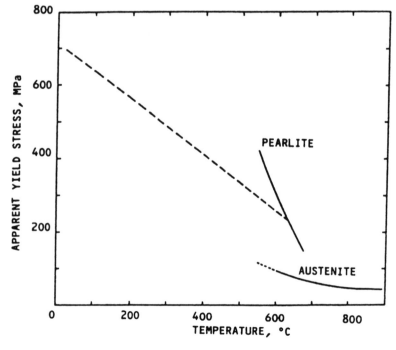

Fig 9-36   Apparent yield strength as a function of temperature for pearlite and austenite. (From same source as Fig. 9-35)

position of austenite; that is, the pearlite was formed while under tensile stress.

As the residual stresses increase during cooling, the yield strength is surpassed, and plastic flow occurs. The stress to produce a given plastic strain depends upon the work hardening character of the material, and this must be known to calculate the residual stresses. Figure 9-37 shows the plastic modulus as a function of temperature; this quantity is related to the work hardening effect.

Figure 9-38 shows the results of a calculation for the formation of pearlite across the cross-section of a cylinder of a eutectoid steel. The axial stress at the surface and

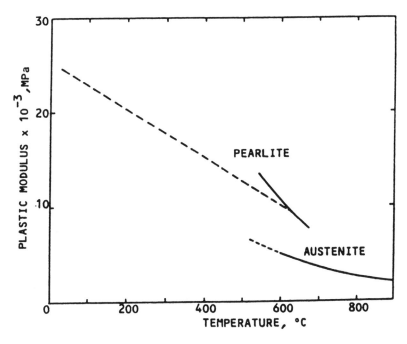

Fig 9-37   Plastic modulus, related to the work hardening characteristic, as a function of temperature for pearlite and austenite. (From same source as Fig. 9-36)

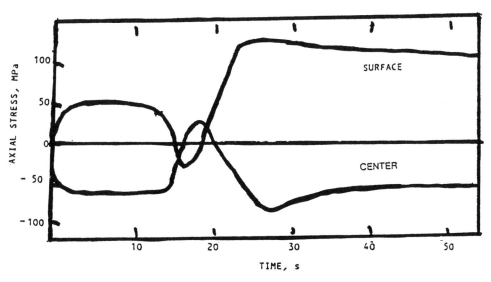

Fig 9-38   Evolution of the calculated axial residual stress as a function of time during quenching. (Adapted from same source as Fig. 9-36)

center in a quenched cylinder of an eutectoid steel is shown as a function of time during quenching. Note the reversal of the stresses at the surface and center as plastic deformation occurs during cooling. Figure 9-39 shows the calculated axial stress distribution after cooling to 25 °C is completed. The surface is in tension and the center in compression.

Kirkaldy's Model for Calculating Jominy Curves

If sufficient data are available, a strictly empirical approach can be taken to calculate hardenability and Jominy curves. One restriction on the use of the relations derived is that their extension to steels which have compositions outside the ranges on which the relations were based is questionable. Therefore, it is desirable to have a theoretical basis for the derivation of such relations, even if experimental data are required to determine values of empirical constants which appear in the relations. The models are complicated by the difficulty in predicting the kinetics of the decomposition of austenite, but they are continually being improved. As an example of the model approach, we examine the procedure developed by Kirkaldy. (See J.S. Kirkaldy and R.C. Sharma, A New Phenomenology for Steel IT and CCT Curves, *Scripta Metallurgica*, Vol 16, p 1193-1198 (1982), and other references given in this paper.)

Figure 9-40 shows a cooling curve superimposed on a continuous cooling TTT diagram (CCT). For this cooling curve the microstructure at 25°C can be predicted, from which the hardness can be estimated. Thus the Jominy curve can be determined by superimposing the

cooling curves corresponding to locations along the bar on the CCT diagram. The cooling curves can be calculated by the methods outlined earlier in this chapter. To estimate the CCT diagram, a model for the formation of primary ferrite or of pearlite is used, which is the crux of the approach of Kirkaldy.

Figure 9-41 shows how the transformation can be tracked along a given cooling curve. The nucleation rate N determines the time t_s for the beginning of transformation. Since this rate is a function of temperature, then the start time t_s for the decomposition of austenite is also temperature dependent. The fraction X of the decomposition product (e.g., pearlite) formed after nucleation depends on both the nucleation rate and the growth rate G. Both of these are functions of temperature and time, so X is a function of temperature and time, and its value at any point along the cooling curve can be obtained by integration (see Fig. 9-41).

Kirkaldy relied on a volume diffusion model to obtain an expression for the start time (called the incubation time), given by

$$t_s = A\,T/[D\,(\Delta T)^2]$$

where A is a constant, T is the absolute temperature (transformation temperature), and ΔT is the degree of undercooling below the A_1 temperature (for pearlite formation). The diffusion coefficient is that for carbon in austenite, corrected for the effect of alloying elements by the relation

$$\frac{1}{D} = \frac{1}{D_c} + \sum_i \frac{k_i C_i}{D_i \Delta T} = \frac{1}{D_c}\left(1 + \sum_i \frac{D_c}{D_i}\frac{k_i C_i}{\Delta T}\right)$$

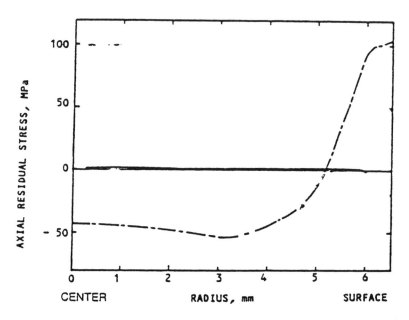

Fig 9-39 Calculated final axial residual stress after quenching to 25°C. (From same source as Fig. 9-36)

This gives

$$t_s = \frac{\sigma T}{(\Delta T)^2} \cdot \frac{1}{D} = \frac{\sigma T}{(\Delta T)^2} \cdot \frac{1}{D_c}\left(1 + \sum_i \frac{D_c}{D_i}\frac{k_i C_i}{\Delta T}\right)$$

D_c is the diffusion coefficient of carbon in austenite. The sum is over the alloying elements each having concentrations C_i. k_i is a coefficient obtained by fitting experimental t_s data. The degree of undercooling is taken to be

$$\Delta T = T_E + \sum_i \beta_j C_j - T$$

where T_E is the A_1 temperature (eutectoid temperature), C_{js}' is the alloy chemical composition and β_{js}' is a constant, determined from experimental phase diagram data.

The growth rate G of pearlite is taken as

$$G = A D (\Delta T)^2$$

where A is a constant. D is the effective diffusion coefficient of carbon, corrected for the effect of alloy content by an equation similar to that used for calculation of the incubation time. ΔT was calculated by the equation given above. A distinction was made for elements which control carbon volume diffusion and elements which themselves diffuse along the pearlite-austenite interface as they partition between the ferrite and the carbide in the pearlite. This was taken into account in the diffusion equation given above.

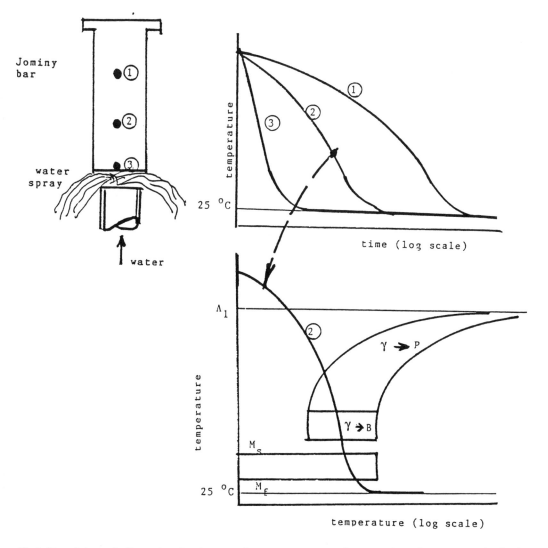

Fig 9-40 Schematic illustration showing a cooling curve corresponding to a given distance on a Jominy bar superimposed on a continuous cooling time-temperature-transformation diagram

Kirkaldy assumed that pearlite nucleates at the center of each austenite grain face. The subsequent progress of the decomposition of the austenite depends on the grain size and the growth rate.

Although the approach illustrated in Fig. 9-41 could be used, Kirkaldy instead first calculated the start of the isothermal decomposition of austenite. Then, he determined the start of decomposition upon continuous cooling by the following procedure. Consider Fig. 9-42, which shows a cooling curve and a curve for the start of the isothermal decomposition of austenite to pearlite. It is desired to estimate the time and temperature at which pearlite starts to form for the cooling curve given. The quantities needed are defined on the curves. By trial and error, the time t_{CCT} is chosen until a temperature is found at which the equality given is obtained. This gives the

point marked on the cooling curve as the start of the formation of pearlite on cooling along this particular curve. The process is repeated for different curves. Figure 9-43 shows an example of the results of this type of calculation.

The Jominy curve calculation is based on estimating the cooling rate (for a given steel) which gives 50% martensite and hence closely corresponds to the inflection point in the Jominy curve. Figure 9-44 illustrates the approach. The growth rate curve is shown with its maximum value corresponding to the minimum time in the IT diagram. The transformation along cooling curve 1 begins at temperature T_1, and as cooling proceeds, the growth rate increases, which forms more products and less martensite, and hence a relatively low hardness. Along the cooling curve 3, the transformation begins at

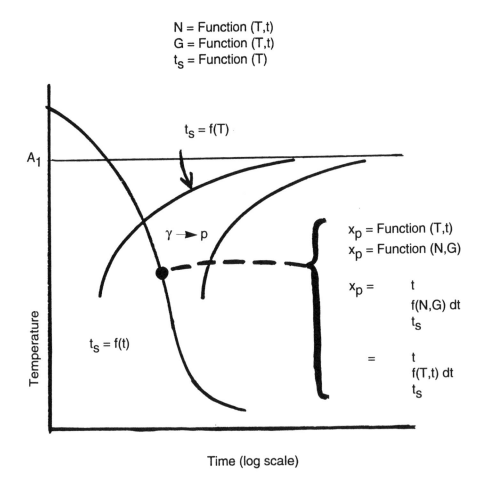

$$N = \text{Function } (T,t)$$
$$G = \text{Function } (T,t)$$
$$t_s = \text{Function } (T)$$

$t_s = f(T)$

A_1

$\gamma \rightarrow p$

$t_s = f(t)$

Temperature

Time (log scale)

$$X_p = \text{Function } (T,t)$$
$$X_p = \text{Function } (N,G)$$

$$X_p = \int_{t_s}^{t} f(N,G)\, dt$$

$$= \int_{t_s}^{t} f(T,t)\, dt$$

Fig 9-41   Schematic illustration of the mathematical relations needed to determine the progress of the decomposition of austenite during cooling

T3 and as cooling progresses the growth rate continues to decrease. Hence a large amount of martensite is formed, and the steel has a relatively high hardness. Cooling curve 2 is taken as that for which 50% martensite forms, and hence corresponds to the inflection point on the Jominy curve for this steel. This inflection point approach was connected to chemical composition and austenite grain size by using experimental data (CCT diagrams and Jominy curves) and developing an empirical relation between the inflection point hardness, the composition and the austenite grain size. The success of the prediction of the inflection point from the empirical formulas is illustrated by the data in Fig. 3-37.

Kirkaldy gives the procedure for a 4068 steel of austenite grain size ASTM 7-8. Figure 9-45 shows the calculated growth rate curve. The IT and CCT start curves are shown in Fig. 9-46, with calculated cooling curves corresponding to the Jominy distances listed.

The success of this particular approach is illustrated by the close agreement of the calculated and experimental Jominy curves shown in Fig. 3-38.

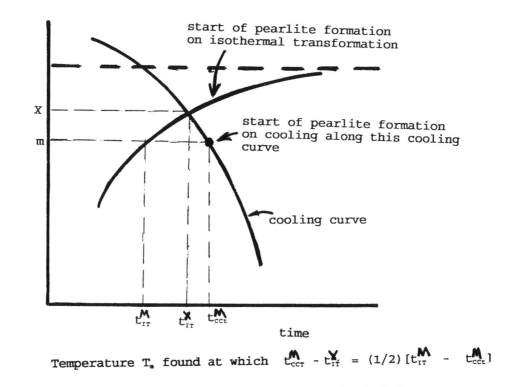

Temperature T_m found at which $t_{CCT}^M - t_{IT}^X = (1/2) [t_{IT}^M - t_{CCt}^M]$

Fig 9-42 Diagram illustrating the terms used to estimate the CCT diagram from the IT diagram

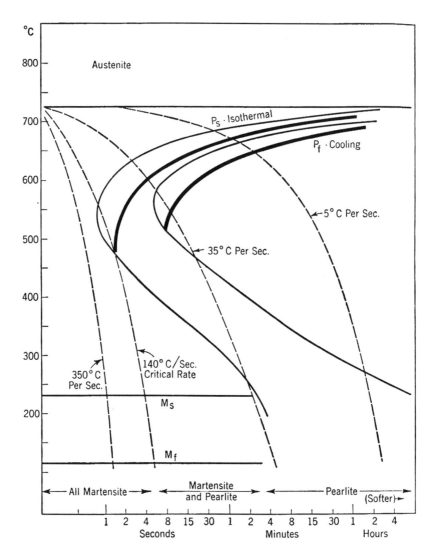

Fig 9-43 Example of the CCT diagram estimated from the IT diagram. (From R.M. Brick and A. Phillips, *Structure and Properties of Alloys*, McGraw-Hill, New York (1949), as adapted from R.A. Grange and J.M. Kiefer, *Trans. ASM*, Vol 29, p 85 (1941))

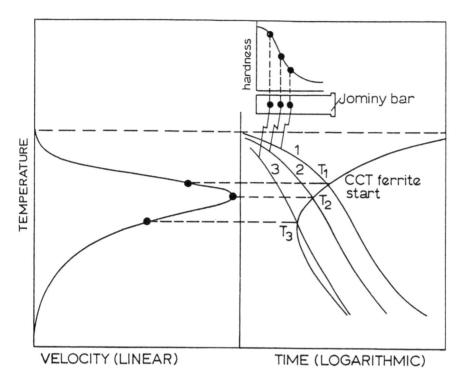

Fig 9-44   Diagram illustrating the determination of the Jominy distance which corresponds to the inflection point on the Jominy curve from the CCT diagram and the growth rate-temperature curve. (Adapted from J.S. Kirkaldy, G.O. Pazionis, and S.E. Feldman, *Heat Treatment '76*, p 169ff, The Metals Society, London (1976))

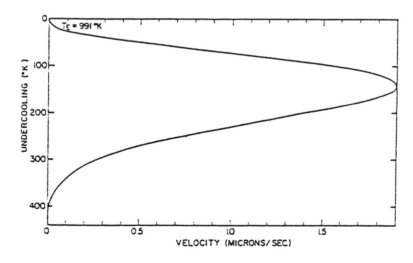

Fig 9-45   Calculated rate of growth of pearlite versus temperature (degree of undercooling below the eutectoid temperature). (From J.S. Kirkaldy, *Met. Trans.*, Vol 4, p 2327-2333 (1973))

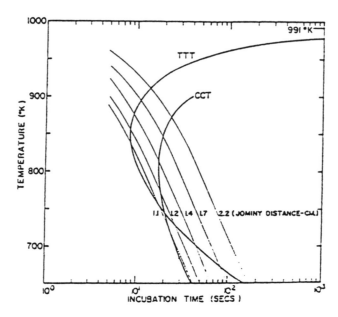

Fig 9-46   Calculated start curve of the decomposition of austenite upon continuous cooling for 4068 steel. (From same source as Fig. 9-45)

Chapter 10

Illustrative Examples

The following problems illustrate the calculation or determination of such items as D_i, the Jominy curve and the severity of quench by methods outlined in previous chapters. One illustrative problem shows how such information can be used to determine a preliminary heat treatment based on specific requirements.

Calculation of Effect of Prior Austenite Grain Size on D_i

For a 4140 steel containing 0.40% C, 0.83% Mn, 0.31% Si, 0.20% Ni, 1.00% Cr, 0.19% Mo, 0.018% P and 0.030% S, calculate the ideal critical diameter using the information in Appendix 1b for austenite grain sizes of ASTM 5, 6, 7 and 8. Plot D_i against the ASTM grain size number.

Solution

The multiplying factors listed below were obtained from Table 1a.1.

$$0.83\% \text{ Mn} \rightarrow +0.576$$
$$0.31\% \text{ Si} \rightarrow +0.085$$
$$0.20\% \text{ Ni} \rightarrow +0.030$$
$$1.00\% \text{ Cr} \rightarrow +0.500$$
$$0.19\% \text{ Mo} \rightarrow +0.196$$
$$0.018\% \text{ P} \rightarrow +0.22$$
$$0.030\% \text{ S} \rightarrow -0.009$$

$$\text{Sum} = +1.400$$

The base D_i values from Appendix 1b are listed below.

$$0.40\% \text{ C, GS } 5 \rightarrow 0.398 \text{ inches}$$
$$0.40\% \text{ C, GS } 6 \rightarrow 0.362 \text{ inches}$$
$$0.40\% \text{ C, GS } 7 \rightarrow 0.329 \text{ inches}$$
$$0.40\% \text{ C, GS } 8 \rightarrow 0.296 \text{ inches}$$

Using these values the following values of D_i are obtained.

$$\text{GS } 5 \rightarrow \text{Sum} = 1.400 + 0.398 = 1.788 \rightarrow D_i = 6.30 \text{ in.}$$

$$\text{GS } 6 \rightarrow \text{Sum} = 1.400 + 0.362 = 1.762 \rightarrow D_i = 5.80 \text{ in.}$$

$$\text{GS } 7 \rightarrow \text{Sum} = 1.400 + 0.329 = 1.729 \rightarrow D_i = 5.35 \text{ in.}$$

$$\text{GS } 8 \rightarrow \text{Sum} = 1.400 + 0.296 = 1.696 \rightarrow D_i = 4.95 \text{ in.}$$

Figure 10-1 shows graphically the dependence of D_i on the prior austenite grain size. If the ASTM grain size number is decreased by a factor of two (grain size increased), D_i decreases by about 30%.

Calculation of Effect of Carbon Content on D_i

Consider a 4xx steel containing 0.83% Mn, 0.31% Si, 0.20% Ni, 1.00% Cr, 0.19% Mo, 0.018% P and 0.30% S. For an austenite grain size of ASTM 7, calculate and plot the ideal critical diameter as a function of carbon content from 0.2 to 0.6% using the information in Appendix 1a.

Solution

To obtain the dependence of D_i on carbon content, the factors in Appendix 1a are used. Figure 10-2 shows that D_i is more than doubled if the carbon content increases from 0.2 to 0.6%.

Calculation of Effect of Chromium Content on D_i

Consider a 4140 steel containing 0.40% C, 0.83% Mn, 0.31% Si, 0.20% Ni, 0.19% Mo, 0.018% P and 0.30% S. For an austenite grain size of ASTM 7, calculate and plot the ideal critical diameter as a function of chromium content from 0.5 to 1.5% using the information in Appendix 1a.

Solution

Figure 10-3 shows the dependence of D_i on the chromium content. Values were obtained from the information in Appendix 1a. Increasing the chromium content from 0.5% to about 1.5% increases D_i by a factor of about two.

Calculation of Effect of Molybdenum Content on D_i

Consider a 4140 steel containing 0.40% C, 0.83% Mn, 0.31% Si, 1.00% Cr, 0.20% Ni, 0.018% P and 0.30% S. For an austenite grain size of ASTM 7, calculate and plot the ideal critical diameter as a function of molybdenum content from 0.05 to 0.5% using the information in Appendix 1a.

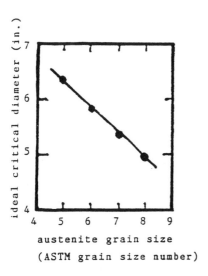

Fig 10-1 Effect of prior austenite grain size on ideal critical diameter

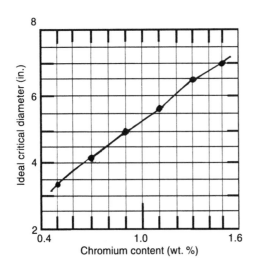

Fig 10-3 Effect of chromium content on ideal critical diameter

Solution

The dependence of D_i on the molybdenum content is shown in Fig. 10-4. Values were obtained from the infor-

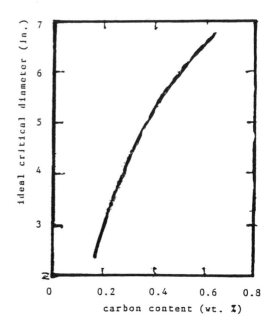

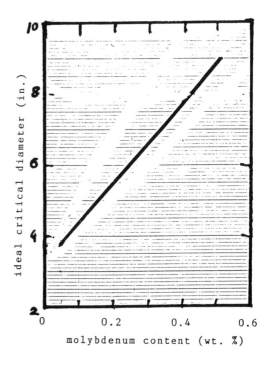

Fig 10-4 Effect of molybdenum content on ideal critical diameter

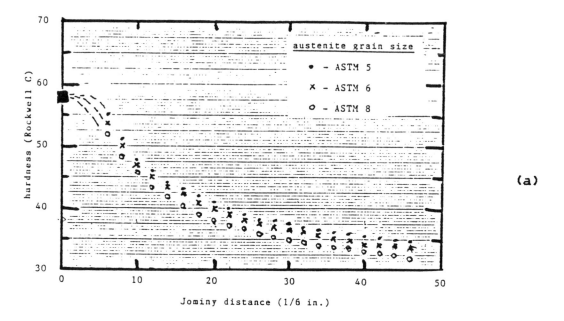

(a)

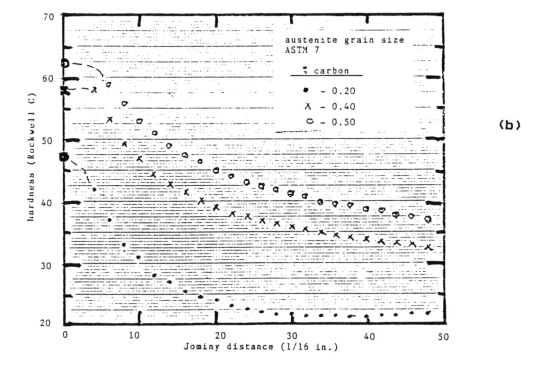

(b)

Fig 10-5   Calculated Jominy curves for various variables *(continued)*

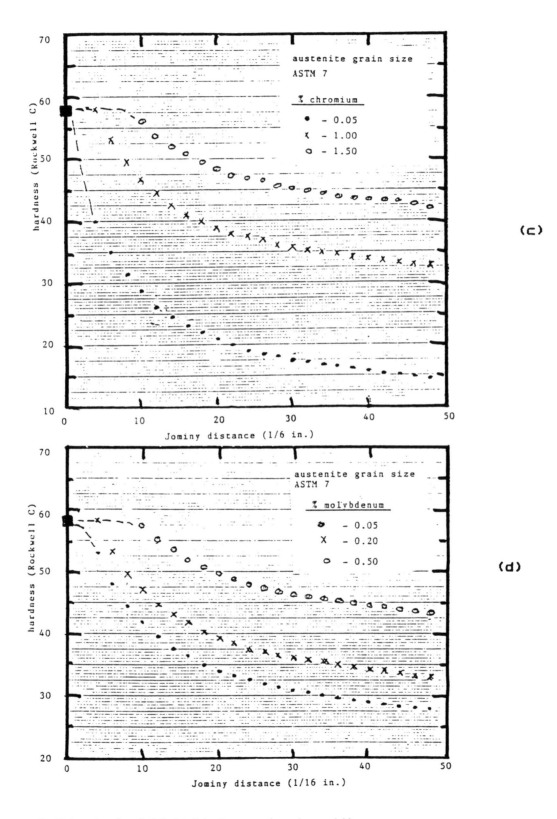

Fig 10-5   (continued) Calculated Jominy curves for various variables

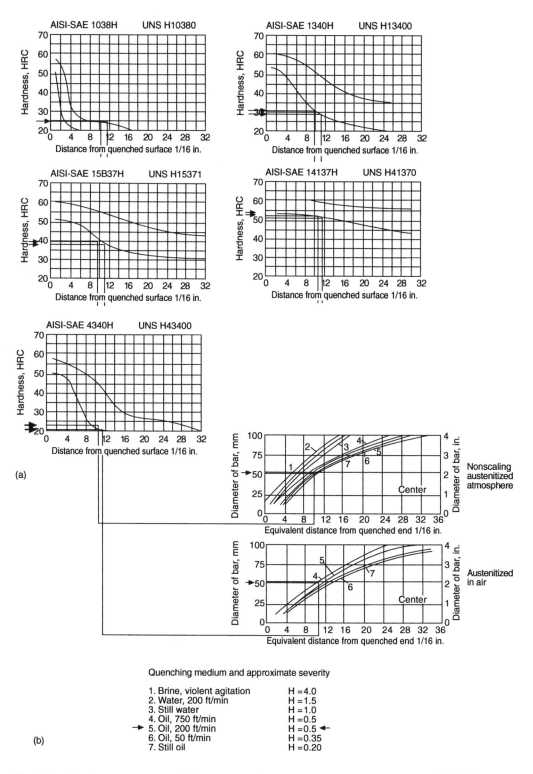

(a)

(b)

Quenching medium and approximate severity

1. Brine, violent agitation	H = 4.0
2. Water, 200 ft/min	H = 1.5
3. Still water	H = 1.0
4. Oil, 750 ft/min	H = 0.5
→ 5. Oil, 200 ft/min	H = 0.5 ←
6. Oil, 50 ft/min	H = 0.35
7. Still oil	H = 0.20

Fig 10-6   (a) Hardenability bands for five steels, and (b) cooling rate correlations at the center of cylinders when quenched into different media. Also included in (b) are curves for two different austenitizing atmospheres. The connecting lines show how the minimum hardness at the center of a 50 mm (1.96 inch) diameter cylinder is obtained when quenched into oil flowing at 200 ft/min.

mation in Appendix 1a, as described in the first problem in this chapter. Increasing the molybdenum content from 0.05 to 0.5% increases D_i by a factor of about two.

Calculation of Jominy Curves

Using the equation by Just in Table 3-5, calculate Jominy curves for the following conditions.

1. A 4140 steel containing 0.40% C, 0.83% Mn, 0.31% Si, 0.20% Ni, 1.00% Cr, 0.19% Mo, 0.018% P and 0.030% S, for austenite grain sizes of ASTM 5, 6 and 8. Plot the curves on the same graph.
2. A 41xx steel containing 0.83% Mn, 0.31% Si, 0.20% Ni, 1.00% Cr, 0.19% Mo, 0.019% P and 0.030% S, using an austenite grain size of ASTM 7, for carbon contents of 0.2, 0.4 and 0.6%. Plot the curves on the same graph.

3. A 4140 steel containing 0.40% C, 0.83% Mn, 0.31% Si, 0.20% Ni, 0.19% Mo, 0.018% P and 0.030% S, using an austenite grain size of ASTM 7, for chromium contents of 0.5, 1.00 and 1.50%. Plot the curves on the same graph.
4. A 4140 steel containing 0.40% C, 0.83% Mn, 0.31% Si, 1.00% Cr, 0.20% Ni, 0.018% P and 0.030% S, using an austenite grain size of ASTM 7, for molybdenum contents of 0.05, 0.20 and 0.50%.

Solution

The calculated Jominy curves are shown in Fig. 10-5. Note in Table 3-5 that the Just equation is valid from 4/16 to 40/16 inches. Thus the calculated initial point should be at 1/16 inch. However, for some of the curves, the values were clearly too high (i.e., higher than the martensite hardness). In those cases, the first calculated points

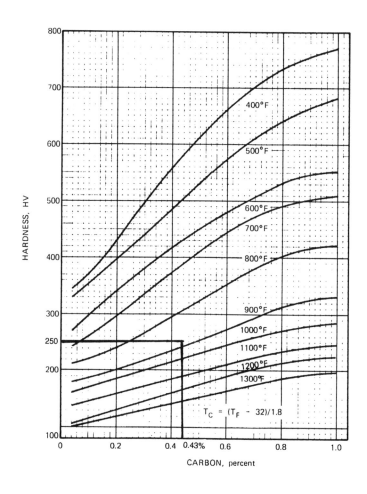

Fig 10-7(a)   Base tempering curves (for one hour) showing the base hardness of 250 HV for a carbon content of 0.43% *(continued)*

are at 6/16 inch. The initial hardness, that of martensite, was calculated by the lower equation in Table 3-5, and is denoted by the heavy point at zero Jominy distance. (The equations associated with Fig. 9-32 and 9-33 could have been used.)

The Jominy curve depends only weakly on the prior austenite grain size (Fig. 10-5a), but it is quite sensitive to the carbon, chromium and molybdenum contents (Fig. 10-5b, c, d).

Determination of Minimum Hardness of Quenched Steels

A 50 mm (1.97 inch) diameter bar is quenched into oil which is flowing at 200 ft/min. For the steels listed below, determine the minimum hardness at the center for austenitizing in air and in a non-scaling atmosphere.

- 1038H
- 1340H
- 15B37H
- 4137H
- 4340H

Solution

The Jominy H-bands are shown in Fig. 10-6a (taken from Appendix 19). The minimum curves are used. The film coefficient of the quenchant (see Chapter 4) depends on the type of quenchant, the relative movement of the quenchant and the component being quenched, and the surface condition (e.g., roughness) of the component. All of these affect the value of the severity of quench H. The cooling rate correlations in Fig. 4-3 give no guidance since the only parameter listed is the H value. However, cooling rate correlation curves are given in Fig. 4-16 for

"oil" flowing at 200 ft/min., listed as a severity of quench of h = 0.5. Curves are for austenitizing both in air and in a non-scaling atmosphere. Figure 10-6b shows how to obtain the center hardness of the 50 mm (1.97 inch) diameter cylinder. The results are:

Steel	Hardness (Rockwell C) (air atmosphere)	Hardness (Rockwell C) (non-scaling atmosphere)
1038H	25	25
1340H	28	30
15B37H	21	22
4137H	38	40
4340H	51	51

Note that the hardness values depend on the shape of the Jominy curve at these Jominy distances. However, since the two Jominy distances are similar, the hardnesses are similar. It is interesting to note that the faster cooling (lower Jominy distance) is achieved for the non-scaling atmosphere.

Determination of Tempered Hardness

A 6145 steel containing 0.43% C, 0.74% Mn, 0.23% Si, 0.92% Cr and 0.16% V is austenitized, then quenched to form martensite. It is then tempered at 1000°F for one hour.

1. Calculate the hardness, and compare the value to an experimental value for this steel. Give the hardness in Rockwell C.
2. Calculate the tempering time required to obtain the same hardness at 900 and 1100°F.
3. Assume a steel cylinder 2.0 inches in diameter is to be tempered from an as-quenched hardness of 58 Rockwell C at the center to the hardness value

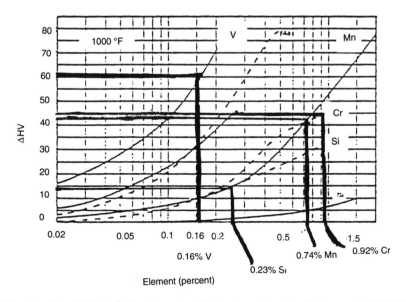

Fig 10-7(b) (continued) Effect of alloy elements on the hardness of martensite tempered at 538°C (1000°F) for one hour *(continued)*

from part 1. Estimate the approximate heat-up time to 1000°F.

Solution

Using the curve in Fig. 10-7a (from Fig. 5-42), a base hardness of 250 Vickers hardness (HV) is obtained. This value is then corrected for the alloying elements by use of the curves in Fig. 10-7b (from Fig. 5-43). For 1000°F, the hardness additions are (Vickers hardness) 43 (0.74% Mn), 14 (0.23% Si), 44 (0.92% Cr) and 61 (0.16% V), which gives a tempered hardness of 390 Vickers. From Appendix 1b, this converts to Rockwell C 40. The data in Fig. 10-7c (from Fig. 5-44) are from the 6145 steel of the given composition, and the experimental hardness for tempering for one hour at 1000°F is 390 Vickers.

The parametric curves in Fig. 10-7d (Fig. 5-45) are used to estimate the time required at 900, 1100 and 1200°F to obtain the same hardness. (See Chapter 5.) The parameter is calculated from

$$(T + 460) (18 + \log t) (0.001)$$

$$= (1000 + 460) (18 + \log 1) (0.001) = 26.3$$

Here T is in °F and the time t is in hours. Using this value and Fig. 10-6d, the times are 11 hours at 900°F and 3 minutes at 1100°F.

The time required to heat the 2.0 inch (51 mm) diameter cylinder to the tempering temperature can be estimated by the same procedure as utilized in Chapter 4 for estimating the cooling time. The "severity of heating" value (H value) must be known. However, the heating

curves shown in Fig. 10-7e (from Fig. 6-32) show that the time to heat the center of a 2.0 inch diameter cylinder to 1000°F (540°C) will be about 5 min. Thus there may be significant softening during heating. The tempering correlation data used in the calculation above was based on a sample heated quickly to the tempering temperature. For samples heating at a slower rate, such as expected for a 2.0 inch diameter cylinder placed in an air furnace, the softening during heating should be taken into account. For many commercial heat treating operations, it is difficult to take this into account. For example, it was estimated above that the desired tempering hardness could be achieved using 3 min. at 1100°F. However, it would be difficult to heat a machine component in a commercial furnace and maintain control of the temperature-time history to achieve such a tempering treatment. Thus the temperature and time are chosen to minimize the effect of tempering during heating to the tempering temperature.

The hardness (at 25 °C) as a function of time during tempering can be estimated. What is required is the hardness as a function of tempering parameter. This can be estimated using the data in Fig. 10-7f. The hardness is approximated by a straight line to get

$$\text{Hardness (HV)} = 850 - 17 \, P$$

For P we use

$$P = (T + 460) (18 + \log t) (0.001)$$

$$= (1000 + 460) (18 + \log t) (0.001)$$

for tempering at 1000°F. The result is shown in Fig. 10-7g. The value calculated for one hour, 403 HV, is based on the assumption that no tempering occurs upon heating. This effect is examined in the last example in this chapter.

Determination of Ideal Critical Diameter

A certain steel has the experimental Jominy curve shown in Fig. 10-8a. Determine the ideal critical diameter.

Solution

Three methods of estimating the ideal critical diameter are given here.

1. Using inflection point on Jominy curve: The microstructure at or near the location corresponding to the inflection point in the Jominy curve contains about 50% martensite (see Fig. 3-14). For the Jominy curve given in the problem, the inflection point occurs at about 9/16 inch (see Fig. 10-8a). As shown in Fig. 10-8b, the center of a cylinder with a diameter of 3.0 inch will have a cooling rate corresponding to this location when quenched into an ideal quench (H = ∞). Thus this diameter will be the ideal critical diameter.

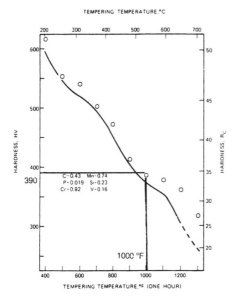

Fig 10-7(c) (continued) Tempered hardness against temperature (one hour tempering time) for a 6145 steel. *(continued)*

2. Method of Tartaglia and Eldis: This method is outlined in Fig. 3-23. Using the given Jominy curve and this method, $D_i = 3.3$ inches.

3. Calculation using chemical composition and austenite grain size: As explained in Chapter 3, in the section "Calculation of the Ideal Critical Diameter," the ideal critical diameter can be calculated from the chemical composition and the prior austenite grain size. The necessary information can be obtained from Appendix 1.

0.49% C—0.372 GS 7	0.49% C—0.338 GS 8
0.98% Mn—0.630	0.98% Mn—0.630
0.29% Si—0.080	0.28% Si—0.080
0.59% Ni—0.085	0.59% Ni—0.085
0.47% Cr—0.304	0.47% Cr—0.304
0.19% Mo—0.196	0.19% Mo—0.196
Sum 1.667	Sum 1.633

This gives $D_i = 4.65$ inches for an austenite grain size of 7 and 4.30 inches for an austenite grain size of 8.

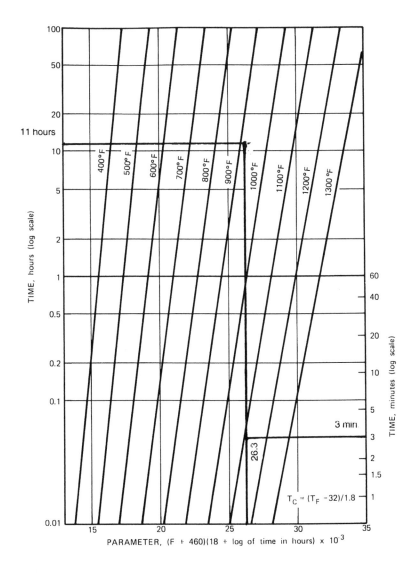

Fig 10-7(d) (continued) Chart showing relationship of tempering parameter to tempering temperature and time.
(continued)

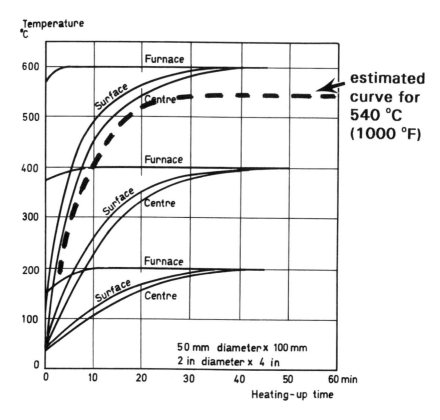

Fig 10-7(e) (continued) Time for heating to various temperatures for steel cylinders of geometry noted in figure. (From K.E. Thelning, *Steel and Its Heat Treatment*, Butterworths, London (1975)) *(continued)*

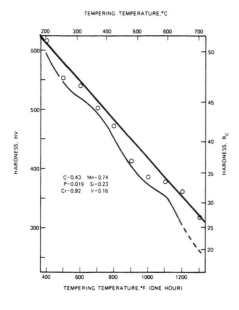

Fig 10-7(f) (continued) Tempered hardness versus tempering parameter for 6145 steel, showing the straight line used in the calculation *(continued)*

The graphs in Fig. 3-26 and 3-27 can be used and give $D_i = 3.8$ inches for a grain size of 7 and $D_i = 3.5$ inches for a grain size of 8. However, the graphs in Fig. 3-28 and 3-29 give $D_i = 3.1$ inches for a grain size of 7 and 3.0 inches for a grain size of 8. These values are nearer those obtained directly from the Jominy curve. The discrepancy between the values of D_i calculated by the two methods illustrates the uncertainty of such correlations for estimating D_i by calculation.

Determination of Severity of Quench

Assume that the continuous cooling time-temperature-transformation diagram in Fig. 10-9a is for an 8630 steel having an austenite grain size of ASTM 7. If a one inch diameter cylinder made of this steel is austenitized and then quenched into water of H = 1.2 and oil of H = 0.4, the cooling curves at the center, at midway to the center and at the surface shown in Fig. 10-9b are obtained.

1. Use each cooling curve to determine the severity of quench, and compare the values to those given for the curves.

2. Will the surface and the center of the cylinder form all martensite for the two quenchants?

Solution

1. The procedure for estimating the severity of quench is illustrated in Fig. 10-9c. The cooling curves are shown with the cooling rate at 704°C, defined by the slope of the tangent, shown in Fig. 10-9b. From these cooling rates the distances on the Jominy bar which have these cooling rates are obtained from Fig. 3-10, as shown in Fig. 10-9c. Then the cooling rate correlations of Fig. 4-13 corresponding to the center of cylinders are used. For the one inch diameter cylinders, the intersection of a line at this location and the lines for the four Jominy distances defines the severity of quench. The values obtained are:

Category	Oil	Water
Based on center	0.2	2.0
Based on surface	0.3	1.5
Values from Fig. 10-9b	0.4	1.2

These values agree reasonably with those given on the figures.

2. To form all martensite, the cooling curve must miss the "nose" of the CCT diagram. If the curve of the location which cools fastest (surface of cylinder upon water quenching) won't do this, then the other locations, which cool slower, will not. In Fig. 10-9a the cooling curves at the surface for the two quenchants have been plotted on the CCT diagram. It is seen that the surface upon water quenching does not miss the nose of the CCT diagram, so that all martensite is not formed for any of the four cooling curves.

Note that it is difficult to estimate a value of the severity of quench from the high cooling rate at the surface of the water quenched sample.

Determination of Severity of Quench

A 2 inch diameter cylinder of AISI-SAE 5055H steel of minimum hardenability is used to estimate the severity of quench of a given medium. After quenching, a "flat" is carefully ground parallel to the axis of the cylinder and to a depth of 0.30 inch. Hardness readings are then taken along the center line of this surface, giving an average value of Rockwell C 50. Determine the severity of quench value for this medium. Does this steel have the type of Jominy curve for best making this type of test?

Solution

The Jominy curve band for 5055H steel is shown in Fig. 10-10a. It is the minimum curve which is applicable here. A hardness of Rockwell C 50 corresponds to a Jominy distance of 6/16 inch. To estimate the H value, the cooling rate correlations in Fig. 4-14 are used. The depth at which the hardness reading was taken was 0.7/1.0 = 0.7 of the radius. Thus the cooling rate correlation curves for this fractional distance must be used, which is shown in

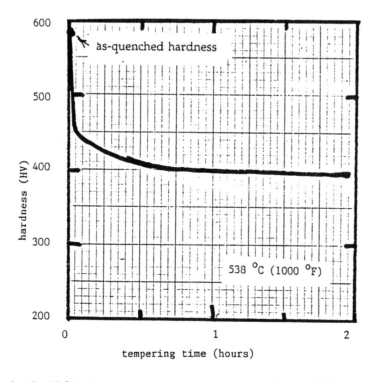

Fig 10-7(g)   (continued) Calculated hardness versus tempering time at 538°C (1000°F)

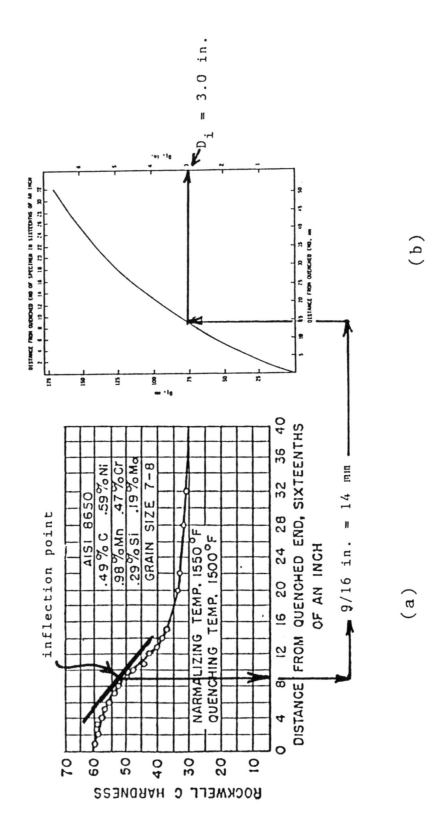

(a)

(b)

Fig 10-8 Jominy curve for 8650 steel, showing method of obtaining value of D_i from cooling rate (Jominy distance at the inflection point)

Fig. 10-10b. From the Jominy distance of 6/16 inch and for a diameter of 2.0 inches, the severity of quench value is H = 0.7.

The best shape of the Jominy curve for this method appears to be one in which the Jominy distance for the measured hardness is not very sensitive to the hardness value, which would correspond to a region in which the Jominy curve is steep, such as in the example above. For example, if the hardness in the example here were 52 or 48 (corresponding to about ±2 Rockwell C accuracy in hardness measurement), then the Jominy distance would be about 5/16 and 7/16 inch, respectively. This would give a severity of quench of about 1.0 and 0.6, respectively.

If the Jominy curve had been flatter, such as that of the maximum hardenability curve in Fig. 10-10a, the Jominy distances corresponding to Rockwell C 52 and 48 would be 13/16 and 17/16 inch, respectively. This would

give H values of about 0.25 and 0.15, respectively, which are quite close. However, if the hardness had been Rockwell C 62 and 58, then the H values would be 0.5 and 0.3, respectively.

The best estimate of the severity of quench by this method is obtained by a judicious choice of bar diameter, the depth at which make the hardness and the shape of the Jominy curve last; the latter depends upon the steel chosen. The best choice of these two quantities also depends upon the value of the severity of quench.

Determination of a Heat Treatment

A 2 inch diameter shaft is to be made from a 3140 steel having the chemical composition 0.39% C, 0.88% Mn, 0.20% Si, 1.2% Ni and 0.70% Cr. Near the mid-length the surface must have a hardness of Rockwell C 50 and the center approximately 40. It should have a "slight"

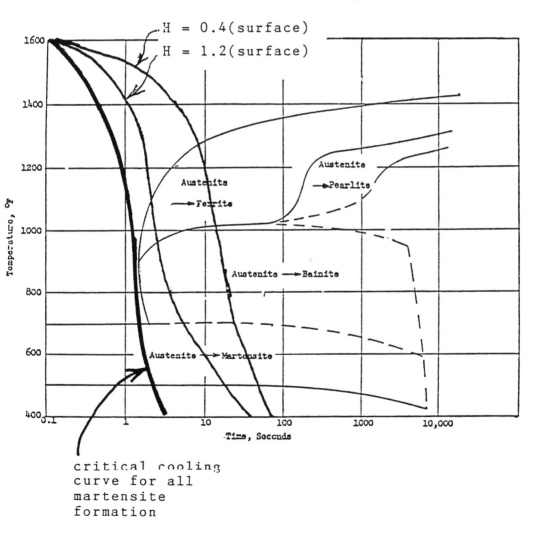

Fig 10-9(a)   Continuous cooling TTT diagram for 8630 steel, with superimposed cooling curves for positions in one inch diameter cylinder when quenched into two quenchants

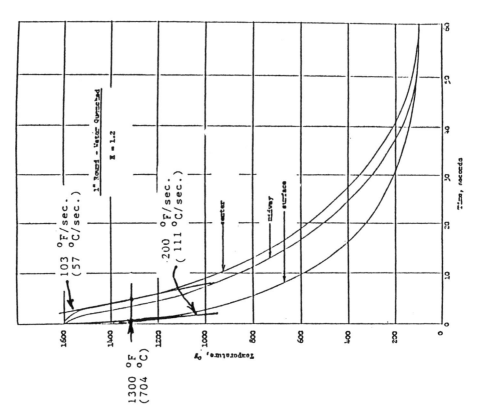

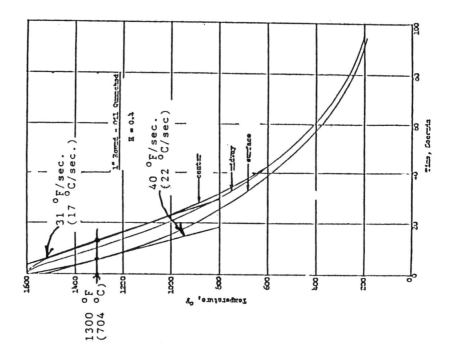

Fig. 10-9(b) Cooling curves at the center, midway and surface of one inch diameter steel cylinders quenched into oil and water

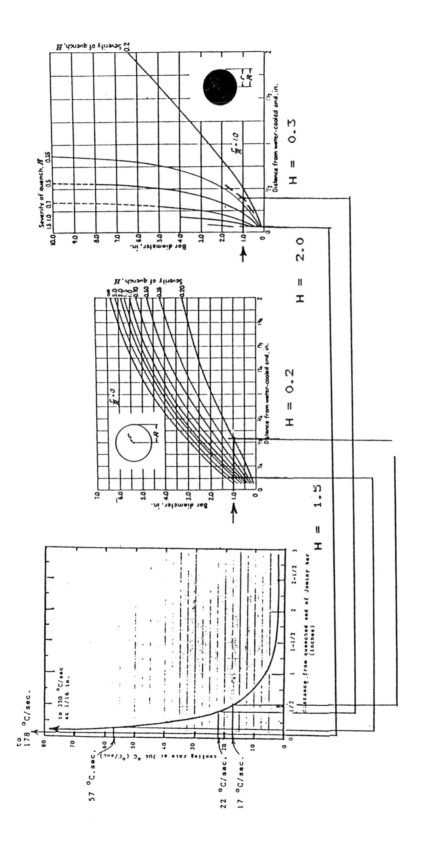

Fig. 10-9(c) Illustration of method to find value of severity of quench H from cooling curves in Fig. 10-9(b)

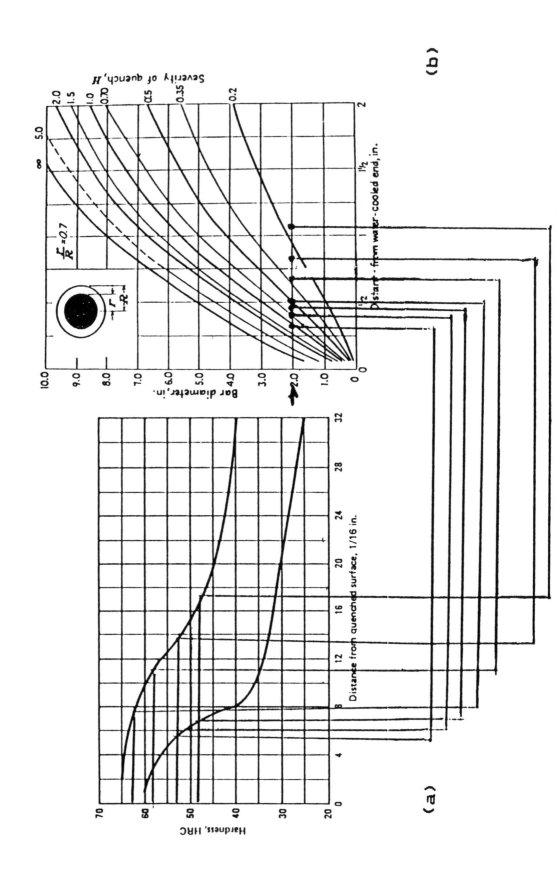

(a)

(b)

stress relief temper. There is a slight change in geometry near each end. Give a heat treatment to meet these requirements.

Solution

The information required is the austenitizing temperature and time, the quenchant to use and the tempering temperature and time. Very rapid cooling is to be avoided because the changing geometry at each end makes the part sensitive to quench cracking. Since only a "slight" stress relief temper is required, a relatively low tempering temperature should be used.

The Jominy curves in Fig. 10-11a were calculated using the equation by Just in Table 3-5 for austenite grain sizes of ASTM 6, 7 and 8. This is the range of expected grain size for austenitizing a steel that is deoxidized (killed) (see Chapter 6). As shown in Fig. 10-11b the curves in Fig. 4-13 were used to obtain the equivalent Jominy distance at the surface and the center of a 2 inch cylinder quenched into media of different severity of quench values. Values of H = 0.2 (still oil quench), 0.6 (agitated oil quench) and 1.0 (water) were used to obtain an indication of the range of cooling rates which would produce the desired hardnesses. The Jominy curve for the smallest grain size (ASTM grain size number 8) was used in this calculation since this will be the lowest hardenabil-

ity of the three grain sizes. Using these H values, the range of Jominy distances listed below was found. The hardness values listed were then obtained from the Jominy curves (see Fig. 10-11b).

H value for ASTM 8	Equivalent Jominy distance (1/16 inch)		Hardness (Rockwell C)	
	Surface	Center	Surface	Center
0.2	13	16	36	33
0.6	4	9	50	40
0.7	3	8	53	42
1.0	1	7	57	43

Recalling that the shaft is to have a "slight" temper, the as-quenched hardness should be slightly higher than the final desired hardness. A hardness of Rockwell C 53 at the surface is used. It is seen from the data in the table that this can be met with a quench of H = 0.7. Using this quench gives a hardness at the center of Rockwell C 42, which is slightly higher than the desired tempered value. Also, H = 0.7 is a moderate quench, so cracking will be avoided.

A tempering treatment which will reduce these hardness values to the specifications now must be chosen. There is an infinite combination of temperatures and times which will produce the desired hardness. However,

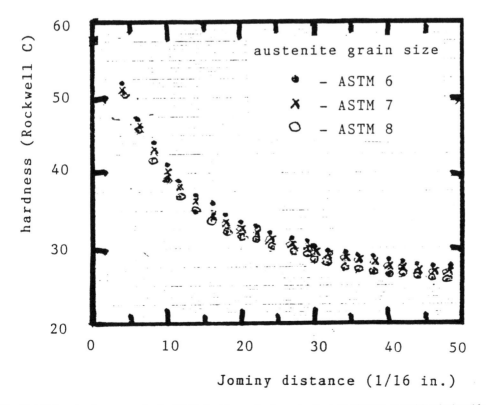

Fig 10-11(a)   Jominy curves for the 3140 steel for austenite grain sizes of ASTM 6, 7 and 8 calculated from the Just equation *(continued)*

a low temperature will reduce energy consumption during heating. The value chosen then depends upon the tempering time desired, but this time is somewhat arbitrary. We choose 2 h, which allows using the method of Crafts and Lamont (Chapter 5). This method also can be used for quenched structures other than all martensite. Using the curves in Fig. 5-47 and 5-48, the data below are obtained.

tempered hardness $R_T = (R_Q - B - D) f + B + A$

Quantity	400°F (205°C)	500°F (260°C)	600°F (315°C)
R_Q	53	53	53
B	47	38	31
D	1.0	1.2	1.5
f	0.64	0.60	0.55
A (0.88% Mn)	0.8	1.10	1.5
A (0.20% Si)	0.5	0.5	1.0
A (1.20% Ni)	0.4	0.4	0.4
A (0.70% Cr)	0.6	1.0	1.8
A (0% Mo)	0	0	0
R_T	53	50	47

These results indicate that a tempering temperature of 500°F (260°C) for 2 h will reduce the surface hardness from Rockwell C 53 to 50. Using this method shows that the center hardness will be unchanged, still 40 Rockwell C. If a different temperature and time combination is desired, then the parametric plot in Fig. 10-11c (from Fig 5-37) for a 3140 steel can be used. Note that the parametric value for Rockwell C 50 is $17.5 = (T + 460) (18 + \log t) (0.001)$, where T is in °F and t is in hours. This can be checked by inserting $T = 500°F$ and $t = 2$ h, which gives a parametric value of 17.6, in excellent agreement.

The concern with embrittlement caused by tempering must be examined. The tempering in this heat treatment is a one-step heat treatment, and thus we are concerned with one-step temper embrittlement (OSTE) or tempered martensite embrittlement. However, 3140 steel is not noted for sensitivity to temper embrittlement.

The austenitizing time and temperature should be chosen to given an austenite grain size of about ASTM 7. For a 3140 steel, the recommended austenitizing temperature range is 1500-1550°F (815-845°C). For a deoxidized (killed) steel the initial austenite grain size will be about 7 and remain at this value for several hours at this temperature (Chapter 6). The heating curves in Fig. 6-32c, for heating a 1.75 inch diameter cylinder in air, show that the furnace temperature is attained in about 20 min.

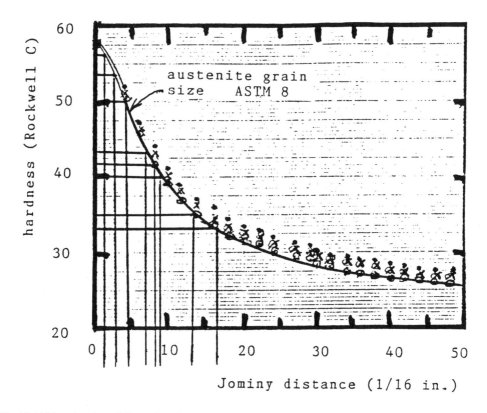

Fig 10-11(b) (continued) Illustration of method to determine the surface and center hardness for the 2 inch diameter shaft using four quenchants (continued)

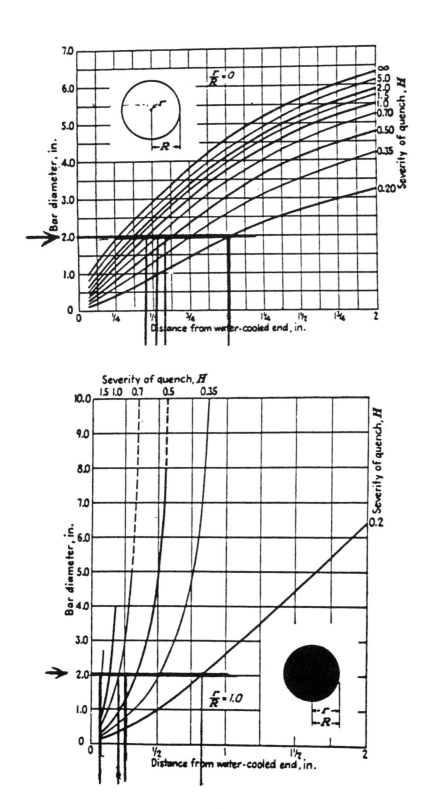

Fig 10-11(b) (continued) Illustration of method to determine the surface and center hardness for the 2 inch diameter shaft using four quenchants (continued)

Thus for the 2 inch diameter cylinder of this problem, one hour will be sufficient to heat the cylinder to the austenitizing temperature. Further, the center of the cylinder should take about 30 min. for homogenization. Superimposing the heating curves in Fig. 6-32c on the diagram in Fig. 6-26 (see Fig. 10-11d) shows that homogeneous austenite will be attained after heating the cylinder in the furnace for one hour (total furnace time).

The recommended complete heat treatment is the following.

1. Place the cylinder in an air furnace at 1500°F (815°C), and hold for one hour (total furnace time).
2. At the end of the one hour, quench the cylinder into a medium of H = 0.7. Moderately agitated oil should be sufficient.
3. Temper the cylinder at 500°F (216°C) for 2 h, then remove it from the furnace and air cool it to room temperature.

Comments

It is important to examine how sensitive the final hardness is to changes in the treatment. This will ensure that possible variation in the heat treatment will not pose a problem. For example, it is important to know how closely the severity of quench must be controlled.

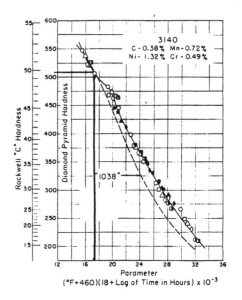

Fig 10-11(c) (continued) Tempered hardness versus tempering parameter for 3140 steel *(continued)*

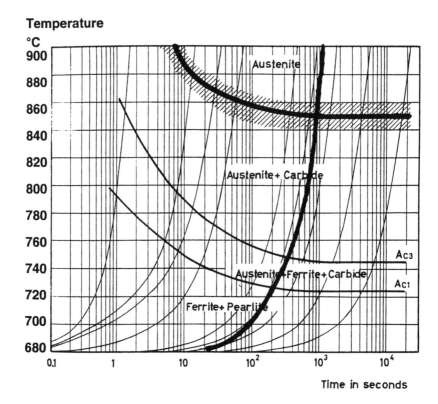

Temperature °C — Time in seconds

Fig 10-11(d) (continued) Diagram for the formation of austenite upon continuous heating (Fig. 6-26), with a curve typical of that upon heating a 2 inch diameter cylinder in air superimposed on the diagram *(continued)*

First, it is useful to keep in mind that the accuracy of hardness measurement on the Rockwell C scale is about ±2. The metallurgist must determine whether the specification has taken this into account. Thus to be conservative, the hardness at the surface after tempering should be Rockwell C 52 (a specification of 50 plus 2 for hardness measurement uncertainty). The procedure described above to determine the severity of quench should be repeated with a hardness higher than 50. Using the above procedure and a hardness of 55 Rockwell C, the Jominy curve in Fig. 10-11a gives a Jominy distance of about 2/16 inch for this hardness. The curve in Fig. 10-11b then gives a severity of quench of about 1.0, which is a water quench. If this quenchant is used, there is concern that the rapid cooling may induce quench cracking problems.

If Rockwell C 57 is obtained upon quenching, then tempering to Rockwell C 53 will require a higher temperature or longer time than already determined. However, using the same procedures as above, a temperature of 500°F (260°C) for 2 h would give a hardness of 52 Rockwell C. This is within the uncertainty of hardness measurements of ±2 of the specification of 50 Rockwell C. This tempering treatment would also produce the desired center hardness.

For a deoxidized 3140 steel, the austenite grain size is not very sensitive to austenitizing temperature or time. Thus a variation of about ±50°F (±24°C) in the austenitizing temperature will have little effect on the austenite grain size. Also there is considerable latitude in the austenitizing times; the grain size should be stable between ASTM 6 and 8 for a few hours in this temperature range.

From this analysis, it is clear that the step which is most susceptible to variations which could affect the final hardness significantly is the quenching process. The most judicious solution to this problem is to change the specification to a steel of higher hardenability.

As a final note, it is pointed out that if the steel had been specified as 3140H, with no chemical composition given, then the analysis should have been made based on the minimum of the hardenability band. The band is shown in Fig. 10-11e. The heavy Jominy curve is that from Fig. 10-11a for the austenite grain size ASTM 8. It is seen that this curve is near the minimum curve, so that the preceding analysis would be valid for a specification of 3140H steel.

Determination of Effect of Tempering During Heat-up to Tempering Temperature

In the problem above on "Determination of Tempered Hardness," the concern was raised as to the amount of softening which occurs during heating to the tempering temperature. The correlations used to estimate tempering hardness were based on the time at the tempering temperature, and probably involved experiments in which small samples were tempered in salt baths to ensure rapid heating to the tempering temperature. In Chapter 5, a method to estimate the tempering which occurs during heating was outlined, and its use will be illustrated in this problem for a 6145 steel.

In the problem above on "Determination of Tempered Hardness", the hardness after tempering for one hour at 1000°F (538°C) was determined to be about DPH 400. This is based on the time at temperature, that is, it assumes that no tempering occurs upon heating. Here we

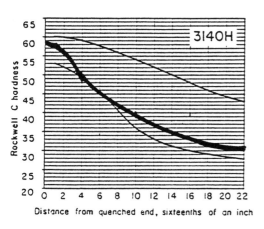

Fig 10-11(e) (continued) Jominy band for 3140H steel. The heavy Jominy curve is the calculated curve shown in Fig. 10-11a for an austenite grain size of ASTM 8. (Jominy band from *Metals Handbook*, 8th edition, *Properties and Selection of Metals*, American Society for Metals, Metals Park, Ohio (1961))

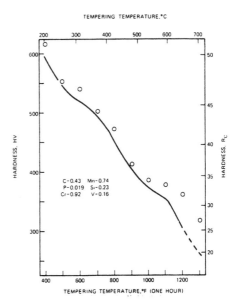

Fig 10-12(a) Tempered hardness against temperature (one hour tempering time) for a 6145 steel *(continued)*

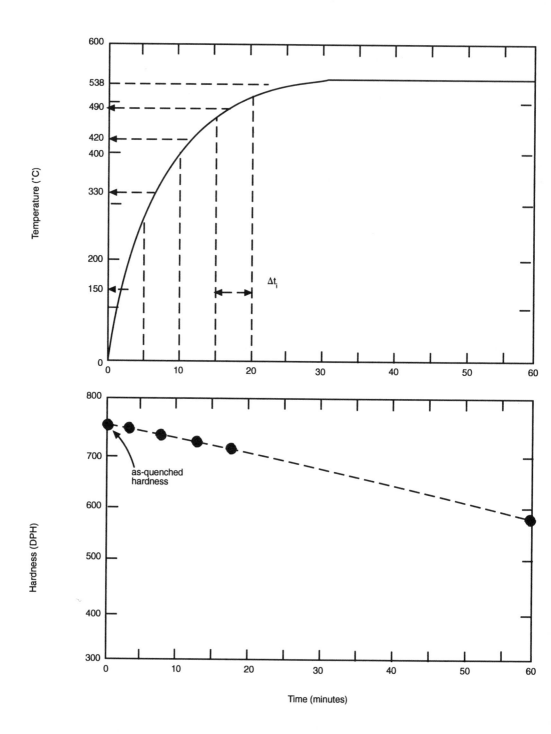

Fig 10-12(b) (continued) Heating curve for tempering at 1000°F (538°C) and associated instantaneous hardness

examine the effect of tempering during the heat-up process.

As in Chaper 5, we assume that during tempering the hardness decrease can be represented by

$$-dH = A \, [\exp(-Q/RT)] \, dt$$

where A is a constant, Q is the activation energy for the process, T is the absolute temperature, t is the time, and H is the hardness. If temperature is changing with time, then the hardness change can be obtained by integrating this equation

$$\int_{H_0}^{H} -dH = A \int_{o}^{t} [\exp(-Q/RT)] dt$$

where H_0 is the initial or quenched hardness at the beginning of tempering (time = 0). The activation energy for the process may not be known, but this relation may be written as

$$-dH = A \, [\exp(-B/T)] \, dt$$

where B is a constant.

During heating, T = f(t), which can be obtained at any location in a simple part (e.g., cylinder) by calculating the curve as described in Chapter 6, or by curve fitting experimental data. For example, the case of interest involves heating in air a cylinder 1 inch in diameter, and we assume that the center heats as shown in Fig. 10-7e. Thus we could fit this temperature-time curve to obtain an analytical expression T = f(t). However, substituting this relation into the equation above would probably result in an expression which is not integratable. Instead, we can write the expression in finite difference form

$$H - H_0 = -A \, [\exp(-B/T)] \, \Delta t_i$$

The heating curve is divided into time increments Δt_i, and the reduction in hardness during each increment is estimated from this expression.

We consider the previous case of tempering the 6145 steel. The temperature was 538°C and the time was one hour. The calculated tempered hardness at the center of the one inch diameter cylinder was about 400 DPH. In the problem here, we will take the one hour to be the time in the furnace. Thus the actual hardness will be less than that

calculated assuming that the center of the cylinder was at temperature for one hour.

First, we must obtain values of A and B in the above equation. To do this, we choose two tempering temperatures and times and determine the corresponding hardnesses. We can do this from the data in Fig. 10-12a. The quenched hardness is taken as 750 DPH (all martensite for 0.45% C of the 6145 steel). At a constant temperature, the equation above becomes

$$H - H_0 = -A \, [\exp(-B/T)] \, t$$

We apply this using tempered hardness data from Fig. 10-12a for two temperatures, 316 and 704°C, each for one hour, to obtain the constants A and B. We get

$$H - H_0 = -1658 \, [\exp(-1645/T)] \, t$$

where T is in K and t is in hours.

This relation is used in the finite difference expression to calculate the hardness contribution. To illustrate the procedure, the heating curve in Fig. 10-7e is divided into 5 minute increments, as shown in Fig. 10-12b. The temperature at the mid-time of each increment is taken to use in the finite difference expression.

$$H - H_0 = -1658 \, \{ \, [\exp(1654/423)] \, [5/60]$$

$$+ [\exp(1654/603)] \, [5/60] + [\exp(1654/693)] \, [5/60]$$

$$+ [\exp(1654/763)] \, [5/60] \, \}$$

or

$$H = 740 - 3 - 9 - 14 - 17 = 740 - 43 = 697.$$

This covers the first 20 minutes of the heat-up time, and Fig. 10-12b shows that the tempering temperature of 540°C is almost attained. To get the remaining reduction in hardness which occurs during the remaining 40 minutes, the same expression is used with a temperature of 540°C and a time of 40 minutes. This lowers the hardness an additional 144 DPH. Thus the final hardness is 553, whereas one hour at temperature gives 400 DPH. The instantaneous hardness during heating is shown in Fig. 10-12b.

Appendices

Appendix 1a.

ASTM Standard A255-89 method for calculating hardenability from composition. (From 1991 Annual Book of ASTM Standards, 01.05, American Society for Testing and Materials, Philadelphia (1991). Copyright ASTM. Reprinted with permission.))

Method for Calculating Hardenability From Composition

1a.1 *Introduction*—This method of Jominy hardenability calculation from the chemical ideal diameter $(DI)^6$ on a steel is based on the original work of M.A. Grossman (**1**)[7] and provides increased accuracy by refinement of the carbon multiplying factors and the correlation of a boron factor (B.F.) with carbon and alloy content.[8] These refinements were based on analysis of thousands of heats of boron and non-boron 1500, 4100, 5000, and 8600 series steels encompassing a range of compositions as follows and a range of DI as contained in Tables 1a.6 through 1a.9. The accuracy of this method and the techniques used to develop it have been documented (**2**). For comparison of this method to others, or for steel compositions outside the mentioned grades the user should refer to other articles concerned with calculating hardenability (**3 to 9**).

Element	Range (%)
Carbon	0.10-0.70
Manganese	0.50-1.65
Silicon	0.15-0.60
Chromium	1.35 max
Nickel	1.50 max
Molybdenum	0.55 max

1a.2 *DI Calculation for Non-Boron Steels*—This calculation relies on a series of hardenability factors (Table 1a.1) for each alloying element in the composition which multiplied together gives a DI value. (For simplicity, only multiplying factors for DI in inch units are given. For DI in millimeters, the DI in inches should be multiplied by 25.4). The effects of phosphorus and sulfur are not considered since they tend to cancel one another. A No. 7 austenitic grain size is assumed since most steels with hardenability control are melted to a fine-grain practice where experience has demonstrated that a high percentage of heats conform to this grain size. An example DI calculation is given as follows for an SAE 4118 modified steel:

Element	%	Multiplying factor (Table 1a.1)
Carbon	0.22	0.119
Manganese	0.80	3.667
Silicon	0.18	1.126
Nickel	0.10	1.036
Chromium	0.43	1.929
Molybdenum	0.25	1.75
Copper	0.10	1.04

where:

$$DI = 0.119 \times 3.667 \times 1.126 \times 1.036 \times 1.929 \times 1.75 \times 1.04 = 1.79 \text{ in. (45.5 mm)}$$

1a.3 *DI Calculation for Boron Steels*—With an effective steel making process the boron factor (signifying the contribution of boron to increased hardenability) is an inverse function of the carbon and alloy content. The

---

[5] The composition of Woods metal is 50% bismuth, 25% lead, and 25% 6in, and the melting point is 200 °F (93 °C).

[6] DI represents the diameter of a round steel bar that will harden at the center to 50% martensite when subjected to an ideal quench (that is, a Grossman quench severity H = infinity).

[7] The boldface numbers in parentheses refer to a list of references at the end of this method.

[8] The multiplying factors for vanadium were taken from W. Crafts and J. Lamont (10) and are known to be less precise due to variations insolubility of vanadium carbides.

higher the carbon or alloy content, or both, the lower the boron factor.

1a.3.1 The actual boron factor is expressed by the following relationship:

$$B.F. =$$

$$\frac{\text{Measured DI (from Jominy data and carbon content)}}{\text{Calculated DI (from composition excluding boron)}}$$

1a.3.2 An example of actual boron factor determination is given as follows for an SAE 15B30 modified steel:

Composition, %	C	Mn	Si	Ni	Cr	Mo	B	Calculated DI (boron excluded)
	0.29	1.25	0.20	0.13	0.07	0.03	0.0015	1.24 in. (31.5 mm)

End-quench test results, in.

"J" position ($^1/_{16}$ in.)	1	2	3	4	5	6	7
Hardness, HRC	50	50	49	48	47	45	41
"J" position ($^1/_{16}$ in.)	8	9	10	12	14	16	
Hardness, HRC	38	33	28	25	22	20	

End-quench test results, mm

"J" position (mm)	1.5	3.0	4.5	6.0	7.5	9.0	10.5
Hardness, HRC	50	50	49	49	47	46	43
"J" position (mm)	12.0	13.5	15.0	18.0	21.0	24.0	
Hardness, HRC	40	35	30	25	23	21	

1a.3.3 Using Table 1a.2 determine the nearest location on the end-quench curve where a hardness corresponding to 50% martensite occurs for the actual carbon content. For the example heat with 0.29 carbon this hardness is 37 HRC occurring at a "J" distance of $^8/_{16}$ in. or 12.9 mm from the quenched end (interpolation required).

1a.3.4 From Table 1a.3 (in.) or Table 1a.4 (mm) a "J" distance of $^8/_{16}$ in. or 12.9 mm equates to a measured DI of 2.97 in. or 76.0 mm (interpolation required).

$$\text{Boron factor} = \frac{2.97 \text{ in.}}{1.24 \text{ in.}} = 2.4 \text{ boron factor} = \frac{76.0 \text{ mm}}{31.3 \text{ mm}} = 2.4$$

1a.3.5 *Calculation of DI With Boron (DI$_B$):*
1a.3.5.1 Calculate the DI without boron. For the above example this DI is 1.24 in. (31.5 mm).
1a.3.5.2 Calculate the alloy factor (the product of all the multiplying factors from Table 1a.1 excluding carbon). For the above example:

Alloy factor

$$= \frac{\text{calculated DI (without boron)}}{\text{carbon multiplying factor}} = \frac{1.24 \text{ in.}}{0.157 \text{ in.}}$$

$$= 8 \text{ or alloy factor} = \frac{31.5 \text{ mm}}{0.157 \text{ in.} \times 25.4 \text{ mm/in.}} = 8$$

1a.3.5.3 Determine the boron multiplying factor from Table 1a.5. For this example with 0.29% carbon and an alloy factor of 8, the boron multiplying factor is 2.36 (interpolation required).
1a.3.5.4 Calculate the DI with boron as follows.

$$DI_B = DI \text{ (without boron)} \times \text{boron factor}$$

$$DI_B = 1.24 \text{ in.} \times 2.36 \text{ or } 31.5 \text{ mm} \times 2.36$$

$$DI_B = 2.93 \text{ in. or } 74.3 \text{ mm}$$

1a.4 *Hardenability Curves from Composition*— With a predetermined DI (DI$_B$ for boron steels), the end-quench hardenability curve can be computed by the following procedure:

1a.4.1 The initial hardness (IH) at the J = $^1/_{16}$-in. or 1.5-mm position is a function of carbon content and independent of hardenability, and is selected from Table 1a.2. For the example non-boron SAE 4118 modified heat containing 0.22% carbon the initial hardness is 45 HRC.

1a.4.2 The hardness at other positions along the end-quench specimen (termed distance hardness) is determined by dividing the initial hardness by the appropriate factor from Table 1a.6 (in.) or 1a.7 (mm) for non-boron steels or from Table 1a.8 (in.) or 1a.9 (mm) for boron steels.

1a.5 For the example non-boron heat with an IH = 45 HRC and a calculated DI of 1.79 in. (45.5 mm) the hardness at the respective end-quench positions can be calculated by dividing 45 by the appropriate dividing factor listed in Table 1a.6 (in.) or 1a.7 (mm) for nonboron steels. (For simplicity the DI should be rounded to the nearest 0.1 in. or 0.5 mm.)

"J" distance ($1/16$) in.)	Dividing factor for 1.8 in. DI (Table 1a.6)	Distance hardness (DH), HRC
1	...	45
2	1.02	44
3	1.10	41
4	1.37	33
5	1.66	27
6	1.92	23
8	2.11	21
10	2.29	20
12	2.53	18

"J" distance (mm)	Dividing factor for 45.5 mm DI (Table 1a.7)	Distance hardness (DH), HRC
1.5	...	45
3.0	1.02	44
4.5	1.10	41
6.0	1.31	34
7.5	1.59	28
9.0	1.82	25
12.0	2.06	22
15.0	2.24	20
18.0	2.46	18

1a.6 *Equations for Tables 1a.5 Through 1a.9*—Equations representing a least squares polynomial fit of the data contained in Eqs 1a.5 through 1a.9 are listed immediately following Table 1a.9. The use of these equations to plot curves may result in random inflection points due to the characteristics of polynomial equations. These inflections will be minor however, and should be disregarded.

Table 1a.1 Multiplying factors, in.

% Alloy	Carbon-grain size 7	Mn	Si	Ni	Cr	Mo	Cu	V
0.01	0.005	1.033	1.007	1.004	1.022	1.03	1.00	1.02
0.02	0.011	1.067	1.014	1.007	1.043	1.06	1.01	1.03
0.03	0.016	1.100	1.021	1.011	1.065	1.09	1.01	1.05
0.04	0.021	1.133	1.028	1.015	1.086	1.12	1.02	1.07
0.05	0.026	1.167	1.035	1.018	1.108	1.15	1.02	1.09
0.06	0.032	1.200	1.042	1.022	1.130	1.18	1.02	1.11
0.07	0.038	1.233	1.049	1.026	1.151	1.21	1.03	1.12
0.08	0.043	1.267	1.056	1.029	1.173	1.24	1.03	1.14
0.09	0.049	1.300	1.063	1.033	1.194	1.27	1.03	1.16
0.10	0.054	1.333	1.070	1.036	1.216	1.30	1.04	1.17
0.11	0.059	1.367	1.077	1.040	1.238	1.33	1.04	1.19
0.12	0.065	1.400	1.084	1.044	1.259	1.36	1.05	1.21
0.13	0.070	1.433	1.091	1.047	1.281	1.39	1.05	1.22
0.14	0.076	1.467	1.098	1.051	1.302	1.42	1.05	1.24
0.15	0.081	1.500	1.105	1.055	1.324	1.45	1.06	1.26
0.16	0.086	1.533	1.112	1.058	1.346	1.48	1.06	1.28
0.17	0.092	1.567	1.119	1.062	1.367	1.51	1.06	1.29
0.18	0.097	1.600	1.126	1.066	1.389	1.54	1.07	1.31
0.19	0.103	1.633	1.133	1.069	1.410	1.57	1.07	1.33
0.20	0.108	1.667	1.140	1.073	1.432	1.60	1.07	1.35
0.21	0.113	1.700	1.147	1.077	1.454	1.63	1.08	...
0.22	0.119	1.733	1.154	1.080	1.475	1.66	1.08	...
0.23	0.124	1.767	1.161	1.084	1.497	1.69	1.09	...
0.24	0.130	1.800	1.168	1.088	1.518	1.72	1.09	...
0.25	0.135	1.833	1.175	1.091	1.540	1.75	1.09	...
0.26	0.140	1.867	1.182	1.095	1.562	1.78	1.10	...
0.27	0.146	1.900	1.189	1.098	1.583	1.81	1.10	...
0.28	0.151	1.933	1.196	1.102	1.605	1.84	1.10	...
0.29	0.157	1.967	1.203	1.106	1.626	1.87	1.11	...
0.30	0.162	2.000	1.210	1.109	1.648	1.90	1.11	...
0.31	0.167	2.033	1.217	1.113	1.670	1.93	1.11	...
0.32	0.173	2.067	1.224	1.117	1.691	1.96	1.12	...
0.33	0.178	2.100	1.231	1.120	1.713	1.99	1.12	...
0.34	0.184	2.133	1.238	1.124	1.734	2.02	1.12	...
0.35	0.189	2.167	1.245	1.128	1.756	2.05	1.13	...
0.36	0.194	2.200	1.252	1.131	1.776	2.08	1.13	...
0.37	0.200	2.233	1.259	1.135	1.799	2.11	1.14	...
0.38	0.205	2.267	1.266	1.139	1.821	2.14	1.14	...
0.39	0.211	2.300	1.273	1.142	1.842	2.17	1.14	...
0.40	0.213	2.333	1.280	1.146	1.864	2.20	1.15	...
0.41	0.216	2.367	1.287	1.150	1.886	2.23	1.15	...
0.42	0.218	2.400	1.294	1.153	1.907	2.26	1.15	...
0.43	0.221	2.433	1.301	1.157	1.929	2.29	1.16	...
0.44	0.223	2.467	1.308	1.160	1.950	2.32	1.16	...
0.45	0.226	2.500	1.315	1.164	1.972	2.35	1.16	...
0.46	0.228	2.533	1.322	1.168	1.994	2.38	1.17	...
0.47	0.230	2.567	1.329	1.171	2.015	2.41	1.17	...
0.48	0.233	2.600	1.336	1.175	2.037	2.44	1.18	...
0.49	0.235	2.633	1.343	1.179	2.058	2.47	1.18	...
0.50	0.238	2.667	1.350	1.182	2.080	2.50	1.18	...
0.51	0.242	2.700	1.357	1.186	2.102	2.53	1.19	...
0.52	0.244	2.733	1.364	1.190	2.123	2.56	1.19	...
0.53	0.246	2.767	1.371	1.193	2.145	2.59	1.19	...
0.54	0.249	2.800	1.378	1.197	2.166	2.62	1.20	...
0.55	0.251	2.833	1.385	1.201	2.188	2.65	1.20	...
0.56	0.253	2.867	1.392	1.204	2.210	...	...	...
0.57	0.256	2.900	1.399	1.208	2.231	...	...	...
0.58	0.258	2.933	1.406	1.212	2.253	...	...	...
0.59	0.260	2.967	1.413	1.215	2.274	...	...	...
0.60	0.262	3.000	1.420	1.219	2.296	...	...	...
0.61	0.264	3.033	1.427	1.222	2.318	...	...	...
0.62	0.267	3.067	1.434	1.226	2.339	...	...	...
0.63	0.269	3.100	1.441	1.230	2.361	...	...	...
0.64	0.271	3.133	1.448	1.233	2.382	...	...	...
0.65	0.273	3.167	1.455	1.237	2.404	...	...	...
0.66	0.275	3.200	1.462	1.241	2.426	...	...	...
0.67	0.277	3.233	1.469	1.244	2.447	...	...	...
0.68	0.279	3.267	1.476	1.248	2.469	...	...	...
0.69	0.281	3.300	1.483	1.252	2.490	...	...	...
0.70	0.283	3.333	1.490	1.256	2.512	...	...	...
0.71	0.285	3.367	1.497	1.259	2.534	...	...	...
0.72	0.287	3.400	1.504	1.262	2.555	...	...	...
0.73	0.289	3.433	1.511	1.266	2.577	...	...	...
0.74	0.291	3.467	1.518	1.270	2.596	...	...	...
0.75	0.293	3.500	1.525	1.273	2.620	...	...	...
0.76	0.295	3.533	1.532	1.276	2.642	...	...	...
0.77	0.297	3.567	1.539	1.280	2.663	...	...	...
0.78	0.299	3.600	1.546	1.284	2.685	...	...	...
0.79	0.301	3.633	1.553	1.287	2.706	...	...	...
0.80	0.303	3.667	1.560	1.291	2.728	...	...	...
0.81	0.305	3.700	1.567	1.294	2.750	...	...	...
0.82	0.307	3.733	1.574	1.298	2.771	...	...	...
0.83	0.309	3.767	1.581	1.301	2.793	...	...	...
0.84	0.310	3.800	1.588	1.306	2.814	...	...	...
0.85	0.312	3.833	1.595	1.309	2.836	...	...	...
0.86	0.314	3.867	1.602	1.313	2.858	...	...	...
0.87	0.316	3.900	1.609	1.317	2.879	...	...	...
0.88	0.318	3.933	1.616	1.320	2.900	...	...	...
0.89	0.319	3.967	1.623	1.324	2.922	...	...	...
0.90	0.321	4.000	1.630	1.327	2.944	...	...	...
0.91	...	4.033	1.637	1.331	2.966	...	...	...
0.92	...	4.067	1.644	1.334	2.987	...	...	...
0.93	...	4.100	1.651	1.338	3.009	...	...	...
0.94	...	4.133	1.658	1.343	3.030	...	...	...
0.95	...	4.167	1.665	1.345	3.052	...	...	...
0.96	...	4.200	1.672	1.349	3.074	...	...	...
0.97	...	4.233	1.679	1.352	3.095	...	...	...
0.98	...	4.267	1.686	1.356	3.117	...	...	...
0.99	...	4.300	1.693	1.360	3.138	...	...	...
1.00	...	4.333	1.700	1.364	3.160	...	...	...
1.01	...	4.367	1.707	1.367	3.182	...	...	...
1.02	...	4.400	1.714	1.370	3.203	...	...	...
1.03	...	4.433	1.721	1.375	3.225	...	...	...
1.04	...	4.467	1.728	1.378	3.246	...	...	...
1.05	...	4.500	1.735	1.382	3.268	...	...	...
1.06	...	4.533	1.742	1.386	3.290	...	...	...
1.07	...	4.567	1.749	1.389	3.311	...	...	...
1.08	...	4.600	1.756	1.393	3.333	...	...	...
1.09	...	4.633	1.763	1.396	3.354	...	...	...
1.10	...	4.667	1.770	1.400	3.376	...	...	...
1.11	...	4.700	1.777	1.403	3.398	...	...	...
1.12	...	4.733	1.784	1.406	3.419	...	...	...
1.13	...	4.767	1.791	1.411	3.441	...	...	...
1.14	...	4.800	1.798	1.414	3.462	...	...	...
1.15	...	4.833	1.805	1.418	3.484	...	...	...
1.16	...	4.867	1.812	1.422	3.506	...	...	...
1.17	...	4.900	1.819	1.426	3.527	...	...	...
1.18	...	4.933	1.826	1.429	3.549	...	...	...
1.19	...	4.967	1.833	1.433	3.570	...	...	...
1.20	...	5.000	1.840	1.437	3.592	...	...	...
1.21	...	5.051	1.847	1.440	3.614	...	...	...
1.22	...	5.102	1.854	1.444	3.635	...	...	...
1.23	...	5.153	1.861	1.447	3.657	...	...	...
1.24	...	5.204	1.868	1.450	3.678	...	...	...

(continued)

Table 1a.1 (Continued)

% Alloy	Carbon-grain size 7	Mn	Si	Ni	Cr	Mo	Cu	V
1.25	...	5.255	1.875	1.454	3.700	...	...	...
1.26	...	5.306	1.882	1.458	3.722	...	...	...
1.27	...	5.357	1.889	1.461	3.743	...	...	...
1.28	...	5.408	1.896	1.465	3.765	...	...	...
1.29	...	5.459	1.903	1.470	3.786	...	...	...
1.30	...	5.510	1.910	1.473	3.808	...	...	...
1.31	...	5.561	1.917	1.476	3.830	...	...	...
1.32	...	5.612	1.924	1.481	3.851	...	...	...
1.33	...	5.663	1.931	1.484	3.873	...	...	...
1.34	...	5.714	1.938	1.487	3.894	...	...	...
1.35	...	5.765	1.945	1.491	3.916	...	...	...
1.36	...	5.816	1.952	1.495	3.938	...	...	...
1.37	...	5.867	1.959	1.498	3.959	...	...	...
1.38	...	5.918	1.966	1.501	3.981	...	...	...
1.39	...	5.969	1.973	1.506	4.002	...	...	...
1.40	...	6.020	1.980	1.509	4.024	...	...	...
1.41	...	6.071	1.987	1.512	4.046	...	...	...
1.42	...	6.122	1.994	1.517	4.067	...	...	...
1.43	...	6.173	2.001	1.520	4.089	...	...	...
1.44	...	6.224	2.008	1.523	4.110	...	...	...
1.45	...	6.275	2.015	1.527	4.132	...	...	...
1.46	...	6.326	2.022	1.531	4.154	...	...	...
1.47	...	6.377	2.029	1.535	4.175	...	...	...
1.48	...	6.428	2.036	1.538	4.197	...	...	...
1.49	...	6.479	2.043	1.541	4.217	...	...	...
1.50	...	6.530	2.050	1.545	4.239	...	...	...
1.51	...	6.581	2.057	1.556	4.262	...	...	...
1.52	...	6.632	2.064	1.561	4.283	...	...	...
1.53	...	6.683	2.071	1.565	4.305	...	...	...
1.54	...	6.734	2.078	1.569	4.326	...	...	...
1.55	...	6.785	2.085	1.574	4.348	...	...	...
1.56	...	6.836	2.092	1.578	4.369	...	...	...
1.57	...	6.887	2.099	1.582	4.391	...	...	...
1.58	...	6.938	2.106	1.586	4.413	...	...	...
1.59	...	6.989	2.113	1.591	4.434	...	...	...
1.60	...	7.040	2.120	1.595	4.456	...	...	...
1.61	...	7.091	2.127	1.600	4.478	...	...	...
1.62	...	7.142	2.134	1.604	4.499	...	...	...
1.63	...	7.193	2.141	1.609	4.521	...	...	...
1.64	...	7.224	2.148	1.613	4.542	...	...	...
1.65	...	7.295	2.155	1.618	4.564	...	...	...
1.66	...	7.346	2.162	1.622	4.586	...	...	...
1.67	...	7.397	2.169	1.627	4.607	...	...	...
1.68	...	7.448	2.176	1.631	4.629	...	...	...
1.69	...	7.499	2.183	1.636	4.650	...	...	...
1.70	...	7.550	2.190	1.640	4.672	...	...	...
1.71	...	7.601	2.197	1.644	4.694	...	...	...
1.72	...	7.652	2.204	1.648	4.715	...	...	...
1.73	...	7.703	2.211	1.652	4.737	...	...	...
1.74	...	7.754	2.218	1.656	4.759	...	...	...
1.75	...	7.805	2.225	1.660	4.780	...	...	...
1.76	...	7.856	2.232	1.664	...	...	...	...
1.77	...	7.907	2.239	1.668	...	...	...	...
1.78	...	7.958	2.246	1.672	...	...	...	...
1.79	...	8.009	2.253	1.676	...	...	...	...
1.80	...	8.060	2.260	1.680	...	...	...	...
1.81	...	8.111	2.267	1.687	...	...	...	...
1.82	...	8.162	2.274	1.694	...	...	...	...
1.83	...	8.213	2.281	1.701	...	...	...	...
1.84	...	8.264	2.288	1.708	...	...	...	...
1.85	...	8.315	2.295	1.715	...	...	...	...
1.86	...	8.366	2.302	1.722	...	...	...	...
1.87	...	8.417	2.309	1.729	...	...	...	...
1.88	...	8.468	2.316	1.736	...	...	...	...
1.89	...	8.519	2.323	1.743	...	...	...	...
1.90	...	8.570	2.330	1.750	...	...	...	...
1.91	...	8.671	2.337	1.753	...	...	...	...
1.92	...	8.672	2.344	1.756	...	...	...	...
1.93	...	8.723	2.351	1.759	...	...	...	...
1.94	...	8.774	2.358	1.761	...	...	...	...
1.95	...	8.825	2.364	1.765	...	...	...	...
1.96	...	...	2.372	1.767	...	...	...	...
1.97	...	...	2.379	1.770	...	...	...	...
1.98	...	...	2.386	1.773	...	...	...	...
1.99	...	...	2.393	1.776	...	...	...	...
2.00	...	...	2.400	1.779	...	...	...	...

Table 1a.2 Carbon content, initial hardness, 50% martensite hardness

% Carbon content	Hardness—HRC Initial 100% martensite	50% martensite	% Carbon content	Hardness—HRC Initial 100% martensite	50% martensite	% Carbon content	Hardness—HRC Initial 100% martensite	50% martensite
0.10	38	26	0.30	50	37	0.50	61	47
0.11	39	27	0.31	51	38	0.51	61	47
0.12	40	27	0.32	51	38	0.52	62	48
0.13	40	28	0.33	52	39	0.53	62	48
0.14	41	28	0.34	53	40	0.54	63	48
0.15	41	29	0.35	53	40	0.55	63	49
0.16	42	30	0.36	54	41	0.56	63	49
0.17	42	30	0.37	55	41	0.57	64	50
0.18	43	31	0.38	55	42	0.58	64	50
0.19	44	31	0.39	56	42	0.59	64	51
0.20	44	32	0.40	56	43	0.60	64	51
0.21	45	32	0.41	57	43	0.61	64	51
0.22	45	33	0.42	57	43	0.62	65	51
0.23	46	34	0.43	58	44	0.63	65	52
0.24	46	34	0.44	58	44	0.64	65	52
0.25	47	35	0.45	59	45	0.65	65	52
0.26	48	35	0.46	59	45	0.66	65	52
0.27	49	36	0.47	59	45	0.67	65	53
0.28	49	36	0.48	59	46	0.68	65	53
0.29	50	37	0.49	60	46	0.69	65	53

Table 1a.3 Jominy distance for 50% martensite vs. DI (in.)

"J" 1/16 in.	DI in.	"J" 1/16 in.	DI in.	"J" 1/16 in.	DI in.
0.5	0.27	11.5	3.74	22.5	5.46
1.0	0.50	12.0	3.83	23.0	5.51
1.5	0.73	12.5	3.94	23.5	5.57
2.0	0.95	13.0	4.04	24.0	5.63
2.5	1.16	13.5	4.13	24.5	5.69
3.0	1.37	14.0	4.22	25.0	5.74
3.5	1.57	14.5	4.32	25.5	5.80
4.0	1.75	15.0	4.40	26.0	5.86
4.5	1.93	15.5	4.48	26.5	5.91
5.0	2.12	16.0	4.57	27.0	5.96
5.5	2.29	16.5	4.64	27.5	6.02
6.0	2.45	17.0	4.72	28.0	6.06
6.5	2.58	17.5	4.80	28.5	6.12
7.0	2.72	18.0	4.87	29.0	6.16
7.5	2.86	18.5	4.94	29.5	6.20
8.0	2.97	19.0	5.02	30.0	6.25
8.5	3.07	19.5	5.08	30.5	6.29
9.0	3.20	20.0	5.15	31.0	6.33
9.5	3.32	20.5	5.22	31.5	6.37
10.0	3.43	21.0	5.28	32.0	6.42
10.5	3.54	21.5	5.33		
11.0	3.64	22.0	5.39		

Table 1a.4 Jominy distance for 50% martensite vs. DI (mm)

"J" mm	DI mm	"J" mm	DI mm	"J" mm	DI mm
1.0	8.4	18.0	94.2	35.0	137.1
2.0	15.7	19.0	97.1	36.0	139.1
3.0	22.9	20.0	100.6	37.0	140.9
4.0	29.7	21.0	103.7	38.0	142.8
5.0	36.3	22.0	106.5	39.0	144.7
6.0	42.9	23.0	109.7	40.0	146.4
7.0	48.2	24.0	112.2	41.0	148.3
8.0	54.2	25.0	114.9	42.0	150.1
9.0	59.5	26.0	117.4	43.0	151.7
10.0	64.2	27.0	119.9	44.0	153.4
11.0	68.6	28.0	122.4	45.0	154.1
12.0	72.1	29.0	124.7	46.0	156.5
13.0	76.4	30.0	127.1	47.0	157.8
14.0	80.1	31.0	129.0	48.0	159.2
15.0	84.0	32.0	131.4	49.0	160.5
16.0	87.6	33.0	133.5	50.0	161.8
17.0	90.1	34.0	135.2		

Table 1a.5 Boron factors vs. % carbon and alloy factor(a)

% Carbon	5	7	9	11	13	15	18	22	26
0.10	6.18	5.38	5.09	4.61	4.28	4.14	3.72	3.68	3.55
0.11	5.76	5.07	4.77	4.35	4.05	3.88	3.54	3.48	3.35
0.12	5.38	4.78	4.48	4.10	3.84	3.65	3.37	3.30	3.18
0.13	5.04	4.52	4.22	3.88	3.64	3.44	3.21	3.14	3.03
0.14	4.72	4.28	3.98	3.68	3.47	3.26	3.07	2.99	2.88
0.15	4.44	4.06	3.77	3.50	3.31	3.09	2.94	2.86	2.76
0.16	4.19	3.86	3.57	3.34	3.16	2.94	2.82	2.74	2.64
0.17	3.96	3.68	3.40	3.19	3.03	2.81	2.71	2.63	2.54
0.18	3.75	3.51	3.24	3.05	2.91	2.70	2.61	2.53	2.44
0.19	3.57	3.36	3.10	2.93	2.80	2.59	2.52	2.44	2.36
0.20	3.40	3.22	2.98	2.82	2.70	2.50	2.43	2.35	2.28
0.21	3.25	3.09	2.86	2.72	2.60	2.42	2.35	2.28	2.20
0.22	3.12	2.98	2.76	2.63	2.52	2.34	2.28	2.20	2.13
0.23	3.00	2.88	2.61	2.55	2.44	2.27	2.21	2.14	2.07
0.24	2.90	2.78	2.59	2.47	2.37	2.21	2.15	2.07	2.01
0.25	2.81	2.70	2.52	2.40	2.30	2.15	2.09	2.01	1.95
0.26	2.73	2.62	2.45	2.34	2.24	2.10	2.03	1.96	1.89
0.27	2.66	2.55	2.39	2.28	2.18	2.05	1.98	1.91	1.84
0.28	2.60	2.49	2.34	2.23	2.13	2.00	1.93	1.86	1.79
0.29	2.54	2.43	2.29	2.18	2.08	1.96	1.88	1.81	1.74
0.30	2.49	2.38	2.24	2.14	2.04	1.92	1.83	1.76	1.70
0.31	2.44	2.33	2.20	2.10	1.99	1.88	1.79	1.72	1.65
0.32	2.40	2.28	2.16	2.06	1.95	1.84	1.74	1.68	1.61
0.33	2.36	2.24	2.12	2.02	1.91	1.80	1.70	1.64	1.57
0.34	2.32	2.20	2.09	1.98	1.87	1.76	1.66	1.60	1.53
0.35	2.29	2.17	2.05	1.95	1.84	1.72	1.63	1.56	1.49
0.36	2.26	2.13	2.02	1.92	1.80	1.69	1.59	1.52	1.45
0.37	2.23	2.10	1.99	1.89	1.77	1.65	1.55	1.49	1.42
0.38	2.20	2.07	1.96	1.85	1.74	1.62	1.52	1.46	1.38
0.39	2.18	2.04	1.93	1.82	1.70	1.58	1.49	1.42	1.35
0.40	2.15	2.01	1.90	1.79	1.67	1.55	1.46	1.39	1.32
0.41	2.12	1.98	1.87	1.76	1.64	1.52	1.43	1.36	1.29
0.42	2.09	1.96	1.84	1.73	1.62	1.49	1.40	1.34	1.26
0.43	2.06	1.93	1.82	1.70	1.58	1.46	1.37	1.31	1.23
0.44	2.04	1.90	1.78	1.68	1.56	1.43	1.35	1.28	1.21
0.45	2.01	1.87	1.75	1.65	1.53	1.40	1.32	1.25	1.19
0.46	1.98	1.85	1.72	1.62	1.51	1.38	1.30	1.23	1.17
0.47	1.94	1.82	1.69	1.59	1.48	1.36	1.28	1.21	1.15
0.48	1.91	1.80	1.67	1.57	1.46	1.34	1.26	1.19	1.13

(continued)

Table 1a.5 (Continued)

% Carbon	5	7	9	11	13	15	18	22	26
0.49	1.89	1.77	1.64	1.54	1.43	1.32	1.24	1.17	1.10
0.50	1.87	1.75	1.61	1.51	1.41	1.30	1.22	1.15	1.08
0.51	1.83	1.72	1.58	1.48	1.39	1.27	1.20	1.12	1.06
0.52	1.80	1.70	1.56	1.46	1.37	1.26	1.18	1.10	1.04
0.53	1.77	1.67	1.53	1.44	1.34	1.24	1.16	1.07	1.02
0.54	1.74	1.65	1.51	1.42	1.32	1.23	1.14	1.05	1.00
0.55	1.71	1.62	1.48	1.39	1.30	1.21	1.12	1.02	1.00
0.56	1.68	1.60	1.46	1.37	1.28	1.20	1.10	1.00	1.00
0.57	1.65	1.57	1.44	1.35	1.26	1.18	1.07	1.00	1.00
0.58	1.62	1.55	1.42	1.33	1.24	1.17	1.05	1.00	1.00
0.59	1.60	1.52	1.40	1.31	1.22	1.14	1.02	1.00	1.00
0.60	1.57	1.50	1.38	1.29	1.20	1.12	1.00	1.00	1.00
0.61	1.54	1.48	1.36	1.27	1.18	1.09	1.00	1.00	1.00
0.62	1.51	1.46	1.34	1.25	1.16	1.06	1.00	1.00	1.00
0.63	1.49	1.43	1.32	1.23	1.13	1.03	1.00	1.00	1.00
0.64	1.47	1.41	1.30	1.21	1.11	1.00	1.00	1.00	1.00
0.65	1.45	1.39	1.29	1.19	1.08	1.00	1.00	1.00	1.00
0.66	1.42	1.37	1.28	1.17	1.05	1.00	1.00	1.00	1.00
0.67	1.40	1.35	1.26	1.15	1.02	1.00	1.00	1.00	1.00
0.68	1.38	1.33	1.24	1.14	1.00	1.00	1.00	1.00	1.00
0.69	1.36	1.31	1.22	1.12	1.00	1.00	1.00	1.00	1.00
0.70	1.35	1.28	1.20	1.10	1.00	1.00	1.00	1.00	1.00
0.71	1.33	1.26	1.18	1.07	1.00	1.00	1.00	1.00	1.00
0.72	1.32	1.25	1.16	1.05	1.00	1.00	1.00	1.00	1.00
0.73	1.30	1.22	1.14	1.02	1.00	1.00	1.00	1.00	1.00
0.74	1.29	1.20	1.12	1.00	1.00	1.00	1.00	1.00	1.00
0.75	1.27	1.17	1.08	1.00	1.00	1.00	1.00	1.00	1.00
0.76	1.26	1.15	1.05	1.00	1.00	1.00	1.00	1.00	1.00
0.77	1.24	1.12	1.02	1.00	1.00	1.00	1.00	1.00	1.00
0.78	1.22	1.10	1.00	1.00	1.00	1.00	1.00	1.00	1.00
0.79	1.20	1.07	1.00	1.00	1.00	1.00	1.00	1.00	1.00
0.80	1.18	1.05	1.00	1.00	1.00	1.00	1.00	1.00	1.00
0.81	1.15	1.02	1.00	1.00	1.00	1.00	1.00	1.00	1.00
0.82	1.12	1.00	1.00	1.00	1.00	1.00	1.00	1.00	1.00
0.83	1.08	1.00	1.00	1.00	1.00	1.00	1.00	1.00	1.00
0.84	1.04	1.00	1.00	1.00	1.00	1.00	1.00	1.00	1.00
0.85	1.02	1.00	1.00	1.00	1.00	1.00	1.00	1.00	1.00
0.86	1.00	1.00	1.00	1.00	1.00	1.00	1.00	1.00	1.00

(a) Alloy factor is the product of all the multiplying factors (Table 1a.1) excluding that for carbon.

REFERENCES

(1) M.A. Grossman, *Hardenability Calculated from Chemical Composition*, AIME Transactions, Vol 150, p 227-259 (1942)

(2) S.K. Banerji and J.E. Morral, *Boron in Steel*, AIME, Warrentown, PA, p 106-126 (1980)

(3) C.A. Siebert, D.V. Doane, and D.H. Breen, The Hardenability of Steels, ASM, Metals Park, Ohio, p 64 ff (1977)

(4) E. Just, *New Formulas for Calculating Hardenability Curves*, Metal Progress, p 87-88 (Nov 1969)

(5) D.V. Doane and J.S. Kirkaldy, Editors, *Hardenability Concepts with Applications to Steel*, The Metallurgical Society of AIME, Warrendale, PA (1978)

(6) W. Hewitt, *Hardenability—Its Prediction from Chemical Composition*, Heat Treatment of Metals, Vol 8, p 33-38 (1981)

(7) J.M. Tartaglia and G.T. Eldis, *Core Hardenability Calculations for Carburizing Steels*, Vol 15A, No. 6, Met. Trans., p 1173-1183 (June 1984)

(8) C.F. Jatczak, *Determining Hardenability from Composition*, Metal Progress, Vol 100, No. 3, p 60 (Sept 1971)

(9) I.R. Kramer, S. Siegel, and J. Brooks, *Factors for the Calculation of Hardenability*, AIME Trans., Vol 163, p 670 (1946)

(10) W. Crafts and Y. Lamont, *The Effects of Some Hardenability*, AIME Transactions, Vol 158, p 162 (1944)

Table 1a.6   Distance hardness dividing factors for non-boron steels, in.

Ideal diameter (DI), in.	Jominy end-quench distance (1/16 in.)																
	2	3	4	5	6	7	8	9	10	12	14	16	18	20	24	28	32
1.0	1.15	1.50	2.15	2.46	2.72	2.81	2.92	3.07	3.22	3.50							
1.1	1.12	1.42	1.98	2.32	2.60	2.70	2.80	2.94	3.07	3.34							
1.2	1.10	1.35	1.85	2.20	2.48	2.59	2.69	2.81	2.94	3.20	3.32	3.44					
1.3	1.08	1.29	1.74	2.09	2.38	2.48	2.58	2.69	2.81	3.07	3.19	3.30	3.53				
1.4	1.07	1.24	1.64	1.99	2.27	2.38	2.47	2.58	2.69	2.95	3.06	3.17	3.37	3.50	3.78		
1.5	1.05	1.19	1.56	1.90	2.18	2.28	2.37	2.47	2.58	2.83	2.94	3.05	3.22	3.35	3.61		
1.6	1.04	1.16	1.49	1.81	2.09	2.19	2.28	2.38	2.47	2.73	2.83	2.94	3.09	3.20	3.45	3.67	3.77
1.7	1.03	1.13	1.43	1.73	2.00	2.10	2.19	2.28	2.38	2.62	2.73	2.83	2.96	3.08	3.30	3.51	3.63
1.8	1.02	1.10	1.37	1.66	1.92	2.02	2.11	2.19	2.29	2.53	2.63	2.73	2.85	2.96	3.17	3.37	3.49
1.9	1.02	1.09	1.33	1.60	1.85	1.94	2.03	2.11	2.20	2.44	2.54	2.64	2.74	2.85	3.05	3.24	3.36
2.0	1.01	1.08	1.29	1.54	1.78	1.87	1.95	2.03	2.12	2.35	2.45	2.55	2.65	2.74	2.94	3.12	3.24
2.1	1.01	1.07	1.26	1.48	1.71	1.80	1.89	1.96	2.05	2.27	2.37	2.47	2.56	2.65	2.83	3.00	3.13
2.2	1.00	1.07	1.23	1.43	1.66	1.73	1.82	1.90	1.98	2.20	2.30	2.39	2.47	2.56	2.74	2.90	3.03
2.3	1.00	1.06	1.21	1.39	1.60	1.68	1.76	1.83	1.91	2.13	2.22	2.32	2.40	2.48	2.65	2.81	2.93
2.4	1.00	1.06	1.18	1.35	1.55	1.62	1.70	1.77	1.85	2.06	2.16	2.25	2.32	2.41	2.57	2.72	2.84
2.5	1.00	1.05	1.16	1.32	1.50	1.57	1.65	1.72	1.80	2.00	2.09	2.19	2.26	2.34	2.50	2.64	2.76
2.6	1.00	1.05	1.15	1.29	1.45	1.52	1.60	1.67	1.74	1.94	2.03	2.13	2.19	2.27	2.43	2.56	2.68
2.7	1.00	1.04	1.13	1.26	1.41	1.48	1.56	1.62	1.69	1.88	1.97	2.07	2.14	2.21	2.37	2.50	2.61
2.8	1.00	1.04	1.12	1.23	1.37	1.44	1.51	1.58	1.65	1.83	1.92	2.02	2.08	2.16	2.31	2.43	2.54
2.9	1.00	1.03	1.11	1.21	1.34	1.40	1.48	1.54	1.60	1.78	1.87	1.97	2.03	2.10	2.25	2.37	2.48
3.0	1.00	1.02	1.10	1.19	1.31	1.37	1.44	1.50	1.57	1.73	1.82	1.92	1.98	2.05	2.20	2.31	2.41
3.1	1.00	1.01	1.09	1.17	1.28	1.34	1.41	1.47	1.53	1.68	1.77	1.87	1.94	2.00	2.14	2.26	2.36
3.2	1.00	1.00	1.08	1.15	1.25	1.31	1.38	1.43	1.49	1.64	1.73	1.83	1.89	1.96	2.10	2.21	2.30
3.3	1.00	1.00	1.07	1.13	1.23	1.29	1.35	1.40	1.46	1.60	1.69	1.79	1.85	1.92	2.05	2.16	2.25
3.4	1.00	1.00	1.06	1.12	1.20	1.26	1.33	1.37	1.43	1.56	1.65	1.75	1.81	1.87	2.00	2.11	2.20
3.5	1.00	1.00	1.05	1.10	1.18	1.24	1.30	1.35	1.40	1.53	1.61	1.71	1.77	1.83	1.96	2.07	2.15
3.6	1.00	1.00	1.04	1.09	1.17	1.22	1.28	1.32	1.37	1.49	1.58	1.68	1.73	1.80	1.92	2.02	2.10
3.7	1.00	1.00	1.04	1.08	1.15	1.20	1.25	1.30	1.35	1.46	1.54	1.64	1.70	1.76	1.87	1.98	2.06
3.8	1.00	1.00	1.03	1.07	1.14	1.18	1.24	1.28	1.32	1.43	1.51	1.61	1.66	1.72	1.83	1.94	2.01
3.9	1.00	1.00	1.03	1.06	1.12	1.17	1.22	1.26	1.30	1.40	1.48	1.58	1.63	1.69	1.79	1.90	1.97
4.0	1.00	1.00	1.02	1.05	1.11	1.15	1.20	1.24	1.28	1.38	1.45	1.55	1.60	1.65	1.76	1.86	1.93
4.1	1.00	1.00	1.01	1.04	1.10	1.14	1.18	1.22	1.26	1.35	1.42	1.52	1.57	1.62	1.72	1.82	1.89
4.2	1.00	1.00	1.00	1.03	1.09	1.13	1.17	1.20	1.24	1.32	1.39	1.49	1.54	1.58	1.68	1.78	1.86
4.3	1.00	1.00	1.00	1.02	1.08	1.12	1.15	1.18	1.22	1.30	1.37	1.46	1.51	1.55	1.65	1.75	1.82
4.4	1.00	1.00	1.00	1.01	1.07	1.10	1.14	1.16	1.21	1.28	1.35	1.43	1.48	1.52	1.61	1.71	1.78
4.5	1.00	1.00	1.00	1.00	1.06	1.09	1.13	1.15	1.19	1.26	1.32	1.41	1.45	1.49	1.58	1.67	1.75
4.6	1.00	1.00	1.00	1.00	1.05	1.08	1.11	1.13	1.18	1.24	1.30	1.39	1.42	1.46	1.54	1.64	1.71
4.7	1.00	1.00	1.00	1.00	1.04	1.07	1.10	1.12	1.16	1.22	1.28	1.36	1.40	1.43	1.50	1.60	1.68
4.8	1.00	1.00	1.00	1.00	1.03	1.06	1.09	1.11	1.15	1.20	1.26	1.34	1.37	1.40	1.47	1.57	1.65
4.9	1.00	1.00	1.00	1.00	1.02	1.05	1.08	1.10	1.13	1.19	1.24	1.32	1.35	1.37	1.44	1.54	1.62
5.0	1.00	1.00	1.00	1.00	1.01	1.04	1.07	1.09	1.12	1.18	1.23	1.30	1.32	1.35	1.41	1.51	1.59
5.1	1.00	1.00	1.00	1.00	1.00	1.03	1.06	1.08	1.11	1.17	1.21	1.28	1.30	1.32	1.38	1.48	1.56
5.2	1.00	1.00	1.00	1.00	1.00	1.02	1.05	1.07	1.10	1.16	1.20	1.26	1.28	1.30	1.36	1.45	1.53
5.3	1.00	1.00	1.00	1.00	1.00	1.01	1.04	1.06	1.09	1.15	1.18	1.24	1.26	1.28	1.33	1.42	1.50
5.4	1.00	1.00	1.00	1.00	1.00	1.00	1.03	1.05	1.08	1.14	1.17	1.22	1.24	1.25	1.31	1.39	1.48
5.5	1.00	1.00	1.00	1.00	1.00	1.00	1.02	1.04	1.07	1.13	1.16	1.21	1.22	1.23	1.30	1.37	1.45
5.6	1.00	1.00	1.00	1.00	1.00	1.00	1.01	1.03	1.06	1.12	1.15	1.19	1.20	1.21	1.28	1.34	1.43
5.7	1.00	1.00	1.00	1.00	1.00	1.00	1.00	1.02	1.05	1.10	1.14	1.18	1.18	1.20	1.26	1.32	1.41
5.8	1.00	1.00	1.00	1.00	1.00	1.00	1.00	1.01	1.04	1.09	1.13	1.16	1.17	1.18	1.25	1.30	1.38
5.9	1.00	1.00	1.00	1.00	1.00	1.00	1.00	1.00	1.03	1.08	1.12	1.15	1.16	1.16	1.24	1.28	1.36
6.0	1.00	1.00	1.00	1.00	1.00	1.00	1.00	1.00	1.02	1.07	1.11	1.13	1.14	1.15	1.22	1.26	1.34
6.1	1.00	1.00	1.00	1.00	1.00	1.00	1.00	1.00	1.01	1.06	1.10	1.12	1.13	1.14	1.21	1.24	1.32
6.2	1.00	1.00	1.00	1.00	1.00	1.00	1.00	1.00	1.00	1.05	1.09	1.11	1.12	1.13	1.20	1.23	1.30
6.3	1.00	1.00	1.00	1.00	1.00	1.00	1.00	1.00	1.00	1.04	1.08	1.10	1.11	1.12	1.19	1.21	1.28
6.4	1.00	1.00	1.00	1.00	1.00	1.00	1.00	1.00	1.00	1.03	1.07	1.09	1.10	1.11	1.18	1.20	1.27
6.5	1.00	1.00	1.00	1.00	1.00	1.00	1.00	1.00	1.00	1.02	1.06	1.08	1.09	1.10	1.17	1.18	1.25
6.6	1.00	1.00	1.00	1.00	1.00	1.00	1.00	1.00	1.00	1.01	1.05	1.07	1.08	1.09	1.16	1.17	1.23
6.7	1.00	1.00	1.00	1.00	1.00	1.00	1.00	1.00	1.00	1.00	1.04	1.06	1.07	1.08	1.14	1.16	1.21
6.8	1.00	1.00	1.00	1.00	1.00	1.00	1.00	1.00	1.00	1.00	1.03	1.05	1.06	1.07	1.12	1.15	1.19
6.9	1.00	1.00	1.00	1.00	1.00	1.00	1.00	1.00	1.00	1.00	1.02	1.04	1.05	1.06	1.10	1.14	1.17
7.0	1.00	1.00	1.00	1.00	1.00	1.00	1.00	1.00	1.00	1.00	1.01	1.03	1.04	1.05	1.08	1.13	1.15

Table 1a.7 Distance hardness dividing factors for non-boron steels, mm

Ideal critical diameter (DI), mm	Jominy end-quench distance (mm)																
	3	4.5	6.0	7.5	9.0	10.5	12.0	13.5	15.0	18.0	21.0	24.0	27.0	33.0	39.0	45.0	51.0
25.0	1.13	1.44	2.01	2.35	2.61	2.77	2.85	2.99	3.14	3.41							
27.5	1.11	1.38	1.89	2.23	2.50	2.68	2.76	2.89	3.02	3.28							
30.0	1.09	1.32	1.76	2.11	2.38	2.56	2.65	2.77	2.89	3.14							
32.5	1.07	1.27	1.66	2.00	2.27	2.46	2.54	2.65	2.77	3.01	3.17						
35.0	1.06	1.22	1.57	1.91	2.17	2.35	2.44	2.55	2.65	2.89	3.04	3.16					
37.5	1.05	1.18	1.50	1.82	2.08	2.26	2.35	2.45	2.55	2.78	2.92	3.04	3.16	3.44			
40.0	1.04	1.15	1.43	1.74	1.99	2.17	2.25	2.35	2.44	2.67	2.81	2.93	3.04	3.29			
42.5	1.03	1.12	1.38	1.66	1.90	2.08	2.16	2.26	2.35	2.57	2.71	2.82	2.92	3.16	3.37	3.55	3.72
45.0	1.02	1.10	1.32	1.60	1.83	2.00	2.08	2.17	2.26	2.48	2.62	2.72	2.82	3.02	3.24	3.41	3.58
47.5	1.02	1.08	1.29	1.54	1.76	1.92	2.00	2.09	2.18	2.39	2.53	2.63	2.72	2.92	3.12	3.28	3.43
50.0	1.01	1.07	1.25	1.49	1.70	1.85	1.92	2.01	2.09	2.30	2.44	2.54	2.63	2.81	3.00	3.16	3.31
52.5	1.01	1.06	1.23	1.44	1.63	1.78	1.86	1.94	2.02	2.22	2.36	2.46	2.55	2.71	2.89	3.04	3.18
55.0	1.00	1.06	1.20	1.39	1.58	1.72	1.79	1.88	1.95	2.15	2.28	2.38	2.46	2.62	2.79	2.94	3.09
57.5	1.00	1.05	1.18	1.35	1.52	1.66	1.73	1.82	1.89	2.09	2.22	2.31	2.39	2.54	2.70	2.85	3.00
60.0	1.00	1.05	1.16	1.32	1.48	1.61	1.67	1.75	1.82	2.02	2.15	2.23	2.31	2.47	2.62	2.76	2.89
62.5	1.00	1.04	1.14	1.29	1.44	1.56	1.62	1.70	1.77	1.95	2.08	2.17	2.24	2.40	2.55	2.68	2.81
65.0	1.00	1.04	1.13	1.26	1.40	1.51	1.57	1.65	1.72	1.89	2.02	2.10	2.18	2.34	2.48	2.60	2.72
67.5	1.00	1.03	1.12	1.24	1.36	1.47	1.53	1.61	1.67	1.84	1.97	2.05	2.13	2.28	2.42	2.54	2.66
70.0	1.00	1.03	1.10	1.21	1.33	1.43	1.49	1.57	1.63	1.79	1.91	1.99	2.07	2.22	2.36	2.47	2.57
72.5	1.00	1.03	1.09	1.19	1.30	1.39	1.45	1.53	1.58	1.74	1.86	1.94	2.02	2.16	2.30	2.41	2.51
75.0	1.00	1.02	1.08	1.17	1.27	1.36	1.41	1.49	1.54	1.70	1.81	1.89	1.97	2.10	2.24	2.34	2.44
77.5	1.00	1.01	1.07	1.15	1.24	1.33	1.38	1.45	1.51	1.65	1.76	1.84	1.92	2.05	2.18	2.28	2.38
80.0	1.00	1.00	1.06	1.13	1.22	1.30	1.35	1.42	1.47	1.61	1.72	1.80	1.88	2.01	2.13	2.23	2.33
82.5	1.00	1.00	1.06	1.12	1.20	1.28	1.33	1.39	1.44	1.57	1.68	1.76	1.84	1.97	2.09	2.19	2.29
85.0	1.00	1.00	1.05	1.11	1.18	1.25	1.30	1.36	1.41	1.54	1.64	1.72	1.80	1.92	2.04	2.09	2.14
87.5	1.00	1.00	1.05	1.09	1.16	1.23	1.28	1.33	1.38	1.51	1.60	1.68	1.76	1.87	1.99	2.05	2.10
90.0	1.00	1.00	1.04	1.08	1.14	1.20	1.25	1.31	1.36	1.47	1.57	1.65	1.73	1.84	1.95	2.01	2.06
92.5	1.00	1.00	1.03	1.07	1.13	1.18	1.23	1.28	1.33	1.44	1.53	1.61	1.69	1.80	1.91	1.96	2.00
95.0	1.00	1.00	1.03	1.07	1.12	1.17	1.21	1.26	1.31	1.41	1.50	1.58	1.66	1.76	1.86	1.92	1.97
97.5	1.00	1.00	1.02	1.06	1.10	1.15	1.20	1.25	1.28	1.38	1.47	1.55	1.63	1.73	1.83	1.89	1.94
100.0	1.00	1.00	1.02	1.05	1.09	1.14	1.18	1.23	1.26	1.36	1.44	1.52	1.60	1.70	1.80	1.86	1.91
102.5	1.00	1.00	1.02	1.04	1.08	1.13	1.17	1.21	1.24	1.34	1.41	1.49	1.56	1.66	1.76	1.82	1.87
105.0	1.00	1.00	1.01	1.03	1.07	1.12	1.16	1.19	1.22	1.31	1.39	1.47	1.53	1.63	1.73	1.78	1.82
107.5	1.00	1.00	1.00	1.02	1.06	1.11	1.14	1.17	1.20	1.28	1.36	1.44	1.50	1.59	1.69	1.75	1.80
110.0	1.00	1.00	1.00	1.01	1.05	1.10	1.13	1.16	1.19	1.27	1.34	1.41	1.47	1.57	1.66	1.71	1.75
112.5	1.00	1.00	1.00	1.01	1.04	1.09	1.12	1.15	1.18	1.25	1.32	1.39	1.44	1.53	1.62	1.67	1.71
115.0	1.00	1.00	1.00	1.00	1.03	1.08	1.10	1.13	1.16	1.23	1.29	1.36	1.42	1.50	1.59	1.64	1.68
117.5	1.00	1.00	1.00	1.00	1.03	1.07	1.09	1.12	1.15	1.21	1.27	1.34	1.40	1.47	1.55	1.60	1.64
120.0	1.00	1.00	1.00	1.00	1.02	1.06	1.08	1.11	1.14	1.20	1.26	1.33	1.38	1.43	1.51	1.57	1.62
122.5	1.00	1.00	1.00	1.00	1.02	1.05	1.07	1.10	1.13	1.18	1.24	1.31	1.36	1.40	1.48	1.54	1.59
125.0	1.00	1.00	1.00	1.00	1.01	1.04	1.06	1.09	1.11	1.17	1.22	1.28	1.33	1.38	1.45	1.51	1.56
127.5	1.00	1.00	1.00	1.00	1.01	1.03	1.05	1.08	1.10	1.16	1.21	1.27	1.31	1.35	1.42	1.48	1.53
130.0	1.00	1.00	1.00	1.00	1.00	1.02	1.04	1.07	1.09	1.15	1.20	1.25	1.29	1.33	1.40	1.45	1.50
130.5	1.00	1.00	1.00	1.00	1.00	1.01	1.03	1.06	1.08	1.14	1.19	1.23	1.27	1.31	1.37	1.43	1.47
135.0	1.00	1.00	1.00	1.00	1.00	1.00	1.02	1.05	1.07	1.13	1.17	1.21	1.25	1.29	1.35	1.40	1.44
137.5	1.00	1.00	1.00	1.00	1.00	1.00	1.01	1.04	1.06	1.12	1.16	1.20	1.23	1.26	1.32	1.38	1.42
140.0	1.00	1.00	1.00	1.00	1.00	1.00	1.01	1.03	1.05	1.10	1.15	1.19	1.21	1.24	1.31	1.35	1.39
142.5	1.00	1.00	1.00	1.00	1.00	1.00	1.00	1.02	1.04	1.10	1.14	1.17	1.19	1.22	1.29	1.33	1.37
145.0	1.00	1.00	1.00	1.00	1.00	1.00	1.00	1.02	1.03	1.08	1.13	1.16	1.18	1.21	1.27	1.31	1.35
147.5	1.00	1.00	1.00	1.00	1.00	1.00	1.00	1.01	1.02	1.07	1.12	1.15	1.16	1.19	1.25	1.29	1.33
150.0	1.00	1.00	1.00	1.00	1.00	1.00	1.00	1.00	1.01	1.06	1.11	1.14	1.15	1.18	1.24	1.28	1.31
152.5	1.00	1.00	1.00	1.00	1.00	1.00	1.00	1.00	1.01	1.05	1.10	1.12	1.13	1.16	1.22	1.27	1.30
155.0	1.00	1.00	1.00	1.00	1.00	1.00	1.00	1.00	1.00	1.04	1.09	1.11	1.12	1.15	1.21	1.25	1.28
157.5	1.00	1.00	1.00	1.00	1.00	1.00	1.00	1.00	1.00	1.03	1.08	1.10	1.11	1.14	1.20	1.24	1.27
160.0	1.00	1.00	1.00	1.00	1.00	1.00	1.00	1.00	1.00	1.03	1.07	1.09	1.10	1.13	1.19	1.23	1.26
162.5	1.00	1.00	1.00	1.00	1.00	1.00	1.00	1.00	1.00	1.02	1.06	1.08	1.09	1.12	1.18	1.22	1.25
165.0	1.00	1.00	1.00	1.00	1.00	1.00	1.00	1.00	1.00	1.01	1.05	1.07	1.08	1.11	1.16	1.20	1.24
167.5	1.00	1.00	1.00	1.00	1.00	1.00	1.00	1.00	1.00	1.01	1.04	1.06	1.07	1.10	1.15	1.18	1.22
170.0	1.00	1.00	1.00	1.00	1.00	1.00	1.00	1.00	1.00	1.00	1.03	1.05	1.06	1.09	1.14	1.17	1.21
172.5	1.00	1.00	1.00	1.00	1.00	1.00	1.00	1.00	1.00	1.00	1.02	1.04	1.05	1.08	1.12	1.16	1.20
175.0	1.00	1.00	1.00	1.00	1.00	1.00	1.00	1.00	1.00	1.00	1.02	1.03	1.04	1.07	1.10	1.14	1.19
177.5	1.00	1.00	1.00	1.00	1.00	1.00	1.00	1.00	1.00	1.00	1.01	1.02	1.03	1.06	1.09	1.12	1.18

Table 1a.8 Distance hardness dividing factors for boron steels, in.

Ideal diameter (DI$_B$), in.	Jominy end-quench distance (1/16 in.)																
	2	3	4	5	6	7	8	9	10	12	14	16	18	20	24	28	32
1.5	1.10	1.14	1.88	2.52	2.90	3.22											
1.6	1.08	1.12	1.65	2.20	2.70	3.02											
1.7	1.07	1.10	1.47	1.95	2.50	2.82	3.00										
1.8	1.06	1.09	1.34	1.75	2.31	2.63	2.82	3.00									
1.9	1.05	1.08	1.25	1.59	2.14	2.45	2.66	2.83	3.08								
2.0	1.04	1.07	1.19	1.46	1.98	2.28	2.51	2.70	2.88	3.34							
2.1	1.03	1.06	1.14	1.36	1.83	2.12	2.36	2.52	2.70	3.15	3.70						
2.2	1.02	1.05	1.11	1.29	1.70	1.98	2.21	2.38	2.53	2.98	3.48	3.87					
2.3	1.02	1.04	1.09	1.24	1.58	1.84	2.08	2.24	2.38	2.82	3.29	3.65					
2.4	1.01	1.03	1.08	1.20	1.48	1.72	1.95	2.11	2.24	2.67	3.11	3.45	3.64				
2.5	1.01	1.03	1.07	1.17	1.39	1.61	1.83	1.99	2.12	2.54	2.95	3.26	3.45	3.62	4.00		
2.6	1.00	1.03	1.06	1.15	1.31	1.52	1.72	1.87	2.00	2.41	2.79	3.09	3.28	3.46	3.86	4.23	
2.7	1.00	1.02	1.05	1.14	1.25	1.43	1.62	1.77	1.90	2.29	2.65	2.93	3.12	3.30	3.67	4.00	
2.8	1.00	1.02	1.05	1.13	1.20	1.36	1.53	1.69	1.80	2.18	2.52	2.78	2.97	3.15	3.50	3.78	4.27
2.9	1.00	1.01	1.04	1.12	1.16	1.30	1.45	1.59	1.72	2.08	2.40	2.64	2.83	3.01	3.33	3.59	4.01
3.0	1.00	1.00	1.04	1.11	1.14	1.24	1.38	1.50	1.64	1.99	2.29	2.52	2.70	2.88	3.18	3.41	3.78
3.1	1.00	1.00	1.03	1.10	1.12	1.20	1.31	1.42	1.57	1.91	2.19	2.40	2.57	2.75	3.03	3.25	3.57
3.2	1.00	1.00	1.03	1.09	1.10	1.17	1.25	1.37	1.51	1.83	2.10	2.30	2.46	2.63	2.90	3.10	3.39
3.3	1.00	1.00	1.02	1.08	1.09	1.14	1.20	1.32	1.45	1.75	2.01	2.20	2.35	2.51	2.77	2.97	3.22
3.4	1.00	1.00	1.02	1.07	1.08	1.12	1.17	1.28	1.40	1.69	1.93	2.10	2.25	2.40	2.66	2.84	3.07
3.5	1.00	1.00	1.01	1.06	1.07	1.10	1.14	1.24	1.35	1.62	1.85	2.01	2.16	2.30	2.55	2.73	2.94
3.6	1.00	1.00	1.00	1.05	1.06	1.09	1.12	1.22	1.31	1.57	1.78	1.93	2.07	2.21	2.45	2.63	2.82
3.7	1.00	1.00	1.00	1.04	1.05	1.08	1.10	1.19	1.27	1.51	1.72	1.86	2.00	2.12	2.35	2.54	2.71
3.8	1.00	1.00	1.00	1.04	1.05	1.07	1.09	1.17	1.24	1.47	1.66	1.80	1.92	2.04	2.26	2.44	2.61
3.9	1.00	1.00	1.00	1.03	1.04	1.06	1.08	1.15	1.21	1.42	1.60	1.74	1.85	1.96	2.18	2.36	2.52
4.0	1.00	1.00	1.00	1.03	1.04	1.06	1.08	1.13	1.19	1.38	1.55	1.68	1.78	1.89	2.11	2.29	2.44
4.1	1.00	1.00	1.00	1.02	1.04	1.06	1.07	1.12	1.16	1.34	1.50	1.63	1.73	1.82	2.04	2.21	2.37
4.2	1.00	1.00	1.00	1.02	1.03	1.05	1.07	1.11	1.14	1.31	1.46	1.58	1.68	1.76	1.98	2.15	2.30
4.3	1.00	1.00	1.00	1.01	1.03	1.04	1.06	1.10	1.13	1.28	1.42	1.54	1.62	1.71	1.92	2.09	2.23
4.4	1.00	1.00	1.00	1.01	1.03	1.04	1.06	1.09	1.11	1.25	1.38	1.50	1.58	1.66	1.86	2.03	2.17
4.5	1.00	1.00	1.00	1.00	1.03	1.04	1.06	1.08	1.10	1.23	1.35	1.46	1.54	1.61	1.81	1.97	2.11
4.6	1.00	1.00	1.00	1.00	1.02	1.04	1.06	1.07	1.09	1.21	1.32	1.43	1.50	1.57	1.76	1.92	2.06
4.7	1.00	1.00	1.00	1.00	1.02	1.03	1.05	1.07	1.09	1.19	1.29	1.40	1.47	1.53	1.72	1.87	2.00
4.8	1.00	1.00	1.00	1.00	1.01	1.03	1.05	1.06	1.08	1.17	1.26	1.37	1.44	1.50	1.67	1.83	1.96
4.9	1.00	1.00	1.00	1.00	1.01	1.03	1.04	1.06	1.07	1.15	1.24	1.35	1.41	1.47	1.63	1.79	1.91
5.0	1.00	1.00	1.00	1.00	1.00	1.02	1.04	1.05	1.06	1.14	1.21	1.32	1.38	1.44	1.60	1.75	1.87
5.1	1.00	1.00	1.00	1.00	1.00	1.01	1.03	1.04	1.05	1.13	1.19	1.30	1.36	1.41	1.56	1.71	1.82
5.2	1.00	1.00	1.00	1.00	1.00	1.01	1.03	1.04	1.05	1.11	1.17	1.28	1.34	1.39	1.53	1.67	1.78
5.3	1.00	1.00	1.00	1.00	1.00	1.00	1.02	1.03	1.04	1.10	1.16	1.26	1.31	1.36	1.50	1.63	1.74
5.4	1.00	1.00	1.00	1.00	1.00	1.00	1.02	1.03	1.04	1.09	1.14	1.24	1.29	1.34	1.47	1.60	1.70
5.5	1.00	1.00	1.00	1.00	1.00	1.00	1.01	1.02	1.03	1.08	1.13	1.22	1.27	1.32	1.44	1.57	1.67
5.6	1.00	1.00	1.00	1.00	1.00	1.00	1.01	1.02	1.03	1.07	1.12	1.20	1.25	1.30	1.41	1.54	1.63
5.7	1.00	1.00	1.00	1.00	1.00	1.00	1.00	1.01	1.03	1.07	1.11	1.19	1.24	1.28	1.39	1.51	1.60
5.8	1.00	1.00	1.00	1.00	1.00	1.00	1.00	1.01	1.02	1.06	1.10	1.17	1.22	1.26	1.37	1.48	1.57
5.9	1.00	1.00	1.00	1.00	1.00	1.00	1.00	1.00	1.02	1.05	1.09	1.16	1.20	1.25	1.35	1.45	1.53
6.0	1.00	1.00	1.00	1.00	1.00	1.00	1.00	1.00	1.01	1.04	1.08	1.14	1.18	1.23	1.33	1.43	1.50
6.1	1.00	1.00	1.00	1.00	1.00	1.00	1.00	1.00	1.01	1.03	1.08	1.13	1.16	1.21	1.30	1.40	1.47
6.2	1.00	1.00	1.00	1.00	1.00	1.00	1.00	1.00	1.00	1.02	1.07	1.11	1.15	1.19	1.28	1.38	1.44
6.3	1.00	1.00	1.00	1.00	1.00	1.00	1.00	1.00	1.00	1.02	1.06	1.10	1.14	1.17	1.26	1.35	1.41
6.4	1.00	1.00	1.00	1.00	1.00	1.00	1.00	1.00	1.00	1.01	1.05	1.09	1.12	1.15	1.24	1.32	1.39
6.5	1.00	1.00	1.00	1.00	1.00	1.00	1.00	1.00	1.00	1.01	1.04	1.08	1.10	1.13	1.21	1.30	1.35
6.6	1.00	1.00	1.00	1.00	1.00	1.00	1.00	1.00	1.00	1.01	1.03	1.07	1.09	1.12	1.18	1.27	1.32
6.7	1.00	1.00	1.00	1.00	1.00	1.00	1.00	1.00	1.00	1.00	1.02	1.06	1.08	1.10	1.16	1.24	1.29
6.8	1.00	1.00	1.00	1.00	1.00	1.00	1.00	1.00	1.00	1.00	1.01	1.05	1.07	1.08	1.14	1.20	1.25
6.9	1.00	1.00	1.00	1.00	1.00	1.00	1.00	1.00	1.00	1.00	1.01	1.05	1.06	1.07	1.12	1.17	1.21
7.0	1.00	1.00	1.00	1.00	1.00	1.00	1.00	1.00	1.00	1.00	1.00	1.04	1.05	1.05	1.10	1.14	1.17

Table 1a.9 Distance hardness dividing factors for boron steels, mm

Ideal Critical Diameter (DIB), mm	Jominy end-quench distance (mm)																
	3	4.5	6.0	7.5	9.0	10.5	12.0	13.5	15.0	18.0	21.0	24.0	27.0	33.0	39.0	45.0	51.0
40.0	1.07	1.11	1.58	2.10	2.56												
42.5	1.06	1.10	1.43	1.89	2.34												
45.0	1.05	1.09	1.32	1.70	2.14	2.53	2.76										
47.5	1.04	1.08	1.23	1.55	1.98	2.36	2.59	2.78									
50.0	1.04	1.07	1.18	1.43	1.82	2.19	2.42	2.64									
52.5	1.03	1.06	1.13	1.34	1.69	2.04	2.27	2.48	2.66	3.02							
55.0	1.02	1.05	1.11	1.27	1.58	1.90	2.12	2.33	2.50	2.85	3.35						
57.5	1.02	1.04	1.09	1.22	1.48	1.77	1.99	2.19	2.35	2.69	3.17						
60.0	1.01	1.03	1.07	1.18	1.40	1.66	1.86	2.06	2.22	2.54	3.00						
62.5	1.01	1.03	1.06	1.16	1.34	1.56	1.74	1.94	2.10	2.41	2.84	3.17					
65.0	1.00	1.03	1.05	1.14	1.29	1.47	1.64	1.83	1.98	2.28	2.70	3.01	3.26	3.60			
67.5	1.00	1.02	1.04	1.12	1.24	1.38	1.55	1.72	1.87	2.17	2.56	2.86	3.10	3.44	3.80	4.38	
70.0	1.00	1.02	1.04	1.11	1.20	1.32	1.47	1.64	1.78	2.06	2.44	2.72	2.95	3.28	3.61	3.96	
72.5	1.00	1.01	1.03	1.10	1.17	1.26	1.39	1.55	1.69	1.97	2.33	2.59	2.80	3.13	3.44	3.74	4.18
75.0	1.00	1.00	1.03	1.09	1.14	1.22	1.33	1.47	1.60	1.88	2.22	2.46	2.67	3.00	3.28	3.55	3.88
77.5	1.00	1.00	1.02	1.08	1.12	1.18	1.27	1.40	1.52	1.80	2.12	2.35	2.54	2.87	3.13	3.37	3.62
80.0	1.00	1.00	1.02	1.07	1.11	1.15	1.22	1.33	1.46	1.72	2.03	2.25	2.43	2.74	2.99	3.21	3.44
82.5	1.00	1.00	1.02	1.07	1.10	1.13	1.18	1.29	1.41	1.66	1.95	2.14	2.31	2.62	2.86	3.07	3.29
85.0	1.00	1.00	1.02	1.06	1.09	1.11	1.15	1.25	1.36	1.60	1.87	2.06	2.23	2.50	2.73	2.94	3.12
87.5	1.00	1.00	1.02	1.06	1.08	1.10	1.13	1.21	1.31	1.54	1.80	1.98	2.13	2.40	2.62	2.82	3.01
90.0	1.00	1.00	1.01	1.05	1.07	1.09	1.11	1.18	1.27	1.48	1.73	1.90	2.05	2.31	2.52	2.71	2.89
92.5	1.00	1.00	1.00	1.04	1.06	1.08	1.10	1.17	1.24	1.44	1.67	1.83	1.97	2.22	2.43	2.61	2.79
95.0	1.00	1.00	1.00	1.03	1.05	1.07	1.09	1.15	1.22	1.39	1.62	1.77	1.90	2.13	2.34	2.51	2.68
97.5	1.00	1.00	1.00	1.03	1.05	1.06	1.08	1.13	1.19	1.35	1.57	1.71	1.83	2.05	2.25	2.42	2.59
100.0	1.00	1.00	1.00	1.02	1.04	1.05	1.07	1.11	1.17	1.32	1.51	1.65	1.77	1.97	2.17	2.34	2.51
102.5	1.00	1.00	1.00	1.02	1.04	1.05	1.07	1.11	1.15	1.29	1.47	1.60	1.71	1.91	2.11	2.27	2.43
105.0	1.00	1.00	1.00	1.01	1.03	1.05	1.06	1.10	1.13	1.25	1.43	1.55	1.66	1.85	2.04	2.20	2.36
107.5	1.00	1.00	1.00	1.01	1.03	1.04	1.06	1.09	1.12	1.23	1.39	1.51	1.62	1.79	1.98	2.14	2.28
110.0	1.00	1.00	1.00	1.01	1.02	1.03	1.05	1.08	1.11	1.21	1.35	1.47	1.57	1.73	1.92	2.07	2.20
112.5	1.00	1.00	1.00	1.01	1.02	1.03	1.05	1.07	1.10	1.18	1.32	1.43	1.53	1.69	1.87	2.02	2.14
115.0	1.00	1.00	1.00	1.00	1.01	1.03	1.05	1.07	1.09	1.17	1.29	1.40	1.49	1.64	1.82	1.97	2.08
117.5	1.00	1.00	1.00	1.00	1.01	1.02	1.05	1.06	1.08	1.16	1.26	1.36	1.45	1.60	1.77	1.92	2.05
120.0	1.00	1.00	1.00	1.00	1.01	1.02	1.04	1.06	1.08	1.15	1.24	1.33	1.42	1.56	1.72	1.87	2.02
122.5	1.00	1.00	1.00	1.00	1.00	1.01	1.04	1.05	1.07	1.13	1.22	1.31	1.40	1.53	1.68	1.83	1.98
125.0	1.00	1.00	1.00	1.00	1.00	1.01	1.03	1.05	1.06	1.12	1.20	1.29	1.37	1.50	1.64	1.79	1.92
127.5	1.00	1.00	1.00	1.00	1.00	1.00	1.03	1.04	1.05	1.11	1.18	1.27	1.35	1.47	1.61	1.75	1.89
130.0	1.00	1.00	1.00	1.00	1.00	1.00	1.02	1.03	1.04	1.10	1.17	1.25	1.33	1.44	1.57	1.71	1.85
132.5	1.00	1.00	1.00	1.00	1.00	1.00	1.02	1.03	1.04	1.08	1.15	1.23	1.30	1.41	1.54	1.67	1.79
135.0	1.00	1.00	1.00	1.00	1.00	1.00	1.01	1.02	1.03	1.07	1.14	1.21	1.28	1.39	1.52	1.64	1.75
137.5	1.00	1.00	1.00	1.00	1.00	1.00	1.01	1.02	1.03	1.07	1.12	1.19	1.26	1.37	1.49	1.60	1.70
140.0	1.00	1.00	1.00	1.00	1.00	1.00	1.00	1.01	1.02	1.06	1.11	1.18	1.24	1.34	1.46	1.57	1.67
142.5	1.00	1.00	1.00	1.00	1.00	1.00	1.00	1.01	1.02	1.05	1.10	1.16	1.22	1.32	1.43	1.54	1.65
145.0	1.00	1.00	1.00	1.00	1.00	1.00	1.00	1.01	1.02	1.05	1.09	1.15	1.21	1.30	1.41	1.51	1.61
147.5	1.00	1.00	1.00	1.00	1.00	1.00	1.00	1.01	1.01	1.04	1.08	1.14	1.19	1.28	1.38	1.48	1.58
150.0	1.00	1.00	1.00	1.00	1.00	1.00	1.00	1.00	1.01	1.04	1.07	1.13	1.18	1.27	1.37	1.46	1.55
152.5	1.00	1.00	1.00	1.00	1.00	1.00	1.00	1.00	1.00	1.03	1.06	1.11	1.16	1.25	1.35	1.44	1.53
155.0	1.00	1.00	1.00	1.00	1.00	1.00	1.00	1.00	1.00	1.02	1.06	1.11	1.15	1.22	1.32	1.41	1.50
157.5	1.00	1.00	1.00	1.00	1.00	1.00	1.00	1.00	1.00	1.01	1.05	1.09	1.13	1.21	1.30	1.38	1.46
160.0	1.00	1.00	1.00	1.00	1.00	1.00	1.00	1.00	1.00	1.01	1.04	1.08	1.12	1.19	1.28	1.35	1.42
162.5	1.00	1.00	1.00	1.00	1.00	1.00	1.00	1.00	1.00	1.01	1.03	1.07	1.11	1.17	1.25	1.33	1.41
165.0	1.00	1.00	1.00	1.00	1.00	1.00	1.00	1.00	1.00	1.01	1.03	1.06	1.09	1.15	1.23	1.30	1.37
167.5	1.00	1.00	1.00	1.00	1.00	1.00	1.00	1.00	1.00	1.01	1.02	1.05	1.08	1.13	1.20	1.27	1.34
170.0	1.00	1.00	1.00	1.00	1.00	1.00	1.00	1.00	1.00	1.00	1.01	1.04	1.07	1.11	1.17	1.24	1.31
172.5	1.00	1.00	1.00	1.00	1.00	1.00	1.00	1.00	1.00	1.00	1.00	1.03	1.05	1.09	1.15	1.20	1.25
175.0	1.00	1.00	1.00	1.00	1.00	1.00	1.00	1.00	1.00	1.00	1.00	1.03	1.05	1.08	1.12	1.17	1.22
177.5	1.00	1.00	1.00	1.00	1.00	1.00	1.00	1.00	1.00	1.00	1.00	1.02	1.04	1.06	1.10	1.14	1.18

Equations for Table 1a.1 multiplying factors

Carbon/grain size 7

Up to 0.39 %, incl	MF = 0.54 (%C)
Over 0.39 to 0.55%, incl	= 0.171 + 0.001 (%C) + 0.265 (%C)^2
Over 0.55 to 0.65%, incl	= 0.115 + 0.268 (%C) – 0.038 (%C)^2
Over 0.65 to 0.75%, incl	= 0.143 + 0.2 (%C)
Over 0.75 to 0.90%, incl	= 0.062 + 0.409 (%C) – 0.135 (%C)^2

Manganese

Up to 1.20%, incl	= 3.3333 (% Mn) + 1.00
Over 1.20 to 1.95%, incl	= 5.10 (%Mn) – 1.12
Silicon to 2.00%, incl	= 1.00 + 0.7 (%Si)
Nickel to 2.00%, incl	= 1.00 + 0.363 (%Ni)
Chromium to 1.75%, incl	= 1.00 + 2.16 (%Cr)
Molybdenum to 0.55%, incl	= 1.00 + 3.00 (%Mo)
Copper to 0.55%, incl	= 1.00 + 0.365 (%Cu)
Vanadium to 0.20%, incl	= 1.00 + 1.73 (%V)

Equations for Table 1a.2 carbon content, initial hardness, 50% martensite hardness

Initial hardness, $H = 35.395 + 6.990x + 312.330x^2 - 821.744x^3 + 1015.479x^4 - 538.346x^5$

50% martensite hardness, $H = 22.974 + 6.214x + 356.364x^2 - 1091.488x + 1464.880x^4 - 750.441x^5$

where: H = Hardness in HRC; x = % carbon

Equations for Table 1a.5 boron factor vs. % carbon and alloy factor

Alloy factor	Boron factor
5 to 0.85% C incl	B.F. = 13.03059 – 99.60059 X + 374.8548 X^2 – 707.3472 X^3 + 649.0012 X^4 – 231.1499 X^5
Over 0.85% C	B.F. = 1.00
7 to 0.81% C incl	B.F. = 10.29157 – 69.64546 X + 245.7061 X^2 – 445.3980 X^3 + 398.8044 X^4 – 140.6225 X^5
Over 0.81% C	B.F. = 1.00
9 to 0.77% C incl	B.F. = 10.45573 – 79.18534 X + 311.9332 X^2 – 630.5490 X^3 + 627.6022 X^4 – 244.4064 X^5
Over 0.77% C	B.F. = 1.00
11 to 0.73% C incl	B.F. = 9.005326 – 64.37669 X + 249.6933 X^2 – 506.0601 X^3 + 509.4772 X^4 – 201.9323 X^5
Over 0.73% C	B.F. = 1.00
13 to 0.67% C incl	B.F. = 8.054231 – 55.10171 X + 213.6752 X^2 – 447.8863 X^3 + 477.8413 X^4 – 204.4974 X^5
Over 0.67% C	B.F. = 1.00
15 to 0.63% C incl	B.F. = 9.001263 – 76.47680 X + 355.8714 X^2 – 872.9646 X^3 + 1067.359 X^4 – 512.7757 X^5
Over 0.63% C	B.F. = 1.00
18 to 0.59% C incl	B.F. = 6.849017 – 46.78647 X + 196.6635 X^2 – 471.3978 X^3 + 587.8504 X^4 – 295.0410 X^5
Over 0.59% C	B.F. = 1.00
22 to 0.55% C incl	B.F. = 7.217034 – 54.73529 X + 248.9901 X^2 – 632.7765 X^3 + 826.1873 X^4 – 431.7227 X^5
Over 0.55% C	B.F. = 1.00
26 to 0.53% C incl	B.F. = 7.162633 – 57.52117 X + 279.6173 X^2 – 756.9353 X^3 + 1042.628 X^4 – 568.5680 X^5
Over 0.53% C	B.F. = 1.00

where: X = % carbon

Equations for Table 1a.6 distance hardness dividing factors for non-boron steels, in.

"J" distance (1/16 in.)	DI(a)	Dividing factor
2	To 2.1, incl	DF = 4.68961 – 11.00832 X + 13.83314 X^2 – 8.80283 X^3 + 2.78698 X^4 – 0.34880 X^5
	Over 2.1	DF = 1.00
3	To 3.1, incl	DF = 2.34904 – 0.28254 X – 1.42995 X^2 + 1.16697 X^3 – 0.33813 X^4 + 0.03403 X^5
	Over 3.1	DF = 1.00
4	To 4.1, incl	DF = 5.66795 – 6.14648 X + 3.52874 X^2 – 1.06026 X^3 + 0.16301 X^4 – 0.01015 X^5
	Over 4.1	DF = 1.00
5	To 4.4, incl	DF = 4.53651 – 2.92609 X + 1.00411 X^2 – 0.17129 X^3 + 0.01369 X^4 – 0.00038 X^5
	Over 4.4	DF = 1.00
6	To 5.0, incl	DF = 4.39436 – 2.16072 X + 0.56027 X^2 – 0.08145 X^3 + 0.00840 X^4 – 0.00053 X^5
	Over 5.0	DF = 1.00
7	To 5.3, incl	DF = 4.20866 – 1.54405 X + 0.08294 X^2 + 0.08613 X^3 – 0.01963 X^4 + 0.00127 X^5
	Over 5.3	DF = 1.00
8	To 5.6, incl	DF = 4.44473 – 1.79085 X + 0.24617 X^2 + 0.03378 X^3 – 0.01189 X^4 + 0.00084 X^5
	Over 5.6	DF = 1.00
9	To 5.8, incl	DF = 4.95421 – 2.43521 X + 0.62983 X^2 – 0.07914 X^3 + 0.00399 X^4 – 0.00001 X^5
	Over 5.8	DF = 1.00
10	To 6.1, incl	DF = 5.31610 – 2.80977 X + 0.84183 X^2 – 0.141781 X^3 + 0.01301 X^4 – 0.00051 X^5
	Over 6.1	DF = 1.00
12	To 6.6, incl	DF = 5.63649 – 2.89264 X + 0.90309 X^2 – 0.17297 X^3 + 0.01881 X^4 – 0.00086 X^5
	Over 6.6	DF = 1.00
14		DF = 5.83176 – 2.99646 X + 0.94088 X^2 – 0.17734 X^3 + 0.01839 X^4 – 0.00079 X^5
16		DF = 6.06952 – 3.15198 X + 0.99297 X^2 – 0.18010 X^3 + 0.01720 X^4 – 0.00066 X^5
18		DF = 7.26492 – 4.50566 X + 1.61688 X^2 – 0.31738 X^3 + 0.03146 X^4 – 0.00122 X^5
20		DF = 7.68728 – 4.90380 X + 1.81034 X^2 – 0.36593 X^3 + 0.03739 X^4 – 0.00150 X^5
24		DF = 9.19586 – 6.71331 X + 2.77208 X^2 – 0.61510 X^3 + 0.06814 X^4 – 0.00295 X^5
28		DF = 9.27904 – 6.21461 X + 2.33158 X^2 – 0.46972 X^3 + 0.04727 X^4 – 0.00186 X^5
32		DF = 8.62857 – 5.16125 X + 1.81214 X^2 – 0.35489 X^3 + 0.03569 X^4 – 0.00143 X^5

where: X = DI in inches. (a) Max DI = 7.0 in.

Equations for Table 1a.7 distance hardness dividing factors for non-boron steels, mm

"J" distance (mm)	DI(a)	Dividing factor
3.0	To 52.5, incl	$DF = 1.65890 - 0.03528\,X + 0.00068\,X^2 - 0.000005\,X^3$
	Over 52.5	$DF = 1.00$
4.5	To 77.5, incl	$DF = 2.76123 - 0.07974\,X + 0.00125\,X^2 - 0.000007\,X^3$
	Over 77.5	$DF = 1.00$
6.0	To 105.0, incl	$DF = 3.67224 - 0.09306\,X + 0.00112\,X^2 - 0.000004\,X^3$
	Over 105.0	$DF = 1.00$
7.5	To 112.5, incl	$DF = 3.99220 - 0.08654\,X + 0.00089\,X^2 - 0.000003\,X^3$
	Over 112.5	$DF = 1.00$
9.0	To 127.5, incl	$DF = 4.16084 - 0.07800\,X + 0.00068\,X^2 - 0.000002\,X^3$
	Over 127.5	$DF = 1.00$
10.5	To 130.5, incl	$DF = 4.30625 - 0.07467\,X + 0.00059\,X^2 - 0.000002\,X^3$
	Over 130.5	$DF = 1.00$
12.0	To 140.0, incl	$DF = 4.40247 - 0.07494\,X + 0.00059\,X^2 - 0.000002\,X^3$
	Over 140.0	$DF = 1.00$
13.5	To 147.5, incl	$DF = 4.52840 - 0.07460\,X + 0.00057\,X^2 - 0.000002\,X^3$
	Over 147.5	$DF = 1.00$
15.0	To 152.5, incl	$DF = 4.70933 - 0.07692\,X + 0.00058\,X^2 - 0.000002\,X^3$
	Over 152.5	$DF = 1.00$
18.0	To 167.5, incl	$DF = 4.94914 - 0.07514\,X + 0.0052\,X^2 - 0.000001\,X^3$
	Over 167.5	$DF = 1.00$
21.0		$DF = 4.93379 - 0.06875\,X + 0.00043\,X^2 - 0.000001\,X^3$
24.0		$DF = 5.03364 - 0.06858\,X + 0.00043\,X^2 - 0.000001\,X^3$
27.0		$DF = 5.06910 - 0.06638\,X + 0.00040\,X^2 - 0.000001\,X^3$
33.0		$DF = 5.44818 - 0.07078\,X + 0.00042\,X^2 - 0.000001\,X^3$
39.0		$DF = 5.57362 - 0.06879\,X + 0.00039\,X^2 - 0.000001\,X^3$
45.0		$DF = 6.00347 - 0.07652\,X + 0.00044\,X^2 - 0.000001\,X^3$
51.0		$DF = 6.37885 - 0.08241\,X + 0.00047\,X^2 - 0.000001\,X^3$

where: X = DI in millimeters. (a) Max DI = 177.5 mm

Equations for Table 1a.8 distance hardness dividing factors for boron steels, in.

"J" distance (1/16 in.)	DI(a)	Dividing factor
2	To 2.5, incl	$DF = 22.97570 - 54.60177\,X + 54.29984\,X^2 - 26.85746\,X^3 + 6.59130\,X^4 - 0.64165\,X^5$
	Over 2.5	$DF = 1.00$
3	To 2.9, incl	$DF = 13.25591 - 28.28828\,X + 26.35541\,X^2 - 12.23150\,X^3 + 2.81374\,X^4 - 0.25263\,X^5$
	Over 2.9	$DF = 1.00$
4	To 3.5, incl	$DF = 28.50611 - 46.70430\,X + 31.90431\,X^2 - 10.91263\,X^3 + 1.86570\,X^4 - 0.12747\,X^5$
	Over 3.5	$DF = 1.00$
5	To 4.4, incl	$DF = 24.56368 - 33.70604\,X + 19.34623\,X^2 - 5.52132\,X^3 + 0.78088\,X^4 - 0.04375\,X^5$
	Over 4.4	$DF = 1.00$
6	To 4.9, incl	$DF = 5.32872 + 1.00334\,X - 3.67571\,X^2 + 1.70752\,X^3 - 0.31024\,X^4 + 0.02018\,X^5$
	Over 4.9	$DF = 1.00$
7	To 5.2, incl	$DF = 5.34598 + 0.98810\,X - 3.15067\,X^2 + 1.33727\,X^3 - 0.22285\,X^4 + 0.01332\,X^5$
	Over 5.2	$DF = 1.00$
8	To 5.6, incl	$DF = 2.61397 + 4.69073\,X - 4.71553\,X^2 + 1.58031\,X^3 - 0.22844\,X^4 + 0.01219\,X^5$
	Over 5.6	$DF = 1.00$
9	To 5.8, incl	$DF = 3.80939 + 2.96448\,X - 3.58847\,X^2 + 1.22906\,X^3 - 0.17730\,X^4 + 0.00938\,X^5$
	Over 5.8	$DF = 1.00$
10	To 6.1, incl	$DF = 11.75138 - 8.15904\,X + 2.57305\,X^2 - 0.42384\,X^3 + 0.03679\,X^4 - 0.00136\,X^5$
	Over 6.1	$DF = 1.00$
12	To 6.6, incl	$DF = 10.94580 - 6.42904\,X + 1.72900\,X^2 - 0.24187\,X^3 + 0.01769\,X^4 - 0.00055\,X^5$
	Over 6.6	$DF = 1.00$
14	To 6.9, incl	$DF = 14.86832 - 10.16374\,X + 3.32700\,X^2 - 0.59480\,X^3 + 0.05639\,X^4 - 0.00221\,X^5$
	Over 6.9	$DF = 1.00$
16		$DF = 14.10267 - 7.94906\,X + 1.93841\,X^2 - 0.22357\,X^3 + 0.01084\,X^4 - 0.00010\,X^5$
18		$DF = 11.29531 - 4.46248\,X + 0.41286\,X^2 + 0.09097\,X^3 - 0.02034\,X^4 + 0.00110\,X^5$
20		$DF = 7.14752 + 0.35500\,X - 1.61359\,X^2 + 0.49403\,X^3 - 0.05879\,X^4 + 0.00251\,X^6$
24		$DF = 12.3738 - 4.50690\,X + 0.29009\,X^2 + 0.12299\,X^3 - 0.02325\,X^4 + 0.00117\,X^5$
28		$DF = 27.50991 - 20.45946\,X + 6.97580\,X^2 - 1.25184\,X^3 + 0.11543\,X^4 - 0.00433\,X^5$
32		$DF = 43.35623 - 35.34260\,X + 12.58238\,X^2 - 2.29821\,X^3 + 0.21196\,X^4 - 0.00785\,X^5$

where: X = DI_B in inches. (a) Max DI_B = 7.0 in.

Equations for Table 1a.9 distance hardness dividing factors for boron steels, mm

"J" distance (mm)	DI_B(a)	Dividing factor
3.0	To 62.5, incl	$DF = 1.36182 - 0.01119\,X + 0.00011\,X^2 + 0.000004\,X^3$
	Over 62.5	$DF = 1.00$
4.5	To 72.5, incl	$DF = 1.33728 - 0.00586\,X - 0.00001\,X^2 + 0.000004\,X^3$
	Over 72.5	$DF = 1.00$
6.0	To 90.0, incl	$DF = 6.69675 - 0.23288\,X + 0.00318\,X^2 - 0.00001\,X^3$
	Over 90.0	$DF = 1.00$
7.5	To 112.5, incl	$DF = 7.56134 - 0.22857\,X + 0.00265\,X^2 - 0.00001\,X^3$
	Over 112.5	$DF = 1.00$
9.0	To 120.0, incl	$DF = 8.54529 - 0.23608\,X + 0.00247\,X^2 - 0.00001\,X^3$
	Over 120.0	$DF = 1.00$
10.5	To 125.0, incl	$DF = 9.21746 - 0.23623\,X + 0.00228\,X^2 - 0.000007\,X^3$
	Over 125.0	$DF = 1.00$
12.0	To 137.5, incl	$DF = 9.06644 - 0.21390\,X + 0.00190\,X^2 - 0.000006\,X^3$
	Over 137.5	$DF = 1.00$
13.5	To 147.5, incl	$DF = 8.85704 - 0.19372\,X + 0.00160\,X^2 - 0.000004\,X^3$
	Over 147.5	$DF = 1.00$
15.0	To 150.0, incl	$DF = 8.87756 - 0.18513\,X + 0.00147\,X^2 - 0.000004\,X^3$
	Over 150.0	$DF = 1.00$
18.0	To 167.5, incl	$DF = 8.55223 - 0.15758\,X + 0.00112\,X^2 - 0.000003\,X^3$
	Over 167.5	$DF = 1.00$
21.0	To 170.0, incl	$DF = 9.46158 - 0.16538\,X + 0.00111\,X^2 - 0.000002\,X^3$
	Over 170.0	
24.0		$DF = 9.97104 - 0.16786\,X + 0.00108\,X^2 - 0.000002\,X^3$
27.0		$DF = 10.73723 - 0.18018\,X + 0.00116\,X^2 - 0.000002\,X^3$
33.0		$DF = 11.57108 - 0.18965\,X + 0.00120\,X^2 - 0.000003\,X^3$
39.0		$DF = 12.80192 - 0.21151\,X + 0.00135\,X^2 - 0.000003\,X^3$
45.0		$DF = 15.29826 - 0.26554\,X + 0.00176\,X^2 - 0.000004\,X^3$
51.0		$DF = 16.05632 - 0.27682\,X + 0.00184\,X^2 - 0.000004\,X^3$

where: $X = DI_B$ in millimeters. (a) Max $DI_B = 177.5$ mm.

Appendix 1b.

Factors for calculating Di for steels as given in the ASTM standard A255-67. (From 1984 Annual Book of ASTM Standards, Vol 0.1.05, American Society for Testing and Materials, Philadelphia (1984). Copyright ASTM. Reprinted with permission.)

Table 1b.1 Calculation of ideal critical diameter

Percent of alloys	Base hardenability characteristic due to carbon and grain size — Grain size				Percent of alloys	Base hardenability characteristic due to carbon and grain size — Grain size			
	No. 5	No. 6	No. 7	No. 8		No. 5	No. 6	No. 7	No.8
0.01	...	...	...	...	0.46	0.428	0.392	0.358	0.325
0.02	...	...	...	...	0.47	0.433	0.397	0.362	0.330
0.03	...	...	...	...	0.48	0.438	0.402	0.366	0.334
0.04	...	...	...	...	0.49	0.443	0.407	0.372	0.338
0.05	...	...	...	...	0.50	0.448	0.412	0.377	0.343
0.06	...	...	...	...	0.51	0.452	0.417	0.382	0.348
0.07	0.021	...	...	...	0.52	0.456	0.422	0.387	0.352
0.08	0.050	0.012	...	...	0.53	0.461	0.427	0.391	0.356
0.09	0.076	0.038	0.005	...	0.54	0.465	0.431	0.396	0.360
0.10	0.101	0.062	0.029	...	0.55	0.469	0.435	0.400	0.364
0.11	0.120	0.084	0.052	0.017	0.56	0.473	0.439	0.404	0.367
0.12	0.138	0.103	0.071	0.037	0.57	0.477	0.443	0.408	0.371
0.13	0.155	0.121	0.088	0.056	0.58	0.481	0.447	0.412	0.375
0.14	0.170	0.136	0.104	0.070	0.59	0.485	0.450	0.416	0.378
0.15	0.184	0.150	0.119	0.084	0.60	0.489	0.454	0.419	0.382
0.16	0.198	0.164	0.133	0.097	0.61	0.493	0.458	0.423	0.386
0.17	0.211	0.176	0.146	0.110	0.62	0.497	0.461	0.427	0.389
0.18	0.224	0.188	0.158	0.122	0.63	0.500	0.464	0.430	0.393
0.19	0.236	0.199	0.169	0.134	0.64	0.504	0.467	0.433	0.396
0.20	0.247	0.210	0.179	0.146	0.65	0.507	0.470	0.436	0.400
0.21	0.258	0.221	0.188	0.156	0.66	0.510	0.473	0.439	0.403
0.22	0.268	0.231	0.198	0.166	0.67	0.513	0.476	0.442	0.407
0.23	0.278	0.241	0.208	0.176	0.68	0.517	0.479	0.446	0.410
0.24	0.288	0.250	0.217	0.184	0.69	0.520	0.482	0.449	0.413
0.25	0.297	0.260	0.225	0.193	0.70	0.523	0.485	0.452	0.415
0.26	0.306	0.269	0.233	0.201	0.71	0.526	0.488	0.455	0.418
0.27	0.314	0.277	0.241	0.209	0.72	0.530	0.491	0.458	0.422
0.28	0.322	0.285	0.250	0.216	0.73	0.533	0.494	0.461	0.425
0.29	0.330	0.292	0.259	0.223	0.74	0.536	0.497	0.464	0.428
0.30	0.337	0.299	0.267	0.230	0.75	0.539	0.500	0.467	0.431
0.31	0.343	0.306	0.274	0.238	0.76	0.542	0.502	0.470	0.433
0.32	0.350	0.313	0.281	0.246	0.77	0.544	0.505	0.473	0.436
0.33	0.356	0.320	0.288	0.253	0.78	0.547	0.508	0.476	0.439
0.34	0.362	0.327	0.295	0.260	0.79	0.549	0.511	0.479	0.441
0.35	0.368	0.333	0.301	0.266	0.80	0.551	0.513	0.481	0.444
0.36	0.374	0.339	0.306	0.272	0.81	0.554	0.516	0.484	0.447
0.37	0.380	0.345	0.312	0.278	0.82	0.556	0.519	0.487	0.450
0.38	0.386	0.351	0.318	0.284	0.83	0.559	0.521	0.490	0.453
0.39	0.392	0.357	0.324	0.290	0.84	0.561	0.524	0.492	0.456
0.40	0.398	0.362	0.329	0.296	0.85	0.563	0.526	0.494	0.458
0.41	0.403	0.368	0.334	0.301	0.86	0.566	0.529	0.497	0.461
0.42	0.408	0.373	0.339	0.306	0.87	0.568	0.531	0.500	0.464
0.43	0.413	0.378	0.344	0.310	0.88	0.571	0.534	0.502	0.467
0.44	0.418	0.383	0.349	0.315	0.89	0.573	0.537	0.504	0.469
0.45	0.423	0.387	0.351	0.320	0.90	0.574	0.539	0.507	0.471

Table 1b.2 Conversion to ideal critical diameter D.I. with example

Conversion of the sum of hardenability characteristics into the ideal critical diameter (D.I.).

Sum	D.I., in.	Sum	D.I., in.	Sum	D.I., in.	Sum	D.I., in.
0.740	0.55	1.312	2.05	1.550	3.55	1.703	5.05
0.778	0.60	1.322	2.10	1.556	3.60	1.708	5.10
0.813	0.65	1.332	2.15	1.562	3.65	1.712	5.15
0.845	0.70	1.342	2.20	1.568	3.70	1.716	5.20
0.875	0.75	1.352	2.25	1.574	3.75	1.720	5.25
0.903	0.80	1.362	2.30	1.580	3.80	1.724	5.30
0.929	0.85	1.371	2.35	1.585	3.85	1.728	5.35
0.954	0.90	1.380	2.40	1.591	3.90	1.732	5.40
0.978	0.95	1.389	2.45	1.597	3.95	1.736	5.45
1.000	1.00	1.398	2.50	1.602	4.00	1.740	5.50
1.021	1.05	1.407	2.55	1.607	4.05	1.744	5.55
1.041	1.10	1.415	2.60	1.613	4.10	1.748	5.60
1.060	1.15	1.423	2.65	1.618	4.15	1.752	5.65
1.079	1.20	1.431	2.70	1.623	4.20	1.756	5.70
1.097	1.25	1.439	2.75	1.628	4.25	1.760	5.75
1.114	1.30	1.447	2.80	1.633	4.30	1.763	5.80
1.130	1.35	1.455	2.85	1.638	4.35	1.767	5.85
1.146	1.40	1.462	2.90	1.643	4.40	1.771	5.90
1.161	1.45	1.470	2.95	1.648	4.45	1.775	5.95
1.176	1.50	1.477	3.00	1.653	4.50	1.778	6.00
1.190	1.55	1.484	3.05	1.658	4.55	1.785	6.10
1.204	1.60	1.491	3.10	1.663	4.60	1.792	6.20
1.217	1.65	1.498	3.15	1.667	4.65	1.799	6.30
1.230	1.70	1.505	3.20	1.672	4.70	1.806	6.40
1.243	1.75	1.512	3.25	1.677	4.75	1.813	6.50
1.255	1.80	1.519	3.30	1.681	4.80	1.820	6.60
1.267	1.85	1.525	3.35	1.686	4.85	1.826	6.70
1.279	1.90	1.531	3.40	1.690	4.90	1.833	6.80
1.290	1.95	1.538	3.45	1.695	4.95	1.839	6.90
1.301	2.00	1.544	3.50	1.699	5.00	1.845	7.00

Example

To calculate the ideal critical diameter of AISI 8740 Steel having No. 7 grain size and of the following composition:

Analysis	Hardenability characteristics
0.40 percent carbon (No. 7 grain size)	0.329
0.85 percent manganese	0.584
0.30 percent silicon	0.083
0.55 percent nickel	0.079
0.50 percent chromium	0.318
0.25 percent molybdenum	0.244
0.010 percent phosphorus	0.011
0.030 percent sulfur	−0.009
Sum of hardenability characteristics	1.639

Ideal critical diameter D.I. = 4.35 in.

Appendix 2.

Common units for converting from the English to the Metric (SI) System. (Reproduced with permission from 1977 Metal Progress Databook, American Society for Metals, Metals Park, OH (1977))

The International System of Units (SI) is a modernized version of the metric system. It is built upon seven base units and two supplementary units. Derived units are related to base and supplementary units for formulas in the right-hand column. Symbols for units with specific names are given in parentheses. The information supplied in this Data Sheet, adapted from the revised *Metric Practice Guide*, Standard ASTM E380, includes a select list of factors for converting customary English units to SI units.

Metric units and conversion factors

Quantity	Unit	Formula
Base units		
length	metre (m)	...
mass	kilogram (kg)	...
time	second (s)	...
electric current	ampere (A)	...
thermodynamic temperature	kelvin (K)	...
amount of substance	mole (mol)	...
luminous intensity	candela (cd)	...
Supplementary units		
plane angle	radian (rad)	...
solid angle	steradian (sr)	...
Derived units		
acceleration	metre per second squared	m/s^2
activity (of a radioactive source)	disintegration per second	(disinte-gration)/s
angular acceleration	radian per second squared	rad/s^2
angular velocity	radian per second	rad/s
area	square metre	m^2
density	kilogram per cubic metre	kg/m^3
electric capacitance	farad (F)	$A \cdot s/V$
electric conductance	siemens (S)	A/V
electric field strength	volt per metre	V/m
electric inductance	henry (H)	$V \cdot s/A$
electric potential difference	volt (V)	W/A
electric resistance	ohm (Ω)	V/A
electromotive force	volt (V)	W/A
energy	joule (J)	$N \cdot m$
entropy	joule per kelvin	J/K
force	newton (N)	$kg \cdot m/s^2$
frequency	hertz (Hz)	(cycle)/s
illuminance	lux (lx)	lm/m^2
luminance	candela per square metre	cd/m^2
luminous flux	lumen (lm)	$cd \cdot sr$
magnetic field strength	ampere per metre	A/m
magnetic flux	weber (Wb)	$V \cdot s$
magnetic flux density	tesla (T)	Wb/m^2
magnetomotive force	ampere (A)	...
power	watt (W)	J/s
pressure	pascal (Pa)	N/m^2
quantity of electricity	coulomb (C)	$A \cdot s$
quantity of heat	joule (J)	$N \cdot m$
radiant intensity	watt per steradian	W/sr
specific heat	joule per kilogram-kelvin	$J/kg \cdot K$
stress	pascal (Pa)	N/m^2
thermal conductivity	watt per metre-kelvin	$W/m \cdot K$
velocity	metre per second	m/s
viscosity, dynamic	pascal-second	$Pa \cdot s$
viscosity, kinematic	square metre per second	m^2/s
voltage	volt (V)	W/A
volume	cubic metre	m^3
wavenumber	reciprocal metre	(wave)/m
work	joule (J)	$N \cdot m$

Source: *Metal Progress Databook*, American Society for Metals (1977)

Metric conversion factors

To convert from	To	Multiply by
atmosphere (760 mm Hg)	Pa	$1.013\ 25 \times 10^3$
Btu (International Table)	J	$1.055\ 056 \times 10^3$
Btu (International Table)/hour	W	$2.930\ 711 \times 10^{-1}$

Metric conversion factors

To convert from	To	Multiply by
calorie (International Table)	J	$4.186\ 800(a)$
centipoise	$Pa \cdot s$	$1.000\ 000(a) \times 10^{-3}$
centistoke	m^2/s	$1.000\ 000(a) \times 10^{-6}$
circular mil	m^2	$5.067\ 075 \times 10^{-10}$
degree Fahrenheit	°C	$tC = (tF - 32)/1.8$
foot	m	$3.048\ 000(a) \times 10^{-1}$
foot^2	m^2	$9.290\ 304(a) \times 10^{-2}$
foot^3	m^3	$2.831\ 685 \times 10^{-2}$
foot-pound-force	J	$1.355\ 818$
foot-pound-force/minute	W	$2.259\ 697 \times 10^{-2}$
foot/second^2	m/s^2	$3.048\ 000(a) \times 10^{-1}$
gallon (U.S. liquid)	m^3	$3.785\ 412 \times 10^{-3}$
horsepower (electric)	W	$7.460\ 000(a) \times 10^2$
inch	m	$2.540\ 000(a) \times 10^{-2}$
inch^2	m^2	$6.451\ 600(a) \times 10^{-4}$
inch^3	m^3	$1.638\ 706 \times 10^{-5}$
inch of mercury (60 F)	Pa	$3.376\ 85 \times 10^3$
inch of water (60 F)	Pa	$2.488\ 4 \times 10^2$
kilogram-force/centimetre^2	Pa	$9.806\ 650(a) \times 10^4$
kip (1000 lbf)	N	$4.448\ 222 \times 10^3$
kip/inch^2 (ksi)	Pa	$6.894\ 757 \times 10^6$
ounce (U.S. fluid)	m^3	$2.957\ 353 \times 10^{-5}$
ounce-force (avoirdupois)	N	$2.780\ 139 \times 10^{-1}$
ounce-mass (avoirdupois)	kg	$2.834\ 952 \times 10^{-2}$
ounce-mass/ft^2	kg/m^2	$3.051\ 52 \times 10^{-1}$
ounce-mass/yard^2	kg/m^2	$3.390\ 575 \times 10^{-2}$
pint (U.S. liquid)	m^3	$4.731\ 765 \times 10^{-4}$
pound-force (lbf avoirdupois)	N	$4.448\ 222$
pound-mass (lbm avoirdupois)	kg	$4.535\ 924 \times 10^{-1}$
pound-force/inch^2 (psi)	Pa	$6.894\ 757 \times 10^3$
pound-mass/inch^3	kg/m^3	$2.767\ 990 \times 10^4$
pound-mass/foot^3	kg/m^3	$1.601\ 846 \times 10$
quart (U.S. liquid)	m^3	$9.463\ 529 \times 10^{-4}$
ton (short, 2000 lbm)	kg	$9.071\ 847 \times 10^2$
torr (mm-Hg)	Pa	$1.333\ 22 \times 10^2$
watt-hour	J	$3.600\ 000(a) \times 10^3$
yard	m	$9.144\ 000(a) \times 10^{-1}$
yard^2	m^2	$8.361\ 274 \times 10^{-1}$
yard^3	m^3	$7.645\ 549 \times 10^{-1}$

(a) Exact. Source: *Metal Progress Databook*, American Society for Metals (1977)

Multiplication factors

Multiplication factors	Prefix	SI symbol
$1\ 000\ 000\ 000\ 000 = 10^{12}$	tera	T
$1\ 000\ 000\ 000 = 10^9$	giga	G
$1\ 000\ 000 = 10^6$	mega	M
$1\ 000 = 10^3$	kilo	k
$100 = 10^2$	hecto(a)	h
$10 = 10^1$	deka(a)	da
$0.1 = 10^{-1}$	deci(a)	d
$0.01 = 10^{-2}$	centi(a)	c
$0.001 = 10^{-3}$	milli	m
$0.000\ 001 = 10^{-6}$	micro	μ
$0.000\ 000\ 001 = 10^{-9}$	nano	n
$0.000\ 000\ 000\ 001 = 10^{-12}$	pico	p
$0.000\ 000\ 000\ 000\ 01 = 10^{-14}$	femto	f
$0.000\ 000\ 000\ 000\ 000\ 001 = 10^{-18}$	atto	a

(a) To be avoided where possible. Source: *Metal Progress Databook*, American Society for Metals

Appendix 3.
Metric energy conversions. (From same source as Appendix 2)

The middle column of figures (in bold-face type) contains the reading (in J or ft-lb) to be converted. If converting from ft-lb to J, read the J equivalent in the column headed "J." If converting from J to ft-lb, read the equivalent in the column headed "ft-lb." 1 ft-lb = 1.355818 J.

ft-lb		J	ft-lb		J	ft-lb		J
0.7376	1	1.3558	37.6157	51	69.1467	77.4440	105	142.3609
1.4751	2	2.7116	38.3532	52	70.5025	81.1318	110	149.1400
2.2127	3	4.0675	39.0908	53	71.8583	84.8196	115	155.9191
2.9502	4	5.4233	39.8284	54	73.2142	88.5075	120	162.6982
3.6878	5	6.7791	40.5659	55	74.5700	92.1953	125	169.4772
4.4254	6	8.1349	41.3035	56	75.9258	95.8831	130	176.2563
5.1629	7	9.4907	42.0410	57	77.2816	99.5709	135	183.0354
5.9005	8	10.8465	42.7786	58	78.6374	103.2587	140	189.8145
6.6381	9	12.2024	43.5162	59	79.9933	106.9465	145	196.5936
7.3756	10	13.5582	44.2537	60	81.3491	110.6343	150	203.3727
8.1132	11	14.9140	44.9913	61	82.7049	114.3221	155	210.1518
8.8507	12	16.2698	45.7288	62	84.0607	118.0099	160	216.9308
9.5883	13	17.6256	46.4664	63	85.4165	121.6977	165	223.7099
10.3259	14	18.9815	47.2040	64	86.7723	125.3856	170	230.4890
11.0634	15	20.3373	47.9415	65	88.1282	129.0734	175	237.2681
11.8010	16	21.6931	48.6791	66	89.4840	132.7612	180	244.0472
12.5386	17	23.0489	49.4167	67	90.8398	136.4490	185	250.8263
13.2761	18	24.4047	50.1542	68	92.1956	140.1368	190	257.6054
14.0137	19	25.7605	50.8918	69	93.5514	143.8246	195	264.3845
14.7512	20	27.1164	51.6293	70	94.9073	147.5124	200	271.1636
15.4888	21	28.4722	52.3669	71	96.2631	154.8880	210	284.7218
16.2264	22	29.8280	53.1045	72	97.6189	162.2637	220	298.2799
16.9639	23	31.1838	53.8420	73	98.9747	169.6393	230	311.8381
17.7015	24	32.5396	54.5796	74	100.3305	177.0149	240	325.3963
18.4390	25	33.8954	55.3172	75	101.6863	184.3905	250	338.9545
19.1766	26	35.2513	56.0547	76	103.0422	191.7661	260	352.5126
19.9142	27	36.6071	56.7923	77	104.3980	199.1418	270	366.0708
20.6517	28	37.9629	57.5298	78	105.7538	206.5174	280	379.6290
21.3893	29	39.3187	58.2674	79	107.1096	213.8930	290	393.1872
22.1269	30	40.6745	59.0050	80	108.4654	221.2686	300	406.7454
22.8644	31	42.0304	59.7425	81	109.8212	228.6442	310	420.3036
23.6020	32	43.3862	60.4801	82	111.1771	236.0199	320	433.8617
24.3395	33	44.7420	61.2177	83	112.5329	243.3955	330	447.4199
25.0771	34	46.0978	61.9552	84	113.8887	250.7711	340	460.9781
25.8147	35	47.4536	62.6928	85	115.2445	258.1467	350	474.5363
26.5522	36	48.8094	63.4303	86	116.6003	265.5224	360	488.0944
27.2898	37	50.1653	64.1679	87	117.9562	272.8980	370	501.6526
28.0274	38	51.5211	64.9055	88	119.3120	280.2736	380	515.2108
28.7649	39	52.8769	65.6430	89	120.6678	287.6492	390	528.7690
29.5025	40	54.2327	66.3806	90	122.0236	295.0248	400	542.3272
30.2400	41	55.5885	67.1182	91	123.3794	302.4005	410	555.8854
30.9776	42	56.9444	67.8557	92	124.7452	309.7761	420	569.4435
31.7152	43	58.3002	68.5933	93	126.0911	317.1517	430	583.0017
32.4527	44	59.6560	69.3308	94	127.4469	324.4273	440	596.5599
33.1903	45	61.0118	70.0684	95	128.8027	331.9029	450	610.1181
33.9279	46	62.3676	70.8060	96	130.1585	339.2786	460	623.6762
34.6654	47	63.7234	71.5435	97	131.5143	346.6542	470	637.2344
35.4030	48	65.0793	72.2811	98	132.8702	354.0298	480	650.7926
36.1405	49	66.4351	73.0186	99	134.2260	361.4054	490	664.3508
36.8781	50	67.7909	73.7562	100	135.5818	368.7811	500	677.9090

Appendix 4.

Metric stress or pressure conversions. (From same source as Appendix 2)

The middle column (in bold-faced type) contains the reading (MPa or ksi) to be converted. If converting from ksi to MPa, read the MPa equivalent in the column headed "MPa." If converting from MPa to ksi, read the ksi equivalent in the column headed "ksi." 1 ksi = 6.894757 Mpa. 1 psi = 6.894757 kPa.

ksi		MPa	ksi		MPa	ksi		MPa	ksi		MPa
0.14504	1	6.895	9.8626	68	468.84	65.267	450	3102.6	179.85	1240	...
0.29008	2	13.790	10.008	69	475.74	66.717	460	3171.6	182.75	1260	...
0.43511	3	20.684	10.153	70	482.63	66.168	470	3240.5	185.65	1280	...
0.58015	4	27.579	10.298	71	489.53	69.618	480	3309.5	188.55	1300	...
0.72519	5	34.474	10.443	72	496.42	71.068	490	3378.4	191.45	1320	...
0.87023	6	41.369	10.588	73	503.32	72.519	500	3447.4	194.35	1340	...
1.0153	7	48.263	10.733	74	510.21	73.969	510	...	197.25	1360	...
1.1603	8	55.158	10.878	75	517.11	75.420	520	...	200.15	1380	...
1.3053	9	62.053	11.023	76	524.00	76.870	530	...	203.05	1400	...
1.4504	10	68.948	11.168	77	530.90	89.320	540	...	205.95	1420	...
1.5954	11	75.842	11.313	78	537.79	79.771	550	...	208.85	1440	...
1.7405	12	82.737	11.458	79	544.69	81.221	560	...	211.76	1460	...
1.8855	13	89.632	11.603	80	551.58	82.672	570	...	214.66	1480	...
2.0305	14	96.527	11.748	81	558.48	84.122	580	...	217.56	1500	...
2.1756	15	103.42	11.893	82	565.87	85.572	590	...	220.46	1520	...
2.3206	16	110.32	12.038	83	572.26	87.023	600	...	223.36	1540	...
2.4656	17	117.21	12.183	84	579.16	88.473	610	...	226.26	1560	...
2.6107	18	124.11	12.328	85	586.05	89.923	620	...	229.16	1580	...
2.7557	19	131.00	12.473	86	592.95	91.374	630	...	232.06	1600	...
2.9008	20	137.90	12.618	87	599.84	92.824	640	...	234.96	1620	...
3.0458	21	144.79	12.763	88	606.74	94.275	650	...	237.86	1640	...
3.1908	22	151.68	12.909	89	613.63	95.725	660	...	240.76	1660	...
3.3359	23	158.58	13.053	90	620.53	97.175	670	...	243.66	1680	...
3.4809	24	165.47	13.198	91	627.42	98.626	680	...	246.56	1700	...
3.6259	25	172.37	13.343	92	634.32	100.08	690	...	249.46	1720	...
3.7710	26	179.26	13.589	93	641.21	101.53	700	...	252.37	1740	...
3.9160	27	186.16	13.634	94	648.11	102.98	710	...	255.27	1760	...
4.0611	28	193.05	13.779	95	655.00	104.43	720	...	258.17	1780	...
4.2061	29	199.95	13.924	96	661.90	105.88	730	...	261.07	1800	...
4.3511	30	206.84	14.069	97	668.79	107.33	740	...	263.97	1820	...
4.4962	31	213.74	14.214	98	675.69	108.78	750	...	266.87	1840	...
4.6412	32	220.63	14.359	99	682.58	110.23	760	...	269.77	1860	...
4.7862	33	227.53	14.504	100	689.48	111.68	770	...	272.67	1880	...
4.9313	34	234.42	15.954	110	758.42	113.13	780	...	275.57	1900	...
5.0763	35	241.32	17.405	120	827.37	114.58	790	...	278.47	1920	...
5.2214	36	248.21	18.855	130	896.32	116.03	800	...	281.37	1940	...
5.3664	37	255.11	20.305	140	965.27	117.48	810	...	284.27	1960	...
5.5114	38	262.00	21.756	150	1034.2	118.93	820	...	287.17	1980	...
5.6565	39	268.90	23.206	160	1103.2	120.38	830	...	290.08	2000	...
5.8015	40	275.79	24.656	170	1172.1	121.83	840	...	292.98	2020	...
5.9465	41	282.69	26.107	180	1241.1	123.28	850	...	295.88	2040	...
6.0916	42	289.58	27.557	190	1310.0	124.73	860	...	298.78	2060	...
6.2366	43	296.47	29.008	200	1379.0	126.18	870	...	301.68	2080	...
6.3817	44	303.37	30.458	210	1447.9	127.63	880	...	304.58	2100	...
6.5267	45	310.26	31.908	220	1516.8	129.08	890	...	307.48	2120	...
6.6717	46	317.16	33.359	230	1585.8	130.53	900	...	310.38	2140	...
6.8168	47	324.05	34.809	240	1654.7	131.98	910	...	313.28	2160	...
6.9618	48	330.95	36.259	250	1723.7	133.43	920	...	316.18	2180	...
7.1068	49	337.84	37.710	260	1792.6	134.89	930	...	319.08	2200	...
7.2519	50	344.74	39.160	270	1861.6	136.34	940	...	321.98	2220	...
7.3969	51	351.63	40.611	280	1930.5	137.79	950	...	324.88	2240	...
7.5420	52	358.53	42.061	290	1999.5	139.24	960	...	327.79	2260	...
7.6870	53	365.42	43.511	300	2068.4	140.69	970	...	330.69	2280	...
6.8320	54	372.32	44.962	310	2137.4	142.14	980	...	333.59	2300	...
7.9771	55	379.21	46.412	320	2206.3	143.59	990	...	336.49	2320	...
8.1221	56	386.11	47.862	330	2275.3	145.04	1000	...	339.39	2340	...
8.2672	57	393.00	49.313	340	2344.2	147.94	1020	...	342.29	2360	...
8.4122	58	399.90	50.763	350	2413.2	150.84	1040	...	345.19	2380	...
8.5572	59	406.79	52.214	360	2482.1	153.74	1060	...	348.09	2400	...
8.7023	60	413.69	53.664	370	2551.1	156.64	1080	...	350.99	2420	...
8.8473	61	420.58	55.114	380	2620.0	159.64	1100	...	353.89	2440	...
8.9923	62	427.47	56.565	390	2689.0	162.44	1120	...	356.79	2460	...
9.1374	63	434.87	58.015	400	2757.9	165.34	1140	...	359.69	2480	...
9.2824	64	441.26	59.465	410	2826.9	168.24	1160	...	362.59	2500	...
9.4275	65	448.16	60.916	420	2895.8	171.14	1180	...			
9.5725	66	455.05	62.386	430	2964.7	171.05	1200	...			
9.7175	67	451.95	63.817	440	3033.7	176.95	1220	...			

Appendix 5.

Temperature conversions. (From same source as Appendix 2)

Look up temperature to be converted in middle column. If in degrees Centigrade, read Fahrenheit equivalent in right-hand column; if in Fahrenheit degrees, read Centigrade equivalent in left-hand column.

		−459.4 to 0						0 to 100			
°C	°F		°C	°F		°C	°F		°C		°F
−273.0	**−459.4**	...	−73.3	**−100**	−148.0		−17.8	**0**	32.0	10.0	**50**	122.0
−267.8	**−450**	...	−72.2	**−98**	−144.4		−17.2	**1**	33.8	10.6	**51**	123.8
−262.2	**−440**	...	−71.1	**−96**	−140.8		−16.7	**2**	35.6	11.1	**52**	125.6
−256.7	**−430**	...	−70.0	**−94**	−137.2		−16.1	**3**	37.4	11.7	**53**	127.4
−251.1	**−420**	...	−68.9	**−92**	−133.6		−15.6	**4**	39.2	12.2	**54**	129.2
−245.6	**−410**	...	−67.8	**−90**	−130.0		−15.0	**5**	41.0	12.8	**55**	131.0
−240.0	**−400**	...	−66.7	**−88**	−126.4		−14.4	**6**	42.8	13.3	**56**	132.8
−234.4	**−390**	...	−65.6	**−86**	−122.8		−13.9	**7**	44.6	13.9	**57**	134.6
−228.9	**−380**	...	−64.4	**−84**	−119.2		−13.3	**8**	46.4	14.4	**58**	136.4
−223.3	**−370**	...	−63.3	**−82**	−115.6		−12.8	**9**	48.2	15.0	**59**	138.2
−217.8	**−360**	...	−62.2	**−80**	−112.0		−12.2	**10**	50.0	15.6	**60**	140.0
−212.2	**−350**	...	−61.1	**−78**	−108.4		−11.7	**11**	51.8	16.1	**61**	141.8
−206.7	**−340**	...	−60.0	**−76**	−104.8		−11.1	**12**	53.6	16.7	**62**	143.6
−201.1	**−330**	...	−58.9	**−74**	−101.2		−10.6	**13**	55.4	17.2	**63**	145.4
−195.6	**−320**	...	−57.8	**−72**	−97.6		−10.0	**14**	57.2	17.8	**64**	147.2
−190.0	**−310**	...	−56.7	**−70**	−94.0		−9.4	**15**	59.0	18.3	**65**	149.0
−184.4	**−300**	...	−55.6	**−68**	−90.4		−8.9	**16**	60.8	18.9	**66**	150.8
−178.9	**−290**	...	−54.4	**−66**	−86.8		−8.3	**17**	62.6	19.4	**67**	152.6
−173.3	**−280**		−53.3	**−64**	−83.2		−7.8	**18**	64.4	20.0	**68**	154.4
−169.5	**−273**	−459.4	−52.2	**−62**	−79.6		−7.2	**19**	66.2	20.6	**69**	156.2
−167.8	**−270**	−454.0	−51.1	**−60**	−76.0		−6.7	**20**	68.0	21.1	**70**	158.0
−162.2	**−260**	−436.0	−50.0	**−58**	−72.4		−6.1	**21**	69.8	21.7	**71**	159.8
−156.7	**−250**	−418.0	−48.9	**−56**	−68.8		−5.6	**22**	71.6	22.2	**72**	161.6
−151.1	**−240**	−400.0	−47.8	**−54**	−65.2		−5.0	**23**	73.4	22.8	**73**	163.4
−145.6	**−230**	−382.0	−46.7	**−52**	−61.6		−4.4	**24**	75.2	23.3	**74**	165.2
−142.8	**−225**	−373.0	−45.6	**−50**	−58.0		−3.9	**25**	77.0	23.9	**75**	167.0
−140.0	**−220**	−364.0	−44.4	**−48**	−54.4		−3.3	**26**	78.8	24.4	**76**	168.8
−137.2	**−215**	−355.0	−43.3	**−46**	−50.8		−2.8	**27**	80.6	25.0	**77**	170.6
−134.4	**−210**	−346.0	−42.2	**−44**	−47.2		−2.2	**28**	82.4	25.6	**78**	172.4
−131.7	**−205**	−337.0	−41.1	**−42**	−43.6		−1.7	**29**	84.2	26.1	**79**	174.2
−128.9	**−200**	−328.0	−40.0	**−40**	−40.0		−1.1	**30**	86.0	26.7	**80**	176.0
−126.1	**−195**	−319.0	−38.9	**−38**	−36.4		−.6	**31**	87.8	27.2	**81**	177.8
−123.3	**−190**	−310.0	−37.8	**−36**	−32.8		0.0	**32**	89.6	27.8	**82**	179.6
−121.0	**−185**	−301.0	−36.7	**−34**	−29.2		.6	**33**	91.4	28.3	**83**	181.4
−117.8	**−180**	−292.0	−35.6	**−32**	−25.6		1.1	**34**	92.3	28.9	**84**	183.2
−115.0	**−175**	−283.0	−34.4	**−30**	−22.0		1.7	**35**	95.0	29.4	**85**	185.0
−112.2	**−170**	−274.0	−33.3	**−28**	−18.4		2.2	**36**	96.8	30.0	**86**	186.8
−109.5	**−165**	−265.0	−32.2	**−26**	−14.8		2.8	**37**	98.6	30.6	**87**	188.6
−106.7	**−160**	−256.0	−31.1	**−24**	−11.2		3.3	**38**	100.4	31.1	**88**	190.4
−103.9	**−155**	−247.0	−30.0	**−22**	−7.6		3.9	**39**	102.2	31.7	**89**	192.2
−101.1	**−150**	−238.0	−28.9	**−20**	−4.0		4.4	**40**	104.0	32.2	**90**	194.0
−98.3	**−145**	−229.0	−27.8	**−18**	−0.4		5.0	**41**	105.8	32.8	**91**	195.8
−95.6	**−140**	−220.0	−26.7	**−16**	+3.2		5.6	**42**	107.6	33.3	**92**	197.6
−92.8	**−135**	−211.0	−25.6	**−14**	+6.8		6.1	**43**	109.4	33.9	**93**	199.4
−90.0	**−130**	−202.0	−24.4	**−12**	+10.4		6.7	**44**	111.2	34.4	**94**	201.2
−87.2	**−125**	−193.0	−23.3	**−10**	+14.0		7.2	**45**	113.0	35.0	**95**	203.0
−84.4	**−120**	−184.0	−22.2	**−8**	+17.6		7.8	**46**	114.8	35.6	**96**	204.8
−82.0	**−115**	−175.0	−21.1	**−6**	+21.2		8.3	**47**	116.6	36.1	**97**	206.6
−78.9	**−110**	−166.0	−20.0	**−4**	+24.8		8.9	**48**	118.4	36.7	**98**	208.4
−75.8	**−105**	−157.0	−18.9	**−2**	+28.4		9.4	**49**	120.2	37.2	**99**	210.2
−73.3	**−100**	−148.0	−17.8	**0**	+32.0		10.0	**50**	122.0	37.8	**100**	212.0

(continued)

(Continued)

					100 to 1000						
°C		°F	°C		°F	°C		°F	°C		°F
39	**102**	216	94	**202**	396	221	**430**	806	357	**675**	1247
40	**104**	219	96	**204**	399	224	**435**	815	360	**680**	1256
41	**106**	223	97	**206**	403	227	**440**	824	363	**685**	1265
42	**108**	226	98	**208**	406	229	**445**	833	366	**690**	1274
43	**110**	230	99	**210**	410	232	**450**	842	368	**695**	1283
44	**112**	234	100	**212**	414	235	**455**	851	371	**700**	1292
46	**114**	237	102	**215**	419	238	**460**	860	374	**705**	1301
47	**116**	241	104	**220**	428	241	**465**	869	377	**710**	1310
48	**118**	244	107	**225**	437	243	**470**	878	379	**715**	1319
49	**120**	248	110	**230**	446	246	**475**	887	382	**720**	1328
50	**122**	252	113	**235**	455	249	**480**	896	385	**725**	1337
51	**124**	255	116	**240**	464	252	**485**	905	388	**730**	1346
52	**126**	259	119	**245**	473	254	**490**	914	391	**735**	1355
53	**128**	262	121	**250**	482	257	**495**	923	393	**740**	1364
54	**130**	266	124	**255**	491	260	**500**	932	396	**745**	1373
56	**132**	270	127	**260**	500	263	**505**	941	399	**750**	1382
57	**134**	273	130	**265**	509	266	**510**	950	402	**755**	1391
58	**136**	277	132	**270**	518	268	**515**	959	404	**760**	1400
59	**138**	280	135	**275**	527	271	**520**	968	407	**765**	1409
60	**140**	284	138	**280**	536	274	**525**	977	410	**770**	1418
61	**142**	288	141	**285**	545	277	**530**	986	413	**775**	1427
62	**144**	291	143	**290**	554	279	**535**	995	416	**780**	1436
63	**146**	295	146	**295**	563	282	**540**	1004	418	**785**	1445
64	**148**	298	149	**300**	572	285	**545**	1013	421	**790**	1454
66	**150**	302	152	**305**	581	288	**550**	1022	424	**795**	1463
67	**152**	306	154	**310**	590	291	**555**	1031	427	**800**	1472
68	**154**	309	157	**315**	599	293	**560**	1040	429	**805**	1481
69	**156**	313	160	**320**	608	296	**565**	1049	432	**810**	1490
70	**158**	316	163	**325**	617	299	**570**	1058	435	**815**	1499
71	**160**	320	166	**330**	626	302	**575**	1067	438	**820**	1508
72	**162**	324	169	**335**	635	304	**580**	1076	441	**825**	1517
73	**164**	327	171	**340**	644	307	**585**	1085	443	**830**	1526
74	**166**	331	174	**345**	653	310	**590**	1094	446	**835**	1535
76	**168**	334	177	**350**	662	313	**595**	1103	449	**840**	1544
77	**170**	338	179	**355**	671	316	**600**	1112	454	**850**	1562
78	**172**	342	182	**360**	680	319	**605**	1121	460	**860**	1580
79	**174**	345	185	**365**	689	321	**610**	1130	466	**870**	1598
80	**176**	349	188	**370**	698	324	**615**	1139	471	**880**	1616
81	**178**	352	191	**375**	707	327	**620**	1148	477	**890**	1624
82	**180**	356	193	**380**	716	330	**625**	1157	482	**900**	1652
83	**182**	360	196	**385**	725	332	**630**	1166	488	**910**	1670
84	**184**	363	199	**390**	734	335	**635**	1175	493	**920**	1688
86	**186**	367	202	**395**	743	338	**640**	1184	499	**930**	1706
87	**188**	370	204	**400**	752	341	**645**	1193	504	**940**	1724
88	**190**	374	207	**405**	761	343	**650**	1202	510	**950**	1742
89	**192**	378	210	**410**	770	346	**655**	1211	516	**960**	1760
90	**194**	381	213	**415**	779	349	**660**	1220	521	**970**	1778
91	**196**	385	216	**420**	788	352	**665**	1229	527	**980**	1796
92	**198**	388	219	**425**	797	354	**670**	1238	532	**990**	1814
93	**200**	392							538	**1000**	1832

(continued)

(Continued)

	1000 to 2000					2000 to 3000				
°C	°F	°C		°F		°C	°F	°C		°F
538	**1000**	1832	816	**1500**	2732	1093	**2000**	3632	1371	**2500**	4532
543	**1010**	1850	821	**1510**	2750	1099	**2010**	3650	1377	**2510**	4550
549	**1020**	1868	827	**1520**	2768	1104	**2020**	3668	1382	**2520**	4568
554	**1030**	1886	832	**1530**	2786	1110	**2030**	3686	1388	**2530**	4586
560	**1040**	1904	838	**1540**	2804	1116	**2040**	3704	1393	**2540**	4604
566	**1050**	1922	843	**1550**	2822	1121	**2050**	3722	1399	**2550**	4622
571	**1060**	1940	849	**1560**	2840	1127	**2060**	3740	1404	**2560**	4640
577	**1070**	1958	854	**1570**	2858	1132	**2070**	3758	1410	**2570**	4658
582	**1080**	1976	860	**1580**	2876	1138	**2080**	3776	1416	**2580**	4676
588	**1090**	1994	866	**1590**	2894	1143	**2090**	3794	1421	**2590**	4694
593	**1100**	2012	871	**1600**	2912	1149	**2100**	3812	1427	**2600**	4712
599	**1110**	2030	877	**1610**	2930	1154	**2110**	3830	1432	**2610**	4730
604	**1120**	2048	882	**1620**	2948	1160	**2120**	3848	1438	**2620**	4748
610	**1130**	2066	888	**1630**	2966	1166	**2130**	3866	1443	**2630**	4766
616	**1140**	2084	893	**1640**	2984	1171	**2140**	3884	1449	**2640**	4784
621	**1150**	2102	899	**1650**	3002	1177	**2150**	3902	1454	**2650**	4802
627	**1160**	2120	904	**1660**	3020	1182	**2160**	3920	1460	**2660**	4820
632	**1170**	2138	910	**1670**	3038	1188	**2170**	3938	1466	**2670**	4838
638	**1180**	2156	916	**1680**	3056	1193	**2180**	3956	1471	**2680**	4856
643	**1190**	2174	921	**1690**	3074	1199	**2190**	3974	1477	**2690**	4874
649	**1200**	2192	927	**1700**	3092	1204	**2200**	3992	1482	**2700**	4892
654	**1210**	2210	932	**1710**	3110	1210	**2210**	4010	1488	**2710**	4910
660	**1220**	2228	938	**1720**	3128	1216	**2220**	4028	1493	**2720**	4928
666	**1230**	2246	943	**1730**	3146	1221	**2230**	4046	1499	**2730**	4946
671	**1240**	2264	949	**1740**	3164	1227	**2240**	4064	1504	**2740**	4964
677	**1250**	2282	954	**1750**	3182	1232	**2250**	4082	1510	**2750**	4982
682	**1260**	2300	960	**1760**	3200	1238	**2260**	4100	1516	**2760**	5000
688	**1270**	2318	966	**1770**	3218	1243	**2270**	4118	1521	**2770**	5018
693	**1280**	2336	971	**1780**	3236	1249	**2280**	4136	1527	**2780**	5036
699	**1290**	2354	977	**1790**	3254	1254	**2290**	4154	1532	**2790**	5054
704	**1300**	2372	982	**1800**	3272	1260	**2300**	4172	1538	**2800**	5072
710	**1310**	2390	988	**1810**	3290	1266	**2310**	4190	1543	**2810**	5090
716	**1320**	2408	993	**1820**	3308	1271	**2320**	4208	1549	**2820**	5108
721	**1330**	2426	999	**1830**	3326	1277	**2330**	4226	1554	**2830**	5126
727	**1340**	2444	1004	**1840**	3344	1282	**2340**	4244	1560	**2840**	5144
732	**1350**	2462	1010	**1850**	3362	1288	**2350**	4262	1566	**2850**	5162
738	**1360**	2480	1016	**1860**	3380	1293	**2360**	4280	1571	**2860**	5180
743	**1370**	2498	1021	**1870**	3398	1299	**2370**	4298	1577	**2870**	5198
749	**1380**	2516	1027	**1880**	3416	1304	**2380**	4316	1582	**2880**	5216
754	**1390**	2534	1032	**1890**	3434	1310	**2390**	4334	1588	**2890**	5234
760	**1400**	2552	1038	**1900**	3452	1316	**2400**	4352	1593	**2900**	5252
766	**1410**	2570	1043	**1910**	3470	1321	**2410**	4370	1599	**2910**	5270
771	**1420**	2588	1049	**1920**	3488	1327	**2420**	4388	1604	**2920**	5288
777	**1430**	2606	1054	**1930**	3506	1332	**2430**	4406	1610	**2930**	5306
782	**1440**	2624	1060	**1940**	3524	1338	**2440**	4424	1616	**2940**	5324
788	**1450**	2642	1066	**1950**	3542	1343	**2450**	4442	1621	**2950**	5342
793	**1460**	2660	1071	**1960**	3560	1349	**2460**	4460	1627	**2960**	5360
799	**1470**	2678	1077	**1970**	3578	1354	**2470**	4478	1632	**2970**	5378
804	**1480**	2696	1082	**1980**	3596	1360	**2480**	4496	1638	**2980**	5396
810	**1490**	2714	1088	**1990**	3614	1366	**2490**	4514	1643	**2990**	5414
816	**1500**	2782	1093	**2000**	3632	1371	**2500**	4532	1649	**3000**	5432

(continued)

(Continued)

	3000 to 4000					4000 to 5000			
°C	°F	°C	°F		°C	°F	°C		°F
1649	3000	5432	1927	3500	6332	2204	4000	7232	2482	4500	8132
1654	3010	5450	1932	3510	6350	2210	4010	7250	2488	4510	8150
1660	3020	5468	1938	3520	6368	2215	4020	7268	2493	4520	8168
1666	3030	5486	1943	3530	6386	2221	4030	7286	2499	4530	8186
1671	3040	5504	1949	3540	6404	2227	4040	7304	2504	4540	8204
1677	3050	5522	1954	3550	6422	2232	4050	7322	2510	4550	8222
1682	3060	5540	1960	3560	6440	2238	4060	7340	2515	4560	8240
1688	3070	5558	1965	3570	6458	2243	4070	7358	2521	4570	8258
1693	3080	5576	1971	3580	6476	2249	4080	7376	2527	4580	8276
1699	3090	3594	1977	3590	6494	2254	4090	7394	2532	4590	8294
1704	3100	5612	1982	3600	6512	2260	4100	7412	2538	4600	8312
1710	3110	5630	1988	3610	6530	2265	4110	7430	2543	4610	8330
1715	3120	5648	1993	3620	6548	2271	4120	7448	2549	4620	8348
1721	3130	5666	1999	3630	6566	2277	4130	7466	2554	4630	8366
1727	3140	5684	2004	3640	6584	2282	4140	7484	2560	4640	8384
1732	3150	5702	2010	3650	6602	2288	4150	7502	2565	4650	8402
1738	3160	5720	2015	3660	6620	2293	4160	7520	2571	4660	8420
1743	3170	5738	2021	3670	6638	2299	4170	7538	2577	4670	8438
1749	3180	5756	2027	3680	6656	2304	4180	7556	2582	4680	8456
1754	3190	5774	2032	3690	6674	2310	4190	7574	2588	4690	8474
1760	3200	5792	2038	3700	6692	2315	4200	7592	2593	4700	8492
1765	3210	5810	2043	3710	6710	2321	4210	7610	2599	4710	8510
1771	3220	5828	2049	3720	6728	2327	4220	7628	2604	4720	8528
1777	3230	5846	2054	3730	6746	2332	4230	7646	2610	4730	8546
1782	3240	5864	2060	3740	6764	2338	4240	7664	2615	4740	8564
1788	3250	5882	2065	3750	6782	2343	4250	7682	2621	4750	8582
1793	3260	5900	2071	3760	6800	2349	4260	7700	2627	4760	8600
1799	3270	5918	2077	3770	6818	2354	4270	7718	2632	4770	8618
1804	3280	5936	2082	3780	6836	2360	4280	7736	2638	4780	8636
1810	3290	5954	2088	3790	6854	2365	4290	7754	2643	4790	8654
1815	3300	5972	2093	3800	6872	2371	4300	7772	2649	4800	8672
1821	3310	5990	2099	3810	6890	2377	4310	7790	2654	4810	8690
1827	3320	6008	2104	3820	6908	2382	4320	7808	2660	4820	8708
1832	3330	6026	2110	3830	6926	2388	4330	7826	2665	4830	8726
1838	3340	6044	2115	3840	6944	2393	4340	7844	2671	4840	8744
1843	3350	6062	2121	3850	6962	2399	4350	7862	2677	4850	8762
1849	3360	6080	2127	3860	6980	2404	4360	7880	2682	4860	8780
1854	3370	6098	2132	3870	6998	2410	4370	7898	2688	4870	8798
1860	3380	6116	2138	3880	7016	2415	4380	7916	2693	4880	8816
1865	3390	6134	2143	3890	7034	2421	4390	7934	2699	4890	8834
1871	3400	6152	2149	3900	7052	2427	4400	7952	2704	4900	8852
1877	3410	6170	2154	3910	7070	2432	4410	7970	2710	4910	8870
1882	3420	6188	2160	3920	7088	2438	4420	7988	2715	4920	8888
1888	3430	6206	2165	3930	7106	2443	4430	8006	2721	4930	8906
1893	3440	6224	2171	3940	7124	2449	4440	8024	2727	4940	8924
1899	3450	6242	2177	3950	7142	2454	4450	8042	2732	4950	8942
1904	3460	6260	2182	3960	7160	2460	4460	8060	2738	4960	8960
1910	3470	6278	2188	3970	7178	2465	4470	8078	2743	4970	8978
1915	3480	6296	2193	3980	7196	2471	4480	8096	2749	4980	8996
1921	3490	6314	2199	3990	7214	2477	4490	8114	2754	4990	9014
1927	3500	6332	2204	4000	7232	2482	4500	8132	2760	5000	9032

Appendix 6.

AISI-SAE system of designations for steels. (From same source as Appendix 2)

Numerals and digits(a)	Type of steel and/or nominal alloy content
Carbon steels	
10xx	Plain carbon (Mn 1.00% max)
11xx	Resulfurized
12xx	Resulfurized and rephosphorized
15xx	Plain carbon (max Mn range— 1.00 to 1.65%)
Manganese steels	
13xx	Mn 1.75
Nickel steels	
23xx	Ni 3.50
25xx	Ni 5.00
Nickel-chromium steels	
31xx	Ni 1.25; Cr 0.65 and 0.80
32xx	Ni 1.75; Cr 1.07
33xx	Ni 3.50; Cr 1.50 and 1.57
34xx	Ni 3.00; Cr 0.77
Molybdenum steels	
40xx	Mo 0.20 and 0.25
44xx	Mo 0.40 and 0.52
Chromium-molybdenum steels	
41xx	Cr 0.50, 0.80 and 0.95; Mo 0.12, 0.20, 0.25 and 0.30

Numerals and digits(a)	Type of steel and/or nominal alloy content
Nickel-chromium-molybdenum steels	
43xx	Ni 1.82; Cr 0.50 and 0.80; Mo 0.25
43BVxx	Ni 1.82; Cr 0.50; Mo 0.12 and 0.25; V 0.03 min
47xx	Ni 1.05; Cr 0.45; Mo 0.20 and 0.35
81xx	Ni 0.30; Cr 0.40; Mo 0.12
86xx	Ni 0.55; Cr 0.50; Mo 0.20
87xx	Ni 0.55; Cr 0.50; Mo 0.25
88xx	Ni 0.55; Cr 0.50; Mo 0.35
93xx	Ni 3.25; Cr 1.20; Mo 0.12
94xx	Ni 0.45; Cr 0.40; Mo 0.12
97xx	Ni 0.55; Cr 0.20; Mo 0.20
98xx	Ni 1.00; Cr 0.80; Mo 0.25
Nickel-molybdenum steels	
46xx	Ni 0.85 and 1.82; Mo 0.20 and 0.25
48xx	Ni 3.50; Mo 0.25
Chromium steels	
50xx	Cr 0.27, 0.40, 0.50 and 0.65
51xx	Cr 0.80, 0.87, 0.92, 0.95, 1.00 and 1.05

Numerals and digits(a)	Type of steel and/or nominal alloy content
Chromium steels	
50xxx	Cr 0.50
51xxx	Cr 1.02 C 1.00 min
52xxx	Cr 1.45
Chromium-vanadium steels	
61xx	Cr 0.60, 0.80 and 0.95; V 0.10 and 0.15 min
Tungsten-chromium steel	
72xx	W 1.75; Cr 0.75
Silicon-manganese steels	
92xx	Si 1.40 and 2.00; Mn 0.65, 0.82 and 0.85; Cr 0.00 and 0.65
High-strength low-alloy steels	
9xx	Various SAE grades
Boron steels	
xxBxx	B denotes boron steel
Leaded steels	
xxLxx	L denotes leaded steel

(a) "xx" in the two (or three) digits fo these designations indicates that the carbon content (in hundredths of a percent) is to be inserted.

Appendix 7.

Compositions of standard carbon steels. (From same source as Appendix 2)

Compositions of standard nonresulfurized carbon steels (1.0 manganese maximum)

Steel designation AISI or SAE	UNS No.	C	Mn	P max	S max
1005(a)	G10050	0.06 max	0.35 max	0.040	0.050
1006(a)	G10060	0.08 max	0.25 max	0.040	0.050
1008	G10080	0.10 max	0.30-0.50	0.040	0.050
1010	G10100	0.08-0.13	0.30-0.60	0.040	0.050
1012	G10120	0.10-0.15	0.30-0.60	0.040	0.050
1015	G10150	0.13-0.18	0.30-0.60	0.040	0.050
1016	G10160	0.13-0.18	0.60-0.90	0.040	0.050
1017	G10170	0.15-0.20	0.30-0.60	0.040	0.050
1018	G10180	0.15-0.20	0.60-0.90	0.040	0.050
1019	G10190	0.15-0.20	0.70-1.00	0.040	0.050
1020	G10200	0.18-0.23	0.30-0.60	0.040	0.050
1021	G10210	0.18-0.23	0.60-0.90	0.040	0.050
1022	G10220	0.18-0.23	0.70-1.00	0.040	0.050
1023	G10230	0.20-0.25	0.30-0.60	0.040	0.050
1025	G10250	0.22-0.28	0.30-0.60	0.040	0.050
1026	G10260	0.22-0.28	0.60-0.90	0.040	0.050
1029	G10290	0.25-0.31	0.60-0.90	0.040	0.050
1030	G10300	0.28-0.34	0.60-0.90	0.040	0.050
1035	G10350	0.32-0.38	0.60-0.90	0.040	0.050
1037	G10370	0.32-0.38	0.70-1.00	0.040	0.050
1038	G10380	0.35-0.42	0.60-0.90	0.040	0.050
1039	G10390	0.37-0.44	0.70-1.00	0.040	0.050
1040	G10400	0.37-0.44	0.60-0.90	0.040	0.050
1042	G10420	0.40-0.47	0.60-0.90	0.040	0.050
1043	G10430	0.40-0.47	0.70-1.00	0.040	0.050
1044	G10440	0.43-0.50	0.30-0.60	0.040	0.050
1045	G10450	0.43-0.50	0.60-0.90	0.040	0.050
1046	G10460	0.43-0.50	0.70-1.00	0.040	0.050
1049	G10490	0.46-0.53	0.60-0.90	0.040	0.050
1050	G10500	0.48-0.55	0.60-0.90	0.040	0.050
1053	G10530	0.48-0.55	0.70-1.00	0.040	0.050
1055	G10550	0.50-0.60	0.60-0.90	0.040	0.050
1059(a)	G10590	0.55-0.65	0.50-0.80	0.040	0.050
1060	G10600	0.55-0.65	0.60-0.90	0.040	0.050
1070	G10700	0.65-0.75	0.60-0.90	0.040	0.050
1078	G10780	0.72-0.85	0.30-0.60	0.040	0.050
1080	G10800	0.75-0.88	0.60-0.90	0.040	0.050
1084	G10840	0.80-0.93	0.60-0.90	0.040	0.050
1086(a)	G10860	0.80-0.93	0.30-0.50	0.040	0.050
1090	G10900	0.85-0.98	0.60-0.90	0.040	0.050
1095	G10950	0.90-1.03	0.30-0.50	0.040	0.050

(a) Standard steel grades for wire rods and wire only

Compositions of standard nonresulfurized carbon steels (over 1.0 manganese)

Steel designation AISI or SAE	UNS No.	C	Mn	P max	S max
1513	G15130	0.10-0.16	1.10-1.40	0.040	0.050
1522	G15220	0.18-0.24	1.10-1.40	0.040	0.050
1524	G15240	0.19-0.25	1.35-1.65	0.040	0.050
1526	G15260	0.22-0.29	1.10-1.40	0.040	0.050
1527	G15270	0.22-0.29	1.20-1.50	0.040	0.050
1541	G15410	0.36-0.44	1.35-1.65	0.040	0.050
1548	G15480	0.44-0.52	1.10-1.40	0.040	0.050
1551	G15510	0.45-0.56	0.85-1.15	0.040	0.050
1552	G15520	0.47-0.55	1.20-1.50	0.040	0.050
1561	G15610	0.55-0.65	0.75-1.05	0.040	0.050
1566	G15660	0.60-0.71	0.85-1.15	0.040	0.050

Compositions of standard resulfurized carbon steels

Steel designation AISI or SAE	UNS No.	C	Mn	P max	S max
1110	G11100	0.08-0.13	0.30-0.60	0.040	0.08-0.13
1117	G11170	0.14-0.20	1.00-1.30	0.040	0.08-0.13
1118	G11180	0.14-0.20	1.30-1.60	0.040	0.08-0.13
1137	G11370	0.32-0.39	1.35-1.65	0.040	0.08-0.13
1139	G11390	0.35-0.43	1.35-1.65	0.040	0.13-0.20
1140	G11400	0.37-0.44	0.70-1.00	0.040	0.08-0.13
1141	G11410	0.37-0.45	1.35-1.65	0.040	0.08-0.13
1144	G11440	0.40-0.48	1.35-1.65	0.040	0.24-0.33
1146	G11460	0.42-0.49	0.70-1.00	0.040	0.08-0.13
1151	G11510	0.48-0.55	0.70-1.00	0.040	0.08-0.13

Compositions of standard rephosphorized and resulfurized carbon steels

Steel designation AISI or SAE	UNS No.	C	Mn	P	S	Pb
1211	G12110	0.13 max	0.60-0.90	0.07-0.12	0.10-0.15	...
1212	G12120	0.13 max	0.70-1.00	0.07-0.12	0.16-0.23	...
1213	G12130	0.13 max	0.70-1.00	0.07-0.12	0.24-0.33	...
1215	G12150	0.09 max	0.75-1.05	0.04-0.09	0.26-0.35	...
12L14	G12144	0.15 max	0.85-1.15	0.04-0.09	0.26-0.35	0.15-0.35

Appendix 8.

Compositions of standard carbon H-steels and standard carbon boron H-steels. (From same source as Appendix 2)

Steel designation AISI or SAE	UNS No.	Chemical composition, %				
		C	Mn	P max	S max	Si
Standard carbon H-steels						
1038H	H10380	0.34-0.43	0.50-1.00	0.040	0.050	0.15-0.30
1045H	H10450	0.42-0.51	0.50-1.00	0.040	0.050	0.15-0.30
1522H	H15220	0.17-0.25	1.00-1.50	0.040	0.050	0.15-0.30
1524H	H15240	0.18-0.26	1.25-1.75(a)	0.040	0.050	0.15-0.30
1526H	H15260	0.21-0.30	1.00-1.50	0.040	0.050	0.15-0.30
1541H	H15410	0.35-0.45	1.25-1.75(a)	0.040	0.050	0.15-0.30
Standard carbon boron H-steels						
15B21H	H15211	0.17-0.24	0.70-1.20	0.040	0.050	0.15-0.30
15B35H	H15351	0.31-0.39	0.70-1.20	0.040	0.050	0.15-0.30
15B37H	H15371	0.30-0.39	1.00-1.50	0.040	0.050	0.15-0.30
15B41H	H15411	0.35-0.45	1.25-1.75(a)	0.040	0.050	0.15-0.30
15B48H	H15481	0.43-0.53	1.00-1.50	0.040	0.050	0.15-0.30
15B62H	H15621	0.54-0.67	1.00-1.50	0.040	0.050	0.40-0.60

(a) Standard AISI-SAE H-steels with 1.75 manganese maximum are classified as carbon steels.

Percent of alloys	Hardenability characteristics of alloys					Percent of alloys	Hardenability characteristics of alloys				
	Mn	Si	Ni	Cr	Mo		Mn	Si	Ni	Cr	Mo
0.01	0.014	0.003	0.002	0.009	0.013	0.46	0.404	0.121	0.067	0.300	0.377
0.02	0.028	0.006	0.003	0.018	0.025	0.47	0.409	0.124	0.069	0.304	0.382
0.03	0.041	0.009	0.005	0.027	0.037	0.48	0.415	0.126	0.070	0.309	0.387
0.04	0.054	0.012	0.006	0.036	0.049	0.49	0.420	0.128	0.072	0.313	0.393
0.05	0.067	0.015	0.008	0.045	0.061	0.50	0.426	0.130	0.073	0.318	0.398
0.06	0.079	0.018	0.009	0.053	0.072	0.51	0.431	0.133	0.074	0.323	0.403
0.07	0.091	0.021	0.011	0.061	0.083	0.52	0.437	0.135	0.076	0.327	0.408
0.08	0.103	0.024	0.012	0.069	0.094	0.53	0.442	0.137	0.077	0.331	0.413
0.09	0.114	0.027	0.014	0.077	0.104	0.54	0.447	0.139	0.078	0.336	0.418
0.10	0.125	0.029	0.015	0.085	0.114	0.55	0.452	0.141	0.079	0.340	0.423
0.11	0.136	0.032	0.017	0.093	0.124	0.56	0.457	0.144	0.081	0.344	0.428
0.12	0.146	0.035	0.019	0.101	0.134	0.57	0.462	0.146	0.082	0.349	0.433
0.13	0.156	0.038	0.020	0.108	0.143	0.58	0.467	0.148	0.084	0.353	0.438
0.14	0.166	0.041	0.022	0.115	0.152	0.59	0.472	0.150	0.085	0.357	0.442
0.15	0.176	0.043	0.023	0.122	0.161	0.60	0.477	0.152	0.086	0.361	0.447
0.16	0.186	0.046	0.024	0.129	0.170	0.61	0.482	0.154	0.087	0.365	0.452
0.17	0.195	0.049	0.026	0.136	0.179	0.62	0.487	0.157	0.088	0.369	0.456
0.18	0.204	0.052	0.028	0.143	0.188	0.63	0.492	0.159	0.090	0.373	0.461
0.19	0.213	0.054	0.029	0.149	0.196	0.64	0.496	0.161	0.091	0.377	0.465
0.20	0.222	0.057	0.030	0.156	0.204	0.65	0.501	0.163	0.092	0.381	0.470
0.21	0.231	0.060	0.032	0.163	0.212	0.66	0.505	0.165	0.094	0.385	0.474
0.22	0.239	0.062	0.033	0.169	0.220	0.67	0.510	0.167	0.095	0.389	0.479
0.23	0.247	0.064	0.035	0.175	0.228	0.68	0.514	0.169	0.096	0.393	0.483
0.24	0.255	0.067	0.037	0.181	0.236	0.69	0.519	0.171	0.097	0.396	0.487
0.25	0.263	0.070	0.038	0.187	0.244	0.70	0.523	0.173	0.099	0.400	0.491
0.26	0.271	0.073	0.040	0.193	0.251	0.71	0.527	0.175	0.100	0.404	0.496
0.27	0.279	0.075	0.041	0.199	0.258	0.72	0.531	0.177	0.101	0.407	0.500
0.28	0.287	0.078	0.042	0.205	0.265	0.73	0.536	0.179	0.102	0.411	0.504
0.29	0.294	0.080	0.044	0.211	0.272	0.74	0.540	0.181	0.104	0.415	0.508
0.30	0.301	0.083	0.045	0.217	0.279	0.75	0.544	0.183	0.105	0.418	0.512
0.31	0.308	0.085	0.047	0.222	0.286	0.76	0.548	0.185	0.106	0.422	0.516
0.32	0.315	0.088	0.048	0.228	0.293	0.77	0.552	0.187	0.107	0.425	0.520
0.33	0.322	0.090	0.049	0.234	0.299	0.78	0.556	0.189	0.109	0.429	0.524
0.34	0.329	0.093	0.051	0.239	0.306	0.79	0.560	0.191	0.110	0.432	0.528
0.35	0.336	0.095	0.052	0.244	0.312	0.80	0.564	0.193	0.111	0.436	0.531
0.36	0.343	0.098	0.053	0.249	0.318	0.81	0.568	0.195	0.112	0.439	0.535
0.37	0.349	0.100	0.055	0.255	0.324	0.82	0.572	0.197	0.113	0.443	0.539
0.38	0.355	0.102	0.057	0.260	0.330	0.83	0.576	0.199	0.114	0.446	0.543
0.39	0.362	0.105	0.058	0.265	0.336	0.84	0.580	0.201	0.116	0.449	0.547
0.40	0.368	0.107	0.059	0.270	0.342	0.85	0.584	0.203	0.117	0.453	0.550
0.41	0.374	0.110	0.061	0.275	0.348	0.86	0.588	0.206	0.118	0.456	0.554
0.42	0.380	0.112	0.062	0.280	0.354	0.87	0.592	0.207	0.120	0.459	0.558
0.43	0.386	0.114	0.063	0.285	0.360	0.88	0.596	0.208	0.121	0.462	0.561
0.44	0.392	0.117	0.064	0.290	0.365	0.89	0.599	0.210	0.122	0.466	0.565
0.45	0.398	0.119	0.066	0.295	0.371	0.90	0.602	0.212	0.123	0.469	0.568

(Continued)

Percent of alloys	Hardenability characteristics (continued)			
	Mn	Si	Ni	Cr
0.91	0.606	0.214	0.124	0.472
0.92	0.609	0.216	0.125	0.475
0.93	0.613	0.218	0.126	0.478
0.94	0.616	0.220	0.128	0.481
0.95	0.620	0.221	0.129	0.485
0.96	0.623	0.223	0.130	0.488
0.97	0.627	0.225	0.131	0.491
0.98	0.630	0.227	0.132	0.494
0.99	0.633	0.229	0.134	0.497
1.00	0.637	0.230	0.135	0.500
1.02	0.643	0.234	0.137	0.506
1.04	0.650	0.238	0.139	0.511
1.06	0.656	0.241	0.142	0.517
1.08	0.662	0.245	0.144	0.522
1.10	0.669	0.248	0.146	0.528
1.12	0.675	0.251	0.148	0.534
1.14	0.681	0.255	0.150	0.539
1.16	0.687	0.258	0.153	0.545
1.18	0.694	0.262	0.155	0.550
1.20	0.702	0.265	0.157	0.555
1.22	0.710	0.268	0.159	0.561
1.24	0.718	0.271	0.161	0.566
1.26	0.725	0.275	0.164	0.571
1.28	0.733	0.278	0.166	0.576
1.30	0.741	0.281	0.168	0.581
1.32	0.749	0.284	0.170	0.586
1.34	0.757	0.287	0.172	0.590
1.36	0.765	0.290	0.175	0.595
1.38	0.772	0.294	0.177	0.600
1.40	0.780	0.297	0.179	0.605
1.42	0.787	0.300	0.181	0.609
1.44	0.794	0.303	0.183	0.614
1.46	0.801	0.306	0.185	0.618
1.48	0.808	0.309	0.187	0.623
1.50	0.815	0.312	0.190	0.627
1.52	0.822	0.315	0.193	0.632
1.54	0.828	0.318	0.196	0.636
1.56	0.835	0.321	0.198	0.641
1.58	0.841	0.323	0.200	0.645
1.60	0.848	0.326	0.203	0.650
1.62	0.854	0.329	0.205	0.653
1.64	0.860	0.332	0.208	0.657
1.66	0.866	0.335	0.210	0.661
1.68	0.872	0.338	0.212	0.665
1.70	0.878	0.340	0.215	0.670
1.72	0.884	0.343	0.217	0.673

Percent of alloys	Hardenability characteristics (continued)			
	Mn	Si	Ni	Cr
1.74	0.890	0.346	0.219	...
1.76	0.896	0.349	0.222	...
1.78	0.902	0.351	0.225	...
1.80	0.908	0.354	0.228	...
1.82	0.914	0.357	0.231	...
1.84	0.920	0.359	0.234	...
1.86	0.925	0.362	0.237	...
1.88	0.930	0.365	0.240	...
1.90	0.936	0.367	0.243	...
1.92	0.941	0.370	0.245	...
1.94	0.946	0.373	0.246	...
1.96	0.951	0.375	0.247	...
1.98	0.955	0.378	0.249	...
2.00	0.960	0.381	0.250	...
2.10	...	...	0.262	...
2.20	...	...	0.275	...
2.30	...	...	0.288	...
2.40	...	...	0.303	...
2.50	...	...	0.318	...
2.60	...	...	0.333	...
2.70	...	...	0.351	...
2.80	...	...	0.369	...
2.90	...	...	0.387	...
3.00	...	...	0.405	...

Percent of alloys	V	P	S	Al	Ti
0.01	0.061	0.011	-0.003	0.006	-0.008
0.02	0.097	0.022	-0.006	0.012	-0.018
0.03	0.137	0.033	-0.009	0.017	-0.025
0.04	0.146	0.044	-0.011	0.022	-0.034
0.05	0.146	0.054	-0.014	0.028	-0.043
0.06	0.140	0.064	-0.018	0.033	-0.053
0.07	0.137	0.073	-0.020	0.039	-0.062
0.08	0.124	0.083	-0.024	0.044	-0.072
0.09	0.111	0.092	-0.027	0.049	-0.081
0.10	0.097	0.101	-0.032	0.054	-0.092
0.11	0.086	...	...	0.059	-0.099
0.12	0.072	...	...	0.064	-0.112
0.13	0.061	...	...	0.069	-0.123
0.14	0.037	...	...	0.074	-0.134
0.15	0.025	...	...	0.079	-0.146

Appendix 9.
Compositions of standard alloy steels. (From same source as Appendix 2)

Compositions of standard alloy steels

Steel designation AISI or SAE	UNS No.	C	Mn	P max	S max	Si	Ni	Cr	Mo
1330	G13300	0.28-0.33	1.60-1.90	0.035	0.040	0.15-0.30	...	...	...
1335	G13350	0.33-0.38	1.60-1.90	0.035	0.040	0.15-0.30	...	...	...
1340	G13400	0.38-0.43	1.60-1.90	0.035	0.040	0.15-0.30	...	...	...
1345	G13450	0.43-0.48	1.60-1.90	0.035	0.040	0.15-0.30	...	...	...
4023	G40230	0.20-0.25	0.70-0.90	0.035	0.040	0.15-0.30	...	...	0.20-0.30
4024	G40240	0.20-0.25	0.70-0.90	0.035	0.035-0.050	0.15-0.30	...	...	0.20-0.30
4027	G40270	0.25-0.30	0.70-0.90	0.035	0.040	0.15-0.30	...	...	0.20-0.30
4028	G40280	0.25-0.30	0.70-0.90	0.035	0.035-0.050	0.15-0.30	...	...	0.20-0.30
4037	G40370	0.35-0.40	0.70-0.90	0.035	0.040	0.15-0.30	...	...	0.20-0.30
4047	G40470	0.45-0.50	0.70-0.90	0.035	0.040	0.15-0.30	...	...	0.20-0.30
4118	G41180	0.18-0.23	0.70-0.90	0.035	0.040	0.15-0.30	...	0.40-0.60	0.08-0.15
4130	G41300	0.28-0.33	0.40-0.60	0.035	0.040	0.15-0.30	...	0.80-1.10	0.15-0.25
4137	G41370	0.35-0.40	0.70-0.90	0.035	0.040	0.15-0.30	...	0.80-1.10	0.15-0.25
4140	G41400	0.38-0.43	0.75-1.00	0.035	0.040	0.15-0.30	...	0.80-1.10	0.15-0.25
4142	G41420	0.40-0.45	0.75-1.00	0.035	0.040	0.15-0.30	...	0.80-1.10	0.15-0.25
4145	G41450	0.43-0.48	0.75-1.00	0.035	0.040	0.15-0.30	...	0.80-1.10	0.15-0.25
4147	G41470	0.45-0.50	0.75-1.00	0.035	0.040	0.15-0.30	...	0.80-1.10	0.15-0.25
4150	G41500	0.48-0.53	0.75-1.00	0.035	0.040	0.15-0.30	...	0.80-1.10	0.15-0.25
4161	G41610	0.56-0.64	0.75-1.00	0.035	0.040	0.15-0.30	...	0.80-1.10	0.15-0.25
4320	G43200	0.17-0.22	0.45-0.65	0.035	0.040	0.15-0.30	1.65-2.00	0.40-0.60	0.20-0.30
4340	G43400	0.38-0.43	0.60-0.80	0.035	0.040	0.15-0.30	1.65-2.00	0.70-0.90	0.20-0.30
E4340	G43406	0.38-0.43	0.65-0.85	0.025	0.025	0.15-0.30	1.65-2.00	0.70-0.90	0.20-0.30
4615	G46150	0.13-0.18	0.45-0.65	0.035	0.040	0.15-0.30	1.65-2.00	...	0.20-0.30
4620	G46200	0.17-0.22	0.45-0.65	0.035	0.040	0.15-0.30	1.65-2.00	...	0.20-0.30
4626	G46260	0.24-0.29	0.45-0.65	0.035	0.040	0.15-0.30	0.70-1.00	...	0.15-0.25
4720	G47200	0.17-0.22	0.50-0.70	0.035	0.040	0.15-0.30	0.90-1.20	0.35-0.55	0.15-0.25
4815	G48150	0.13-0.18	0.40-0.60	0.035	0.040	0.15-0.30	3.25-3.75	...	0.20-0.30
4817	G48170	0.15-0.20	0.40-0.60	0.035	0.040	0.15-0.30	3.25-3.75	...	0.20-0.30
4820	G48200	0.18-0.23	0.50-0.70	0.035	0.040	0.15-0.30	3.25-3.75	...	0.20-0.30
5117	G51170	0.15-0.20	0.70-0.90	0.035	0.040	0.15-0.30	...	0.70-0.90	...
5120	G51200	0.17-0.22	0.70-0.90	0.035	0.040	0.15-0.30	...	0.70-0.90	...
5130	G51300	0.28-0.33	0.70-0.90	0.035	0.040	0.15-0.30	...	0.80-1.10	...
5132	G51320	0.30-0.35	0.60-0.80	0.035	0.040	0.15-0.30	...	0.75-1.00	...
5135	G51350	0.33-0.38	0.60-0.80	0.035	0.040	0.15-0.30	...	0.80-1.05	...
5140	G51400	0.38-0.43	0.70-0.90	0.035	0.040	0.15-0.30	...	0.70-0.90	...
5150	G51500	0.48-0.53	0.70-0.90	0.035	0.040	0.15-0.30	...	0.70-0.90	...
5155	G51550	0.51-0.59	0.70-0.90	0.035	0.040	0.15-0.30	...	0.70-0.90	...
5160	G51600	0.56-0.64	0.75-1.00	0.035	0.040	0.15-0.30	...	0.70-0.90	...
E51100	G51986	0.98-1.10	0.25-0.45	0.025	0.025	0.15-0.30	...	0.90-1.15	...
E52100	G52986	0.98-1.10	0.25-0.45	0.025	0.025	0.15-0.30	...	1.30-1.60	...
6118	G61180	0.16-0.21	0.50-0.70	0.035	0.040	0.15-0.30	...	0.50-0.70	0.10-0.15 V
6150	G61500	0.48-0.53	0.70-0.90	0.035	0.040	0.15-0.30	...	0.80-1.10	0.15 V min
8615	G86150	0.13-0.18	0.70-0.90	0.035	0.040	0.15-0.30	0.40-0.70	0.40-0.60	0.15-0.25
8617	G86170	0.15-0.20	0.70-0.90	0.035	0.040	0.15-0.30	0.40-0.70	0.40-0.60	0.15-0.25
8620	G86200	0.18-0.23	0.70-0.90	0.035	0.040	0.15-0.30	0.40-0.70	0.40-0.60	0.15-0.25
8622	G86220	0.20-0.25	0.70-0.90	0.035	0.040	0.15-0.30	0.40-0.70	0.40-0.60	0.15-0.25
8625	G86250	0.23-0.28	0.70-0.90	0.035	0.040	0.15-0.30	0.40-0.70	0.40-0.60	0.15-0.25
8627	G86270	0.25-0.30	0.70-0.90	0.035	0.040	0.15-0.30	0.40-0.70	0.40-0.60	0.15-0.25
8630	G86300	0.28-0.33	0.70-0.90	0.035	0.040	0.15-0.30	0.40-0.70	0.40-0.60	0.15-0.25
8637	G86370	0.35-0.40	0.75-1.00	0.035	0.040	0.15-0.30	0.400.70	0.40-0.60	0.15-0.25
8640	G86400	0.38-0.43	0.75-1.00	0.035	0.040	0.15-0.30	0.40-0.70	0.40-0.60	0.15-0.25
8642	G86420	0.40-0.45	0.75-1.00	0.035	0.040	0.15-0.30	0.40-0.70	0.40-0.60	0.15-0.25
8645	G86450	0.43-0.48	0.75-1.00	0.035	0.040	0.15-0.30	0.40-0.70	0.40-0.60	0.15-0.25
8655	G86550	0.51-0.59	0.75-1.00	0.035	0.040	0.15-0.30	0.40-0.70	0.40-0.60	0.15-0.25
8720	G87200	0.18-0.23	0.70-0.90	0.035	0.040	0.15-0.30	0.40-0.70	0.40-0.60	0.20-0.30
8740	G87400	0.38-0.43	0.75-1.00	0.035	0.040	0.15-0.30	0.40-0.70	0.40-0.60	0.20-0.30
8822	G88220	0.20-0.25	0.75-1.00	0.035	0.040	0.15-0.30	0.40-0.70	0.40-0.60	0.30-0.40
9260	G92600	0.56-0.64	0.75-1.00	0.035	0.040	1.80-2.20	...	...	...

Compositons of Standard Boron (Alloy) Steels

Steel designation AISI or SAE	UNS No.	C	Mn	P max	S max	Si	Ni	Cr	Mo
50B44	G50441	0.43-0.48	0.75-1.00	0.035	0.040	0.15-0.30	...	0.40-0.60	...
50B46	G50461	0.44-0.49	0.75-1.00	0.035	0.040	0.15-0.30	...	0.20-0.35	...
50B50	G50501	0.48-0.53	0.75-1.00	0.035	0.040	0.15-0.30	...	0.40-0.60	...
50B60	G50601	0.56-0.64	0.75-1.00	0.035	0.040	0.15-0.30	...	0.40-0.60	...
51B60	G51601	0.56-0.64	0.75-1.00	0.035	0.040	0.15-0.30	...	0.70-0.90	...
81B45	G81451	0.43-0.48	0.75-1.00	0.035	0.040	0.15-0.30	0.20-0.40	0.35-0.55	0.08-0.15
94B17	G94171	0.15-0.20	0.75-1.00	0.035	0.040	0.15-0.30	0.30-0.60	0.30-0.50	0.08-0.15
94B30	G94301	0.28-0.33	0.75-1.00	0.035	0.040	0.15-0.30	0.30-0.60	0.30-0.50	0.08-0.15

Appendix 10.
Compositions of standard alloy H-steels. (From same source as Appendix 2)

Compositions of standard alloy H-steels

Steel designation AISI or SAE	UNS No.	C	Mn	P max	S max	Si	Ni	Cr	Mo
1330H	H13300	0.27-0.33	1.45-2.05	0.035	0.040	0.15-0.30	...	...	...
1335H	H13350	0.32-0.38	1.45-2.05	0.035	0.040	0.15-0.30	...	...	...
1340H	H13400	0.37-0.44	1.45-2.05	0.035	0.040	0.15-0.30	...	...	...
1345H	H13450	0.42-0.49	1.45-2.05	0.035	0.040	0.15-0.30	...	...	...
4027H	H40270	0.24-0.30	0.60-1.00	0.035	0.040	0.15-0.30	...	...	0.20-0.30
4028H	H40280	0.24-0.30	0.60-1.00	0.035	0.035-0.050	0.15-0.30	...	...	0.20-0.30
4032H	H40320	0.29-0.35	0.60-1.00	0.035	0.040	0.15-0.30	...	...	0.20-0.30
4037H	H40370	0.34-0.41	0.60-1.00	0.035	0.040	0.15-0.30	...	...	0.20-0.30
4042H	H40420	0.39-0.46	0.60-1.00	0.035	0.040	0.15-0.30	...	...	0.20-0.30
4047H	H40470	0.44-0.51	0.60-1.00	0.035	0.040	0.15-0.30	...	...	0.20-0.30
4118H	H41180	0.17-0.23	0.60-1.00	0.035	0.040	0.15-0.30	...	0.30-0.70	0.08-0.15
4130H	H41300	0.27-0.33	0.30-0.70	0.035	0.040	0.15-0.30	...	0.75-1.20	0.15-0.25
4135H	H41350	0.32-0.38	0.60-1.00	0.035	0.040	0.15-0.30	...	0.75-1.20	0.15-0.25
4137H	H41370	0.34-0.41	0.60-1.00	0.035	0.040	0.15-0.30	...	0.75-1.20	0.15-0.25
4140H	H41400	0.37-0.44	0.65-1.10	0.035	0.040	0.15-0.30	...	0.75-1.20	0.15-0.25
4142H	H41420	0.39-0.46	0.65-1.10	0.035	0.040	0.15-0.30	...	0.75-1.20	0.15-0.25
4145H	H41450	0.42-0.49	0.65-1.10	0.035	0.040	0.15-0.30	...	0.75-1.20	0.15-0.25
4147H	H41470	0.44-0.51	0.65-1.10	0.035	0.040	0.15-0.30	...	0.75-1.20	0.15-0.25
4150H	H41500	0.47-0.54	0.65-1.10	0.035	0.040	0.15-0.30	...	0.75-1.20	0.15-0.25
4161H	H41610	0.55-0.65	0.65-1.10	0.035	0.040	0.15-0.30	...	0.65-0.95	0.25-0.35
4320H	H43200	0.17-0.23	0.40-0.70	0.035	0.040	0.15-0.30	1.55-2.00	0.35-0.65	0.20-0.30
4340H	H43400	0.37-0.44	0.55-0.90	0.035	0.040	0.15-0.30	1.55-2.00	0.65-0.95	0.20-0.30
E4340H	H43406	0.37-0.44	0.60-0.95	0.025	0.025	0.15-0.30	1.55-2.00	0.65-0.95	0.20-0.30
4620H	H46200	0.17-0.23	0.35-0.75	0.035	0.040	0.15-0.30	1.55-2.00	...	0.20-0.30
4626H	H46260	0.23-0.29	0.40-0.70	0.035	0.040	0.15-0.30	0.65-1.05	...	0.15-0.25
4720H	H47200	0.17-0.23	0.45-0.75	0.035	0.040	0.15-0.30	0.85-1.25	0.30-0.60	0.15-0.25
4815H	H48150	0.12-0.18	0.30-0.70	0.035	0.040	0.15-0.30	3.20-3.80	...	0.20-0.30
4817H	H48170	0.14-0.20	0.30-0.70	0.035	0.040	0.15-0.30	3.20-3.80	...	0.20-0.30
4820H	H48200	0.17-0.23	0.40-0.80	0.035	0.040	0.15-0.30	3.20-3.80	...	0.20-0.30
5046H	H50460	0.43-0.50	0.65-1.10	0.035	0.040	0.15-0.30	...	0.13-0.43	...
5120H	H51200	0.17-0.23	0.60-1.00	0.035	0.040	0.15-0.30	...	0.60-1.00	...
5130H	H51300	0.27-0.33	0.60-1.00	0.035	0.040	0.15-0.30	...	0.75-1.20	...
5132H	H51320	0.29-0.35	0.50-0.90	0.035	0.040	0.15-0.30	...	0.65-1.10	...
5135H	H51350	0.32-0.38	0.50-0.90	0.035	0.040	0.15-0.30	...	0.70-1.15	...
5140H	H51400	0.37-0.44	0.60-1.00	0.035	0.040	0.15-0.30	...	0.60-1.00	...
5150H	H51500	0.47-0.54	0.60-1.00	0.035	0.040	0.15-0.30	...	0.60-1.00	...
5155H	H51550	0.50-0.60	0.60-1.00	0.035	0.040	0.15-0.30	...	0.60-1.00	...
5160H	H51600	0.55-0.65	0.65-1.00	0.035	0.040	0.15-0.30	...	0.60-1.00	...
6118H	H61180	0.15-0.21	0.40-0.80	0.035	0.040	0.15-0.30	...	0.40-0.80	0.10-0.15
6150H	H61500	0.47-0.54	0.60-1.00	0.035	0.040	0.15-0.30	...	0.75-1.20	0.15 V min
8617H	H86170	0.14-0.20	0.60-0.95	0.035	0.040	0.15-0.30	0.35-0.75	0.35-0.65	0.15-0.25
8620H	H86200	0.17-0.23	0.60-0.95	0.035	0.040	0.15-0.30	0.35-0.75	0.35-0.65	0.15-0.25
8622H	H86220	0.19-0.25	0.60-0.95	0.035	0.040	0.15-0.30	0.35-0.75	0.35-0.65	0.15-0.25
8625H	H86250	0.22-0.28	0.60-0.95	0.035	0.040	0.15-0.30	0.35-0.75	0.35-0.65	0.15-0.25
8627H	H86270	0.24-0.30	0.60-0.95	0.035	0.040	0.15-0.30	0.35-0.75	0.35-0.65	0.15-0.25
8630H	H86300	0.27-0.33	0.60-0.95	0.035	0.040	0.15-0.30	0.35-0.75	0.35-0.65	0.15-0.25
8637H	H86370	0.34-0.41	0.70-1.05	0.035	0.040	0.15-0.30	0.35-0.75	0.35-0.65	0.15-0.65
8640H	H86400	0.37-0.44	0.70-1.05	0.035	0.040	0.15-0.30	0.35-0.75	0.35-0.65	0.15-0.25
8642H	H86420	0.39-0.46	0.70-1.05	0.035	0.040	0.15-0.30	0.35-0.75	0.35-0.65	0.15-0.25
8645H	H86450	0.42-0.49	0.70-1.05	0.035	0.040	0.15-0.30	0.35-0.75	0.35-0.65	0.15-0.25
8650H	H86500	0.47-0.54	0.70-1.05	0.035	0.040	0.15-0.30	0.35-0.75	0.35-0.65	0.15-0.25
8655H	H86550	0.50-0.60	0.70-1.05	0.035	0.040	0.15-0.30	0.35-0.75	0.35-0.65	0.15-0.25
8660H	H86600	0.55-0.65	0.70-1.05	0.035	0.040	0.15-0.30	0.35-0.75	0.35-0.65	0.15-0.25
8720H	H87200	0.17-0.23	0.60-0.95	0.035	0.040	0.15-0.30	0.35-0.75	0.35-0.65	0.20-0.30
8740H	H87400	0.37-0.44	0.70-1.05	0.035	0.040	0.15-0.30	0.35-0.75	0.35-0.65	0.20-0.30
8822H	H88220	0.19-0.25	0.70-1.05	0.035	0.040	0.15-0.30	0.35-0.75	0.35-0.65	0.30-0.40
9260H	H92600	0.55-0.65	0.65-1.10	0.035	0.040	1.70-2.20	...	...	...
9310H	H93100	0.07-0.13	0.40-0.70	0.035	0.040	0.15-0.30	2.95-3.55	1.00-1.45	0.08-0.15

(continued)

(Continued)

Compositions of standard boron (alloy) H-steels

Steel designation AISI or SAE	UNS No.	Chemical composition, %							
		C	Mn	P max	S max	Si	Ni	Cr	Mo
50B40H	H50401	0.37-0.44	0.65-1.10	0.035	0.040	0.15-0.30	...	0.30-0.70	...
50B44H	H50441	0.42-0.49	0.65-1.10	0.035	0.040	0.15-0.30	...	0.30-0.70	...
50B46H	H50461	0.43-0.50	0.65-1.10	0.035	0.040	0.15-0.30	...	0.13-0.43	...
50B50H	H50501	0.47-0.54	0.65-1.10	0.035	0.040	0.15-0.30	...	0.30-0.70	...
50B60H	H50601	0.55-0.65	0.65-1.10	0.035	0.040	0.15-0.30	...	0.30-0.70	...
51B60H	H51601	0.55-0.65	0.65-1.10	0.035	0.040	0.15-0.30	...	0.60-1.00	...
81B45H	H81451	0.42-0.49	0.70-1.05	0.035	0.040	0.15-0.30	0.15-0.45	0.30-0.60	0.08-0.15
86B30H	H86301	0.27-0.33	0.60-0.95	0.035	0.040	0.15-0.30	0.35-0.75	0.35-0.65	0.15-0.25
86B45H	H86451	0.42-0.49	0.70-1.05	0.035	0.040	0.15-0.30	0.35-0.75	0.35-0.65	0.15-0.25
94B15H	H94151	0.12-0.18	0.70-1.05	0.035	0.040	0.15-0.30	0.25-0.65	0.25-0.55	0.08-0.15
94B17H	H94171	0.14-0.20	0.70-1.05	0.035	0.040	0.15-0.30	0.25-0.65	0.25-0.55	0.08-0.15
94B30H	H94301	0.27-0.33	0.70-1.05	0.035	0.040	0.15-0.30	0.25-0.65	0.25-0.55	0.08-0.15

Appendix 11.

Cross-reference to steels. (Reprinted from Heat Treater's Guide: Practices and Procedures for Irons and Steels, 2nd edition, ASM International, Materials Park, Ohio (1995))

The following index was developed to help the Heat Treater cross-index chemically similar specifications. The specifications are listed alpha-numerically by country of origin. It is recommended that this index serve only as a guide. Any determination of the true equivalency of any two alloys should only be made after careful comparison of their chemical compositions. For further information on the chemical compositions and mechanical properties of the alloys listed in this index the reader may find it useful to consult such publications as the *Worldwide Guide to Equivalent Irons and Steels*, ASM, 1979, and *Woldman's Engineering Alloys*, ASM, 1979.

France

Designation	AISI
AFNOR	
100 C 6	E52100
20 MC 5	5120
20 MC 5	5120H
20 NCD 2	8617
20 NCD 2	8617H
20 NCD 2	8620
20 NCD 2	8620H
22 NCD 2	8617
22 NCD 2	8617H
22 NCD 2	8620
22 NCD 2	8620H
2237 Z 230 CVA 12.04	D7
25 CD 4(S)	4130
25 CD 4(S)	4130
25 CD 4(S)	4130H
25 CD 4(S)	4130H
2881 Y 10 NC 6	P3
2882 10 NC 12	P6
32 C 4	5130H
32 C 4	5132
3432 Z 38 CDW 5	A8
35 CD 4	4135
35 CD 4	4135H
35 CD 4 TS	4135
35 CD 4 TS	4135H
35 M 5	1039
35 MF 4	1140
3541 Z 40 WCV 5	H14
3548 Z 65 WDCV 6.05	H42
3548 Z 65 WDCV 6.05	T1
38 C 4	5132H
38 C 4	5135
40 CD 4	4137
40 CD 4	4137H
40 CD 4	4140
40 CD 4	4140
40 CD 4	4140H
40 CD 4	4140H
40 M 5	1335
40 M 5	1335H
40 M 5	1541
40 M 5	1541H
42 C 2	5140H
42 C 2	5150
42 C 4	5135H
42 C 4	5140
42 CD 4	4137
42 CD 4	4137H
42 CD 4	4140
42 CD 4	4140
42 CD 4	4140H
42 CD 4	4140H

France

Designation	AISI
AFNOR	
45 C 2	5140H
45 C 2	5150
45 MF 4	1146
50 CV 4	6150
50 CV 4	6150
50 CV 4	6150H
50 CV 4	6150H
55 C 3	5155
55 C 3	5155H
55 WC 20	S1
60 S 7	9260
60 S 7	9260H
61 SC 7	9260
61 SC 7	9260H
A35-590-1102 Y (1) 105	W1
A35-590 1103 Y (1) 90	W1
A35-590 1104 Y (1) 80	W1
A35-590 1105 Y (1) 70	W1
A35-590 1161 Y 120 V	W2
A35-590 1162 Y 105 V	W2
A35-590 1163 Y 90 V	W2
A35-590 1164 Y 75 V	W2
A35-590 1200 Y (2) 140	W1
A35-590 1201 Y (2) 120	W1
A35-590 1232 Y 105 C	W2
A35-590 2130 Y 100 C 2	W2

Germany

Designation	AISI
DIN	
1.0204	1008
1.0402	1020
1.0419	1016
1.0501	1035
1.0503	1043
1.0601	1060
1.0647	1084
1.0702	1110
1.0711	1212
1.0715	1213
1.0718	12L14
1.0726	1140
1.0727	1146
1.0909	9260
1.0909	9260H
1.0912	1345
1.0912	1345H
1.1121	1010
1.1133	1022
1.1133	1522
1.1141	1015

Germany

Designation	AISI
DIN	
1.1141	1017
1.1151	1023
1.1157	1039
1.1158	1025
1.1160	1524
1.1160	1524H
1.1161	1526
1.1161	1527
1.1161	1541
1.1165	1330
1.1165	1330H
1.1167	1335
1.1167	1335H
1.1172	1030
1.1176	1038
1.1176	1038H
1.1186	1040
1.1191	1042
1.1191	1045
1.1191	1045H
1.1201	1049
1.1209	1055
1.1210	1050
1.1226	1548
1.1226	1552
1.1231	1070
1.1248	1078
1.1260	1566
1.1273	1090
1.1274	1095
1.1525	W1
1.1545	W1
1.1625	W1
1.1645	W2
1.1654	W1
1.1663	W1
1.167	1541H
1.1673	W1
1.1744	W1
1.1750	W1
1.1820	W1
1.1830	W1
1.5069	1340H
1.5523	15B21H
1.5527	15B41H
1.5713	P3
1.6523	8617
1.6523	8617H
1.6523	8620
1.6523	8620H
1.6543	8622
1.6543	8622H

Germany

Designation	AISI
DIN	
1.6543	8720
1.6543	8720H
1.6543	8822
1.6543	8822H
1.6545	8630
1.6545	8630H
1.6546	8640
1.6546	8640
1.6546	8640H
1.6546	8640H
1.6546	8740
1.6546	8740H
1.6562	E4340
1.6562	E4340H
1.6565	4340
1.6565	4340
1.6565	4340H
1.6565	4340H
1.7006	5140H
1.7006	5150
1.7007	50B40
1.7007	50B40H
1.7030	5130
1.7033	5130H
1.7033	5132
1.7034	5132H
1.7034	5135
1.7035	5135H
1.7035	5140
1.7138	50B50
1.7138	50B50H
1.7147	5120
1.7147	5120H
1.7176	5155
1.7176	5155H
1.7218	4130
1.7218	4130
1.7218	4130H
1.7218	4130H
1.7220	4135
1.7220	4135H
1.7223	4142H
1.7225	4137
1.7225	4137H
1.7225	4140
1.7225	4140
1.7225	4140H
1.7225	4140H
1.7228	4147
1.7228	4147H
1.7228	4150
1.7228	4150H
1.7511	6118
1.7511	6118H
1.7783	H11
1.7784	H11
1.8159	6150
1.8159	6150
1.8159	6150H
1.8159	6150H

Italy

Designation	AISI
UNI	
10 S 20	1212
100 Cr 6	E52100
20 NiCrMo 2	8617
20 NiCrMo 2	8617H
20 NiCrMo 2	8620
20 NiCrMo 2	8620H
25 CrMo 4	4130
25 CrMo 4	4130
25 CrMo 4	4130H
25 CrMo 4	4130H
25 CrMo 4 KB	4130
25 CrMo 4 KB	4130
25 CrMo 4 KB	4130H
25 CrMo 4 KB	4130H
30 NiCrMo 2 KB	8630
30 NiCrMo 2 KB	8630H
34 Cr 4 KB	5130H
34 Cr 4 KB	5132
34 CrMo 4 KB	4135
34 CrMo 4 KB	4135H
35 CrMo 4	4135
35 CrMo 4	4135H
35 CrMo 4 F	4135
35 CrMo 4 F	4135H
38 Cr 4 KB	5132H
38 Cr 4 KB	5135
38 CrB 1 KB	50B40
38 CrB 1 KB	50B40H
38 CrMo 4	4142H
38 CrMo 4 KB	4140
38 CrMo 4 KB	4140
38 CrMo 4 KB	4140H
38 CrMo 4 KB	4140H
40 Cr 4	5135H
40 Cr 4	5140
40 CrMo 4	4137
40 CrMo 4	4137H
40 CrMo 4	4140
40 CrMo 4	4140
40 CrMo 4	4140H
40 CrMo 4	4140H
40 NiCrMo 2 KB	8640
40 NiCrMo 2 KB	8640
40 NiCrMo 2 KB	8640H
40 NiCrMo 2 KB	8640H
40 NiCrMo 2 KB	8740
40 NiCrMo 2 KB	8740H
40 NiCrMo 7	E4340H
40 NiCrMo 7 KB	E4340H
41 Cr 4 KB	5135H
41 Cr 4 KB	5140
50 CrV 4	6150
50 CrV 4	6150
50 CrV 4	6150H
50 CrV 4	6150H
58 W Cr 9 KU	S1
88 MnV 8 KU	O2
9 Smn 23	1213
9 SMnPb 23	12L14
C 20	1020
C 35	1035
C 45	1043

Italy

Designation	AISI
UNI	
C 60	1060
CB 10 FU	1008
CB 35	1030
G 22 Mn 3	1522H
G 38 CrMo 4 KB	4137
G 38 CrMo 4 KB	4137H
G 40 CrMo 4	4137
G 40 CrMo 4	4137H
G 40 CrMo 4	4140
G 40 CrMo 4	4140
G 40 CrMo 4	4140H
G 40 CrMo 4	4140H
G22 Mn 3	1022

Japan

Designation	AISI
JIS	
40 NiCrMo 7	E4340
40 NiCrMo 7 KB	E4340
G4401 SK 1	W1
G4401 SK 2	W1
G4401 SK 3	W1
G4401 SK 4	W1
G4401 SK 5	W1
G4401 SK 6	W1
G4401 SK 7	W1
G4401 SKC 3	W1
S 10 C	1010
S 12 C 9 CK	1010
S 15 C	1015
S 15 C	1017
S 15 CK	1015
S 15 CK	1017
S 17 C	1015
S 17 C	1017
S 20 C	1023
S 20 CK	1023
S 22 C	1023
S 28 C	1025
S 40 C	1040
S 45 C	1042
S 45 C	1045
S 45 C	1045H
S 48 C	1042
S 48 C	1045
S 48 C	1045H
S 50 C	1049
S 53 C	1050
S 55 C	1050
S25 C	1025
SCCrM 1	4130
SCCrM 1	4130
SCCrM 1	4130H
SCCrM 1	4130H
SCCrM 3	4135
SCCrM 3	4135H
SCM 1	4135
SCM 1	4135H
SCM 2	4130
SCM 2	4130
SCM 2	4130H

Japan

Designation	AISI
JIS	
SCM 2	4130H
SCM 4	4137
SCM 4	4137H
SCM 4	4140
SCM 4	4140
SCM 4	4140H
SCM 4	4140H
SCM 4 H	4137
SCM 4 H	4137H
SCM 4 H	4140
SCM 4 H	4140
SCM 4 H	4140H
SCM 4 H	4140H
SCM 5	4147
SCM 5	4147H
SCM 5	4150
SCM 5	4150H
SCM 5 H	4147
SCM 5 H	4147H
SCM 5 H	4150
SCM 5 H	4150H
SCMn 2	1330
SCMn 2	1330H
SCMn 3	1335
SCMn 3	1335H
SCMn 3	1541
SCMn 3	1541H
SCr 2	5130H
SCr 2	5132
SCr 2 H	5130H
SCr 2 H	5132
SCr 3 H	5132H
SCr 3 H	5135
SCr 4 H	5135H
SCr 4 H	5140
SMn 1 H	1330
SMn 1 H	1330H
SMn 2	1335
SMn 2	1335H
SMn 2	1541
SMn 2	1541H
SMn 2 H	1335
SMn 2 H	1335H
SMn 2 H	1541
SMn 2 H	1541H
SMnC 21	1022
SMnC 21	1522H
SNCM 21	8617
SNCM 21	8617H
SNCM 21	8620
SNCM 21	8620H
SNCM 21 H	8617
SNCM 21 H	8617H
SNCM 21 H	8620
SNCM 21 H	8620H
SNCM 8	4340
SNCM 8	4340
SNCM 8	4340H
SNCM 8	4340H
SUM 11	1110
SUM 12	1110
SUM 21	1212

Japan

Designation	AISI
JIS	
SUM 22	1213
SUM 22 L	12L14
SUM 24 L	12L14
SUP 10	6150
SUP 10	6150
SUP 10	6150H
SUP 10	6150H
SUP 11	50B50
SUP 11	50B50H
SUP 4	1095

Sweden

Designation	AISI
SS14	
1370	1015
1370	1017
1450	1020
1550	1035
1650	1043
1660	1049
1672	1042
1672	1045
1672	1045H
1770	1070
1774	1078
1778	1070
1870	1095
1914	12L14
1957	1140
1973	1146
2120	1335
2120	1335H
2120	1541
2120	1541H
2225	4130
2225	4130
2225	4130H
2225	4130H
2230	6150
2230	6150
2230	6150H
2230	6150H
2234	4135
2234	4135H
2242	H13
2244	4137
2244	4137H
2244	4140
2244	4140
2244	4140H
2244	4140H

United Kingdom

Designation	AISI
B.S.	
4659 BS5	S5
040 A 20	1020
060 A 35	1035
060 A 47	1043

United Kingdom

Designation	AISI
B.S.	
060 A 62	1060
060 A 96	1095
070 M 20	1020
080 A 32	1035
080 A 35	1035
080 A 37	1035
080 A 40	1040
080 H 46	1043
080 M 36	1035
080 M 40	1043
080 M 46	1043
120 M 36	1039
150 M 36	1039
2 S 117	5135H
2 S 117	5140
2 S 119	4340
2 S 119	4340
2 S 119	4340H
2 S 119	4340H
2 S 516	1345
2 S 516	1345H
2 S 517	1345
2 S 517	1345H
2 S. 130	348
2 S. 93	1040
220 M 07	1213
250 A 58	9260
250 A 58	9260H
3 S 95	4340
3 S 95	4340
3 S 95	4340H
3 S 95	4340H
3111 Type 6	4340
3111 Type 6	4340
3111 Type 6	4340H
3111 Type 6	4340H
4559 BW1A	W1
4659 (SA W1)	W1
4659 BW1B	W1
4659 BW1C	W1
5 S 80	431
530 A 30	5130
530 A 32	5130H
530 A 32	5132
530 A 36	5132H
530 A 36	5135
530 A 40	5135H
530 A 40	5140
530 H 3	5135
530 H 30	5130
530 H 32	5130H
530 H 32	5132
530 H 36	5132H
530 H 40	5135H
530 H 40	5140
530 M 40	5135H
530 M 40	5140
534 A 99	E52100
535 A 99	E52100
708 A 37	4135
708 A 37	4135H
708 A 40	4137H

United Kingdom	
Designation	AISI
B.S.	
708 A 42	4137
708 A 42	4137H
708 A 42	4140
708 A 42	4140
708 A 42	4140H
708 A 42	4140H
708 M 40	4137
708 M 40	4140
708 M 40	4140
708 M 40	4140H
708 M 40	4140H
709 A 40	4137H
709 M 40	4137
709 M 40	4140
709 M 40	4140
709 M 40	4140H
709 M 40	4140H
735 A 50	6150
735 A 50	6150
735 A 50	6150H
735 A 50	6150H
805 A 20	8622
805 A 20	8622H
805 A 20	8720
805 A 20	8720H
805 A 20	8822
805 A 20	8822H
805 H 20	8617
805 H 20	8617H
805 H 20	8620
805 H 20	8620H
805 M 20	8617
805 M 20	8617H
805 M 20	8620
805 M 20	8620H
817 M 40	4340
817 M 40	4340
817 M 40	4340H
817 M 40	4340H
CDS 105/106	1039
CDS 110	4130
CDS 110	4130
CDS 110	4130H
CDS 110	4130H
En. 44 B	1095
En. 47	6150
En. 47	6150
En. 47	6150H
En. 47	6150H

United States	
Designation	AISI
Type 3	5132H
Type 7	8640
Type 7	8640
Type 7	8640H
Type 7	8640H
Type 7	8740
Type 7	8740H
Type 8	E4340
Type 8	E4340H

United States
AISI Designation
1005
1006
1008
1010
1012
1013
1015
1016
1017
1018
1019
1020
1021
1022
1023
1025
1026
1029
1030
1035
1037
1038
1038H
1039
1040
1042
1043
1044
1045
1045H
1046
1049
1050
1053
1055
1059
1060
1064
1065
1069
1070
1075
1078
1080
1084
1085
1086
1090
1095
1108
1110
1113
1117
1118
1137
1139
1140
1141
1144
1146
1151
1211
1212
1213

United States
AISI Designation
1215
12L14
1330
1330H
1335
1335H
1340
1340H
1345
1345H
15-5PH
1513
1522
1522H
1524
1524H
1526
1526H
1527
1536
1541
1541H
I548
1551
1552
1561
1566
15B21H
15B21RH
15B28H
15B30H
15B35H
15B35RH
15B37H
15B41H
15B48H
15B62H
4118
4118H
4118RH
4120H
4120RH
4130
4130
4130H
4130H
4130RH
4135
4135H
4137
4137H
4140
4140
4140H
4140H
4140RH
4142
4142H
4145
4145H
4145RH
4147
4147H
4150

United States		United States		United States	
AISI Designation		**AISI Designation**		**Designation**	**AISI**
4150H		1B60H		**AMS**	
4161		6118		294	4620
4161H		6118H		5010 D	1212
4161RH		6150		5024 C	1137
4320		6150		5032	1020
4320H		6150H		5040	1010
4320RH		6150H		5042	1010
4330V		81B45		5044	1010
4335V		81B45H		5045	1020
4340		8615		5047	1010
4340		8617		5053	1010
4340H		8617H		5060	1015
4340H		8620		5069	1018
4615		8620H		5070	1022
4620		8622		5075	1025
4620H		8622H		5077	1025
4620RH		8622RH		5080	1035
4626		8625		5082	1035
4626H		8625H		5085	1050
4718H		8627		5110	1080
4720		8627H		5112	1090
4720H		8630		5115	1070
4815		8630H		5121	1095
4815H		8637		5122	1095
4817		8637H		5132	1095
4817H		8640		5331	4340
4820		8640		5331	4340
4820H		8640H		5333	8615
4820RH		8640H		6272	8617
5046		8642		6274	8620
5046H		8642H		6275	94B17
50B40		8645		6275 A	94B15
50B40H		8645H		6276	8620
50B40RH		8650		6277	8620
50B44		8650H		6280	8630
50B44H		8655		6281	8630
50B46		8655H		6290	4615
50B46H		8660		6322	8740
50B50		8660H		6323	8740
50B50H		86B30H		6325	8740
50B60		86B45		6327	8740
50B60H		86B45H		6350	4130
5117		8720		6350	4130
5120		8720H		6355	8630
5120H		8720RH		6356	4130
5130		8740		6356	4130
5130H		8740H		6358	8740
5130RH		8822		6359	4340
5132		8822H		6359	4340
5132H		8822RH		6360	4130
5135		9260		6360	4130
5135H		9260H		6361	4130
5140		9310H		6361	4130
5140H		9310RH			
5140RH		94B15		6362	4130
5147H		94B15H		6362	4130
5150		94B17		6365 C	4135
5150H		94B17H		6370	4130
5155		94B30		6370	4130
5155H		94B30H		6371	4130
5160		W1		6371	4130
5160H		W2		6372 C	4135
5160RH		W5		6373	4130
51B60				6373	4130

United States

Designation	AISI
AMS	
6381	4140
6381	4140
6382	4140
6382	4140
6390	4140
6390	4140
6395	4140
6395	4140
6414	4340
6414	4340
6415	4340
6415	4340
6437	H11 591
6440	E52100
6443	E51100
6444	E52100
6446	E51100
6447	E52100
6448	6150
6448	6150
6449	E51100
6450	6150
6450	6150
6455	6150
6455	6150
6485	H11 591
6487	H11 591
6488	H11 591
6530	8630
6550	8630
7240	1060
7304	1095
ASME	
A107	1213
A107 (B1113)	1213
A108	1213
A108 (B1113)	1213
ASTM	
743	CE-30
914	15B21H
A107	1110
A107	1117
A107	1118
A107	1137
A107	1141
A107	1151
A107	1211
A107	1212
A107	12L14
A107 (B1111)	1211
A107 (B1212)	1212
A108	1008
A108	1010
A108	1016
A108	1017
A108	1018
A108	1117
A108	1118
A108	1141
A108	1144
A108	1151

United States

Designation	AISI
ASTM	
A108	1211
A108	1212
A108	12L14
A108 (B1111)	1211
A108 (B1212)	1212
A109	1137
A273	1026
A273	1029
A273	1042
A274	4135
A274	4720
A274	8660
A274	E52100
A29	9260
A295	E51100
A304	1330
A304	1330H
A304	1335H
A304	1340H
A304	1345H
A304	15B28H
A304	15B30H
A304	4027H
A304	4028H
A304	4032H
A304	4037H
A304	4042H
A304	4047H
A304	4118H
A304	4130H
A304	4130H
A304	4135H
A304	4137H
A304	4140H
A304	4140H
A304	4142H
A304	4145H
A304	4147H
A304	4150H
A304	4161H
A304	4320H
A304	4340H
A304	4340H
A304	4620H
A304	4626H
A304	4718H
A304	4720H
A304	4815H
A304	4817H
A304	4820H
A304	5046H
A304	50B40H
A304	50B44H
A304	50B46H
A304	50B50H
A304	50B60H
A304	5120H
A304	5130H
A304	5132H
A304	5135H
A304	5140H
A304	5150H
A304	5155H

United States

Designation	AISI
ASTM	
A304	5160H
A304	51B60H
A304	6118H
A304	6150H
A304	6150H
A304	81B45H
A304	8617H
A304	8620H
A304	8622H
A304	8625H
A304	8627H
A304	8630H
A304	8637H
A304	8640
A304	8640
A304	8640H
A304	8640H
A304	8642H
A304	8645H
A304	8650H
A304	8655H
A304	8660H
A304	86B30H
A304	86B45H
A304	8720H
A304	8740H
A304	8822H
A304	9260H
A304	9310H
A304	94B15H
A304	94B17H
A304	94B30H
A304	E4340H
A311	1137
A311	1141
A311	1144
A311	1151
A322	1330
A322	1335
A322	1340
A322	1345
A322	4023
A322	4024
A322	4027
A322	4028
A322	4032
A322	4037
A322	4042
A322	4047
A322	4118
A322	4130
A322	4130
A322	4137
A322	4140
A322	4140
A322	4142
A322	4145
A322	4147
A322	4150
A322	4161
A322	4320
A322	4340
A322	4340

United States		United States		United States	
Designation	**AISI**	**Designation**	**AISI**	**Designation**	**AISI**
ASTM		**ASTM**		**ASTM**	
A322	4615	A331	5132	A510	1030
A322	4620	A331	5135	A510	1035
A322	4626	A331	5140	A510	1037
A322	4720	A331	5150	A510	1038
A322	4815	A331	5155	A510	1039
A322	4817	A331	5160	A510	1040
A322	4820	A331	6150	A510	1042
A322	5120	A331	6150	A510	1043
A322	5132	A331	8620	A510	1044
A322	5135	A331	8630	A510	1045
A322	5140	A331	8655	A510	1046
A322	5150	A331	8740	A510	1049
A322	5155	A331	9260	A510	1050
A322	5160	A331	E4340	A510	1053
A322	6150	A331	E52100	A510	1055
A322	6150	A332	8660	A510	1060
A322	8615	A351	CF-3	A510	1070
A322	8620	A351	CF-8C	A510	1078
A322	8630	A351	CF-8M	A510	1080
A322	8640	A351	CH-20	A510	1084
A322	8640	A351	CN-7M	A510	1090
A322	8650	A355	4135	A510	1095
A322	8655	A505	4118	A510	1524
A322	8660	A505	4130	A510	1526
A322	8720	A505	4130	A510	1527
A322	8740	A505	4137	A510	1541
A322	9260	A505	4140	A510	1548
A322	E51100	A505	4140	A510	1551
A322	E52100	A505	4142	A510	1552
A331	1330	A505	4145	A510	1561
A331	1335	A505	4147	A510	1566
A331	1340	A505	4150	A512	1025
A331	1345	A505	4320	A512	1030
A331	4023	A505	4340	A513	1016
A331	4024	A505	4340	A513	1017
A331	4027	A505	4615	A513	1018
A331	4028	A505	4620	A513	1019
A331	4037	A505	4815	A513	4130
A331	4042	A505	4820	A513	4130
A331	4047	A505	5132	A513	8620
A331	4118	A505	5140	A513 (1024)	1524
A331	4130	A505	5150	A513 (1027)	1527
A331	4130	A505	5160	A519	1008
A331	4137	A505	E4340	A519	1010
A331	4140	A505	E51100	A519	1012
A331	4140	A505	E52100	A519	1015
A331	4142	A508	403 763	A519	1017
A331	4145	A510	1008	A519	1018
A331	4147	A510	1010	A519	1019
A331	4150	A510	1012	A519	1020
A331	4161	A510	1015	A519	1021
A331	4320	A510	1016	A519	1022
A331	4340	A510	1017	A519	1025
A331	4340	A510	1018	A519	1026
A331	4615	A510	1019	A519	1030
A331	4620	A510	1020	A519	1035
A331	4626	A510	1021	A519	1040
A331	4720	A510	1022	A519	1045
A331	4815	A510	1023	A519	1050
A331	4817	A510	1025	A519	1330
A331	4820	A510	1026	A519	1335
A331	5120	A510	1029	A519	1340

United States		United States		United States	
Designation	**AISI**	**Designation**	**AISI**	**Designation**	**AISI**
ASTM		**ASTM**		**ASTM**	
A519	1345	A544	1035	A576	1022
A519	1524	A544	1038	A576	1023
A519	1541	A545	1008	A576	1025
A519	4023	A545	1010	A576	1026
A519	4024	A545	1012	A576	1029
A519	4027	A545	1015	A576	1030
A519	4028	A545	1016	A576	1035
A519	4037	A545	1018	A576	1037
A519	4042	A545	1019	A576	1038
A519	4047	A545	1021	A576	1039
A519	4118	A545	1022	A576	1040
A519	4130	A545	1026	A576	1042
A519	4130	A545	1035	A576	1043
A519	4135	A545	1038	A576	1044
A519	4137	A545	1524	A576	1045
A519	4140	A545	1541	A576	1046
A519	4140	A546	1030	A576	1049
A519	4142	A546	1035	A576	1050
A519	4145	A546	1038	A576	1053
A519	4147	A546	1039	A576	1055
A519	4150	A546	1040	A576	1060
A519	4320	A546	1541	A576	1070
A519	4340	A547	1335	A576	1078
A519	4340	A547	1340	A576	1080
A519	4720	A547	4037	A576	1084
A519	4817	A547	4137	A576	1090
A519	4820	A547	4140	A576	1095
A519	5046	A547	4140	A646	4130
A519	50B40	A547	4142	A646	4130
A519	50B44	A547	4340	A646	4140
A519	50B46	A547	4340	A646	4140
A519	50B50	A548	10165	A646	4340
A519	50B60	A548	1018	A646	4340
A519	5120	A548	1019	A659	1015
A519	5132	A548	1021	A659	1016
A519	5135	A548	1022	A659	1017
A519	5140	A549	1008	A659	1018
A519	5150	A549	1010	A659	1020
A519	5155	A549	1012	A659	1021
A519	5160	A549	1015	A659	1023
A519	51B60	A549	1016	A682	1030
A519	81B45	A549	1017	A682	1035
A519	8650	A549	1018	A682	1040
A519	8660	A575	1008	A682	10454
A519	86B45	A575	1010	A682	1050
A519	94B15	A575	1012	A682	1055
A519	94B17	A575	1015	A682	1060
A519	94B30	A575	1017	A682	1070
A519	E4340	A575	1020	A682	1080
A519	E51100	A575	1023	A682	1095
A519	E52100	A575	1025	A686 (W-1)	W1
A534	4023	A575	1044	A686 (W-2)	W2
A535	4320	A576	1008	A686 (W-5)	W5
A535	4620	A576	1010	A914	15B35H
A535	4720	A576	1012	A914	15B35RH
A535	4820	A576	1015	A914	3310RH
A535	E52100	A576	1016	A914	4027H
A544	1017	A576	1017	A914	4118H
A544	1018	A576	1018	A914	4120H
A544	1020	A576	1019	A914	4120RH
A544	1022	A576	1020	A914	4130H
A544	1030	A576	1021	A914	4140H

United States

Designation	AISI
ASTM	
A914	4145H
A914	4161H
A914	4320H
A914	4620H
A914	4820H
A914	50B40H
A914	5130H
A914	5140H
A914	5160H
A914	8620
A914	8720H
Federal	
QQ-S-635 (C1030)	1030
QQ-S-635 (C1035)	1035
QQ-S-635 (C1042)	1042
QQ-S-635 (C1045)	1045
QQ-S-635 (C1050)	1050
QQ-S-635 (C1080)	1080
QQ-S-637	1141
QQ-S-637	1215
QQ-S-637 (C1008)	1008
QQ-S-637 (C1110)	1110
QQ-S-637 (C1117)	1117
QQ-S-637 (C1118)	1118
QQ-S-637 (C1137)	1137
QQ-S-637 (C1139)	1139
QQ-S-637 (C1140)	1140
QQ-S-637 (C1144)	1144
QQ-S-637 (C1146)	1146
QQ-S-637 (C1151)	1151
QQ-S-637 (C1211)	1211
QQ-S-637 (C1212)	1212
QQ-S-637 (C1913)	1213
QQ-S-698 (C1008)	1008
QQ-S-698 (C1015)	1015
QQ-S-700 (C1025)	1025
QQ-S-700 (C1030)	1030
QQ-S-700 (C1035)	1035
QQ-S-700 (C1045)	1045
QQ-S-700 (C1050)	1050
QQ-S-700 (C1055)	1055
QQ-S-700 (C1084)	1084
QQ-S-700 (C1095)	1095
MIL-SPEC	
MIL-S-11310 (CS1008)	1008
MIL-S-11310 (CS1010)	1010
MIL-S-11310 (CS1012)	1012
MIL-S-11310 (CS 1017)	1017
MIL-S-11310 (CS1018)	1018
MIL-S-11310 (CS1020)	1020
MIL-S-11310 (CS1020)	1022
MIL-S-11310 (CS1025)	1025
MIL-S-11310 (CS1030)	1030
MIL-S-11310 (CS1040)	1040
MIL-S-11595 (ORD4150)	4150
MIL-S-11713 (2)	1070
MIL-S-16788 (CS1095)	1095
MIL-S-16974	1015
MIL-S-16974	1050
MIL-S-16974	1060
MIL-S-16974	1080
MIL-S-16974	1330

United States

Designation	AISI
MIL-SPEC	
MIL-S-16974	1335
MIL-S-16974	1340
MIL-S-16974	41309
MIL-S-16974	4130
MIL-S-16974	4135
MIL-S-16974	4140
MIL-S-16974	4140
MIL-S-16974	4145
MIL-S-16974	4340
MIL-S-16974	4340
MIL-S-16974	8620
MIL-S-16974	8625
MIL-S-16974	8630
MIL-S-16974	8640
MIL-S-16974	8640
MIL-S-16974	8645
MIL-S-18411	1117
MIL-S-18733	4135
MIL-S-20137A	1151
MIL-S-22141	E52100
MIL-S-6049	8740
MIL-S-7420	E52100
MIL-S-7493	4615
MIL-S-7493	4620
MIL-S-8503	6150
MIL-S-8503	6150
SAE	
1268	6118H
3310RH	3310RH
J1268	1038H
J1268	1045H
J1268	1330H
J1268	1522H
J1268	1524H
J1268	1526H
J1268	1541H
J1268	15B21H
J1268	15B28H
J1268	15B30H
J1268	15B35H
J1268	15B35RH
J1268	15B37H
J1268	15B41H
J1268	15B48H
J1268	15B62H
J1268	4027H
J1268	4032H
J1268	4037H
J1268	4042H
J1268	4047H
J1268	4118H
J1268	4120H
J1268	4120RH
J1268	4130H
J1268	4135H
J1268	4137H
J1268	4140H
J1268	4142H
J1268	4145H
J1268	4147H
J1268	4150H
J1268	4161H

United States

Designation	AISI
SAE	
J1268	4320H
J1268	4340H
J1268	4620H
J1268	4718H
J1268	4720H
J1268	4815H
J1268	4817H
J1268	4820H
J1268	5046H
J1268	50B40H
J1268	50B44H
J1268	50B46H
J1268	50B50H
J1268	50B60H
J1268	5120H
J1268	5130H
J1268	5132H
J1268	5135H
J1268	5140H
J1268	5150H
J1268	5155H
J1268	5160H
J1268	51B60H
J1268	6150H
J1268	81B45H
J1268	8617H
J1268	8620
J1268	8625H
J1268	8627H
J1268	8630H
J1268	8637H
J1268	8640H
J1268	8642H
J1268	8645H
J1268	8650H
J1268	8655H
J1268	8660H
J1268	86B30H
J1268	86B45H
J1268	8720H
J1268	8740H
J1268	9260H
J1268	9310H
J1268	94B15H
J1268	94B17H
J1268	94B30H
J1397 (formerly J770)	4615
J1397 (formerly J770)	4626H
J1868	15B21H
J1868	15B35H
J1868	15B35RH
J1868	3310RH
J1868	4027H
J1868	4118H
J1868	4120H
J1868	4120RH
J1868	4130H
J1868	4140H
J1868	4145H
J1868	4320H
J1868	4620H
J1868	50B40H
J1868	5130H

United States		United States		United States	
Designation	**AISI**	**Designation**	**AISI**	**Designation**	**AISI**
SAE		SAE		SAE	
J1868	5140H	J403	1551	J404	8637
J1868	5160H	J403	1552	J404	8640
J1868	8620	J403	1561	J404	8640
J1868	8720H	J403	1566	J404	8642
J403	1008	J404	1330	J404	8645
J403	1010	J404	1335	J404	8650
J403	1012	J404	1340	J404	8655
J403	1015	J404	1345	J404	8660
J403	1016	J404	4023	J404	86B45
J403	1017	J404	4024	J404	8720
J403	1018	J404	4027	J404	8740
J403	1019	J404	4028	J404	8822
J403	1020	J404	4032	J404	9260
J403	1021	J404	4037	J404	94B15
J403	1022	J404	4042	J404	94B17
J403	1023	J404	4047	J404	94B30
J403	1025	J404	4118	J404	E4340
J403	1026	J404	4130	J404	E51100
J403	1029	J404	4130	J404	E52100
J403	1030	J404	4135	J407	1335H
J403	1035	J404	4137	J407	1340H
J403	1037	J404	4140	J407	1345H
J403	1038	J404	4140	J407	4028H
J403	1039	J404	4142	J407	4130H
J403	1040	J404	4145	J407	4140H
J403	1042	J404	4147	J407	4340H
J403	1043	J404	4150	J407	6150H
J403	1044	J404	4161	J407	8620H
J403	1045	J404	4320	J407	8622H
J403	1046	J404	4340	J407	8640H
J403	1049	J404	4340	J407	8822H
J403	1050	J404	4620	J407	E4340H
J403	1053	J404	4626	J412	1008
J403	1055	J404	4720	J412	1010
J403	1060	J404	4815	J412	1012
J403	1070	J404	4817	J412	1015
J403	1078	J404	4820	J412	1016
J403	1080	J404	5046	J412	1017
J403	1084	J404	50B40	J412	1018
J403	1090	J404	50B44	J412	1019
J403	1095	J404	50B46	J412	1020
J403	1110	J404	50B50	J412	1021
J403	1117	J404	50B60	J412	1022
J403	1118	J404	5120	J412	1023
J403	1137	J404	5130	J412	1025
J403	1139	J404	5132	J412	1026
J403	1140	J404	5135	J412	1029
J403	1141	J404	5140	J412	1030
J403	1144	J404	5150	J412	1035
J403	1146	J404	5155	J412	1037
J403	1151	J404	5160	J412	1038
J403	1211	J404	51B60	J412	1039
J403	1212	J404	6118	J412	1040
J403	1213	J404	6150	J412	1042
J403	12L14	J404	6150	J412	1043
J403	1513	J404	81B45	J412	1044
J403	1522	J404	8615	J412	1045
J403	1524	J404	8617	J412	1046
J403	1526	J404	8622	J412	1049
J403	1527	J404	8625	J412	1050
J403	1541	J404	8627	J412	1053
J403	1548	J404	8630	J412	1055

United States			United States			United States	
Designation	**AISI**		**Designation**	**AISI**		**Designation**	**AISI**
SAE			SAE			SAE	
J412	1060		J412	5046		J414	1070
J412	1070		J412	50B40		J414	1078
J412	1078		J412	50B44		J414	1080
J412	1080		J412	50B46		J414	1084
J412	1084		J412	50B50		J414	1090
J412	1090		J412	50B60		J414	1095
J412	1095		J412	5130		J414	1117
J412	1110		J412	5132		J414	1118
J412	1117		J412	5135		J414	1137
J412	1118		J412	5140		J414	1140
J412	1137		J412	5150		J414	1141
J412	1140		J412	5155		J414	1144
J412	1141		J412	5160		J414	1146
J412	1144		J412	51B60		J414	1151
J412	1146		J412	6150		J414	12L14
J412	1151		J412	6150		J414	1524
J412	1215		J412	81B45		J414	1541
J412	12L14		J412	8630		J414	1548
J412	1330		J412	8637		J414	1551
J412	1335		J412	8640		J414	1552
J412	1340		J412	8640		J437 (W108)	W1
J412	1345		J412	8642		J437 (W109)	W1
J412	1513		J412	8645		J437 (W110)	W1
J412	1522		J412	8650		J437 (W112)	W1
J412	1524		J412	8655		J438 (W108)	W1
J412	1526		J412	8660		J438 (W109)	W1
J412	1527		J412	86B45		J438 (W110)	W1
J412	1541		J412	8740		J438 (W112)	W1
J412	1548		J412	9260		J438 (W209)	W2
J412	1551		J412	94B30		J438 (W210)	W2
J412	1552		J412	E51100		J770	1330
J412	1561		J412	E52100		J770	1335
J412	1566		J414	1008		J770	1340
J412	4023		J414	1010		J770	1345
J412	4024		J414	1012		J770	4023
J412	4027		J414	1015		J770	4024
J412	4028		J414	1016		J770	4027
J412	4032		J414	1017		J770	4028
J412	4037		J414	1018		J770	4032
J412	4042		J414	1019		J770	4037
J412	4047		J414	1020		J770	4042
J412	4118		J414	1021		J770	4047
J412	4130		J414	1022		J770	4118
J412	4130		J414	1023		J770	4130
J412	4135		J414	1025		J770	4130
J412	4137		J414	1026		J770	4135
J412	4140		J414	1030		J770	4137
J412	4140		J414	1035		J770	4140
J412	4142		J414	1037		J770	4140
J412	4145		J414	1038		J770	4142
J412	4147		J414	1039		J770	4145
J412	4150		J414	1040		J770	4147
J412	4161		J414	1042		J770	4150
J412	4320		J414	1043		J770	4161
J412	4340		J414	1044		J770	4320
J412	4340		J414	1045		J770	4340
J412	4620		J414	1046		J770	4340
J412	4626		J414	1049		J770	4620
J412	4720		J414	1050		J770	4626
J412	4815		J414	1053		J770	4720
J412	4817		J414	1055		J770	4815
J412	4820		J414	1060		J770	4817

United States		United States		United States	
Designation	**AISI**	**Designation**	**AISI**	**Designation**	**AISI**
SAE		**UNS**		**UNS**	
J770	4820	G10250	1025	G41370	4137
J770	5046	G10260	1026	G41400	4140
J770	50B40	G10290	1029	G41400	4140
J770	50B44	G10300	1030	G41420	4142
J770	50B46	G10350	1035	G41450	4145
J770	50B50	G10370	1037	G41470	4147
J770	50B60	G10380	1038	G41500	4150
J770	5120	G10390	1039	G41610	4161
J770	5130	G10430	1043	G43200	4320
J770	5132	G10440	1044	G43400	4340
J770	5135	G10450	1045	G43400	4340
J770	5140	G10460	1046	G43406	E4340
J770	5150	G10490	1049	G46150	4615
J770	5155	G10500	1050	G46200	4620
J770	5160	G10530	1053	G46260	4626
J770	51B60	G10550	1055	G47200	4720
J770	6118	G10600	1060	G48150	4815
J770	6150	G10700	1070	G48170	4817
J770	6150	G10780	1078	G48200	4820
J770	81B45	G10800	1080	G50401	50B40
J770	8615	G10840	1084	G50441	50B44
J770	8617	G11100	1110	G50460	5046
J770	8622	G11170	1117	G50461	50B46
J770	8625	G11180	1118	G50501	50B50
J770	8627	G11390	1139	G50601	50B60
J770	8630	G11400	1140	G51170	5117
J770	8637	G11410	1141	G51200	5120
J770	8640	G11440	1144	G51300	5130
J770	8640	G11460	1146	G51320	5132
J770	8642	G11510	1151	G51350	5135
J770	8645	G12110	1211	G51400	5140
J770	8650	G12120	1212	G51500	5150
J770	8655	G12130	1213	G51550	5155
J770	8660	G12144	12L14	G51600	5160
J770	86B45	G12150	1215	G51601	51B60
J770	8720	G13300	1330	G51986	E51100
J770	8740	G13350	1335	G52986	E52100
J770	8822	G13400	1340	G61180	6118
J770	9260	G13450	1345	G61500	6150
J770	94B15	G15130	1513	G61500	6150
J770	94B17	G15220	1522	G81451	81B45
J770	94B30	G15240	1524	G86150	8615
J770	E4340	G15260	1526	G86170	8617
J770	E51100	G15270	1527	G86200	8620
J770	E52100	G15410	1541	G86220	8622
J8668	4820H	G15480	1548	G86250	8625
		G15510	1551	G86270	8627
UNS		G15520	1552	G86300	8630
G10080	1008	G15610	1561	G86301	86B30H
G10100	1010	G15660	1566	G86370	8637
G10120	1012	G40230	4023	G86400	8640
G10150	1015	G40240	4024	G86400	8640
G10160	1016	G40270	4027	G86420	8642
G10170	1017	G40280	4028	G86450	8645
G10180	1018	G40320	4032	G86451	86B45
G10190	1019	G40370	4037	G86500	8650
G10200	1020	G40420	4042	G86550	8655
G10200	1090	G40470	4047	G86600	8660
G10200	1095	G41180	4118	G87200	8720
G10200	1137	G41300	4130	G87400	8740
G10210	1021	G41300	4130	G88220	8822
G10220	1022	G41350	4135	G92600	9260
G10230	1023				

United States		United States		United States	
Designation	**AISI**	**Designation**	**AISI**	**Designation**	**AISI**
UNS		UNS		UNS	
G93100	9310H	H41350	4135H	H51400	5140H
G94151	94B15	H41370	4137H	H51500	5150H
G94171	94B17	H41400	4140H	H51550	5155H
G94301	94B30	H41400	4140H	H51600	5160H
H10380	1038H	H41420	4142H	H51601	51B60H
H10450	1045H	H41450	4145H	H61180	6118H
H13300	1330H	H41470	4147H	H61500	6150H
H13350	1335H	H41500	4150H	H61500	6150H
H13400	1340H	H41610	4161H	H81451	81B45H
H13450	1345H	H43200	4320H	H86170	8617H
H15211	15B21H	H43400	4340H	H86200	8620H
H15220	1522H	H43400	4340H	H86220	8622H
H15240	1524H	H43406	E4340H	H86250	8625H
H15260	1526H	H46200	4620H	H86270	8627H
H15351	15B35H	H46260	4626H	H86300	8630H
H15351	15B35RH	H47200	4720H	H86370	8637H
H15371	15B37H	H48150	4815H	H86400	8640H
H15410	1541H	H48170	4817H	H86400	8640H
H15411	15B41H	H48200	4820H	H86420	8642H
H15481	15B48H	H494171	94B17H	H86450	8645H
H15621	15B62H	H50401	50B40H	H86451	86B45H
H40270	4027H	H50441	50B44H	H86500	8650H
H40280	4028H	H50460	5046H	H86550	8655H
H40320	4032H	H50461	50B46H	H86600	8660H
H40370	4037H	H50501	50B50H	H87200	8720H
H40420	4042H	H50601	50B60H	H87400	8740H
H40470	4047H	H51200	5120H	H88220	8822H
H41180	4118H	H51300	5130H	H92600	9260H
H41300	4130H	H51320	5132H	H94151	94B15H
H41300	4130H	H51350	5135H	H94301	94B30H

Appendix 12.

Description of hardness code and specification of hardness numbers for metals. (From Kenneth H. Budinski, Engineering Materials: Properties & Selection, Vol 3e, p 37, 38 (1989). Reprinted by permission of Prentice-Hall, Englewood Cliffs, New Jersey)

Specify hardness according to the code described below.

This code is in agreement with the method of designation used by the following standards organizations:

1. American Society for Testing and Materials (ASTM)
2. American National Standards Institute (ANSI)
3. International Standards Organization (ISO)

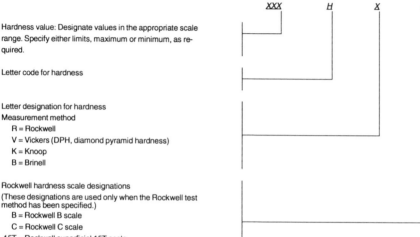

Hardness value: Designate values in the appropriate scale range. Specify either limits, maximum or minimum, as required.

Letter code for hardness

Letter designation for hardness
Measurement method
   R = Rockwell
   V = Vickers (DPH, diamond pyramid hardness)
   K = Knoop
   B = Brinell

Rockwell hardness scale designations
(These designations are used only when the Rockwell test method has been specified.)
   B = Rockwell B scale
   C = Rockwell C scale
  15T = Rockwell superficial 15T scale
  15N = Rockwell superficial 15N scale etc.

Example

1.	50-60 HRC		means: a hardness value of 50 to 60 using the Rockwell C scale.
2.	85 HR15T	MAX	means: a maximum hardness value of 85 using the Rockwell Superficial 15T scale.
3.	185-240 HV		means: a hardness value of 185-240 using the Vickers hardness tester and a test load of 1 kilogram-force.
		1Kgf	
4.	500 HK 200gf	MIN	means: a minimum hardness value of 500 using the Knoop hardness tester and a test load of 200 grams-force.

Appendix 13.

Comparison of hardness tests. (From same source as Appendix 2)

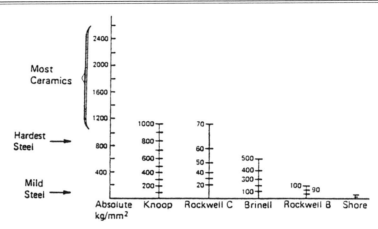

Hardness test	Indenter	Load	Application
Knoop or Vickers	Diamond	1 g to 2000 g	Microhardness of soft steels to ceramics
Brinell	Ball	500 & 3000 kg	Soft steels & metals to 40 HRC
Rockwell B	Ball	100 kg	Soft steels & nonferrous metals
Rockwell T	Ball	15, 30 & 45 kg	Thin soft metals
Rockwell N	Diamond	15, 30 & 45 kg	Hard thin sheet metals
Rockwell A	Diamond	50 kg	Cemented carbides
Rockwell R	Ball	10 kg	Polymers
Shore Durometer	Needle	Spring	Elastomers
Rockwell C	Diamond	150 kg	Hardened metals (thick)

Appendix 14.

Approximate equivalent hardness numbers and tensile strengths for Vickers hardness numbers for steel. (From same source as Appendix 2)

Vickers hardness No.	Brinell hardness No., 3000-kg load, 10-mm ball Standard ball	Tungsten carbide ball	Rockwell hardness No. A scale, 60-kg load, Brale indenter	B scale, 100-kg load, 1/16-in.-diam ball	C scale, 150-kg load, Brale indenter	D scale, 100-kg load, Brale indenter	Rockwell superficial hardness No., superficial Brale indenter 15N scale, 15-kg load	30N scale, 30-kg load	45N scale, 45-kg load	Knoop hardness No., 500-g load and greater	Shore Sclero-scope hardness No.	Tensile strength (approx), 1000 psi	Vickers hardness No.
940	...	...	85.6	...	68.0	76.9	93.2	84.4	75.4	920	97	...	940
920	...	...	85.3	...	67.5	76.5	93.0	84.0	74.8	908	96	...	920
900	...	...	85.0	...	67.0	76.1	92.9	83.6	74.2	895	95	...	900
880	...	(767)	84.7	...	66.4	75.7	92.7	83.1	74.6	882	93	...	880
860	...	(757)	84.4	...	65.9	75.3	92.5	82.7	73.1	867	92	...	860
840	...	(745)	84.1	...	65.3	74.8	92.3	82.2	72.2	852	91	...	840
820	...	(733)	83.8	...	64.7	74.3	92.1	81.7	71.8	837	90	...	820
800	...	(722)	83.4	...	64.0	73.8	91.8	81.1	71.0	822	88	...	800
780	...	(710)	83.0	...	63.3	73.3	91.5	30.4	70.2	806	87	...	780
760	...	(698)	82.6	...	62.5	72.6	91.2	79.7	69.4	788	86	...	760
740	...	(684)	82.2	...	61.8	72.1	91.0	79.1	68.6	772	84	...	740
720	...	(670)	81.8	...	61.0	71.5	90.7	78.4	67.7	754	83	...	720
700	...	(656)	81.3	...	60.1	70.8	90.3	77.6	66.7	735	81	...	700
690	...	(647)	81.1	...	59.7	70.5	90.1	77.2	66.2	725	...	...	690
680	...	(638)	80.8	...	59.2	70.1	89.8	76.8	65.7	716	80	355	680
670	...	(630)	80.6	...	58.8	69.8	89.7	76.4	65.3	706	...	348	670
660	...	620	80.3	...	58.3	69.4	89.5	75.9	64.7	697	79	342	660
650	...	611	80.0	...	57.8	69.0	89.2	75.5	64.1	687	78	336	650
640	...	601	79.8	...	57.3	68.7	89.0	75.1	63.5	677	77	328	640
630	...	591	79.5	...	56.8	68.3	88.8	74.6	63.0	667	76	323	630
620	...	582	79.2	...	56.3	67.9	88.5	74.2	62.4	657	75	317	620
610	...	573	78.9	...	55.7	67.5	88.2	73.6	61.7	646	...	310	610
600	...	564	78.6	...	55.2	67.0	88.0	73.2	61.2	636	74	303	600
590	...	554	78.4	...	54.7	66.7	87.8	72.7	60.5	625	73	298	590
580	...	545	78.0	...	54.1	66.2	87.5	72.1	59.9	615	72	293	580
570	...	535	77.8	...	53.6	65.8	87.2	71.7	59.3	604	...	288	570
560	...	525	77.4	...	53.0	65.4	86.9	71.2	58.6	594	71	283	560
550	(505)	517	77.0	...	52.3	64.8	86.6	70.5	57.8	583	70	276	550
540	(496)	507	76.7	...	51.7	64.4	86.3	70.0	57.0	572	69	270	540
530	(488)	497	76.4	...	51.1	63.9	86.0	69.5	56.2	561	68	265	530
520	(480)	488	76.1	...	50.5	63.5	85.7	69.0	55.6	550	67	250	520
510	(473)	479	75.7	...	49.8	62.9	85.4	68.3	54.7	539	...	254	510
500	(565)	471	75.3	...	49.1	62.2	85.0	67.7	53.9	528	66	247	500
490	(456)	460	74.9	...	48.4	61.6	84.7	67.1	53.1	517	65	241	490
480	(448)	452	74.5	...	47.7	61.3	84.3	66.4	52.2	505	64	235	480
470	441	442	74.1	...	46.9	60.7	83.9	65.7	51.3	494	...	228	470
460	433	433	73.6	...	46.1	60.1	83.6	64.9	50.4	482	62	223	460
450	425	425	73.3	...	45.3	59.4	83.2	64.3	49.4	471	...	217	450
440	415	415	72.8	...	44.5	58.8	82.8	63.5	48.4	459	59	212	440
430	405	405	72.3	...	43.6	58.2	82.3	62.7	47.4	447	58	205	430
420	397	397	71.8	...	42.7	57.5	81.8	61.9	46.4	435	57	199	420
410	388	388	71.4	...	41.8	56.8	81.4	61.1	45.3	423	56	193	410
400	379	379	70.8	...	40.8	56.0	80.8	60.2	44.1	412	55	187	400
390	369	369	70.3	...	39.8	55.2	80.3	59.3	42.9	400	...	181	390
380	360	360	69.8	(110.0)	38.8	54.4	79.8	58.4	41.7	389	52	175	380
370	350	350	69.2	...	37.7	53.6	79.2	57.4	40.4	378	51	170	370
360	341	341	68.7	(109.0)	36.6	52.8	78.6	56.4	39.1	367	50	164	360
350	331	331	68.1	...	35.5	51.9	78.0	55.4	37.8	356	48	159	350
340	322	322	67.6	(108.0)	34.4	51.1	77.4	54.4	36.5	346	47	155	340
330	313	313	67.0	...	33.3	50.2	76.8	53.6	35.2	337	46	150	330
320	303	303	66.4	(107.0)	32.2	49.4	76.2	52.3	33.9	328	45	146	320
310	294	294	65.8	...	31.0	48.4	75.6	51.3	32.5	318	...	142	310
300	284	284	65.2	(105.5)	29.8	47.5	74.9	50.2	31.1	309	42	138	300
295	280	280	64.8	...	29.2	47.1	74.6	49.7	30.4	305	...	136	295
290	275	275	64.5	(104.5)	28.5	46.5	74.2	49.0	29.5	300	41	133	290
285	270	270	64.2	...	27.8	46.0	73.8	48.4	28.7	296	...	131	285
280	265	265	63.8	(103.5)	27.1	45.3	73.4	47.8	27.9	291	40	129	280
275	261	261	63.5	...	26.4	44.9	73.0	47.2	27.1	286	39	127	275
270	256	256	63.1	(102.0)	25.6	44.3	72.6	45.4	26.2	282	38	124	270
265	252	252	62.7	...	24.8	43.7	72.1	45.7	25.2	277	...	122	265
260	247	247	62.4	(101.0)	24.0	43.1	71.6	45.0	24.3	272	37	120	260
255	243	243	62.0	...	23.1	42.2	71.1	44.2	23.2	267	...	117	255
250	238	238	61.6	99.5	22.2	41.7	70.6	43.4	22.2	262	36	115	250

(continued)

(Continued)

Vickers hardness No.	Brinell hardness No., 3000-kg load, 10-mm ball Standard ball	Tungsten carbide ball	Rockwell hardness No. A scale, 60-kg load, Brale indenter	B scale, 100-kg load, 1/16-in.-diam ball	C scale, 150-kg load, Brale indenter	D scale, 100-kg load, Brale indenter	Rockwell superficial hardness No., superficial Brale indenter 15N scale, 15-kg load	30N scale, 30-kg load	45N scale, 45-kg load	Knoop hardness No., 500-g load and greater	Shore Sclero-scope hardness No.	Tensile strength (approx), 1000 psi	Vickers hardness No.
245	233	233	61.2	...	21.3	41.1	70.1	42.5	21.1	258	35	113	245
240	228	228	60.7	98.1	20.3	40.3	69.6	41.7	19.9	253	34	111	240
230	219	219	...	96.7	(18.0)	...	...	...	...	243	33	106	230
220	209	209	...	95.0	(15.7)	...	...	...	...	234	32	101	220
210	200	200	...	93.4	(13.4)	...	...	...	...	226	30	97	210
200	190	190	...	91.5	(11.0)	...	...	...	...	216	29	92	200
190	181	181	...	89.5	(8.5)	...	...	...	...	206	28	88	190
180	171	171	...	87.1	(6.0)	...	...	...	...	196	26	84	180
170	162	162	...	85.0	(3.0)	...	...	...	...	185	25	79	170
160	152	152	...	81.7	(0.0)	...	...	...	...	175	23	75	160
150	143	143	...	78.7	...	...	...	...	...	164	22	71	150
140	133	133	...	75.0	...	...	...	...	...	154	21	66	140
130	124	124	...	71.2	...	...	...	...	...	143	20	62	130
120	114	114	...	66.7	...	...	...	...	...	133	18	57	120
110	105	105	...	62.3	...	...	...	...	...	123	...	...	110
100	95	95	...	56.2	...	...	...	...	...	112	...	...	100
95	90	90	...	52.0	...	...	...	...	...	107	...	...	95
90	86	86	...	48.0	...	...	...	...	...	102	...	...	90
85	81	81	...	41.0	...	...	...	...	...	97	...	...	85

For carbon and alloy steels in the annealed, normalized, and quenched-and-tempered conditions; less accurate for cold worked condition and for austenitic steels. The values in **boldface type** correspond to the values in the joint SAE-ASM-ASTM hardness conversions as printed in ASTM E140, Table 1. The values in parentheses are beyond normal range and are given for information only.

Appendix 15.

Approximate equivalent hardness numbers and tensile strengths for Brinell hardness numbers for steel. (From same source as Appendix 2)

Brinell indentation diam,mm	Brinell hardness No., 3000-kg load, 10-mm ball — Standard ball	Tungsten carbide ball	Vickers hardness No.	A scale, 60-kg load, Brale indenter	B scale, 100-kg load, 1/16-in.- diam ball	C scale, 150-kg load, Brale indenter	D scale, 100-kg load, Brale indenter	15N scale, 15-kg load	30N scale, 30-kg load	45N scale, 45-kg load	Knoop hardness No., 500-g load and greater	Shore Sclero- scope hardness No.	Tensile strength (approx), 1000psi	Brinell indentation diam,mm
2.25	...	(745)	840	84.1	...	65.3	74.8	92.3	82.2	72.2	852	91	...	2.25
2.30	...	(712)	783	83.1	...	63.4	73.4	91.6	80.5	70.4	808	...	...	2.30
2.35	...	(682)	737	82.2	...	61.7	72.0	91.0	79.0	68.5	768	84	...	2.35
2.40	...	(653)	697	81.2	...	60.0	70.7	90.2	77.5	66.5	732	81	...	2.40
2.45	...	627	667	80.5	...	58.7	69.7	89.6	76.3	65.1	703	79	347	2.45
2.50	...	601	640	79.8	...	57.3	68.7	89.0	75.1	63.5	677	77	328	2.50
2.55	...	578	615	79.1	...	56.0	67.7	88.4	73.9	62.1	652	75	313	2.55
2.60	...	555	591	78.4	...	54.7	66.7	87.8	72.7	60.6	626	73	298	2.60
2.65	...	534	569	77.8	...	53.5	65.8	87.2	71.6	59.2	604	71	288	2.65
2.70	...	514	547	76.9	...	52.1	64.7	86.5	70.3	57.6	579	70	273	2.70
2.75	(495)	...	539	76.7	...	51.6	64.3	86.3	69.9	56.9	571	...	269	2.75
2.75	...	495	528	76.3	...	51.0	63.8	85.9	69.4	56.1	558	68	263	2.75
2.80	(477)	...	516	75.9	...	50.3	63.2	85.6	68.7	55.2	545	...	257	2.80
2.80	...	477	508	75.6	...	49.6	62.7	85.3	68.2	54.5	537	66	252	2.80
2.85	(461)	...	495	75.1	...	48.8	61.9	84.9	67.4	53.5	523	...	244	2.85
2.85	...	461	491	74.9	...	48.5	61.7	84.7	67.2	53.2	518	65	242	2.85
2.90	444	...	474	74.3	...	47.2	61.0	84.1	66.0	51.7	499	...	231	2.90
2.90	...	444	472	74.2	...	47.1	60.8	84.0	65.8	51.5	496	63	229	2.90
2.95	429	429	455	73.4	...	45.7	59.7	83.4	64.6	49.9	476	61	220	2.95
3.00	415	415	440	72.8	...	44.5	58.8	82.8	63.5	48.4	459	59	212	3.00
3.05	401	401	425	72.0	...	43.1	57.8	82.0	62.3	46.9	441	58	202	3.05
3.10	388	388	410	71.4	...	41.8	56.8	81.4	61.1	45.3	423	56	193	3.10
3.15	375	375	396	70.6	...	40.4	55.7	80.6	59.9	43.6	407	54	184	3.15
3.20	363	363	383	70.0	...	39.1	54.6	80.0	58.7	42.0	392	52	177	3.20
3.25	352	352	372	69.3	(110.0)	37.9	53.8	79.3	57.6	40.5	379	51	172	3.25
3.30	341	341	360	68.7	(109.0)	36.6	52.8	78.6	58.4	39.1	367	50	164	3.30
3.35	331	331	350	68.1	(108.5)	35.5	51.9	78.0	55.4	37.8	356	48	159	3.35
3.40	321	321	339	67.5	(108.0)	34.3	51.0	77.3	54.3	36.4	345	47	154	3.40
3.45	311	311	328	66.9	(107.5)	33.1	50.0	76.7	53.3	34.4	336	46	149	3.45
3.50	302	302	319	66.3	(107.0)	32.1	49.3	76.1	52.2	33.8	327	45	146	3.50
3.55	293	293	309	65.7	(106.0)	30.9	48.3	75.5	51.2	32.4	318	43	142	3.55
3.60	285	285	301	65.3	(105.5)	29.9	47.6	75.0	50.3	31.2	310	42	138	3.60
3.65	277	277	292	64.6	(104.5)	28.8	46.7	74.4	49.3	29.9	302	41	134	3.65
3.70	269	269	284	64.1	(104.0)	27.6	45.9	73.7	48.3	28.5	294	40	131	3.70
3.75	262	262	276	63.6	(103.0)	26.6	45.0	73.1	47.3	27.3	286	39	127	3.75
3.80	255	255	269	63.0	(102.0)	25.4	44.2	72.5	46.2	26.0	279	38	123	3.80
3.85	248	248	261	62.5	(101.0)	24.2	43.2	71.7	45.1	24.5	272	37	120	3.85
3.90	241	241	253	61.8	100.0	22.8	42.0	70.9	43.9	22.8	265	36	116	3.90
3.95	235	235	247	61.4	99.0	21.7	41.4	70.3	42.9	21.5	259	35	114	3.95
4.00	229	229	241	60.8	98.2	20.5	40.5	69.7	41.9	20.1	253	34	111	4.00
4.05	223	223	234	...	97.3	(19.0)	...	...	...	...	247	...	107	4.05
4.10	217	217	228	...	96.4	(17.7)	...	...	...	...	242	33	105	4.10
4.15	212	212	222	...	95.5	(16.4)	...	...	...	...	237	32	102	4.15
4.20	207	207	218	...	94.6	(15.2)	...	...	...	...	232	31	100	4.20
4.25	201	201	212	...	93.7	(13.8)	...	...	...	...	227	...	98	4.25
4.30	197	197	207	...	92.8	(12.7)	...	...	...	...	222	30	95	4.30
4.35	192	192	202	...	91.9	(11.5)	...	...	...	...	217	29	93	4.35
4.40	187	187	196	...	90.9	(10.2)	...	...	...	...	212	...	90	4.40
4.45	183	183	192	...	90.0	(9.0)	...	...	...	...	207	28	89	4.45
4.50	179	179	188	...	89.0	(8.0)	...	...	...	...	202	27	87	4.50
4.55	174	174	182	...	88.0	(6.7)	...	...	...	...	198	...	85	4.55
4.60	170	170	178	...	87.0	(5.4)	...	...	...	...	194	26	83	4.60
4.65	167	167	175	...	86.0	(4.4)	...	...	...	...	190	...	81	4.65
4.70	163	163	171	...	85.0	(3.3)	...	...	...	...	186	25	79	4.70
4.75	159	159	167	...	83.9	(2.0)	...	...	...	...	182	...	78	4.75
4.80	156	156	163	...	82.9	(0.9)	...	...	...	...	178	24	76	4.80
4.85	152	152	159	...	81.9	...	...	...	...	...	174	...	75	4.85
4.90	149	149	156	...	80.8	...	...	...	...	...	170	23	73	4.90
4.95	146	146	153	...	79.7	...	...	...	...	...	166	...	72	4.95
5.00	143	143	150	...	78.6	...	...	...	...	...	163	22	71	5.00
5.10	137	137	143	...	76.4	...	...	...	...	...	157	21	67	5.10

(continued)

(Continued)

Brinell indenta- tion diam,mm	Brinell hardness No., 3000-kg load, 10-mm ball		Vickers hardness No.	Rockwell hardness No.				Rockwell superficial hardness No., superficial Brale indenter			Knoop hardness No., 500-g load and greater	Shore Sclero- scope hardness No.	Tensile strength (approx), 1000 psi	Brinell indenta- tion diam,mm
	Standard ball	Tungsten carbide ball		A scale, 60-kg load, Brale indenter	B scale, 100-kg load, 1/16-in.- diam ball	C scale, 150-kg load, Brale indenter	D scale, 100-kg load, Brale indenter	15N scale, 15-kg load	30N scale, 30-kg load	45N scale, 45-kg load				
5.20	131	131	137	...	74.2	...	...	...	...	...	151	...	65	5.20
5.30	126	126	132	...	72.0	...	...	...	...	...	145	20	63	5.30
5.40	121	121	127	...	69.8	...	...	...	...	...	140	19	60	5.40
5.50	116	116	122	...	67.6	...	...	...	...	...	135	18	58	5.50
5.60	111	111	117	...	65.4	...	...	...	...	...	131	17	56	5.60

For carbon and alloy steels in the annealed, normalized, and quenched-and-tempered conditions; less accurate for cold worked condition and for austenitic steels. The values in **boldface type** correspond to the values in the joint SAE-ASM-ASTM hardness conversions as printed in ASTM E140, Table 3. Values in parentheses are beyond normal range and are given for information only. Brinell numbers are based on the diameter of impressed indentation. If the ball distorts (flattens) during test, Brinell numbers will vary in accordance with the degree of such distortion when related to hardnesses determined with a Vickers diamond pyramid, Rockwell Brale, or other indenter that does not sensibly distort. At high hardnesses, therefore, the relationship between Brinell and Vickers or Rockwell scales is affected by the type of ball used. Standard steel balls tend to flatten slightly more than tungsten carbide balls, resulting in a larger indentation and a lower Brinell number than shown by a tungsten carbide ball. Thus, on a specimen of about 539 to 547 HV, a standard ball will leave a 2.75-mm indentation (495 HB), and a tungsten carbide ball a 2.70-mm indentation (514 HB). Conversely, identical indentation diameters for both types of ball will correspond to different Vickers and Rockwell values. Thus, if indentations in two different specimens both are 2.75 mm in diameter (495 HB), the specimen tested with a standard ball has a Vickers hardness of 539 whereas the specimen tested with a tungsten carbide ball has a Vickers hardness of 528.

Appendix 16.

Approximate equivalent hardness numbers and tensile strengths for Rockwell C and B hardness numbers for steel. (From same source as Appendix 2)

Rockwell C-scale hardness No.	Vickers hardness No.	Brinell hardness No., 3000-kg load 10-mm ball Standard ball	Tungsten carbide ball	A scale, 60-kg load, Brale indenter	B scale, 100-kg load, 1/16-in. diam ball	D scale, 100-kg load, Brale indenter	15N scale, 15-kg load	30N scale, 30-kg load	45N scale, 45-kg load	Knoop hardness No., 500-g load and greater	Shore Sclero-scope hardness No.	Tensile strength (approx), 1000 psi	Rockwell C-scale hardness No.
Rockwell C-Scale Hardness Numbers													
68	940	...	...	85.6	...	76.9	93.2	84.4	75.4	920	97	...	68
67	900	...	...	85.0	...	76.1	92.9	83.6	74.2	895	95	...	67
66	865	...	...	84.5	...	75.4	92.5	82.8	73.3	870	92	...	66
65	832	...	(739)	83.9	...	74.5	92.2	81.9	72.0	846	91	...	65
64	800	...	(722)	83.4	...	73.8	91.8	81.1	71.0	822	88	...	64
63	772	...	(705)	82.8	...	73.0	91.4	80.1	69.9	799	87	...	63
62	746	...	(688)	82.3	...	72.2	91.1	79.3	68.8	776	85	...	62
61	720	...	(670)	81.8	...	71.5	90.7	78.4	67.7	754	83	...	61
60	697	...	(654)	81.2	...	70.7	90.2	77.5	66.6	732	81	...	60
59	674	...	(634)	80.7	...	69.9	89.8	76.6	65.5	710	80	351	59
58	653	...	615	80.1	...	69.2	89.3	75.7	64.3	690	78	338	58
57	633	...	595	79.6	...	68.5	88.9	74.8	63.2	670	76	325	57
56	613	...	577	79.0	...	67.7	88.3	73.9	62.0	650	75	313	56
55	595	...	560	78.5	...	66.9	87.9	73.0	60.9	630	74	301	55
54	577	...	543	78.0	...	66.1	87.4	72.0	59.8	612	72	292	54
53	560	...	525	77.4	...	65.4	86.9	71.2	58.6	594	71	283	53
52	544	(500)	512	76.8	...	64.6	86.4	70.2	57.4	576	69	273	52
51	528	(487)	496	76.3	...	63.8	85.9	69.4	56.1	558	68	264	51
50	513	(475)	481	75.9	...	63.1	85.5	68.5	55.0	542	67	255	50
49	498	(464)	469	75.2	...	62.1	85.0	67.6	53.8	526	66	246	49
48	484	(451)	455	74.7	...	61.4	84.5	66.7	52.5	510	64	238	48
47	471	442	443	74.1	...	60.8	83.9	65.8	51.4	495	63	229	47
46	458	432	432	73.6	...	60.0	83.5	64.8	50.3	480	62	221	46
45	446	421	421	73.1	...	59.2	83.0	64.0	49.0	466	60	215	45
44	434	409	409	72.5	...	58.5	82.5	63.1	47.8	452	58	208	44
43	423	400	400	72.0	...	57.7	82.0	62.2	46.7	438	57	201	43
42	412	390	390	71.5	...	56.9	81.5	61.3	45.5	426	56	194	42
41	402	381	381	70.9	...	56.2	80.9	60.4	44.3	414	55	188	41
40	392	371	371	70.4	...	55.4	80.4	59.5	43.1	402	54	182	40
39	382	362	362	69.9	...	54.6	79.9	58.6	41.9	391	52	177	39
38	372	353	353	69.4	...	53.8	79.4	57.7	40.8	380	51	171	38
37	363	344	344	68.9	...	53.1	78.8	56.8	39.6	370	50	166	37
36	354	336	336	68.4	(109.0)	52.3	78.3	55.9	38.4	360	49	161	36
35	345	327	327	67.9	(108.5)	51.5	77.7	55.0	37.2	351	48	157	35
34	336	319	319	67.4	(108.0)	50.8	77.2	54.2	36.1	342	47	153	34
33	327	311	311	66.8	(107.5)	50.0	76.6	53.3	34.9	334	46	149	33
32	318	301	301	66.3	(107.0)	49.2	76.1	52.1	33.7	326	44	145	32
31	310	294	294	65.8	(106.0)	48.4	75.6	51.3	32.5	318	43	141	31
30	302	286	286	65.3	(105.5)	47.7	75.0	50.4	31.3	311	42	138	30
29	294	279	279	64.7	(104.5)	47.0	74.5	49.5	30.1	304	41	135	29
28	286	271	271	64.3	(104.0)	46.1	73.9	48.6	28.9	297	40	131	28
27	279	264	264	63.8	(103.0)	45.2	73.3	47.7	27.8	290	39	128	27
26	272	258	258	63.3	(102.5)	44.6	72.8	46.8	26.7	284	38	125	26
25	266	253	253	62.8	(101.5)	43.8	72.2	45.9	25.5	278	38	122	25
24	260	247	247	62.4	(101.0)	43.1	71.6	45.0	24.3	272	37	119	24
23	254	243	243	62.0	100.0	42.1	71.0	44.0	23.1	266	36	117	23
22	248	237	237	61.5	99.0	41.6	70.5	43.2	22.0	261	35	114	22
21	243	231	231	61.0	98.5	40.9	69.9	42.3	20.7	256	35	112	21

(continued)

(Continued)

Rockwell B-scale hardness No.	Vickers hardness No.	Brinell hardness No., 10-mm ball		Rockwell hardness No.			Rockwell superficial hardness No., 1/16-in. diam ball			Knoop hardness No., 500-g load and greater	Shore Scleroscope hardness No.	Tensile strength (approx), 1000 psi	Rockwell B-scale hardness No.
		500-kg load	3000-kg load	A scale, 60-kg load, Brale indenter	C scale, 150-kg load, Brale indenter	F scale, 60-kg load, 1/16-in. diam ball	15T scale, 15-kg load	30T scale, 30-kg load	45T scale, 45-kg load				

Rockwell B-Scale Hardness Numbers

98	228	189	228	60.2	(19.9)	...	92.5	81.8	70.9	241	34	107	98
97	222	184	222	59.5	(18.6)	...	92.1	81.1	69.9	236	33	104	97
96	216	179	216	58.9	(17.2)	...	91.8	80.4	68.9	231	32	102	96
95	210	175	210	58.3	(15.7)	...	91.5	79.8	67.9	226	...	99	95
94	205	171	205	57.6	(14.3)	...	91.2	79.1	66.9	221	31	97	94
93	200	167	200	57.0	(13.0)	...	90.8	78.4	65.9	216	30	94	93
92	195	163	195	56.4	(11.7)	...	90.5	77.8	64.8	211	...	92	92
91	190	160	190	55.8	(10.4)	...	90.2	77.1	63.8	206	29	90	91
90	185	157	185	55.2	(9.2)	...	89.9	76.4	62.8	201	28	88	90
89	180	154	180	54.6	(8.0)	...	89.5	75.8	61.8	196	27	86	89
88	176	151	176	54.0	(6.9)	...	89.2	75.1	60.8	192	...	84	88
87	172	148	172	53.4	(5.8)	...	88.9	74.4	59.8	188	26	82	87
86	169	145	169	52.8	(4.7)	...	88.6	73.8	58.8	184	26	81	86
85	165	142	165	52.3	(3.6)	...	88.2	73.1	57.8	180	25	79	85
84	162	140	162	51.7	(2.5)	...	87.9	72.4	56.8	176	...	78	84
83	159	137	159	51.1	(1.4)	...	87.6	71.8	55.8	173	24	76	83
82	156	135	156	50.6	(0.3)	...	87.3	71.1	54.8	170	24	75	82
81	153	133	153	50.0	...	...	86.9	70.4	53.8	167	...	73	81
80	150	130	150	49.5	...	...	86.6	69.7	52.8	164	23	72	80
79	147	128	147	48.9	...	...	86.3	69.1	51.8	161	...	70	79
78	144	126	144	48.4	...	...	86.0	68.4	50.8	158	22	69	78
77	141	124	141	47.9	...	...	85.6	67.7	49.8	155	22	68	77
76	139	122	139	47.3	...	...	85.3	67.1	48.8	152	...	67	70
75	137	120	137	46.8	...	99.6	85.0	66.4	47.8	150	21	66	75
74	135	118	135	46.3	...	99.1	84.7	65.7	46.8	148	21	65	74
73	132	116	132	45.8	...	98.5	84.3	65.1	45.8	145	...	64	73
72	130	114	130	45.3	...	98.0	84.0	64.4	44.8	143	20	63	72
71	127	112	127	44.8	...	97.4	83.7	63.7	43.8	141	20	62	71
70	125	110	125	44.3	...	96.8	83.4	63.1	42.8	139	...	61	70
69	123	109	123	43.8	...	96.2	83.0	62.4	41.8	137	19	60	69
68	121	107	121	43.3	...	95.6	82.7	61.7	40.8	135	19	59	68
67	119	106	119	42.8	...	95.1	82.4	61.0	39.8	133	19	58	67
66	117	104	117	42.3	...	94.5	82.1	60.4	38.7	131	...	57	66
65	116	102	116	41.8	...	93.9	81.8	59.7	37.7	129	18	56	65
64	114	101	114	41.4	...	93.4	81.4	59.0	36.7	127	18	...	62
63	112	99	112	40.9	...	92.8	81.1	58.4	35.7	125	18	...	63
62	110	98	110	40.4	...	92.2	80.8	57.7	34.7	124	...	...	63
61	108	96	108	40.0	...	91.7	80.5	57.0	33.7	122	17	...	62
60	107	95	107	39.5	...	91.1	80.1	56.4	32.7	120	...	...	60
59	106	94	106	39.0	...	90.5	79.8	55.7	31.7	118	...	...	59
58	104	92	104	38.6	...	90.0	79.5	55.0	30.7	117	...	...	59
57	103	91	103	38.1	...	89.4	79.2	54.4	29.7	115	...	...	57
56	101	90	101	37.7	...	88.8	78.8	53.7	28.7	114	...	...	56
55	100	89	100	37.2	...	88.2	78.5	53.0	27.7	112	...	...	55

For carbon and alloy steels in the annealed, normalized, and quenched-and-tempered conditions; less accurate for cold worked condition and for austenitic steels. The values in **boldface type** correspond to the values in the joint SAE-ASM-ASTM hardness conversions as printed in ASTM E140, Table 2. The values in parentheses are beyond normal range and are given for information only.

Appendix 17.

The relationship between the ASTM grain size and the average "diameter" of the grain. (Adapted from 1966 Book of ASTM Standards, Part 31, American Society for Testing and Materials, Philadelphia (1966), copyright ASTM, reprinted with permission)

ASTM micro-grain size number	Calculated "diameter" of average grain		ASTM micro-grain size number	Calculated "diameter" of average grain	
	mm	in.		mm	in.
		×10⁻³			×10⁻³
00	0.508	20.0	7.5	0.027	1.05
0	0.359	14.1	...	0.025	0.984
0.5	0.302	11.9	8.0	0.0224	0.884
1.0	0.254	10.0	...	0.0200	0.787
...	0.250	9.84	8.5	0.0189	0.743
1.5	0.214	8.41	9.0	0.0159	0.625
...	0.200	7.87	...	0.0150	0.591
...	0.180	7.09	9.5	0.0134	0.526
2.0	0.179	7.07	10.0	0.0112	0.442
2.5	0.151	5.95	...	0.0100	0.394
...	0.150	5.91	10.5	0.00944	0.372
3.0	0.127	5.00	...	0.00900	0.354
...	0.120	4.72	...	0.00800	0.315
3.5	0.107	4.20	11.0	0.00794	0.313
...	0.099	3.90	...	0.00700	0.276
4.0	0.0898	3.54	11.5	0.00667	0.263
4.5	0.076	2.97	...	0.00600	0.236
...	0.070	2.76	12.0	0.00561	0.221
5.0	0.064	2.50	...	0.00500	0.197
...	0.060	2.36	12.5	0.00472	0.186
5.5	0.053	2.10	...	0.00400	0.158
...	0.050	1.97	13.0	0.00397	0.156
6.0	0.045	1.77	13.5	0.00334	0.131
...	0.040	1.58	...	0.00300	0.118
6.5	0.038	1.49	14.0	0.00281	0.111
...	0.035	1.38	...	0.00250	0.098
7.0	0.032	1.25			
...	0.030	1.18			

Appendix 18.

A comment on magnification markers. (From C.R. Brooks, Principles of the Surface Treatment of Steels, Technomic Publishing Company, Lancaster, PA (1992))

It is customary to indicate the magnification of a photograph of a microstructure (micrograph), but when the photograph size is changed (e.g., enlarged), the original magnification must be corrected. A method of avoiding this is to place on the micrograph a bar or marker that has the correct dimension for the magnification of the photograph. Then if the magnification of the photograph is changed, the marker also changes dimensions to maintain the correct dimension at the new magnification.

For example, consider a micrograph at 100×. Then a marker 1 cm long would correspond to a dimension of $1/100 = 0.01$ cm. It is common to express this in micrometers (microns). Since a micron is equal to 10^{-4} cm, then the 0.01 cm dimension could also be labeled as 100 µm ($0.01 \times 10,000$). If the micrograph is enlarged 2.5 times, then the marker becomes $2.5 \times 1 = 2.5$ cm long, and is still labeled as 100 µm.

In general,

$$M = x/(y \times 10^{-4})$$

where M is the magnification, x is the marker length in cm, and y is the marker value in µm on the micrograph.

At very high magnification, the micron marker value may be less than 1. For example, if the magnification is 40,000×, then 1 cm would correspond to 0.25 µm. In such cases, the marker corresponding to a certain value in Angstroms (Å) may be used. An Angstrom is equal to 10^{-8} cm, so in this case the marker dimension y in Å would be obtained from the equation above to be 40,000 $= 1(y \times 10^{-8})$, so $y = 2500$ Å.

For the SI system, the nanometer is used. One nanometer equals 10 Å, so for the case above, the marker would be labeled 250 nm.

The use of such markers is very useful because the actual sizes of microstructural features can be determined. For example, if the micron marker is labeled 2 µm and is 1 cm long, and a particle is present which is about 0.5 cm long in the micrograph, then its *actual* dimension in the sample is about 1 µm.

Appendix 19.

Hardenability bands for H-steels. (From Metals Handbook, 9th edition, Vol. 1, Properties and Selection: Irons and Steels, ASM International, Materials Park, Ohio (1978), p 497-525)

AISI-SAE 1038H UNS H10380

Specified hardness limits

Distance from quenched surface		Hardness, HRC		Distance from quenched surface		Hardness, HRC	
1/16 in.	mm	Max	Min	1/16 in.	mm	Max	Min
1	1.58	58	51	6	9.48	28	21
1.5	2.37	56	42	6.5	10.27	27	20
2	3.16	55	34	7	11.06	27	...
2.5	3.95	53	29	7.5	11.85	26	...
3	4.74	49	26	8	12.64	26	...
3.5	5.58	43	24	9	14.22	25	...
4	6.32	37	23	10	15.80	25	...
4.5	7.11	33	22	12	18.96	24	...
5	7.90	30	22	14	22.12	23	...
5.5	8.69	29	21	16	25.28	21	...

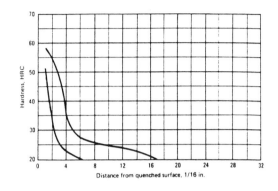

AISI-SAE 1045H UNS H1045H

Specified hardness limits

Distance from quenched surface		Hardness, HRC		Distance from quenched surface		Hardness, HRC	
1/16 in.	mm	Max	Min	1/16 in.	mm	Max	Min
1	1.58	62	55	7	11.06	31	25
1.5	2.37	61	52	7.5	11.85	30	24
2	3.16	59	42	8	12.64	30	24
2.5	3.95	56	34	9	14.22	29	23
3	4.74	52	31	10	15.80	29	22
3.5	5.53	46	29	12	18.96	28	21
4	6.32	38	28	14	22.12	27	20
4.5	7.11	34	27	16	25.28	26	...
5	7.90	33	26	18	28.44	25	...
5.5	8.69	32	26	20	31.60	23	...
6	9.48	32	25	22	34.76	22	...
6.5	10.27	31	25	24	37.92	21	...

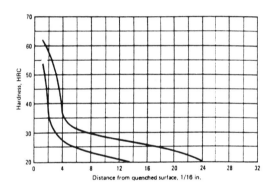

AISI-SAE 1330H UNS H13300

Specified hardness limits

Distance from quenched surface		Hardness, HRC		Distance from quenched surface		Hardness, HRC	
1/16 in.	mm	Max	Min	1/16 in.	mm	Max	Min
1	1.58	56	49	13	20.54	38	20
2	3.16	56	47	14	22.12	37	...
3	4.74	55	44	15	23.70	36	...
4	6.32	53	40	16	25.28	35	...
5	7.90	52	35	18	28.44	34	...
6	9.48	50	31	20	31.60	33	...
7	11.06	48	28	22	34.76	32	...
8	12.64	45	26	24	37.92	31	...
9	14.22	43	25	26	41.08	31	...
10	15.80	42	23	28	44.24	31	...
11	17.38	40	22	30	47.40	30	...
12	18.96	39	21	32	50.56	30	...

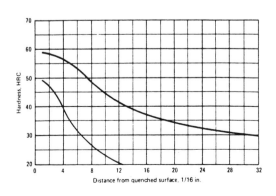

AISI-SAE 1335H UNS H13350

Specified hardness limits

Distance from quenched surface		Hardness, HRC		Distance from quenched surface		Hardness, HRC	
1/16 in.	mm	Max	Min	1/16 in.	mm	Max	Min
1	1.58	58	51	13	20.54	40	23
2	3.16	57	49	14	22.12	39	22
3	4.74	56	47	15	23.70	38	22
4	6.32	55	44	16	25.28	37	21
5	7.90	54	38	18	28.44	35	20
6	9.48	52	34	20	31.60	34	...
7	11.06	50	31	22	34.76	33	...
8	12.64	48	29	24	37.92	32	...
9	14.22	46	27	26	41.08	31	...
10	15.80	44	26	28	44.24	31	...
11	17.38	42	25	30	47.40	30	...
12	18.96	41	24	32	50.56	30	...

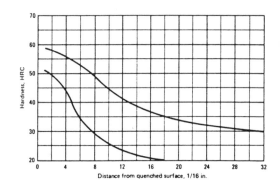

AISI-SAE 1340H UNS H13400

Specified hardness limits

Distance from quenched surface		Hardness, HRC		Distance from quenched surface		Hardness, HRC	
1/16 in.	mm	Max	Min	1/16 in.	mm	Max	Min
1	1.58	60	53	13	20.54	46	26
2	3.16	60	52	14	22.12	44	25
3	4.74	59	51	15	23.70	42	25
4	6.32	58	49	16	25.28	41	24
5	7.90	57	46	18	28.44	39	23
6	9.48	56	40	20	31.60	38	23
7	11.06	55	35	22	34.76	37	22
8	12.64	54	33	24	37.92	36	22
9	14.22	52	31	26	41.08	35	21
10	15.80	51	29	28	44.24	35	21
11	17.38	50	28	30	47.40	34	20
12	18.96	48	27	32	50.56	34	20

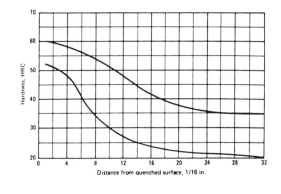

AISI-SAE 1345H UNS H13450

Specified hardness limits

Distance from quenched surface		Hardness, HRC		Distance from quenched surface		Hardness, HRC	
1/16 in.	mm	Max	Min	1/16 in.	mm	Max	Min
1	1.58	63	56	13	20.54	54	29
2	3.16	63	56	14	22.12	53	29
3	4.74	62	55	15	23.70	52	28
4	6.32	61	54	16	25.28	51	28
5	7.90	61	51	18	28.44	49	27
6	9.48	60	44	20	31.60	47	27
7	11.06	60	38	22	34.76	45	26
8	12.64	59	35	24	37.92	44	26
9	14.22	58	33	26	41.08	47	25
10	15.80	57	32	28	44.24	46	25
11	17.38	56	31	30	47.40	45	24
12	18.96	55	30	32	50.56	45	24

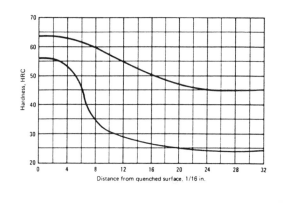

AISI-SAE 15B21 H UNS H15211

Specified hardness limits

Distance from quenched surface		Hardness, HRC		Distance from quenched surface		Hardness, HRC	
1/16 in.	mm	Max	Min	1/16 in.	mm	Max	Min
1	1.58	48	41	6	9.48	35	...
1.5	2.37	48	41	6.5	10.27	32	...
2	3.16	47	40	7	11.06	27	...
2.5	3.95	47	39	7.5	11.85	22	...
3	4.74	46	38	8	12.64	20	...
3.5	5.53	45	36	9	14.22	...	...
4	6.32	44	30	10	15.80	...	...
4.5	7.11	42	23	12	18.96	...	...
5	7.90	40	20	14	22.12	...	...
5.5	8.69	38	...	16	25.28	...	...

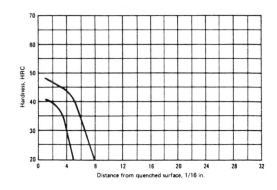

AISI-SAE 1522H UNS H15220

Specified hardness limits

Distance from quenched surface		Hardness, HRC		Distance from quenched surface		Hardness, HRC	
1/16 in.	mm	Max	Min	1/16 in.	mm	Max	Min
1	1.58	50	41	6	9.48	30	...
1.5	2.37	48	41	6.5	10.27	28	...
2	3.16	47	32	7	11.06	27	...
2.5	3.95	46	27	7.5	11.58	...	...
3	4.74	45	22	8	12.64	25	...
3.5	5.53	42	21	9	14.22	23	...
4	6.32	39	20	10	15.80	22	...
4.5	7.11	37	...	12	18.96	20	...
5	7.90	34	...	14	22.12	...	...
5.5	8.69	32	...	16	25.28	...	...

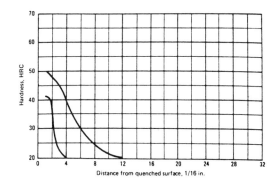

AISI-SAE 1524H UNS H15240

Specified hardness limits

Distance from quenched surface		Hardness, HRC		Distance from quenched surface		Hardness, HRC	
1/16 in.	mm	Max	Min	1/16 in.	mm	Max	Min
1	1.58	51	42	6	9.48	32	...
1.5	2.37	49	42	6.5	10.27	30	...
2	3.16	48	38	7	11.06	29	...
2.5	3.95	47	34	7.5	11.58	28	...
3	4.74	45	29	8	12.64	27	...
3.5	5.53	43	25	9	14.22	26	...
4	6.32	39	22	10	15.80	25	...
4.5	7.11	38	20	12	18.96	23	...
5	7.90	35	...	14	22.12	22	...
5.5	8.69	34	...	16	25.28	20	...

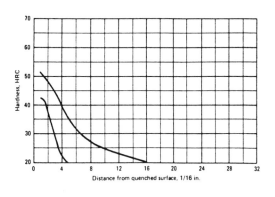

AISI-SAE 1526H UNS H15260

Specified hardness limits

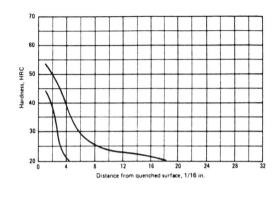

Distance from quenched surface		Hardness, HRC		Distance from quenched surface		Hardness, HRC	
1/16 in.	mm	Max	Min	1/16 in.	mm	Max	Min
1	1.58	53	44	6.5	10.27	28	...
1.5	2.37	50	42	7	11.06	27	...
2	3.16	49	38	7.5	11.85	26	...
2.5	3.95	47	33	8	12.64	26	...
3	4.74	46	26	9	14.22	24	...
3.5	5.58	42	25	10	15.80	24	...
4	6.32	39	21	12	18.96	23	...
4.5	7.11	37	20	14	22.12	22	...
5	7.90	33	...	16	25.28	21	...
5.5	8.69	31	...	18	28.44	20	...
6	9.48	30	...				

AISI-SAE 15B35H UNS H15351

Specified hardness limits

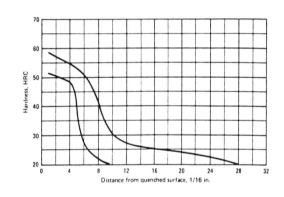

Distance from quenched surface		Hardness, HRC		Distance from quenched surface		Hardness, HRC	
1/16 in.	mm	Max	Min	1/16 in.	mm	Max	Min
1	1.58	58	51	13	20.54	...	...
2	3.16	56	50	14	22.12	26	...
3	4.74	55	49	15	23.70	...	...
4	6.32	54	48	16	25.28	25	...
5	7.90	53	39	18	28.44	...	...
6	9.48	51	28	20	31.60	24	...
7	11.06	47	24	22	34.76	...	...
8	12.64	41	22	24	37.92	22	...
9	14.22	...	...	26	41.08	...	...
10	15.80	30	20	28	44.24	20	...
11	17.38	...	...	30	47.40	...	...
12	18.96	27	...	32	50.56	...	...

AISI-SAE 15B37H UNS H15371

Specified hardness limits

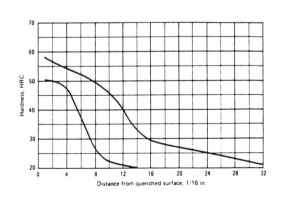

Distance from quenched surface		Hardness, HRC		Distance from quenched surface		Hardness, HRC	
1/16 in.	mm	Max	Min	1/16 in.	mm	Max	Min
1	1.58	58	50	13	20.54	...	...
2	3.16	56	50	14	22.12	33	20
3	4.74	55	49	15	23.70	...	...
4	6.32	54	48	16	25.28	29	...
5	7.90	53	43	18	28.44	...	...
6	9.48	52	37	20	31.60	27	...
7	11.06	51	33	22	34.76	...	...
8	12.64	50	26	24	37.92	25	...
9	14.22	...	...	26	41.08	...	...
10	15.80	45	22	28	44.26	23	...
11	17.38	...	...	30	47.40	...	...
12	18.96	40	21	32	50.56	21	...

AISI-SAE 1541H UNS H15410

Specified hardness limits

Distance from quenched surface		Hardness, HRC		Distance from quenched surface		Hardness, HRC	
1/16 in.	mm	Max	Min	1/16 in.	mm	Max	Min
1	1.58	60	53	7	11.06	44	25
1.5	2.37	59	52	7.5	11.85	41	24
2	3.16	59	50	8	12.64	39	23
2.5	3.95	58	47	9	14.22	35	23
3	4.74	57	44	10	15.80	33	22
3.5	5.58	56	41	12	18.96	32	21
4	6.32	55	38	14	22.12	31	20
4.5	7.11	53	35	16	25.28	30	...
5	7.90	52	32	18	28.44	30	...
5.5	8.69	50	29	20	31.60	29	...
6	9.48	48	27	22	34.76	28	...
6.5	10.27	46	26	24	37.92	26	...

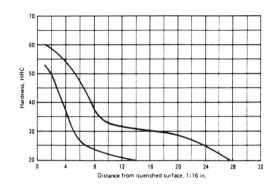

AISI-SAE 15B41H UNS H15411

Specified hardness limits

Distance from quenched surface		Hardness, HRC		Distance from quenched surface		Hardness, HRC	
1/16 in.	mm	Max	Min	1/16 in.	mm	Max	Min
1	1.58	60	53	13	20.54	52	26
2	3.16	59	52	14	22.12	51	25
3	4.74	59	52	15	23.70	50	25
4	6.32	58	51	16	25.28	49	24
5	7.90	58	51	18	28.44	46	23
6	9.46	57	50	20	31.60	42	22
7	11.06	57	49	22	34.76	39	21
8	12.64	56	48	24	37.92	36	21
9	14.22	55	44	26	41.08	34	20
10	15.80	55	37	28	44.24	33	...
11	17.38	54	32	30	47.40	31	...
12	18.96	53	28	32	50.56	31	...

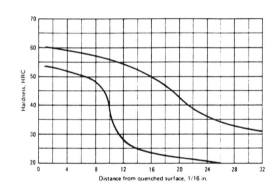

AISI-SAE 15B48H UNS H15481

Specified hardness limits

Distance from quenched surface		Hardness, HRC		Distance from quenched surface		Hardness, HRC	
1/16 in.	mm	Max	Min	1/16 in.	mm	Max	Min
1	1.58	63	56	13	20.54	48	27
2	3.16	62	56	14	22.12	45	27
3	4.74	62	55	15	23.70	41	26
4	6.32	61	54	16	25.28	38	26
5	7.90	60	53	18	28.44	34	25
6	9.48	59	52	20	31.60	32	24
7	11.06	58	42	22	34.76	31	23
8	12.64	57	34	24	37.92	30	22
9	14.22	56	31	26	41.08	29	21
10	15.80	55	30	28	44.24	29	20
11	17.38	53	29	30	47.40	28	...
12	18.96	51	28	32	50.56	28	...

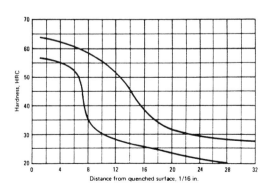

AISI-SAE 15B62H UNS H15621

Specified hardness limits

Distance from quenched surface		Hardness, HRC		Distance from quenched surface		Hardness, HRC	
1/16 in.	mm	Max	Min	1/16 in.	mm	Max	Min
1	1.58	...	60	13	20.54	62	35
2	3.16	...	60	14	22.12	62	34
3	4.74	...	60	15	23.70	61	33
4	6.32	...	60	16	25.28	60	33
5	7.90	65	59	18	28.44	58	32
6	9.48	65	58	20	31.60	54	31
7	11.06	64	57	22	34.76	48	30
8	12.64	64	52	24	37.92	43	30
9	14.22	64	43	26	41.08	40	29
10	15.80	63	39	28	44.24	37	28
11	17.38	63	37	30	47.40	35	27
12	18.96	63	35	32	50.56	34	26

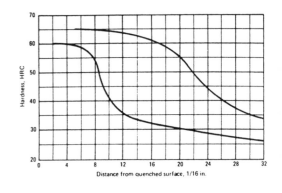

AISI-SAE 4028H UNS H40280

Specified hardness limits

Distance from quenched surface		Hardness, HRC		Distance from quenched surface		Hardness, HRC	
1/16 in.	mm	Max	Min	1/16 in.	mm	Max	Min
1	1.58	52	45	13	20.54	23	...
2	3.16	50	40	14	22.12	22	...
3	4.74	46	31	15	23.70	22	...
4	6.32	40	25	16	25.28	21	...
5	7.90	34	22	18	28.44	21	...
6	9.48	30	20	20	31.60	20	...
7	11.06	28	...	22	34.76	...	...
8	12.64	26	...	24	37.92	...	...
9	14.22	25	...	26	41.08	...	...
10	15.80	25	...	28	44.24	...	...
11	17.38	24	...	30	47.40	...	...
12	18.96	23	...	32	50.56	...	...

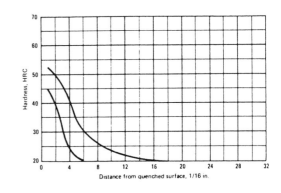

AISI-SAE 4032H UNS H40320

Specified hardness limits

Distance from quenched surface		Hardness, HRC		Distance from quenched surface		Hardness, HRC	
1/16 in.	mm	Max	Min	1/16 in.	mm	Max	Min
1	1.58	57	50	13	20.54	24	...
2	3.16	54	45	14	22.12	24	...
3	4.74	51	36	15	23.70	23	...
4	6.32	46	29	16	25.28	23	...
5	7.90	39	25	18	28.44	23	...
6	9.48	34	23	20	31.60	22	...
7	11.06	31	22	22	34.76	22	...
8	12.64	29	21	24	37.92	21	...
9	14.22	28	20	26	41.08	21	...
10	15.80	26	...	28	44.24	20	...
11	17.38	26	...	30	47.40	...	...
12	18.96	25	...	32	50.56	...	...

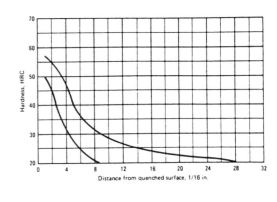

AISI-SAE 4037H UNS H40370

Specified hardness limits

Distance from quenched surface		Hardness, HRC		Distance from quenched surface		Hardness, HRC	
1/16 in.	mm	Max	Min	1/16 in.	mm	Max	Min
1	1.58	59	52	13	20.54	26	...
2	3.16	57	49	14	22.12	26	...
3	4.74	54	42	15	23.70	26	...
4	6.32	51	35	16	25.28	25	...
5	7.90	45	30	18	28.44	25	...
6	9.48	38	26	20	31.60	25	...
7	11.06	34	23	22	34.76	25	...
8	12.64	32	22	24	37.92	24	...
9	14.22	30	21	26	41.08	24	...
10	15.80	29	20	28	44.24	24	...
11	17.38	28	...	30	47.40	23	...
12	18.96	27	...	32	50.56	23	...

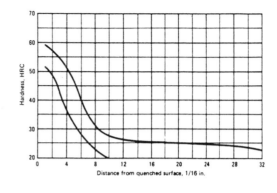

AISI-SAE 4042H UNS H40420

Specified hardness limits

Distance from quenched surface		Hardness, HRC		Distance from quenched surface		Hardness, HRC	
1/16 in.	mm	Max	Min	1/16 in.	mm	Max	Min
1	1.58	62	55	13	20.54	30	23
2	3.16	60	52	14	22.12	30	23
3	4.74	58	48	15	23.70	29	22
4	6.32	55	40	16	25.28	29	22
5	7.90	50	33	18	28.44	28	22
6	9.48	45	29	20	31.60	28	21
7	11.06	39	27	22	34.76	28	20
8	12.64	36	26	24	37.92	27	20
9	14.22	34	25	26	41.08	27	...
10	15.80	33	24	28	44.24	27	...
11	17.38	32	24	30	47.40	26	...
12	18.96	31	23	32	50.56	26	...

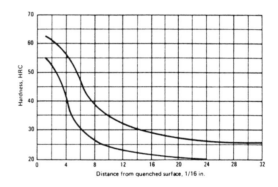

AISI-SAE 4047H UNS H40470

Specified hardness limits

Distance from quenched surface		Hardness, HRC		Distance from quenched surface		Hardness, HRC	
1/16 in.	mm	Max	Min	1/16 in.	mm	Max	Min
1	1.58	64	57	13	20.54	34	25
2	3.16	62	55	14	22.12	33	25
3	4.74	60	50	15	23.70	33	25
4	6.32	58	42	16	25.28	32	25
5	7.90	55	35	18	28.44	31	24
6	9.48	52	32	20	31.60	30	24
7	11.06	47	30	22	34.76	30	23
8	12.64	43	28	24	37.92	30	23
9	14.22	40	28	26	41.08	30	22
10	15.80	38	27	28	44.24	29	22
11	17.38	37	26	30	47.40	29	21
12	18.96	35	26	32	50.56	29	21

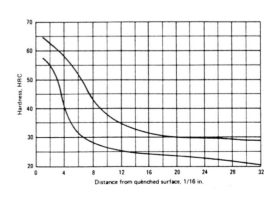

AISI-SAE 4118H UNS H41180

Specified hardness limits

Distance from quenched surface		Hardness, HRC		Distance from quenched surface		Hardness, HRC	
1/16 in.	mm	Max	Min	1/16 in.	mm	Max	Min
1	1.58	48	41	13	20.54	21	...
2	3.16	46	36	14	22.12	20	...
3	4.74	41	27	15	23.70	...	...
4	6.32	35	23	16	25.28	...	...
5	7.90	31	20	18	28.44	...	...
6	9.48	28	...	20	31.60	...	...
7	11.06	27	...	22	34.76	...	...
8	12.64	26	...	24	37.92	...	...
9	14.22	24	...	26	41.08	...	...
10	15.80	23	...	28	44.24	...	...
11	17.38	22	...	30	47.40	...	...
12	18.96	21	...	32	50.56	...	...

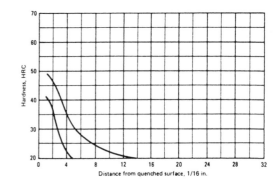

AISI-SAE 4130H UNS H41300

Specified hardness limits

Distance from quenched surface		Hardness, HRC		Distance from quenched surface		Hardness, HRC	
1/16 in.	mm	Max	Min	1/16 in.	mm	Max	Min
1	1.58	56	49	13	20.54	34	24
2	3.16	55	46	14	22.12	34	24
3	4.74	53	42	15	23.70	33	23
4	6.32	51	38	16	25.28	33	23
5	7.90	49	34	18	28.44	32	22
6	9.48	47	31	20	31.60	32	21
7	11.06	44	29	22	34.76	32	20
8	12.64	42	27	24	37.92	31	...
9	14.22	40	26	26	41.08	31	...
10	15.80	38	26	28	44.24	30	...
11	17.38	36	25	30	47.40	30	...
12	18.96	35	25	32	50.56	29	...

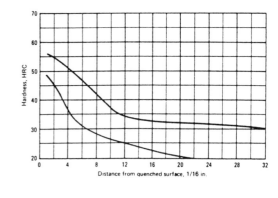

AISI-SAE 4135H UNS H41350

Specified hardness limits

Distance from quenched surface		Hardness, HRC		Distance from quenched surface		Hardness, HRC	
1/16 in.	mm	Max	Min	1/16 in.	mm	Max	Min
1	1.58	58	51	13	20.54	48	32
2	3.16	58	50	14	22.12	47	31
3	4.74	57	49	15	23.70	46	30
4	6.32	56	48	16	25.28	45	30
5	7.90	56	47	18	28.44	44	29
6	9.48	55	45	20	31.60	42	28
7	11.06	54	42	22	34.76	41	27
8	12.64	53	40	24	37.92	40	27
9	14.22	52	38	26	41.08	39	27
10	15.80	51	36	28	44.24	38	26
11	17.38	50	34	30	47.40	38	26
12	18.96	49	33	32	50.56	37	26

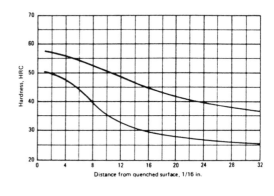

AISI-SAE 4137H   UNS H41370

Specified hardness limits

Distance from quenched surface		Hardness, HRC		Distance from quenched surface		Hardness, HRC	
1/16 in.	mm	Max	Min	1/16 in.	mm	Max	Min
1	1.58	59	52	13	20.54	51	35
2	3.16	59	51	14	22.12	50	34
3	4.74	58	50	15	23.70	49	33
4	6.32	58	49	16	25.28	48	33
5	7.90	57	49	18	28.44	46	32
6	9.48	57	48	20	31.60	45	31
7	11.06	56	45	22	34.76	44	30
8	12.64	55	43	24	37.92	43	30
9	14.22	55	40	26	41.08	42	30
10	15.80	54	39	28	44.24	42	29
11	17.38	53	37	30	47.40	41	29
12	18.96	52	36	32	50.56	41	29

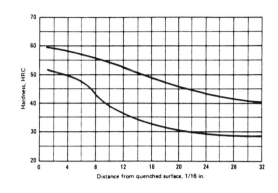

AISI-SAE 4140H   UNS H41400

Specified hardness limits

Distance from quenched surface		Hardness, HRC		Distance from quenched surface		Hardness, HRC	
1/16 in.	mm	Max	Min	1/16 in.	mm	Max	Min
1	1.58	60	53	13	20.54	55	38
2	3.16	60	53	14	22.12	54	37
3	4.74	60	52	15	23.70	54	36
4	6.32	59	51	16	25.29	53	35
5	7.90	59	51	18	28.44	52	34
6	9.48	58	50	20	31.60	51	33
7	11.06	58	48	22	34.76	49	33
8	12.64	57	47	24	37.92	48	32
9	14.22	57	44	26	41.08	47	32
10	15.80	56	42	28	44.24	46	31
11	17.38	56	40	30	47.40	45	31
12	18.96	55	39	32	50.56	44	30

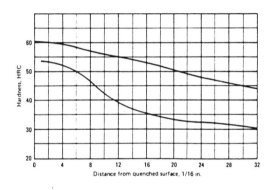

AISI-SAE 4142H   UNS H41420

Specified hardness limits

Distance from quenched surface		Hardness, HRC		Distance from quenched, surface		Hardness, HRC	
1/16 in.	mm	Max	Min	1/16 in.	mm	Max	Min
1	1.58	62	55	13	20.54	58	42
2	3.16	62	55	14	22.12	57	41
3	4.74	62	54	15	23.70	57	40
4	6.32	61	53	16	25.28	56	39
5	7.90	61	53	18	28.44	55	37
6	9.48	61	52	20	31.60	54	36
7	11.06	60	51	22	34.76	53	35
8	12.64	60	50	24	37.92	53	34
9	14.22	60	49	26	41.08	52	34
10	15.80	59	47	28	44.24	51	34
11	17.38	59	46	30	47.40	51	33
12	18.96	58	44	32	50.56	50	33

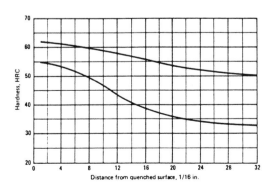

AISI-SAE 4145H UNS H41450

Specified hardness limits

Distance from quenched surface		Hardness, HRC		Distance from quenched surface		Hardness, HRC	
1/16 in.	mm	Max	Min	1/16 in.	mm	Max	Min
1	1.58	63	56	13	20.54	59	46
2	3.16	63	55	14	22.12	59	45
3	4.74	62	55	15	23.70	58	43
4	6.32	62	54	16	25.28	58	42
5	7.90	62	53	18	28.44	57	40
6	9.48	61	53	20	31.60	57	38
7	11.06	61	52	22	34.76	56	37
8	12.64	61	52	24	37.92	55	36
9	14.22	60	51	26	41.08	55	35
10	15.80	60	50	28	44.24	55	35
11	17.38	60	49	30	47.40	55	34
12	18.96	59	48	32	50.56	54	34

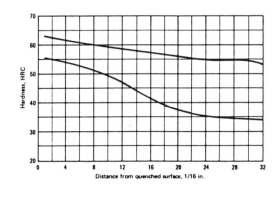

AISI-SAE 4147H UNS H41470

Specified hardness limits

Distance from quenched surface		Hardness, HRC		Distance from quenched surface		Hardness, HRC	
1/16 in.	mm	Max	Min	1/16 in.	mm	Max	Min
1	1.58	64	57	13	20.54	61	49
2	3.16	64	57	14	22.12	61	48
3	4.74	64	56	15	23.70	60	46
4	6.32	64	56	16	25.28	60	45
5	7.90	63	55	18	28.44	59	42
6	9.48	63	55	20	31.60	59	40
7	11.06	63	55	22	34.76	58	39
8	12.64	63	54	24	37.92	57	38
9	14.22	63	54	26	41.08	57	37
10	15.80	62	53	28	44.24	57	37
11	17.38	62	52	30	47.40	56	37
12	18.96	62	51	32	50.56	56	36

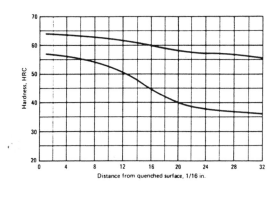

AISI-SAE 4150H UNS H41500

Specified hardness limits

Distance from quenched surface		Hardness, HRC		Distance from quenched surface		Hardness, HRC	
1/16 in.	mm	Max	Min	1/16 in.	mm	Max	Min
1	1.58	65	59	13	20.54	63	51
2	3.16	65	59	14	22.12	62	50
3	4.74	65	59	15	23.70	62	48
4	6.32	65	58	16	25.28	62	47
5	7.90	65	58	18	28.44	61	45
6	9.48	65	57	20	31.60	60	43
7	11.06	65	57	22	34.76	59	41
8	12.64	64	56	24	37.92	59	40
9	14.22	64	56	26	41.08	58	39
10	15.80	64	55	28	44.24	58	38
11	17.38	64	54	30	47.40	58	38
12	18.96	63	53	32	50.56	58	38

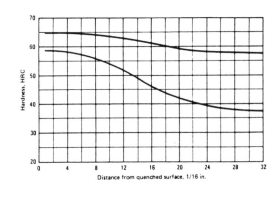

AISI-SAE 4161H   UNS H41610

Specified hardness limits

Distance from quenched surface		Hardness, HRC		Distance from quenched surface		Hardness, HRC	
1/16 in.	mm	Max	Min	1/16 in.	mm	Max	Min
1	1.58	65	60	13	20.54	64	58
2	3.16	65	60	14	22.12	64	58
3	4.74	65	60	15	23.70	64	57
4	6.32	65	60	16	25.28	64	56
5	7.90	65	60	18	28.44	64	55
6	9.48	65	60	20	31.60	63	53
7	11.06	65	60	22	34.76	63	50
8	12.64	65	60	24	37.92	63	48
9	14.22	65	59	26	41.08	63	45
10	15.80	65	59	28	44.24	63	43
11	17.38	65	59	30	47.40	63	42
12	18.96	64	59	32	50.56	63	41

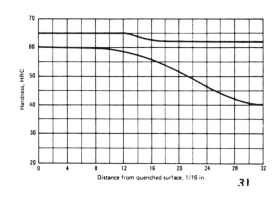

AISI-SAE 4320H   UNS H43200

Specified hardness limits

Distance from quenched surface		Hardness, HRC		Distance from quenched surface		Hardness, HRC	
1/16 in.	mm	Max	Min	1/16 in.	mm	Max	Min
1	1.58	48	41	13	20.54	28	...
2	3.16	47	38	14	22.12	27	...
3	4.74	45	35	15	23.70	27	...
4	6.32	43	32	16	25.28	26	...
5	7.90	41	29	18	28.44	25	...
6	9.48	38	27	20	31.60	25	...
7	11.06	36	25	22	34.76	24	...
8	12.64	34	23	24	37.92	24	...
9	14.22	33	22	26	41.08	24	...
10	15.80	31	21	28	44.24	24	...
11	17.38	30	20	30	47.40	24	...
12	18.96	29	20	32	50.56	24	...

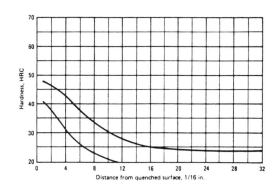

AISI-SAE 4340H   UNS H43400

Specified hardness limits

Distance from quenched surface		Hardness, HRC		Distance from quenched surface		Hardness, HRC	
1/16 in.	mm	Max	Min	1/16 in.	mm	Max	Min
1	1.58	60	53	13	20.54	59	50
2	3.16	60	53	14	22.12	58	49
3	4.74	60	53	15	23.70	58	49
4	6.32	60	53	16	25.28	58	48
5	7.90	60	53	18	28.44	58	47
6	9.48	60	53	20	31.60	57	46
7	11.06	60	53	22	34.76	57	45
8	12.64	60	52	24	37.92	57	44
9	14.22	60	52	26	41.08	57	43
10	15.80	60	52	28	44.24	56	42
11	17.38	59	51	30	47.40	56	41
12	18.96	59	51	32	50.56	56	40

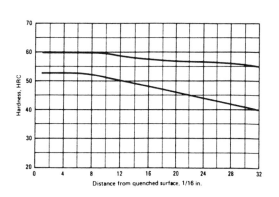

AISI-SAE 4620H UNS H46200

Specified hardness limits

Distance from quenched surface		Hardness, HRC		Distance from quenched surface		Hardness, HRC	
1/16 in.	mm	Max	Min	1/16 in.	mm	Max	Min
1	1.58	48	41	13	20.54	22	...
2	3.16	45	35	14	22.12	22	...
3	4.74	42	27	15	23.70	22	...
4	6.32	39	24	16	25.28	21	...
5	7.90	34	21	18	28.44	21	...
6	9.48	31	...	20	31.60	20	...
7	11.06	29	...	22	34.76	...	...
8	12.64	27	...	24	37.92	...	...
9	14.22	26	...	26	41.08	...	...
10	15.80	25	...	28	44.24	...	...
11	17.38	24	...	30	47.40	...	...
12	18.96	23	...	32	50.56	...	...

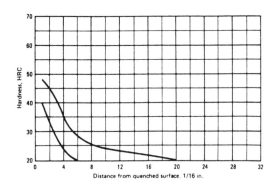

AISI-SAE 4621H UNS H46210

Specified hardness limits

Distance from quenched surface		Hardness, HRC		Distance from quenched surface		Hardness, HRC	
1/16 in.	mm	Max	Min	1/16 in.	mm	Max	Min
1	1.58	48	41	13	20.54	26	...
2	3.16	47	38	14	22.12	25	...
3	4.74	46	34	15	23.70	25	...
4	6.32	44	30	16	25.28	24	...
5	7.90	41	27	18	28.44	24	...
6	9.48	37	25	20	31.60	23	...
7	11.06	34	23	22	34.76	23	...
8	12.64	32	22	24	37.92	22	...
9	14.22	30	20	26	41.08	22	...
10	15.80	28	...	28	44.24	22	...
11	17.38	27	...	30	47.40	21	...
12	18.96	26	...	32	50.56	21	...

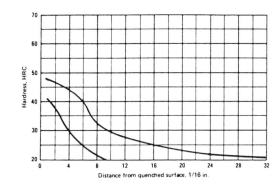

AISI-SAE 4626H UNS H46260

Specified hardness limits

Distance from quenched surface		Hardness, HRC		Distance from quenched surface		Hardness, HRC	
1/16 in.	mm	Max	Min	1/16 in.	mm	Max	Min
1	1.58	51	45	13	20.54	21	...
2	3.16	48	36	14	22.12	20	...
3	4.74	41	29	15	23.70	...	...
4	6.32	33	24	16	25.28	...	...
5	7.90	29	21	18	28.44	...	...
6	9.48	27	...	20	31.60	...	...
7	11.06	25	...	22	34.76	...	...
8	12.64	24	...	24	37.92	...	...
9	14.22	23	...	26	41.08	...	...
10	15.80	22	...	28	44.24	...	...
11	17.38	22	...	30	47.40	...	...
12	18.96	21	...	32	50.56	...	...

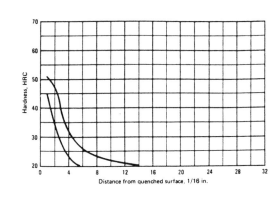

AISI-SAE 4718H UNS H47180

Specified hardness limits

Distance from quenched surface		Hardness, HRC		Distance from quenched surface		Hardness, HRC	
1/16 in.	mm	Max	Min	1/16 in.	mm	Max	Min
1	1.58	47	40	13	20.54	29	21
2	3.16	47	40	14	22.12	28	21
3	4.74	45	38	15	23.70	27	20
4	6.32	43	33	16	25.28	27	20
5	7.90	40	29	18	28.44	27	...
6	9.48	37	27	20	31.60	26	...
7	11.06	35	25	22	34.76	26	...
8	12.64	33	24	24	37.92	25	...
9	14.22	32	23	26	41.08	25	...
10	15.80	31	22	28	44.24	24	...
11	17.38	30	22	30	47.40	24	...
12	18.96	29	21	32	50.56	24	...

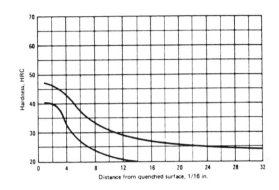

AISI-SAE 4720H UNS H47200

Specified hardness limits

Distance from quenched surface		Hardness, HRC		Distance from quenched surface		Hardness, HRC	
1/16 in.	mm	Max	Min	1/16 in.	mm	Max	Min
1	1.58	48	41	13	20.54	24	...
2	3.16	47	39	14	22.12	23	...
3	4.74	33	31	15	23.70	23	...
4	6.32	39	27	16	25.28	22	...
5	7.90	35	23	18	28.44	21	...
6	9.48	32	21	20	31.60	21	...
7	11.06	29	...	22	34.76	21	...
8	12.64	28	...	24	37.92	20	...
9	14.22	27	...	26	41.08	...	...
10	15.80	26	...	28	44.24	...	...
11	17.38	25	...	30	47.40	...	...
12	18.96	24	...	32	50.56	...	...

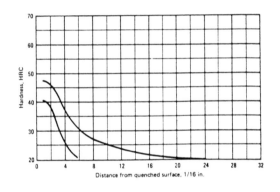

AISI-SAE 4815H UNS H48150

Specified hardness limits

Distance from quenched surface		Hardness, HRC		Distance from quenched surface		Hardness, HRC	
1/16 in.	mm	Max	Min	1/16 in.	mm	Max	Min
1	1.58	45	38	13	20.54	28	...
2	3.16	44	37	14	22.12	28	...
3	4.74	44	34	15	23.70	27	...
4	6.32	42	30	16	25.28	27	...
5	7.90	41	27	18	28.44	26	...
6	9.48	39	24	20	31.60	25	...
7	11.06	37	22	22	34.76	24	...
8	12.64	35	21	24	37.92	24	...
9	14.22	33	20	26	41.08	24	...
10	15.80	31	...	28	44.24	23	...
11	17.38	30	...	30	47.40	23	...
12	18.96	29	...	32	50.56	23	...

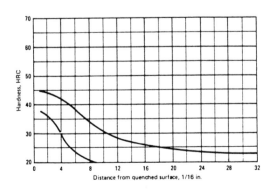

AISI-SAE 4817H UNS H48170

Specified hardness limits

Distance from quenched surface		Hardness, HRC		Distance from quenched surface		Hardness, HRC	
1/16 in.	mm	Max	Min	1/16 in.	mm	Max	Min
1	1.58	46	39	13	20.54	30	...
2	3.16	46	38	14	22.12	29	...
3	4.74	45	35	15	23.70	28	...
4	6.32	44	32	16	25.28	28	...
5	7.90	42	29	18	28.44	27	...
6	9.48	41	27	20	31.60	26	...
7	11.06	39	25	22	34.76	25	...
8	12.64	37	23	24	37.92	25	...
9	14.22	35	22	26	41.08	25	...
10	15.80	33	21	28	44.24	25	...
11	17.38	32	20	30	47.40	24	...
12	18.96	31	20	32	50.56	24	...

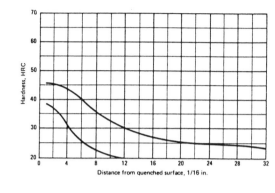

AISI-SAE 4820H UNS H48200

Specified hardness limits

Distance from quenched surface		Hardness, HRC		Distance from quenched surface		Hardness, HRC	
1/16 in.	mm	Max	Min	1/16 in.	mm	Max	Min
1	1.58	48	41	13	20.54	34	22
2	3.16	48	40	14	22.12	33	22
3	4.74	47	39	15	23.70	32	21
4	6.32	46	38	16	25.28	31	21
5	7.90	45	34	18	28.44	29	20
6	9.48	43	31	20	31.60	28	20
7	11.06	42	29	22	34.76	28	...
8	12.64	40	27	24	37.92	27	...
9	14.22	39	26	26	41.08	27	...
10	15.80	37	25	28	44.24	26	...
11	17.38	36	24	30	47.40	26	...
12	18.96	35	23	32	50.56	25	...

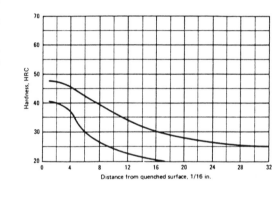

AISI-SAE 50B40H UNS H50401

Specified hardness limits

Distance from quenched surface		Hardness, HRC		Distance from quenched surface		Hardness, HRC	
1/16 in.	mm	Max	Min	1/16 in.	mm	Max	Min
1	1.58	60	53	13	20.54	49	27
2	3.16	60	53	14	22.12	47	26
3	4.74	59	52	15	23.70	44	25
4	6.32	59	51	16	25.28	41	25
5	7.90	58	50	18	28.44	38	23
6	9.48	58	48	20	31.60	36	21
7	11.06	57	44	22	34.76	35	...
8	12.64	57	39	24	37.92	34	...
9	14.22	56	34	26	41.08	33	...
10	15.80	55	31	28	44.24	32	...
11	17.38	53	29	30	47.40	30	...
12	18.96	51	28	32	50.56	29	...

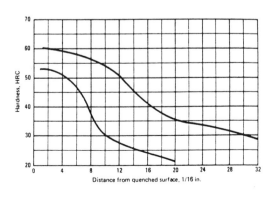

AISI-SAE 50B44H UNS H50441

Specified hardness limits

Distance from quenched surface		Hardness, HRC		Distance from quenched surface		Hardness, HRC	
1/16 in.	mm	Max	Min	1/16 in.	mm	Max	Min
1	1.58	63	56	13	20.54	54	29
2	3.16	63	56	14	22.12	52	29
3	4.74	62	55	15	23.70	50	28
4	6.32	62	55	16	25.28	48	27
5	7.90	61	54	18	28.44	44	26
6	9.48	61	52	20	31.60	40	24
7	11.06	60	48	22	34.76	38	23
8	12.64	60	43	24	37.92	37	21
9	14.22	59	38	26	41.08	36	20
10	15.80	58	34	28	44.24	35	...
11	17.38	57	31	30	47.40.	34	...
12	18.96	56	30	32	50.56	33	...

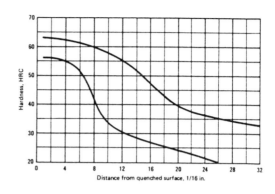

AISI-SAE 5046H UNS H50460

Specified hardness limits

Distance from quenched surface		Hardness, HRC		Distance from quenched surface		Hardness, HRC	
1/16 in.	mm	Max	Min	1/16 in.	mm	Max	Min
1	1.58	63	56	13	20.54	32	22
2	3.16	62	55	14	22.12	31	22
3	4.74	60	45	15	23.70	31	21
4	6.32	56	32	16	25.28	30	21
5	7.90	52	28	18	28.44	29	20
6	9.48	46	27	20	31.60	28	...
7	11.16	39	26	22	34.76	27	...
8	12.64	35	25	24	37.92	26	...
9	14.22	34	24	26	41.08	25	...
10	15.80	33	24	28	44.24	24	...
11	17.38	33	23	30	47.40	23	...
12	18.96	32	23	32	50.56	23	...

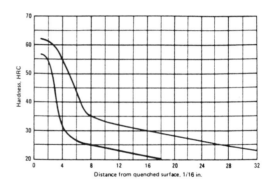

AISI-SAE 5120H UNS H51200

Specified hardness limits

Distance from quenched surface		Hardness, HRC		Distance from quenched surface		Hardness, HRC	
1/16 in.	mm	Max	Min	1/16 in.	mm	Max	Min
1	1.58	48	40	13	20.54	21	...
2	3.16	46	34	14	22.12	21	...
3	4.74	41	28	15	23.70	20	...
4	6.32	36	23	16	25.28	...	...
5	7.90	33	20	18	28.44	...	...
6	9.48	30	...	20	31.60	...	...
7	11.06	28	...	22	34.76	...	...
8	12.64	27	...	24	37.92	...	...
9	14.22	25	...	26	41.08	...	...
10	15.80	24	...	28	44.24	...	...
11	17.38	23	...	30	47.40	...	...
12	18.96	22	...	32	50.56	...	...

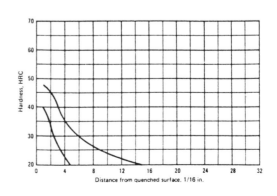

AISI-SAE 5130H   UNS H51300

Specified hardness limits

Distance from quenched surface 1/16 in.	mm	Hardness, HRC Max	Min	Distance from quenched surface 1/16 in.	mm	Hardness, HRC Max	Min
1	1.58	56	49	13	20.54	35	21
2	3.16	55	46	14	22.12	34	20
3	4.74	53	42	15	23.70	34	...
4	6.32	51	39	16	25.28	33	...
5	7.90	49	35	18	28.44	32	...
6	9.48	47	32	20	31.60	31	...
7	11.06	45	30	22	34.76	30	...
8	12.64	42	28	24	37.92	29	...
9	14.22	40	26	26	41.08	27	...
10	15.80	38	25	28	44.24	26	...
11	17.38	37	23	30	47.40	25	...
12	18.96	36	22	32	50.56	24	...

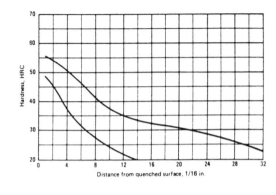

AISI-SAE 50B46H   UNS H50461

Specified hardness limits

Distance from quenched surface 1/16 in.	mm	Hardness, HRC Max	Min	Distance from quenched surface 1/16 in.	mm	Hardness, HRC Max	Min
1	1.58	63	56	13	20.54	40	26
2	3.16	62	54	14	22.12	38	25
3	4.74	61	52	15	23.70	37	25
4	6.32	60	50	16	25.28	36	24
5	7.90	59	41	18	28.44	35	23
6	9.48	58	32	20	31.60	34	22
7	11.06	57	31	22	34.76	33	21
8	12.64	56	30	24	37.92	32	20
9	14.22	54	29	26	41.08	31	...
10	15.80	51	28	28	44.24	30	...
11	17.38	47	27	30	47.40	29	...
12	18.96	43	26	32	50.56	28	...

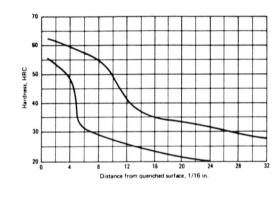

AISI-SAE 50B50H   UNS H50501

Specified hardness limits

Distance from quenched surface 1/16 in.	mm	Hardness, HRC Max	Min	Distance from quenched surface 1/16 in.	mm	Hardness, HRC Max	Min
1	1.58	65	59	13	20.54	58	32
2	3.16	65	59	14	22.12	57	31
3	4.74	64	58	15	23.70	56	30
4	6.32	64	57	16	25.28	54	29
5	7.90	63	56	18	28.44	50	28
6	9.48	63	55	20	31.60	47	27
7	11.06	62	52	22	34.76	44	26
8	12.64	62	47	24	37.92	41	25
9	14.22	61	42	26	41.08	39	24
10	15.80	60	37	28	44.24	38	22
11	17.38	60	35	30	47.40	37	21
12	18.96	59	33	32	50.56	36	20

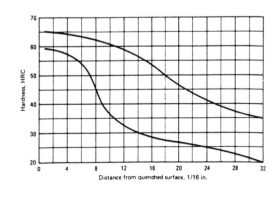

AISI-SAE 50B60H UNS H50601

Specified hardness limits

Distance from quenched surface		Hardness, HRC		Distance from quenched surface		Hardness, HRC	
1/16 in.	mm	Max	Min	1/16 in.	mm	Max	Min
1	1.58	...	60	13	20.54	63	36
2	3.16	...	60	14	22.12	63	35
3	4.74	...	60	15	23.70	63	34
4	6.32	...	60	16	25.28	62	34
5	7.90	...	60	18	28.44	60	33
6	9.48	...	59	20	31.60	58	31
7	11.06	...	57	22	34.76	55	30
8	12.64	65	53	24	37.92	53	29
9	14.22	65	47	26	41.08	51	28
10	15.80	64	42	28	44.24	49	27
11	17.38	64	39	30	47.40	47	26
12	18.96	64	37	32	50.56	44	25

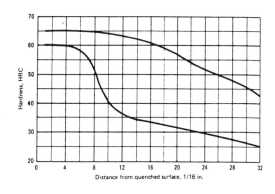

AISI-SAE 5147H UNS H51470

Specified hardness limits

Distance from quenched surface		Hardness, HRC		Distance from quenched surface		Hardness, HRC	
1/16 in.	mm	Max	Min	1/16 in.	mm	Max	Min
1	1.58	64	57	13	20.54	58	33
2	3.16	64	56	14	22.12	57	32
3	4.74	63	55	15	23.70	57	32
4	6.32	62	54	16	25.28	56	31
5	7.90	62	53	18	28.44	55	30
6	9.48	61	52	20	31.60	54	29
7	11.06	61	49	22	34.76	53	27
8	12.64	60	45	24	37.92	52	26
9	14.22	60	40	26	41.08	51	25
10	15.80	59	37	28	44.24	50	24
11	17.38	59	35	30	47.40	49	22
12	18.96	58	34	32	50.56	48	21

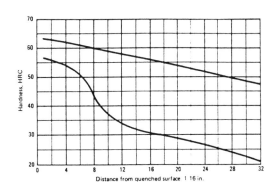

AISI-SAE 5135H UNS H51350

Specified hardness limits

Distance from quenched surface		Hardness, HRC		Distance from quenched surface		Hardness, HRC	
1/16 in.	mm	Max	Min	1/16 in.	mm	Max	Min
1	1.58	58	51	13	20.54	39	23
2	3.16	57	49	14	22.12	38	22
3	4.74	56	47	15	23.70	37	21
4	6.32	55	43	16	25.28	37	21
5	7.90	54	38	18	28.44	36	20
6	9.48	52	35	20	31.60	35	...
7	11.06	50	32	22	34.76	34	...
8	12.64	47	30	24	37.92	33	...
9	14.22	45	28	26	41.08	32	...
10	15.80	43	27	28	44.24	32	...
11	17.38	41	25	30	47.40	31	...
12	18.96	40	24	32	50.56	30	...

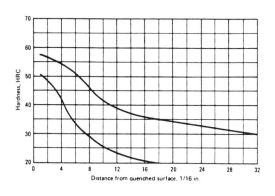

AISI-SAE 5140H UNS H51400

Specified hardness limits

Distance from quenched surface		Hardness, HRC		Distance from quenched surface		Hardness, HRC	
1/16 in.	mm	Max	Min	1/16 in.	mm	Max	Min
1	1.58	60	53	13	20.54	42	27
2	3.16	59	52	14	22.12	40	27
3	4.74	58	50	15	23.70	39	25
4	6.32	57	48	16	25.28	38	25
5	7.90	56	43	18	28.44	37	24
6	9.48	54	38	20	31.60	36	23
7	11.06	52	35	22	34.76	35	21
8	12.64	50	33	24	37.92	34	20
9	14.22	48	31	26	41.08	34	...
10	15.80	46	30	28	44.24	33	...
11	17.38	45	29	30	47.40	33	...
12	18.96	43	28	32	50.56	32	...

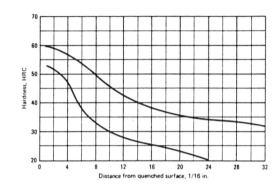

AISI-SAE 5145H UNS H51450

Specified hardness limits

Distance from quenched surface		Hardness, HRC		Distance from quenched surface		Hardness, HRC	
1/16 in.	mm	Max	Min	1/16 in.	mm	Max	Min
1	1.58	63	56	13	20.54	48	30
2	3.16	62	55	14	22.12	47	29
3	4.74	61	53	15	23.70	45	28
4	6.32	60	51	16	25.28	44	28
5	7.90	59	48	18	28.44	42	26
6	9.48	58	42	20	31.60	41	25
7	11.06	57	38	22	34.76	39	24
8	12.64	56	35	24	37.92	38	23
9	14.22	55	33	26	41.08	37	22
10	15.80	53	32	28	44.24	37	21
11	17.38	52	31	30	47.40	36	...
12	18.96	50	30	32	50.56	35	...

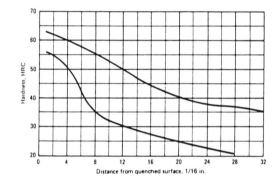

AISI-SAE 5132H UNS H51320

Specified hardness limits

Distance from quenched surface		Hardness, HRC		Distance from quenched surface		Hardness, HRC	
1/16 in.	mm	Max	Min	1/16 in.	mm	Max	Min
1	1.58	57	50	13	20.54	35	21
2	3.16	56	47	14	22.12	34	20
3	4.74	54	43	15	23.70	34	...
4	6.32	52	40	16	25.28	33	...
5	7.90	50	35	18	28.44	32	...
6	9.48	48	32	20	31.60	31	...
7	11.06	45	29	22	34.76	30	...
8	12.64	42	27	24	37.92	29	...
9	14.22	40	25	26	41.08	28	...
10	15.80	38	24	28	44.24	27	...
11	17.38	37	23	30	47.40	26	...
12	18.96	36	22	32	50.56	25	...

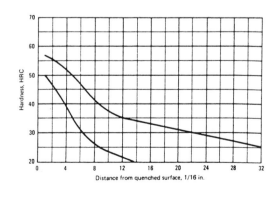

AISI-SAE 5160H UNS H51600

Specified hardness limits

Distance from quenched surface 1/16 in.	mm	Hardness, HRC Max	Min	Distance from quenched surface 1/16 in.	mm	Hardness, HRC Max	Min
	1.58	...	60	13	20.54	58	35
	3.16	...	60	14	22.12	56	35
	4.74	...	60	15	23.70	54	34
	6.32	65	59	16	25.28	52	34
	7.90	65	58	18	28.44	48	33
	9.48	64	56	20	31.60	47	32
	11.06	64	52	22	34.76	46	31
	12.64	63	47	24	37.92	45	30
	14.22	62	42	26	41.08	44	29
10	15.80	61	39	28	44.24	43	28
1	17.38	60	37	30	47.40	43	28
2	18.96	59	36	32	50.56	42	27

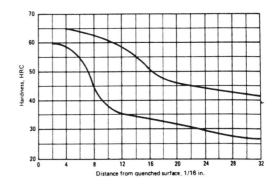

AISI-SAE 51B60H UNS H51601

Specified hardness limits

Distance from quenched surface 1/16 in.	mm	Hardness, HRC Max	Min	Distance from quenched surface 1/16 in.	mm	Hardness, HRC Max	Min
	1.58	...	60	13	20.54	65	40
	3.16	...	60	14	22.12	64	39
	4.74	...	60	15	23.70	64	38
	6.32	...	60	16	25.28	63	37
	7.90	...	60	18	28.44	61	36
	9.48	...	59	20	31.60	59	34
	11.06	...	58	22	34.76	57	33
	12.64	...	57	24	37.92	55	31
	14.22	...	54	26	41.08	53	30
10	15.80	...	50	28	44.24	51	28
1	17.38	...	44	30	47.40	49	27
2	18.96	65	41	32	50.56	47	25

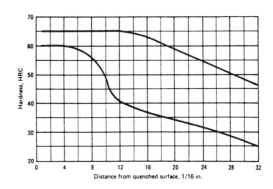

AISI-SAE 6118H UNS H61180

Specified hardness limits

Distance from quenched surface 1/16 in.	mm	Hardness, HRC Max	Min	Distance from quenched surface 1/16 in.	mm	Hardness, HRC Max	Min
1	1.58	46	39	13	20.54	24	...
2	3.16	44	36	14	22.12	23	...
3	4.74	38	28	15	23.70	23	...
4	6.32	33	24	16	25.28	22	...
5	7.90	30	22	18	28.44	22	...
6	9.148	28	20	20	31.60	21	...
7	11.06	27	...	22	34.76	21	...
8	12.64	26	...	24	37.92	20	...
9	14.22	26	...	26	41.08	...	...
10	15.80	25	...	28	44.24	...	...
11	17.38	25	...	30	47.40	...	...
12	18.96	24	...	32	50.56	...	...

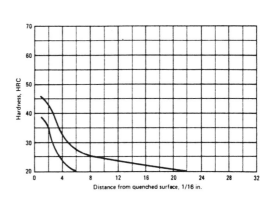

AISI-SAE 5150H UNS H51500

Specified hardness limits

Distance from quenched surface		Hardness, HRC		Distance from quenched surface		Hardness, HRC	
1/16 in.	mm	Max	Min	1/16 in.	mm	Max	Min
1	1.58	65	59	13	20.54	51	31
2	3.16	65	58	14	22.12	50	31
3	4.74	64	57	15	23.70	48	30
4	6.32	63	56	16	25.28	47	30
5	7.90	62	53	18	28.44	45	29
6	9.48	61	49	20	31.60	43	28
7	11.06	60	42	22	34.76	42	27
8	12.64	59	38	24	37.92	41	26
9	14.22	58	36	26	41.08	40	25
10	15.80	56	34	28	44.24	39	24
11	17.38	55	33	30	47.40	39	23
12	18.96	53	32	32	50.56	38	22

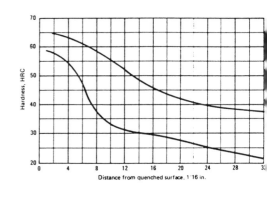

AISI-SAE 5155H UNS H51550

Specified hardness limits

Distance from quenched surface		Hardness, HRC		Distance from quenched surface		Hardness, HRC	
1/16 in.	mm	Max	Min	1/16 in.	mm	Max	Min
1	1.58	...	60	13	20.54	55	34
2	3.16	65	59	14	22.12	52	33
3	4.74	64	58	15	23.70	51	33
4	6.32	64	57	16	25.28	49	32
5	7.90	63	55	18	28.44	47	31
6	9.48	63	52	20	31.60	45	31
7	11.06	62	47	22	34.76	44	30
8	12.64	62	41	24	37.92	43	29
9	14.22	61	37	26	41.08	42	28
10	15.80	60	36	28	44.24	41	27
11	17.38	59	35	30	47.40	41	26
12	18.96	57	34	32	50.56	40	25

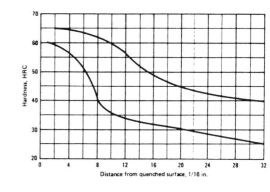

AISI-SAE 8620H UNS H86200

Specified hardness limits

Distance from quenched surface		Hardness, HRC		Distance from quenched surface		Hardness, HRC	
1/16 in.	mm	Max	Min	1/16 in.	mm	Max	Min
1	1.58	48	41	13	20.54	25	...
2	3.16	47	37	14	22.12	25	...
3	4.74	44	32	15	23.70	24	...
4	6.32	41	27	16	25.28	24	...
5	7.90	37	23	18	28.44	23	...
6	9.48	34	21	20	31.60	23	...
7	11.06	32	...	22	34.76	23	...
8	12.64	30	...	24	37.92	23	...
9	14.22	29	...	26	41.08	23	...
10	15.80	28	...	28	44.24	22	...
11	17.38	27	...	30	47.40	22	...
12	18.96	26	...	32	50.56	22	...

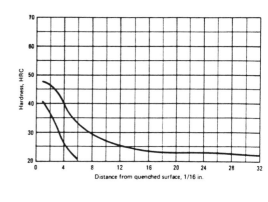

AISI-SAE 8622H UNS H86220

Specified hardness limits

Distance from quenched surface		Hardness, HRC		Distance from quenched surface		Hardness, HRC	
1/16 in.	mm	Max	Min	1/16 in.	mm	Max	Min
1	1.58	50	43	13	20.54	27	...
2	3.16	49	39	14	22.12	26	...
3	4.74	47	34	15	23.70	26	...
4	6.32	44	30	16	25.28	25	...
5	7.90	40	26	18	28.44	25	...
6	9.48	37	24	20	31.60	24	...
7	11.06	34	22	22	34.76	24	...
8	12.64	32	20	24	37.92	24	...
9	14.22	31	...	26	41.08	24	...
10	15.80	30	...	28	44.24	24	...
11	17.38	29	...	30	47.40	24	...
12	18.96	28	...	32	50.56	24	...

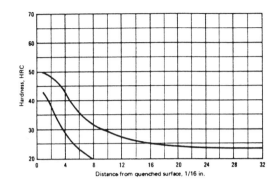

AISI-SAE 6150H UNS H61500

Specified hardness limits

Distance from quenched surface		Hardness, HRC		Distance from quenched surface		Hardness, HRC	
1/16 in.	mm	Max	Min	1/16 in.	mm	Max	Min
1	1.58	65	59	13	20.54	57	37
2	3.16	65	58	14	22.12	55	36
3	4.74	64	57	15	23.70	54	35
4	6.32	64	56	16	25.28	52	35
5	7.90	63	55	18	28.44	50	34
6	9.48	63	53	20	31.60	48	32
7	11.06	62	50	22	34.76	47	31
8	12.64	61	47	24	37.92	46	30
9	14.22	61	43	26	41.08	45	29
10	15.80	60	41	28	44.24	44	27
11	17.38	59	39	30	47.40	43	26
12	18.96	58	38	32	50.56	42	25

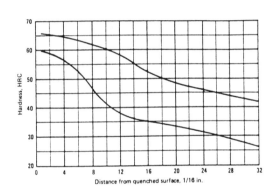

AISI-SAE 81B45H UNS H81451

Specified hardness limits

Distance from quenched surface		Hardness, HRC		Distance from quenched surface		Hardness, HRC	
1/16 in.	mm	Max	Min	1/16 in.	mm	Max	Min
1	1.58	63	56	13	20.54	58	38
2	3.16	63	56	14	22.12	57	37
3	4.74	63	56	15	23.70	57	36
4	6.32	63	56	16	25.28	56	35
5	7.90	63	55	18	28.44	55	34
6	9.48	63	54	20	31.60	53	32
7	11.06	62	53	22	34.76	52	31
8	12.64	62	51	24	37.92	50	30
9	14.22	61	48	26	41.08	49	29
10	15.80	60	44	28	44.24	47	28
11	17.38	60	41	30	47.40	45	28
12	18.96	59	39	32	50.56	43	27

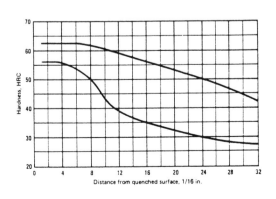

AISI-SAE 8617H UNS H86170

Specified hardness limits

Distance from quenched surface		Hardness, HRC		Distance from quenched surface		Hardness, HRC	
1/16 in.	mm	Max	Min	1/16 in.	mm	Max	Min
1	1.58	46	39	13	20.54	23	...
2	3.16	44	33	14	22.12	22	...
3	4.74	41	27	15	23.70	22	...
4	6.32	38	24	16	25.28	21	...
5	7.90	34	20	18	28.44	21	...
6	9.48	31	...	20	31.60	20	...
7	11.06	28	...	22	34.76	...	...
8	12.64	27	...	24	37.92	...	...
9	14.22	26	...	26	41.08	...	...
10	15.80	25	...	28	44.24	...	...
11	17.38	24	...	30	47.40	...	...
12	18.96	23	...	32	59.56	...	...

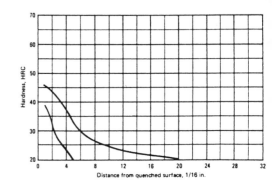

AISI-SAE 8642H UNS H86420

Specified hardness limits

Distance from quenched surface		Hardness, HRC		Distance from quenched surface		Hardness, HRC	
1/16 in.	mm	Max	Min	1/16 in.	mm	Max	Min
1	1.58	62	55	13	20.54	50	32
2	3.16	62	54	14	22.12	49	31
3	4.74	62	53	15	23.70	48	30
4	6.32	61	52	16	25.28	46	29
5	7.90	61	50	18	28.44	44	28
6	9.48	60	48	20	31.60	42	28
7	11.06	59	45	22	34.76	41	27
8	12.64	58	42	24	37.92	40	27
9	14.22	57	39	26	41.08	40	26
10	15.80	55	37	28	44.24	39	26
11	17.38	54	34	30	47.40	39	26
12	18.96	52	33	32	50.56	39	26

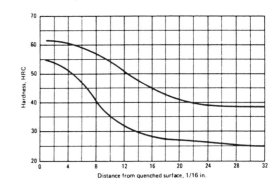

AISI-SAE 8627H UNS H86270

Specified hardness limits

Distance from quenched surface		Hardness, HRC		Distance from quenched surface		Hardness, HRC	
1/16 in.	mm	Max	Min	1/16 in.	mm	Max	Min
1	1.58	54	47	13	20.54	31	21
2	3.16	52	43	14	22.12	30	21
3	4.74	50	38	15	23.70	30	20
4	6.32	48	35	16	25.28	29	20
5	7.90	45	32	18	28.44	28	...
6	9.48	43	29	20	31.60	28	...
7	11.06	40	27	22	34.76	28	...
8	12.64	38	26	24	37.92	27	...
9	14.22	36	24	26	41.08	27	...
10	15.80	34	24	28	44.24	27	...
11	17.38	33	23	30	47.40	27	...
12	18.96	32	22	32	50.56	27	...

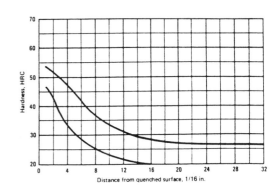

AISI-SAE 8630H   UNS H86300

Specified hardness limits

Distance from quenched surface 1/16 in.	mm	Hardness, HRC Max	Min	Distance from quenched surface 1/16 in.	mm	Hardness, HRC Max	Min
	1.58	56	49	13	20.54	33	23
	3.16	55	46	14	22.12	33	22
	4.74	54	43	15	23.70	32	22
	6.32	52	39	16	25.28	31	21
	7.90	50	35	18	28.44	30	21
	9.48	47	32	20	31.60	30	20
	11.06	44	29	22	34.76	29	20
	12.64	41	28	24	37.92	29	...
	14.22	39	27	26	41.08	29	...
0	15.80	37	26	28	44.24	29	...
1	17.38	35	25	30	47.40	29	...
2	18.96	34	24	32	50.56	29	...

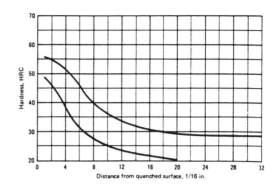

AISI-SAE 86B30H   UNS H86301

Specified hardness limits

Distance from quenched surface 1/16 in.	mm	Hardness, HRC Max	Min	Distance from quenched surface 1/16 in.	mm	Hardness, HRC Max	Min
	1.58	56	49	13	20.54	51	39
	3.16	55	49	14	22.12	50	38
	4.74	55	48	15	23.70	50	36
	6.32	55	48	16	25.28	49	35
	7.90	54	48	18	28.44	48	34
	9.48	54	48	20	31.60	47	32
	11.06	53	48	22	34.76	45	31
	12.64	53	47	24	37.92	44	29
	14.22	52	46	26	41.08	43	28
0	15.80	52	44	28	44.24	41	27
1	17.38	52	42	30	47.40	40	26
2	18.96	51	40	32	50.56	39	25

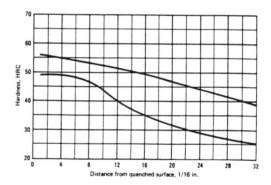

AISI-SAE 8625H   UNS H86250

Specified hardness limits

Distance from quenched surface 1/16 in.	mm	Hardness, HRC Max	Min	Distance from quenched surface 1/16 in.	mm	Hardness, HRC Max	Min
	1.58	52	45	13	20.54	29	...
	3.16	51	41	14	22.12	28	...
	4.74	48	36	15	23.70	28	...
	6.32	46	32	16	25.28	27	...
	7.90	43	29	18	28.44	27	...
	9.48	40	27	20	31.60	26	...
	11.06	37	25	22	34.76	26	...
	12.64	35	23	24	37.92	26	...
	14.22	33	22	26	41.08	26	...
0	15.80	32	21	28	44.24	25	...
1	17.38	31	20	30	47.40	25	...
2	18.96	30		32	50.56	25	...

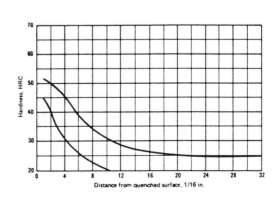

AISI-SAE 8645H UNS H86450

Specified hardness limits

Distance from quenched surface 1/16 in.	mm	Hardness, HRC Max	Min	Distance from quenched surface 1/16 in.	mm	Hardness, HRC Max	Min
1	1.58	63	56	13	20.54	54	34
2	3.16	63	56	14	22.12	52	33
3	4.74	63	55	15	23.70	51	32
4	6.32	63	54	16	25.28	49	31
5	7.90	62	52	18	28.44	47	30
6	9.48	61	50	20	31.60	45	29
7	11.06	61	48	22	34.76	43	28
8	12.64	60	45	24	37.92	42	28
9	14.22	59	41	26	41.08	42	27
10	15.80	58	39	28	44.24	41	27
11	17.38	56	37	30	47.40	41	27
12	18.96	55	35	32	50.56	41	27

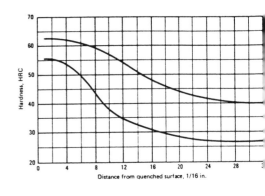

AISI-SAE 86B45H UNS H86451

Specified hardness limits

Distance from quenched surface 1/16 in.	mm	Hardness, HRC Max	Min	Distance from quenched surface 1/16 in.	mm	Hardness, HRC Max	Min
1	1.58	63	56	13	20.54	59	49
2	3.16	63	56	14	22.12	59	48
3	4.74	62	55	15	23.70	58	46
4	6.32	62	54	16	25.28	58	45
5	7.90	62	54	18	28.44	58	42
6	9.48	61	53	20	31.60	58	39
7	11.06	61	52	22	34.76	57	37
8	12.64	60	52	24	37.92	57	35
9	14.22	60	51	26	41.08	57	34
10	15.80	60	51	28	44.24	57	32
11	17.38	59	50	30	47.40	56	32
12	18.96	59	50	32	50.56	56	31

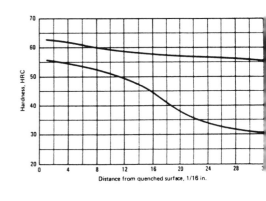

AISI-SAE 8650H UNS H86500

Specified hardness limits

Distance from quenched surface 1/16 in.	mm	Hardness, HRC Max	Min	Distance from quenched surface 1/16 in.	mm	Hardness, HRC Max	Min
1	1.58	65	59	13	20.54	58	37
2	3.16	65	58	14	22.12	58	36
3	4.74	65	57	15	23.70	57	35
4	6.32	64	57	16	25.28	56	34
5	7.90	64	56	18	28.44	55	33
6	9.48	63	54	20	31.60	53	32
7	11.06	63	53	22	34.76	52	31
8	12.64	62	50	24	37.92	50	31
9	14.22	61	47	26	41.08	49	30
10	15.80	60	44	28	44.24	47	30
11	17.38	60	41	30	47.40	46	29
12	18.96	59	39	32	50.56	45	29

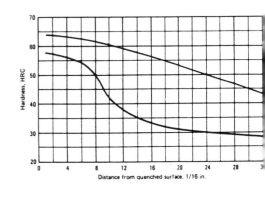

AISI-SAE 8637H UNS H86370

Specified hardness limits

Distance from quenched surface		Hardness, HRC		Distance from quenched surface		Hardness, HRC	
1/16 in.	mm	Max	Min	1/16 in.	mm	Max	Min
1	1.58	59	52	13	20.54	44	29
2	3.16	58	51	14	22.12	43	28
3	4.74	58	50	15	23.70	41	27
4	6.32	57	48	16	25.28	40	26
5	7.90	56	45	18	28.44	39	25
6	9.48	55	42	20	31.60	37	25
7	11.06	54	39	22	34.76	36	24
8	12.64	53	36	24	37.92	36	24
9	14.22	51	34	26	41.08	35	24
10	15.80	49	32	28	44.24	35	24
11	17.38	47	31	30	47.40	35	23
12	18.96	46	30	32	50.56	35	23

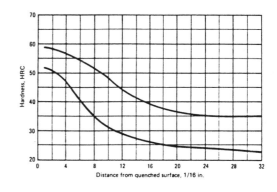

AISI-SAE 8640H UNS H86400

Specified hardness limits

Distance from quenched surface		Hardness, HRC		Distance from quenched surface		Hardness, HRC	
1/16 in.	mm	Max	Min	1/16 in.	mm	Max	Min
1	1.58	60	53	13	20.54	47	30
2	3.16	60	53	14	22.12	45	29
3	4.74	60	52	15	23.70	44	28
4	6.32	59	51	16	25.28	42	28
5	7.90	59	49	18	28.44	41	26
6	9.48	58	46	20	31.60	39	26
7	11.06	57	42	22	34.76	38	25
8	12.64	55	39	24	37.92	38	25
9	14.22	54	36	26	41.08	37	24
10	15.80	52	34	28	44.24	37	24
11	17.38	50	32	30	47.40	37	24
12	18.96	49	31	32	50.56	37	24

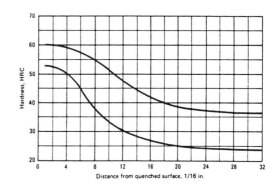

AISI-SAE 8740H UNS H87400

Specified hardness limits

Distance from quenched surface		Hardness, HRC		Distance from quenched surface		Hardness, HRC	
1/16 in.	mm	Max	Min	1/16 in.	mm	Max	Min
1	1.58	60	53	13	20.54	49	31
2	3.16	60	53	14	22.12	48	31
3	4.74	60	52	15	23.70	46	30
4	6.32	60	51	16	25.28	45	29
5	7.90	59	49	18	28.44	43	28
6	9.48	58	46	20	31.60	42	28
7	11.06	57	43	22	34.76	41	27
8	12.64	56	40	24	37.92	40	27
9	14.22	55	37	26	41.08	39	27
10	15.80	53	35	28	44.24	39	27
11	17.38	52	34	30	47.40	38	26
12	18.96	50	32	32	50.56	38	26

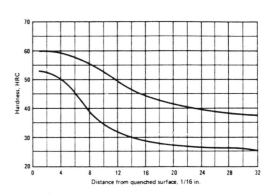

AISI-SAE 8822H   UNS H88220

Specified hardness limits

Distance from quenched surface		Hardness, HRC		Distance from quenched surface		Hardness, HRC	
1/16 in.	mm	Max	Min	1/16 in.	mm	Max	Min
1	1.58	50	43	13	20.54	31	22
2	3.16	49	42	14	22.12	30	22
3	4.74	48	39	15	23.70	30	21
4	6.32	46	33	16	25.28	29	21
5	7.90	43	29	18	28.44	29	20
6	9.48	40	27	20	31.60	28	...
7	11.06	37	25	22	34.76	27	...
8	12.64	35	24	24	37.92	27	...
9	14.22	34	24	26	41.08	27	...
10	15.80	33	23	28	44.24	27	...
11	17.38	32	23	30	47.40	27	...
12	18.96	31	22	32	50.56	27	...

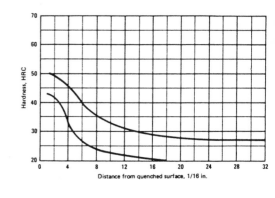

AISI-SAE 8655H   UNS H86550

Specified hardness limits

Distance from quenched surface		Hardness, HRC		Distance from quenched surface		Hardness, HRC	
1/16 in.	mm	Max	Min	1/16 in.	mm	Max	Min
1	1.58	...	60	13	20.54	64	41
2	3.16	...	59	14	22.12	63	40
3	4.74	...	59	15	23.70	63	39
4	6.32	...	58	16	25.28	62	38
5	7.90	...	57	18	28.44	61	37
6	9.48	...	56	20	31.60	60	35
7	11.06	...	55	22	34.76	59	34
8	12.64	...	54	24	37.92	58	34
9	14.22	...	52	26	41.08	57	33
10	15.80	65	49	28	44.24	56	33
11	17.38	65	46	30	47.40	55	32
12	18.96	64	43	32	50.56	53	32

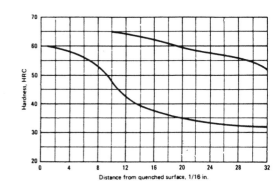

AISI-SAE 8660H   UNS H86600

Specified hardness limits

Distance from quenched surface		Hardness, HRC		Distance from quenched surface		Hardness, HRC	
1/16 in.	mm	Max	Min	1/16 in.	mm	Max	Min
1	1.58	...	60	13	20.54	...	45
2	3.16	...	60	14	22.12	...	44
3	4.74	...	60	15	23.70	...	43
4	6.32	...	60	16	25.28	65	42
5	7.90	...	60	18	28.44	64	40
6	9.48	...	59	20	31.60	64	39
7	11.06	...	58	22	34.76	63	38
8	12.64	...	57	24	37.92	62	37
9	14.22	...	55	26	41.08	62	36
10	15.80	...	53	28	44.24	61	36
11	17.38	...	50	30	47.40	60	35
12	18.96	...	47	32	50.56	60	35

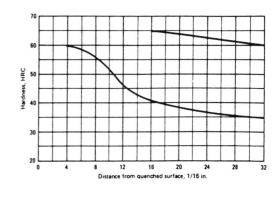

ISI-SAE 8720H UNS H87200

Specified hardness limits

Distance from quenched surface 1/16 in.	mm	Hardness, HRC Max	Hardness, HRC Min	Distance from quenched surface 1/16 in.	mm	Hardness, HRC Max	Hardness, HRC Min
	1.58	48	41	13	20.54	26	...
	3.16	47	38	14	22.12	26	...
	4.74	45	35	15	23.70	25	...
	6.32	42	30	16	25.28	25	...
	7.90	38	26	18	28.44	24	...
	9.48	35	24	20	31.60	24	...
	11.06	33	22	22	34.76	23	...
	12.64	31	21	24	37.92	23	...
	14.22	30	20	26	41.08	23	...
	15.80	29	...	28	44.24	23	...
	17.38	28	...	30	47.40	22	...
	18.96	27	...	32	50.56	22	...

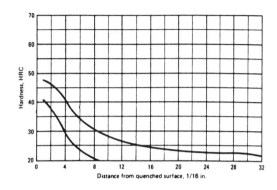

ISI-SAE 9310H UNS H93100

Specified hardness limits

Distance from quenched surface 1/16 in.	mm	Hardness, HRC Max	Hardness, HRC Min	Distance from quenched surface 1/16 in.	mm	Hardness, HRC Max	Hardness, HRC Min
	1.58	43	36	13	20.54	37	26
	3.16	43	35	14	22.12	36	26
	4.74	43	35	15	23.70	36	26
	6.32	42	34	16	25.28	35	26
	7.90	42	32	18	28.44	35	26
	9.48	42	31	20	31.60	35	25
	11.06	42	30	22	34.76	34	25
	12.64	41	29	24	37.92	34	25
	14.22	40	28	26	41.08	34	25
	15.80	40	27	28	44.24	34	25
	17.38	39	27	30	47.40	33	24
	18.96	38	26	32	50.56	33	24

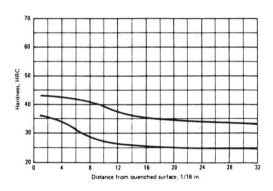

ISI-SAE 94B15H UNS H94151

Specified hardness limits

Distance from quenched surface 1/16 in.	mm	Hardness, HRC Max	Hardness, HRC Min	Distance from quenched surface 1/16 in.	mm	Hardness, HRC Max	Hardness, HRC Min
	1.58	45	38	13	20.54	30	...
	3.16	45	38	14	22.12	29	...
	4.74	44	37	15	23.70	28	...
	6.32	44	36	16	25.28	27	...
	7.90	43	32	18	28.44	26	...
	9.48	42	28	20	31.60	25	...
	11.06	40	25	22	34.76	24	...
	12.64	38	23	24	37.92	23	...
	14.22	36	21	26	41.08	23	...
	15.80	34	20	28	44.24	22	...
	17.38	33	...	30	47.40	22	...
	18.96	31	...	32	50.56	22	...

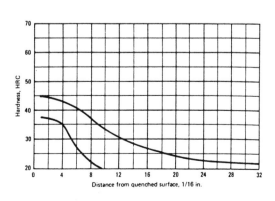

AISI-SAE 94B17H   UNS H94171

Specified hardness limits

Distance from quenched surface 1/16 in.	mm	Hardness, HRC Max	Min	Distance from quenched surface 1/16 in.	mm	Hardness, HRC Max	Min
1	1.58	46	39	13	20.54	33	...
2	3.16	46	39	14	22.12	32	...
3	4.74	45	38	15	23.70	31	...
4	6.32	45	37	16	25.28	30	...
5	7.90	44	34	18	28.44	28	...
6	9.48	43	29	20	31.60	27	...
7	11.06	42	26	22	34.76	26	...
8	12.64	41	24	24	37.92	25	...
9	14.22	40	23	26	41.08	24	...
10	15.80	38	21	28	44.24	24	...
11	17.38	36	20	30	47.40	23	...
12	18.96	34		32	50.56	23	...

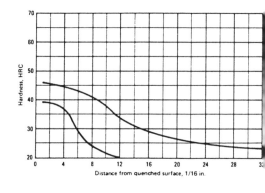

AISI-SAE 94B30H   UNS H94301

Specified hardness limits

Distance from quenched surface 1/16 in.	mm	Hardness, HRC Max	Min	Distance from quenched surface 1/16 in.	mm	Hardness, HRC Max	Min
1	1.58	56	49	13	20.54	50	30
2	3.16	56	49	14	22.12	49	29
3	4.74	55	48	15	23.70	48	28
4	6.32	55	48	16	25.28	46	27
5	7.90	54	47	18	28.44	44	25
6	9.48	54	46	20	31.60	42	24
7	11.06	53	44	22	34.76	40	23
8	12.64	53	42	24	37.92	38	23
9	14.22	52	39	26	41.08	37	22
10	15.80	52	37	28	44.24	35	21
11	17.38	51	34	30	47.40	34	21
12	18.96	51	32	32	50.56	34	20

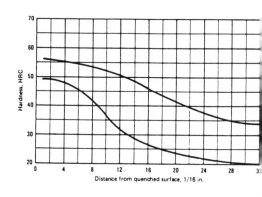

AISI-SAE 9260H   UNS H92600

Specified hardness limits

Distance from quenched surface 1/16 in.	mm	Hardness, HRC Max	Min	Distance from quenched surface 1/16 in.	mm	Hardness, HRC Max	Min
1	1.58	...	60	13	20.54	45	33
2	3.16	...	60	14	22.12	43	33
3	4.74	65	57	15	23.70	42	32
4	6.32	64	53	16	25.28	40	32
5	7.90	63	46	18	28.44	38	31
6	9.48	62	41	20	31.60	37	31
7	11.06	60	38	22	34.76	36	30
8	12.64	58	36	24	37.92	36	30
9	14.22	55	36	26	41.08	35	29
10	15.80	52	35	28	44.24	35	29
11	17.38	49	34	30	47.40	35	28
12	18.96	47	34	32	50.56	34	28

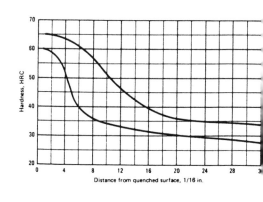

Appendix 20.

Glossary of selected terms. (From G. Krauss, Steels: Heat Treatment and Processing Principles, ASM International, Materials Park, Ohio (1990))

A

A_{cm}, A_1, A_3, A_4. Same as Ae_{cm}, Ae_1, Ae_3 and Ae_4.

Ac_{cm}, Ac_1, Ac_3, Ac_4. Defined under *transformation temperature*.

acicular ferrite. A highly substructured non-equiaxed ferrite that forms upon continuous cooling by a mixed diffusion and shear mode of transformation that begins at a temperature slightly higher than the temperature transformation range for upper bainite. It is distinguished from bainite in that it has a limited amount of carbon available; thus, there is only a small amount of carbide present.

Ae_{cm}, Ae_1, Ae_3, Ae_4. Defined under *transformation temperature*.

age hardening. Hardening by aging, usually after rapid cooling or cold working. See also *aging*.

age softening. Spontaneous decrease of strength and hardness that takes place at room temperature in certain strain-hardened alloys, especially those of aluminum.

aging. A change in the properties of certain metals and alloys that occurs at ambient or moderately elevated temperatures after hot working or a heat treatment (quench aging in ferrous alloys, natural or artificial aging in ferrous and nonferrous alloys) or after a cold working operation (strain aging). The change in properties is often, but not always, due to a phase change (precipitation), but never involves a change in chemical composition of the metal or alloy. See also *age hardening, artificial aging, interrupted aging, natural aging, overaging, precipitation hardening, precipitation heat treatment, progressive aging, quench aging, step aging.*

air-hardening steel. A steel containing sufficient carbon and other alloying elements to harden fully during cooling in air or other gaseous mediums from a temperature above its transformation range. The term should be restricted to steels that are capable of being hardened by cooling in air in fairly large sections, about 2 in. (50 mm) or more in diameter. Same as self-hardening steel.

alpha ferrite. See *ferrite*.

alpha iron. The body-centered cubic form of pure iron, stable below 910 °C (1670 °F).

Alumel. A nickel-base alloy containing about 2.5% Mn, 2% Al and 1% Si used chiefly as a component of pyrometric thermocouples.

annealing. A generic term denoting a treatment, consisting of heating to and holding at a suitable temperature followed by cooling at a suitable rate, used primarily to soften metallic materials, but also to simultaneously produce desired changes in other properties or in microstructure. The purpose of such changes may be, but is not confined to: improvement of machinability, facilitation of cold work, improvement of mechanical or electrical properties, and/or increase in stability of dimensions.

When the term is used without qualification, full annealing is implied. When applied only for the relief of stress, the process is properly called stress relieving or stress-relief annealing.

In ferrous alloys, annealing usually is done above the upper critical temperature, but the time-temperature cycles vary widely in both maximum temperature attained and in cooling rate employed, depending on composition, material condition, and results desired. When applicable, the following commercial process names should be used: black annealing, blue annealing, box annealing, bright annealing, cycle annealing, flame annealing, full annealing, graphitizing, in-process annealing, isothermal annealing, malleabilizing, orientation annealing, process annealing, quench annealing, spheroidizing, subcritical annealing.

In nonferrous alloys, annealing cycles are designed to: (1) remove part or all of the effects of cold working (recrystallization may or may not be involved); (2) cause substantially complete coalescence of precipitates from solid solution in relatively coarse form; or (3) both, depending on composition and material condition. Specific process names in commercial use are final annealing, full annealing, intermediate annealing, partial annealing, recrystallization annealing, stress-relief annealing, anneal to temper.

annealing carbon. Fine, apparently amorphous carbon particles formed in white cast iron and certain steels during prolonged annealing. Also called temper carbon.

annealing twin. A twin form in a crystal during recrystallization.

anneal to temper. A final partial anneal that softens a cold worked nonferrous alloy to a specified level of hardness or tensile strength.

Ar_{cm}, Ar_1, Ar_3, Ar_4, Ar', Ar''. Defined under *transformation temperature*.

artificial aging. Aging above room temperature. See also *aging*. Compare with *natural aging*.

athermal transformation. A reaction that proceeds without benefit of thermal fluctuations; that is, thermal activation is not required. Such reactions are diffusionless and can take place with great speed when the driving force is sufficiently high. For example, many martensitic transformations occur athermally on cooling, even at relatively low temperatures, because of the progressively increasing driving force. In contrast, a reaction that occurs at constant temperature is an *isothermal transformation*; thermal activation is necessary in this case and the reaction proceeds as a function of time.

ausforming. Hot deformation of metastable austenite within controlled ranges of temperature and time that avoids formation of nonmartensitic transformation products.

austempering. A heat treatment for ferrous alloys in which a part is quenched from the austenitizing temperature at a rate fast enough to avoid formation of ferrite or pearlite and then held at a temperature just above M_s until transformation to bainite is complete.

austenite. A solid solution of one or more elements in face-centered cubic iron. Unless otherwise designated (such as nickel austenite), the solute is generally assumed to be carbon.

austenitic grain size. The size attained by the grains of steel when heated to the austenitic region; may be revealed by appropriate etching of cross sections after cooling to room temperature.

austenitizing. Forming austenite by heating a ferrous alloy into the transformation range (partial austenitizing) or above the transformation range (complete austenitizing). When used without qualification, the term implies complete austenitizing.

B

bainite. A metastable aggregate of ferrite and cementite resulting from the transformation of austenite at temperatures below the pearlite range but above M_s. Its appearance is feathery if formed in the upper part of the bainite transformation range; acicular, resembling tempered martensite, if formed in the lower part.

baking. (1) Heating to a low temperature to remove gases. (2) Curing or hardening surface coatings such as paints by exposure to heat. (3) Heating to drive off moisture, as in the baking of sand cores after molding.

bark. The decarburized layer just beneath the scale that results from heating steel in an oxidizing atmosphere.

black annealing. Box annealing or pot annealing ferrous alloy sheet, strip, wire. See also *box annealing.*

black oxide. A black finish on a metal produced by immersing it in hot oxidizing salts or salt solutions.

blank carburizing. Simulating the carburizing operation without introducing carbon. This is usually accomplished by using an inert material in place of the carburizing agent, or by applying a suitable protective coating to the ferrous alloy.

blank nitriding. Simulating the nitriding operation without introducing nitrogen. This is usually accomplished by using an inert material in place of the nitriding agent, or by applying a suitable protective coating to the ferrous alloy.

block brazing. An obsolete brazing process in which the joint was heated using hot blocks.

blue annealing. Heating hot rolled ferrous sheet in an open furnace to a temperature within the transformation range and then cooling in air, in order to soften the metal. The formation of a bluish oxide on the surface is incidental.

blue brittleness. Brittleness exhibited by some steels after being treated to some temperature within the range of about 200 to 370°C (400 to 700°F), particularly if the steel is worked at the elevated temperature. Killed steels are virtually free of this kind of brittleness.

bluing. Subjecting the scale-free surface of a ferrous alloy to the action of air, steam, or other agents at a suitable temperature, thus forming a thin blue film of oxide and improving the appearance and resistance to corrosion. *Note:* This term is ordinarily applied to sheet, strip, or finished parts. It is used also to denote the heating of springs after fabrication to improve their properties.

box annealing. Annealing a metal or alloy in a sealed container under conditions that minimize oxidation. In box annealing a ferrous alloy, the charge is usually heated slowly to a temperature below the transformation range, but sometimes above or within it, and is then cooled slowly; this process is also called close annealing or pot annealing. See also *black annealing.*

brazing. A group of welding processes that join solid materials together by heating them to a suitable temperature and by using a filler metal having a liquidus above 450°C (840°F) and below the solidus of the base materials. The filler metal is distributed between the closely fitted surfaces of the joint by capillary attraction.

brazing alloy. See preferred term *brazing filler metal.*

brazing filler metal. A nonferrous filler metal used in *brazing* and braze welding.

brazing sheet. Brazing filler metal in sheet form or flat-rolled metal clad with brazing filler metal on one or both sides.

breaks. Creases or ridges usually in "untempered" or in aged material where the yield point has been exceeded. Depending on the origin of the break, it may be termed a cross break, a coil break, an edge break, or a sticker break.

bright annealing. Annealing in a protective medium to prevent discoloration of the bright surface.

burning. (1) Permanently damaging a metal or alloy by heating to cause either incipient melting or intergranular oxidation. See also *overheating.* (2) In grinding, getting the work hot enough to cause discoloration or to change the microstructure by tempering or hardening.

C

calorizing. Imparting resistance to oxidation to an iron or steel surface by heating in aluminum powder at 800 to 1000°C (1472 to 1832°F).

carbonitriding. A case hardening process in which a suitable ferrous material is heated above the lower transformation temperature in a gaseous atmosphere of such composition as to cause simultaneous absorption of carbon and nitrogen by the surface and, by diffusion, create a concentration gradient. The process is completed by cooling at a rate that produces the desired properties in the workpiece.

carbonization. Conversion of an organic substance into elemental carbon. (Should not be confused with carburization.)

carbon potential. A measure of the ability of an environment containing active carbon to alter or maintain, under prescribed conditions, the carbon level of the steel. *Note:* In any particular environment, the carbon level attained will depend on such factors as temperature, time, and steel composition.

carbon restoration. Replacing the carbon lost in the surface layer from previous processing by carburizing this layer to substantially the original carbon level. Sometimes called recarburizing.

carburizing. Absorption and diffusion of carbon into solid ferrous alloys by heating, to a temperature usually above Ac3, in contact with a suitable carbonaceous material. A form of *case hardening* that produces a carbon gradient extending inward from the surface, enabling the surface layer to be hardened either by quenching directly from the carburizing temperature or by cooling to room temperature, then reaustenitizing and quenching.

carburizing flame. A gas flame that will introduce carbon into some heated metals, as during a gas welding operation. A carburizing flame is a *reducing flame*, but a reducing flame is not necessarily a carburizing flame.

case. That portion of a ferrous alloy, extending inward from the surface, whose composition has been altered so that it can be *case hardened*. Typically considered to be the portion of the alloy (1) whose composition has been measurably altered from the original composition, (2) that appears dark on an etched cross section, or (3) that has a hardness, after hardening, equal to or greater than a specified value. Contrast with *core*.

case hardening. A generic term covering several processes applicable to steel that change the chemical composition of the surface layer by absorption of carbon, nitrogen, or a mixture of the two and, by diffusion, create a concentration gradient. The processes commonly used are carburizing and quench hardening; cyaniding; nitriding; and carbonitriding. The use of the applicable specific process name is preferred.

cementation. The introduction of one or more elements into the outer portion of a metal object by means of diffusion at high temperature.

cementite. A compound of iron and carbon, known chemically as iron carbide and having the approximate chemical formula Fe_3C. It is characterized by an orthorhombic crystal structure. When it occurs as a phase in steel, the chemical composition will be altered by the presence of manganese and other carbide-forming elements.

checks. Numerous, very fine cracks in a coating or at the surface of a metal part. Checks may appear during processing or during service and are most often associated with thermal treatment or thermal cycling. Also called check marks, checking, *heat checks*.

Chromel. (1) A 90Ni-10Cr alloy used in thermocouples. (2) A series of nickel-chromium alloys, some with iron, used for heat-resistant applications.

close annealing. Same as *box annealing*.

coarsening. An increase in the grain size, usually, but not necessarily, by *grain growth*.

coherency. The continuity of lattice of precipitate and parent phase (solvent) maintained by mutual strain and not separated by a phase boundary.

coherent precipitate. A crystalline precipitate that forms from solid solution with an orientation that maintains continuity between the crystal lattice of the precipitate and the lattice of the matrix, usually accompanied by some strain in both lattices. Because the lattices fit at the interface between precipitate and matrix, there is no discernible phase boundary.

cold treatment. Exposing to suitable subzero temperatures for the purpose of obtaining desired conditions or properties such as dimensional or microstructural stability. When the treatment involves the transformation of retained austenite, it is usually followed by tempering.

columnar structure. A coarse structure of parallel elongated grains formed by unidirectional growth, most often observed in castings, but sometimes in structures resulting from diffusional growth accompanied by a solid-state transformation.

combined carbon. The part of the total carbon in steel or cast iron that is present as other than *free carbon*.

conditioning heat treatment. A preliminary heat treatment used to prepare a material for desired reaction to a subsequent heat treatment. For the term to be meaningful, the exact heat treatment must be specified.

congruent transformation. An isothermal or isobaric phase change in which both of the phases concerned have the same composition throughout the process.

constantan. A group of copper-nickel alloys containing 45 to 60% copper with minor amounts of iron and manganese and characterized by relatively constant electrical resistivity irrespective of temperature; used in resistors and thermocouples.

constitution diagram. A graphical representation of the temperature and composition limits of phase fields in an alloy system as they actually exist under the specific conditions of heating or cooling (synonymous with phase diagram). A constitution diagram may be an equilibrium diagram, an approximation to an equilibrium diagram, or a representation of metastable conditions or phases. Compare with *equilibrium diagram*.

continuous precipitation. Precipitation from a supersaturated solid solution in which the precipitate particles grow by long-range diffusion without recrystallization of the matrix. Continuous precipitates grow from nuclei distributed more or less uniformly throughout the matrix. They usually are randomly oriented, but may form a Widmanstätten structure. Also called general precipitation. Compare with *discontinuous precipitation, localized precipitation*.

controlled cooling. Cooling from an elevated temperature in a predetermined manner, to avoid hardening, cracking, or internal damage, or to produce desired microstructure or mechanical properties.

cooling curve. A curve showing the relation between time and temperature during the cooling of a material.

cooling stresses. Residual stresses resulting from nonuniform distribution of temperature during cooling.

core. In a ferrous alloy prepared for *case hardening*, that portion of the alloy that is not part of the *case*. Typically considered to be the portion that (1) appears light on an etched cross section, (2) has an essentially unaltered chemical composition, or (3) has a hardness, after hardening, less than a specified value.

critical cooling rate. The rate of continuous cooling required to prevent undesirable transformation. For steel, it is the minimum rate at which austenite must be continuously cooled to suppress transformations above the M_s temperature.

critical point. (1) The temperature or pressure at which a change in crystal structure, phase or physical properties occurs. Same as *transformation temperature*. (2) In an equilibrium diagram, that specific value of composition, temperature, and pressure, or combinations thereof, at which the phases of a heterogeneous system are in equilibrium.

critical strain. The strain just sufficient to cause *recrystallization*; because the strain is small, usually only a few percent, recrystallization takes place from only a few nuclei, which produces a recrystallized structure consisting of very large grains.

critical temperature. (1) Synonymous with *critical point* if the pressure is constant. (2) The temperature above which the vapor phase cannot be condensed to liquid by an increase in pressure.

critical temperature ranges. Synonymous with *transformation ranges*, which is the preferred term.

Curie temperature. The temperature of magnetic transformation below which a metal or alloy is ferromagnetic and above which it is paramagnetic.

cyaniding. A case hardening process in which a ferrous material is heated above the lower transformation range in a molten salt containing cyanide to cause simultaneous absorption of carbon and nitrogen at the surface and, by diffusion, create a concentration gradient. Quench hardening completes the process.

cycle annealing. An annealing process employing a predetermined and closely controlled time-temperature cycle to produce specific properties or microstructures.

D

dead soft. A *temper* of nonferrous alloys and some ferrous alloys corresponding to the condition of minimum hardness and tensile strength produced by *full annealing*.

decalescence. A phenomenon, associated with the transformation of alpha iron to gamma iron on the heating (superheating) of iron or steel, revealed by the darkening of the metal surface owing to the sudden decrease in temperature caused by the fast absorption of the latent heat of transformation. Contrast with *recalescence*.

decarburization. Loss of carbon from the surface layer of a carbon-containing alloy due to reaction with one or more chemical substances in a medium that contacts the surface.

degrees of freedom. The number of independent variables (such as temperature, pressure, or concentration within the phases present) that may be altered at will without causing a phase change in an alloy system at equilibrium; or the number of such variables that must be fixed arbitrarily to define the system completely.

delta ferrite. See *ferrite*.

differential heating. Heating that intentionally produces a temperature gradient within an object such that, after cooling, a desired stress distribution or variation in properties is present within the object.

diffusion. (1) Spreading of a constituent in a gas, liquid, or solid, tending to make the composition of all parts uniform. (2) The spontaneous movement of atoms or molecules to new sites within a material.

diffusion coefficient. A factor of proportionality representing the amount of substance diffusing across a unit area through a unit concentration gradient in unit time.

direct quenching. (1) Quenching carburized parts directly from the carburizing operation. (2) Also used for quenching pearlitic malleable parts directly from the malleabilizing operation.

discontinuous precipitation. Precipitation from a supersaturated solid solution in which the precipitate particles grow by short-range diffusion, accompanied by recrystallization of the matrix in the region of precipitation. Discontinuous precipitates grow into the matrix from nuclei near grain boundaries, forming cells of alternate lamellae of precipitate and depleted (and recrystallized) matrix. Often referred to as cellular or nodular precipitation. Compare with *continuous precipitation, localized precipitation*.

double aging. Employment of two different aging treatments to control the type of precipitate formed from a supersaturated matrix in order to obtain the desired properties. The first aging treatment, sometimes referred to as intermediate or stabilizing, is usually carried out at higher temperature than the second.

double tempering. A treatment in which a quench-hardened ferrous metal is subjected to two complete tempering cycles, usually at substantially the same temperature, for the purpose of ensuring completion of the tempering reaction and promoting stability of the resulting microstructure.

drawing. A misnomer for *tempering*.

dry cyaniding. (obsolete) Same as *carbonitriding*.

E

embrittlement. Reduction in the normal ductility of a metal due to a physical or chemical change. Examples include *blue brittleness, hydrogen embrittlement,* and *temper brittleness.*

enantiotropy. The relation of crystal forms of the same substance in which one form is stable above a certain temperature and the other form stable below that temperature. Ferrite and austenite are enantiotropic in ferrous alloys, for example.

end-quench hardenability test. A laboratory procedure for determining the hardenability of a steel or other ferrous alloy; widely referred to as the *Jominy test*. Hardenability is determined by heating a standard specimen above the upper critical temperature, placing the hot specimen in a fixture so that a stream of cold water impinges on one end, and, after cooling to room temperature is completed, measuring the hardness near the surface of the specimen at regularly spaced intervals along its length. The data are normally plotted as hardness versus distance from the quenched end.

equilibrium diagram. A graphical representation of the temperature, pressure, and composition limits of phase fields in an alloy system as they exist under conditions of complete equilibrium. In metal systems, pressure is usually considered constant.

eutectic. (1) An isothermal reversible reaction in which a liquid solution is converted into two or more intimately mixed solids on cooling, the number of solids formed being the same as the number of components in the system. (2) An alloy having the composition indicated by the eutectic point on an equilibrium diagram. (3) An alloy structure of intermixed solid constituents formed by a eutectic reaction.

eutectic carbide. Carbide formed during freezing as one of the mutually insoluble phases participating in the eutectic reaction of ferrous alloys.

eutectic melting. Melting of localized microscopic areas whose composition corresponds to that of the eutectic in the system.

eutectoid. (1) An isothermal reversible reaction in which a solid solution is converted into two or more intimately mixed solids on cooling, the number of solids formed being the same as the number of components in the system. (2) An alloy having the composition indicated by the eutectoid point on an equilibrium diagram. (3) An alloy structure of intermixed solid constituents formed by a eutectoid reaction.

extra hard. A *temper* of nonferrous alloys and some ferrous alloys characterized by tensile strength and hardness about one-third of the way from *full hard* to *extra spring* temper.

extra spring. A *temper* of nonferrous alloys and some ferrous alloys corresponding approximately to a cold worked state above *full hard* beyond which further cold work will not measurably increase the strength and hardness.

F

ferrite. A solid solution of one or more elements in body-centered cubic iron. Unless otherwise designated (for instance, as chromium ferrite), the solute is generally assumed to be carbon. On some equilibrium diagrams, there are two ferrite regions separated by an austenite area. The lower area is alpha ferrite; the upper, delta ferrite. If there is no designation, alpha ferrite is assumed.

ferritizing anneal. A treatment given as-cast gray or ductile (nodular) iron to produce an essentially ferritic matrix. For the term to be meaningful, the final microstructure desired or the time-temperature cycle used must be specified.

file hardness. Hardness as determined by the use of a file of standardized hardness on the assumption that a material that cannot be cut with the file is as hard as, or harder than, the file. Files covering a range of hardnesses may be employed.

final annealing. An imprecise term used to denote the last anneal given to a nonferrous alloy prior to shipment.

finishing temperature. The temperature at which hot working is completed.

flame annealing. Annealing in which the heat is applied directly by a flame.

flame hardening. A process for hardening the surfaces of hardenable ferrous alloys in which an intense flame is used to heat the surface layers above the upper transformation temperature, whereupon the workpiece is immediately quenched.

flame straightening. Correcting distortion in metal structures by localized heating with a gas flame.

fog quenching. Quenching in a fine vapor or mist.

free carbon. The part of the total carbon in steel or cast iron that is present in elemental form as graphite or temper carbon. Contrast with *combined carbon*.

free ferrite. Ferrite that is formed directly from the decomposition of hypoeutectoid austenite during cooling, without the simultaneous formation of cementite. Also proeutectoid ferrite.

freezing range. That temperature range between liquidus and solidus temperatures in which molten and solid constituents coexist.

full annealing. An imprecise term that denotes an annealing cycle to produce minimum strength and hardness. For the term to be meaningful, the composition and starting condition of the material and the time-temperature cycle used must be stated.

full hard. A *temper* of nonferrous alloys and some ferrous alloys corresponding approximately to a cold worked state beyond which the material can no longer be formed by bending. In specifications, a full hard temper is commonly defined in terms of minimum hardness or minimum tensile strength (or, alternatively, a range of hardness or strength) corresponding to a specific percentage of cold reduction following a full anneal. For aluminum, a full hard temper is equivalent to a reduction of 75% from *dead soft*; for austenitic stainless steels, a reduction of about 50 to 55%.

furnace brazing. A mass-production *brazing* process in which the filler metal is preplaced on the joint, then the entire assembly is heated to brazing temperature in a furnace. Usually, a protective furnace atmosphere is required, and wetting of the joint surfaces is accomplished without using a brazing flux.

fusion. A change of state from solid to liquid; melting.

G

gamma iron. The face-centered cubic form of pure iron, stable from 910 to 1400 °C (1670 to 2550 °F).

gas cyaniding. A misnomer for *carbonitriding*.

grain growth. An increase in the average size of the grains in polycrystalline metal, usually as a result of heating at elevated temperature.

grain size. For metals, a measure of the areas or volumes of grains in a polycrystalline material, usually expressed as an average when the individual sizes are fairly uniform. In metals containing two or more phases, the grain size refers to that of the matrix unless otherwise specified. Grain sizes are reported in terms of number of grains per unit area or volume, average diameter, or as a grain-size number derived from area measurements.

graphitization. Formation of graphite in iron or steel. Where graphite is formed during solidification, the phenomenon is called primary graphitization; where formed later by heat treatment, secondary graphitization.

graphitizing. Annealing a ferrous alloy in such a way that some or all of the carbon is precipitated as graphite.

growth. In cast iron, a permanent increase in dimensions resulting from repeated or prolonged heating at temperatures above 480 °C (900 °F) due either to graphitizing of carbides or to oxidation.

H

half hard. A *temper* of nonferrous alloys and some ferrous alloys characterized by tensile strength about midway between that of *dead soft* and *full hard* tempers.

hardenability. The relative ability of a ferrous alloy to form martensite when quenched from a temperature above the upper critical temperature. Hardenability is commonly measured as the distance below a quenched surface where the metal exhibits a specific hardness (50 HRC, for example) or a specific percentage of martensite in the microstructure.

hardening. Increasing hardness by suitable treatment, usually involving heating and cooling. When applicable, the following more specific terms should be used: *age hardening, case hardening, flame hardening, induction hardening, precipitation hardening* and *quench hardening*.

hard temper. Same as *full hard* temper.

heat-resisting alloy. An alloy developed for very high temperature service where relatively high stresses (tensile, thermal, vibratory, or shock) are encountered and where oxidation resistance is frequently required.

heat tinting. Coloration of a metal surface through oxidation by heating to reveal details of the microstructure.

heat treatable alloy. An alloy that can be hardened by heat treatment.

heat treating film. A thin coating or film, usually an oxide, formed on the surface of metals during heat treatment.

heat treatment. Heating and cooling a solid metal or alloy in such a way as to obtain desired conditions or properties. Heating for the sole purpose of hot working is excluded from the meaning of this definition.

homogeneous carburizing. Use of a carburizing process to convert a low-carbon ferrous alloy to one of uniform and higher carbon content throughout the section.

homogenizing. Holding at high temperature to eliminate or decrease chemical segregation by diffusion.

hot quenching. An imprecise term used to cover a variety of quenching procedures in which a quenching medium is maintained at a prescribed temperature above 70 °C (160 °F).

hydrogen brazing. A term sometimes used to denote brazing in a hydrogen-containing atmosphere, usually in a furnace; use of the appropriate process name is preferred.

hydrogen embrittlement. A condition of low ductility in metals resulting from the absorption of hydrogen.

I

induction brazing. *Brazing* in which the required heat is generated by subjecting the workpiece to electromagnetic induction.

induction hardening. A surface-hardening process in which only the surface layer of a suitable ferrous workpiece is heated by electromagnetic induction to above the upper critical temperature and immediately quenched.

induction heating. Heating by combined electrical resistance and hysteresis losses induced by subjecting a metal to the varying magnetic field surrounding a coil carrying alternating current.

intermediate annealing. Annealing wrought metals at one or more stages during manufacture and before final treatment.

interrupted aging. Aging at two or more temperatures, by steps, and cooling to room temperature after each step. See also *aging*. Compare with *progressive aging* and *step aging*.

interrupted quenching. A quenching procedure in which the workpiece is removed from the first quench at a temperature substantially higher than that of the quenchant and is then subjected to a second quenching system having a different cooling rate than the first.

isothermal annealing. Austenitizing a ferrous alloy and then cooling to and holding at a temperature at which austenite transforms to a relatively soft ferrite carbide aggregate.

isothermal transformation. A change in phase that takes place at a constant temperature. The time required for transformation to be completed, and in some instances the time delay before transformation begins, depends on the amount of supercooling below (or superheating above) the equilibrium temperature for the same transformation.

J

Jominy test. See *end-quench hardenability test.*

L

ledeburite. The eutectic of the iron-carbon system, the constituents being austenite and cementite. The austenite decomposes into ferrite and cementite on cooling below the Ar_1.

liquid phase sintering. *Sintering* a powder metallurgy compact under conditions that maintain a liquid metallic phase within the compact during all or part of the sintering schedule. The liquid phase may be derived from a component of the green compact or may be infiltrated into the compact from an outside source.

localized precipitation. Precipitation from a supersaturated solid solution similar to *continuous precipitation,* except that the precipitate particles form at preferred locations, such as along slip planes, grain boundaries, or incoherent twin boundaries.

M

malleabilizing. Annealing white cast iron in such a way that some or all of the combined carbon is transformed to graphite or, in some instances, part of the carbon is removed completely.

maraging. A precipitation-hardening treatment applied to a special group of iron-base alloys to precipitate one or more intermetallic compounds in a matrix of essentially carbon-free martensite. *Note:* The first developed series of maraging steels contained, in addition to iron, more than 10% nickel and one or more supplemental hardening elements. In this series, aging is done at 480 °C (900 °F).

marquenching. See *martempering.*

martempering. (1) A hardening procedure in which an austenitized ferrous workpiece is quenched into an appropriate medium whose temperature is maintained substantially at the M_s of the workpiece, held in the medium until its temperature is uniform throughout—but not long enough to permit bainite to form—and then cooled in air. The treatment is frequently followed by tempering. (2) When the process is applied to carburized material, the controlling M_s temperature is that of the case. This variation of the process is frequently called marquenching.

martensite. A generic term for microstructures formed by diffusionless phase transformation in which the parent and product phases have a specific crystallographic relationship. Martensite is characterized by an acicular pattern in the microstructure in both ferrous and nonferrous alloys. In alloys where the solute atoms occupy interstitial positions in the martensitic lattice (such as carbon in iron), the structure is hard and highly strained; but where the solute atoms occupy substitutional positions (such as nickel in iron), the martensite is soft and ductile. The amount of high-temperature phase that transforms to martensite on cooling depends to a large extent on the lowest temperature attained, there being a rather distinct beginning temperature (M_s) and a temperature at which the transformation is essentially complete (M_f).

martensite range. The temperature interval between M_s and M_f.

martensitic transformation. A reaction that takes place in some metals on cooling, with the formation of an acicular structure called *martensite.*

McQuaid-Ehn test. A test to reveal grain size after heating into the austenitic temperature range. Eight standard McQuaid-Ehn grain sizes rate the structure. No. 8 being finest, No. 1 coarsest.

metallurgy. The science and technology of metals and alloys. Process metallurgy is concerned with the extraction of metals from their ores and with the refining of metals; physical metallurgy, with the physical and mechanical properties of metals as affected by composition, processing, and environmental conditions; and mechanical metallurgy, with the response of metals to applied forces.

M_f temperature. For any alloy system, the temperature at which martensite formation on cooling is essentially finished. See *transformation temperature* for the definition applicable to ferrous alloys.

microhardness. The hardness of a material as determined by forcing an indenter such as a Vickers or Knoop indenter into the surface of a material under very light load; usually, the indentations are so small that they must be measured with a microscope. Capable of determining hardness of different microconstituents within a structure, or of measuring steep hardness gradients such as those encountered in case hardening.

mill scale. The heavy oxide layer formed during hot fabrication or heat treatment of metals.

monotropism. The ability of a solid to exist in two or more forms (crystal structures), but in which one form is the stable modification at all temperatures and pressures. Ferrite and martensite are a monotropic pair below Ac_1 in steels, for example. May also be spelled monotrophism.

M_s temperature. For any alloy system, the temperature at which martensite starts to form on cooling. See *transformation temperature* for the definition applicable to ferrous alloys.

N

natural aging. Spontaneous aging of a supersaturated solid solution at room temperature. See also *aging.* Compare with *artificial aging.*

neutral flame. A gas flame in which there is no excess of either fuel or oxygen in the inner flame. Oxygen from ambient air is used to complete the combustion of CO_2 and H_2 produced in the inner flame.

nitriding. Introducing nitrogen into the surface layer of a solid ferrous alloy by holding at a suitable temperature (below Ac_1 for ferritic steels) in contact with a nitrogenous material, usually ammonia or molten cyanide of appropriate composition. Quenching is not required to produce a hard case.

nitrocarburizing. Any of several processes in which both nitrogen and carbon are absorbed into the surface layers of a ferrous material at temperatures below the lower critical temperature and, by diffusion, create a concentration gradient. Nitrocarburizing is done mainly to provide an antiscuffing surface layer and to improve fatigue resistance. Compare with *carbonitriding*.

normalizing. Heating a ferrous alloy to a suitable temperature above the transformation range and then cooling in air to a temperature substantially below the transformation range.

O

optical pyrometer. An instrument for measuring the temperature of heated material by comparing the intensity of light emitted with a known intensity of an incandescent lamp filament.

overaging. Aging under conditions of time and temperature greater than those required to obtain maximum change in a certain property, so that the property is altered in the direction of the initial value. See also *aging*.

overheating. Heating a metal or alloy to such a high temperature that its properties are impaired. When the original properties cannot be restored by further heat treating, by mechanical working, or by a combination of working and heat treating, the overheating is known as *burning*.

oxidizing flame. A gas flame produced with excess oxygen in the inner flame.

P

packing material. Any material in which powder metallurgy compacts are embedded during the presintering or sintering operations.

partial annealing. An imprecise term used to denote a treatment given cold worked material to reduce the strength to a controlled level or to effect stress relief. To be meaningful, the type of material, the degree of cold work, and the time-temperature schedule must be stated.

patenting. In wiremaking, a heat treatment applied to medium-carbon or high-carbon steel before the drawing of wire or between drafts. This process consists of heating to a temperature above the transformation range and then cooling to a temperature below Ae_1 in air or in a bath of molten lead or salt.

pearlite. A metastable lamellar aggregate of ferrite and cementite resulting from the transformation of austenite at temperatures above the bainite range.

postheating. Heating weldments immediately after welding, for tempering, for stress relieving, or for providing a controlled rate of cooling to prevent formation of a hard or brittle structure.

pot annealing. Same as *box annealing*.

precipitation hardening. Hardening caused by the precipitation of a constituent from a supersaturated solid solution. See also *age hardening* and *aging*.

precipitation heat treatment. *Artificial aging* in which a constituent precipitates from a supersaturated solid solution.

preheating. Heating before some further thermal or mechanical treatment. For tool steel, heating to an intermediate temperature immediately before final austenitizing. For some nonferrous alloys, heating to a high temperature for a long time, to homogenize the structure before working. In welding and related processes, heating to an intermediate temperature for a short time immediately before welding, brazing, soldering, cutting, or thermal spraying.

presintering. The heating of a powder metallurgy compact to a temperature lower than the normal temperature for final sintering, usually to increase the ease of handling or forming the compact or to remove a lubricant or binder before sintering.

process annealing. An imprecise term denoting various treatments used to improve workability. For the term to be meaningful, the condition of the material and the time-temperature cycle used must be stated.

progressive aging. Aging by increasing the temperature in steps or continuously during the aging cycle. See also *aging*. Compare with *interrupted aging* and *step aging*.

pseudocarburizing. See *blank carburizing*.

pseudonitriding. See *blank nitriding*.

pusher furnace. A type of continuous furnace in which parts to be heated are periodically charged into the furnace in containers, which are pushed along the hearth against a line of previously charged containers thus advancing the containers toward the discharge end of the furnace, where they are removed.

Q

quarter hard. A *temper* of nonferrous alloys and some ferrous alloys characterized by tensile strength about midway between that of *dead soft* and *half hard* tempers.

quench-age embrittlement. Embrittlement of low-carbon steel evidenced by a loss of ductility on aging at room temperature following rapid cooling from a temperature below the lower critical temperature.

quench aging. Aging induced by rapid cooling after *solution heat treatment*.

quench annealing. Annealing an austenitic ferrous alloy by *solution heat treatment* followed by rapid quenching.

quench cracking. Fracture of a metal during quenching from elevated temperature. Most frequently observed in hardened carbon steel, alloy steel, or tool steel parts of high hardness and low toughness. Cracks often emanate from fillets, holes, corners, or other stress raisers and result from high stresses due to the volume changes accompanying transformation to martensite.

quench hardening. (1) Hardening suitable alpha-beta alloys (most often certain copper or titanium alloys) by solution treating and quenching to develop a martensitic-like structure. (2) In ferrous alloys, hardening by austenitizing and then cooling at a rate such that a substantial amount of austenite transforms to martensite.

quenching. Rapid cooling. When applicable, the following more specific terms should be used: *direct quenching, fog quenching, hot quenching, interrupted quenching, selective quenching, spray quenching,* and *time quenching.*

R

recalescence. A phenomenon, associated with the transformation of gamma iron to alpha iron on the cooling (supercooling) of iron or steel, revealed by the brightening (reglowing) of the metal surface owing to the sudden increase in temperature caused by the fast liberation of the latent heat of transformation. Contrast with *decalescence.*

recarburize. (1) To increase the carbon content of molten cast iron or steel by adding carbonaceous material, high-carbon pig iron, or a high-carbon alloy. (2) To carburize a metal part to return surface carbon lost in processing; also known as carbon restoration.

recovery. Reduction or removal of work-hardening effects, without motion of large-angle grain boundaries.

recrystallization. (1) The formation of a new, strain-free grain structure from that existing in cold worked metal, usually accomplished by heating. (2) The change from one crystal structure to another, as occurs on heating or cooling through a critical temperature.

recrystallization annealing. Annealing cold worked metal to produce a new grain structure without phase change.

recrystallization temperature. The approximate minimum temperature at which complete recrystallization of a cold worked metal occurs within a specified time.

recuperator. Equipment for transferring heat from gaseous products of combustion to incoming air or fuel. The incoming material passes through pipes surrounded by a chamber through which the outgoing gases pass.

reducing flame. A gas flame produced with excess fuel in the inner flame.

refractory. (1) A material of very high melting point with properties that make it suitable for such uses as furnace linings and kiln construction. (2) The quality of resisting heat.

refractory alloy. (1) A heat-resistant alloy. (2) An alloy having an extremely high melting point. See also *refractory metal.* (3) An alloy difficult to work at elevated temperatures.

refractory metal. A metal having an extremely high melting point; for example, tungsten, molybdenum, tantalum, niobium (columbium), chromium, vanadium, and rhenium. In the broad sense, it refers to metals having melting points above the range of iron, cobalt, and nickel.

regenerator. Same as *recuperator* except the gaseous products of combustion heat brick checkerwork in a chamber connected to the exhaust side of the furnace while the incoming air and fuel are being heated by the brick checkerwork in a second chamber, connected to the entrance side. At intervals, the gas flow is reversed so that incoming air and fuel contact hot checkerwork while that in the second chamber is being reheated by exhaust gases.

resist. (1) A material applied to a part of the surface of an article to prevent reaction of metal from that area during chemical or electrochemical processes. (2) A material applied to prevent the flow of brazing filler metal into unwanted area.

resistance brazing. Brazing by resistance heating, the joint being part of the electrical circuit.

reverberatory furnace. A furnace with a shallow hearth, usually unregenerative, having a roof that deflects the flame and radiates heat toward the hearth or the surface of the charge.

Rockwell hardness test. An indentation hardness test based on the depth of penetration of a specified penetrator into the specimen under certain arbitrarily fixed conditions.

rotary furnace. A circular furnace constructed so that the hearth and workpieces rotate around the axis of the furnace during heating.

S

selective heating. Intentionally heating only certain portions of a workpiece.

selective quenching. Quenching only certain portions of an object.

self-hardening steel. See preferred term, *air-hardening steel.*

shrink forming. Forming metal wherein the inner fibers of a cross section undergo a reduction in a localized area by the application of heat, cold upset, or mechanically induced pressures.

siliconizing. Diffusing silicon into solid metal, usually steel, at an elevated temperature.

sinter. To heat a mass of fine particles for a prolonged time below the melting point, usually to cause agglomeration.

sintering. The bonding of adjacent surfaces in a mass of particles by molecular or atomic attraction on heating at high temperatures below the melting temperature of any constituent in the material. Sintering strengthens a powder mass and normally produces densification and, in powdered metals, recrystallization. See also *liquid phase sintering.*

slack quenching. The incomplete hardening of steel due to quenching from the austenitizing temperature at a rate slower than the critical cooling rate for the particular steel, resulting in the formation of one or more transformation products in addition to martensite.

slot furnace. A common batch furnace where stock is charged and removed through a slot or opening.

snap temper. A precautionary interim stress-relieving treatment applied to high-hardenability steels immediately after quenching to prevent cracking because of delay in tempering them at the prescribed higher temperature.

soaking. Prolonged holding at a selected temperature to effect homogenization of structure or composition.

soft temper. Same as *dead soft* temper.

solution heat treatment. Heating an alloy to a suitable temperature, holding at that temperature long enough to cause one or more constituents to enter into solid solution, and then cooling rapidly enough to hold these constituents in solution.

sorbite. (obsolete) A fine mixture of ferrite and cementite produced either by regulating the rate of cooling of steel or by tempering steel after hardening. The first type is very fine pearlite difficult to resolve under the microscope; the second type is tempered martensite.

spheroidite. An aggregate of iron or alloy carbides of essentially spherical shape dispersed throughout a matrix of ferrite.

spheroidizing. Heating and cooling to produce a spheroidal or globular form of carbide in steel. Spheroidizing methods frequently used are: (1) Prolonged holding at a temperature just below Ae_1. (2) Heating and cooling alternately between temperatures that are just above and just below Ae_1. (3) Heating to a temperature above Ae_1 or Ae_3 and then cooling very slowly in the furnace or holding at a temperature just below Ae_1. (4) Cooling at a suitable rate from the minimum temperature at which all carbide is dissolved, to prevent the reformation of a carbide network, and then reheating in accordance with method 1 or 2 above. (Applicable to hypereutectoid steel containing a carbide network.)

spinodal structure. A fine homogeneous mixture of two phases that form by the growth of composition waves in a solid solution during suitable heat treatment. The phases of a spinodal structure differ in composition from each other and from the parent phase but have the same crystal structure as the parent phase.

spray quenching. Quenching in a spray of liquid.

spring temper. A *temper* of nonferrous alloys and some ferrous alloys characterized by tensile strength and hardness about two-thirds of the way from *full hard* to *extra spring* temper.

stabilizing treatment. (1) Before finishing to final dimensions, repeatedly heating a ferrous or nonferrous part to or slightly above its normal operating temperature and then cooling to room temperature to ensure dimensional stability in service. (2) Transforming retained austenite in quenched hardenable steels, usually by *cold treatment.* (3) Heating a solution-treated stabilized grade of austenitic stainless steel to 870 to 900 °C (1600 to 1650 °F) to precipitate all carbon as TiC, NbC, or TaC so that *sensitization* is avoided on subsequent exposure to elevated temperature.

Stead's brittleness. A condition of brittleness that causes transcrystalline fracture in the coarse grain structure that results from prolonged annealing of thin sheets of low-carbon steel previously rolled at a temperature below about 705 °C (1300 °F). The fracture usually occurs at about 45° to the direction of rolling.

step aging. Aging at two or more temperatures, by steps, without cooling to room temperature after each step. See also *aging.* Compare with *interrupted aging* and *progressive aging.*

stoking. (obsolete) Presintering, or sintering, in such a way that powder metallurgy compacts are advanced through the furnace at a fixed rate by manual or mechanical means; also called continuous sintering.

stop-off. See *resist.*

stopping off. (1) Applying a *resist.* (2) Depositing a metal (copper, for example) in localized areas to prevent carburization, decarburization, or nitriding in those areas.

strain-age embrittlement. A loss in ductility accompanied by an increase in hardness and strength that occurs when low-carbon steel (especially rimmed or capped steel) is aged following plastic deformation. The degree of embrittlement is a function of aging time and temperature, occurring in a matter of minutes at about 200 °C (400 °F) but requiring a few hours to a year at room temperature.

stress relieving. Heating to a suitable temperature, holding long enough to reduce residual stresses, and then cooling slowly enough to minimize the development of new residual stresses.

subcritical annealing. A process anneal performed on ferrous alloys at a temperature below Ac_1.

superalloy. See *heat-resisting alloy.*

supercooling. Cooling below the temperature at which an equilibrium phase transformation can take place, without actually obtaining the transformation.

superheating. Heating above the temperature at which an equilibrium phase transformation should occur without actually obtaining the transformation.

surface hardening. A generic term covering several processes applicable to a suitable ferrous alloy that produces, by quench hardening only, a surface layer that is harder or more wear resistant than the core. There is no significant alteration of the chemical composition of the surface layer. The processes commonly used are induction hardening, flame hardening, and shell hardening. Use of the applicable specific process name is preferred.

T

temper. (1) In heat treatment, reheating hardened steel or hardened cast iron to some temperature below the eutectoid temperature for the purpose of decreasing hardness and increasing toughness. The process also is sometimes applied to normalized steel. (2) In tool steels, temper is sometimes used, but inadvisedly, to denote the carbon content. (3) In nonferrous alloys and in some ferrous alloys (steels that cannot be hardened by heat treatment), the hardness and strength produced by mechanical or thermal treatment, or both, and characterized by a certain structure, mechanical properties, or reduction in area during cold working.

temper brittleness. Brittleness that results when certain steels are held within, or are cooled slowly through, a certain range of temperature below the transformation range. The brittleness is manifested as an upward shift in ductile-to-brittle transition temperature, but only rarely produces a low value of reduction of area in a smooth-bar tension test of the embrittled material.

temper carbon. Same as *annealing carbon*.

temper color. A thin, tightly adhering oxide skin (only a few molecules thick) that forms when steel is tempered at a low temperature, or for a short time, in air or a mildly oxidizing atmosphere. The color, which ranges from straw to blue depending on the thickness of the oxide skin, varies with both tempering time and temperature.

thermocouple. A device for measuring temperatures, consisting of lengths of two dissimilar metals or alloys that are electrically joined at one end and connected to a voltage-measuring instrument at the other end. When one junction is hotter than the other, a thermal electromotive force is produced that is roughly proportional to the difference in temperature between the hot and cold junctions.

thermomechanical working. A general term covering a variety of processes combining controlled thermal and deformation treatments to obtain synergistic effects such as improvement in strength without loss of toughness. Same as thermal-mechanical treatment.

three-quarters hard. A *temper* of nonferrous alloys and some ferrous alloys characterized by tensile strength and hardness about midway between those of *half hard* and *full hard* tempers.

time quenching. Interrupted quenching in which the time in the quenching medium is controlled.

total carbon. The sum of the free and combined carbon (including carbon in solution) in a ferrous alloy.

transformation-induced plasticity. A phenomenon, occurring chiefly in certain highly alloyed steels that have been heat treated to produce metastable austenite or metastable austenite plus martensite, whereby, on subsequent deformation, part of the austenite undergoes strain-induced transformation to martensite. Steels capable of transforming in this manner, commonly referred to as TRIP steels, are highly plastic after heat treatment, but exhibit a very high rate of strain hardening and thus have high tensile and yield strengths after plastic deformation

at temperatures between about 20 and 500 °C (70 and 930 °F). Cooling to –195°C (–320 °F) may or may not be required to complete the transformation to martensite. Tempering usually is done following transformation.

transformation ranges. Those ranges of temperature within which a phase forms during heating and transforms during cooling. The two ranges are distinct, sometimes overlapping, but never coinciding. The limiting temperatures of the ranges depend on the composition of the alloy and on the rate of change of temperature, particularly during cooling. See also *transformation temperature*.

transformation temperature. The temperature at which a change in phase occurs. The term is sometimes used to denote the limiting temperature of a transformation range. The following symbols are used for iron and steels:

Ac_{cm}. In hypereutectoid steel, the temperature at which the solution of cementite in austenite is completed during heating.

Ac_1. The temperature at which austenite begins to form during heating.

Ac_3. The temperature at which transformation of ferrite to austenite is completed during heating.

Ac_4. The temperature at which austenite transforms to delta ferrite during heating.

Ae_{cm}, Ae_1, Ae_3, Ae_4. The temperatures of phase changes at equilibrium.

Ar_{cm}. In hypereutectoid steel, the temperature at which precipitation of cementite starts during cooling.

Ar_1. The temperature at which transformation of austenite to ferrite or to ferrite plus cementite is completed during cooling.

Ar_3. The temperature at which austenite begins to transform to ferrite during cooling.

Ar_4. The temperature at which delta ferrite transforms to austenite during cooling.

Ar'. The temperature at which transformation of austenite to pearlite starts during cooling.

M_f. The temperature at which transformation of austenite to martensite finishes during cooling.

M_s (or Ar''). The temperature at which transformation of austenite to martensite starts during cooling.

Note: All these changes except the formation of martensite occur at lower temperatures during cooling than during heating, and depend on the rate of change of temperature.

TRIP steel. A commercial steel product exhibiting *transformation-induced plasticity*.

troostite. (obsolete) A previously unresolvable rapidly etching fine aggregate of carbide and ferrite produced either by tempering martensite at low temperature or by quenching a steel at a rate slower than the critical cooling rate. Preferred terminology for the first product is tempered martensite; for the latter, fine pearlite.

U

undercooling. Same as *supercooling*.

Index